The Which? Guide to Country Pubs

WHICH? BOOKS

Which? Books is the book publishing arm of Consumers' Association, which was set up in 1957 to improve the standards of goods and services available to the public. Everything Which? publishes aims to help consumers, by giving them the independent information they need to make informed decisions. These publications, known throughout Britain for their quality, integrity and impartiality, have been held in high regard for four decades.

Independence does not come cheap: the guides carry no advertising, and no restaurant or pub can buy an entry in our guides, or treat our inspectors to free meals or accommodation. This policy, and our practice of rigorously re-researching our guides for each edition, helps us to provide our readers with information of a standard and quality that cannot be surpassed.

The Which?
Guide to
Country Pubs

EDITED BY **ANDREW TURVIL**

CONSUMERS' ASSOCIATION

Which? Books are commissioned and researched by
Consumers' Association and published by Which? Ltd,
2 Marylebone Road, London NW1 4DF
Email address: books@which.net

Distributed by The Penguin Group:
Penguin Books Ltd, 27 Wrights Lane, London W8 5TZ

First edition 1993
Second edition 1995
Third edition 1997
Fourth edition 1999
Fifth edition 2001

British Library Cataloguing in Publication Data
A catalogue record for this book is available from the British Library

ISBN 0 85202 853 9

For a full list of Which? books, please write to:
Which? Books, Castlemead, Gascoyne Way,
Hertford X, SG14 1LH
or access our web site at www.which.net

Cover design by Price Watkins
Cover photograph by James Duncan
Typographic design by Paul Saunders

Typeset by Saxon Graphics Ltd, Derby
Printed and bound by Clays Ltd, St Ives plc

Contents

How to use the Guide

The Guide is divided into two parts. At the front is the main section, which lists country pubs throughout Britain selected for the quality of their food, drink and atmosphere; the selections are based on reports from the general public backed up by independent inspections. Towards the back you will find the 'Out and About' section, which features more than 300 additional pubs which are also well worth a visit. These have been selected less on the basis of the food they offer (some do not offer food at all; in other cases, we have had insufficient feedback to be able to assess cooking), but rather for other qualities that set them apart – perhaps for their superlative beers, hospitality, character, setting, history or other attribute.

Layout
Both parts of the Guide are further divided into the following sections: England, Scotland and Wales. Pubs are listed alphabetically by locality; they are put in their true *geographical* location, rather than at their postal address. If a pub is difficult to find, directions are given (after the address and telephone number). It is always worth checking by telephone if you are unsure about the exact location of an out-of-the-way pub.

How to find a pub in a particular area
Go to the maps at the back of the book and choose the general area that you want. Towns and villages where pubs in the Guide are located are marked with a tankard symbol; turn to that locality in the appropriate section of the book, where you will find details of the pub (or pubs) there.

Symbols and awards
❀ ❀ denotes a pub where the quality of the bar food is comparable to that of a 'serious' restaurant – i.e. ingredients are consistently first-class and imagination and style are hallmarks of the kitchen. See page 10 for a list of these pubs.

❀ signifies that the pub offers above-average bar food that shows ambition and good ideas, or simple pub fare prepared particularly well. See page 10 for list.

🍺 denotes a pub serving exceptional draught beers. See page 12 for list.

🍷 indicates a pub serving better-than-average wines, imaginatively chosen and decently priced, with a good selection (usually six or more) by the glass. See page 14 for list.

▲ indicates a pub which offers accommodation.

NEW ENTRY   appears after a pub's name if it did not feature in the last edition as a main entry (although it might have featured as an Out and About). See page 16 for list.

LOCAL PRODUCE   *'Flashes'* These highlight a particular point of interest in selected main entries, such as 'cheese', 'setting' or 'whisky', indicating that the pub has something special, perhaps unique, about it.

Note that web sites are also included for the first time in this edition if a pub has one.

Sample dishes

These are listed at the end of each main entry and are examples of typical dishes from the menu. Prices are based on figures provided by the pub licensee; in most cases, prices have been rounded up to the nearest 25 pence. Note that items listed may not always be available (particularly if they are 'specials').

Food and drink

Details of bar food mentioned in the entries are based on all the feedback we have received since the last edition of the Guide was published, including official inspections, notes from readers, and information provided by the licensees. Many pubs vary their menus from day to day, so specific items may no longer be in the kitchen's repertoire. If dishes are available in a separate restaurant and not in the bar, we mention that in the entry. Similarly, the range of draught beers may differ from time to time, especially if a pub has guest brews. Any real ciders are also listed. Information about wine is geared to what is generally available in the bar; in some pubs with a separate restaurant, you may need to request to see the full wine list (most pubs will oblige). The number of wines available by the glass is usually given in the text.

'Details'

The information given in the section at the end of each entry has been supplied by the pub and may be subject to change. If you are making a special journey, it is always worthwhile phoning beforehand to check opening and bar food times, and any other details that are important to you, such as restrictions on children or dogs, wheelchair access, the availability of no-smoking areas, etc.

✪ Licensee: the current licensee is given, followed by the name of the pub's owner (such as a brewery) in brackets; 'freehouse' is given if that is the case.

✪ 'Open' times: these are the pub's full licensing hours. (Sunday hours are given separately if different.) Opening times may vary, especially in pubs that rely heavily on seasonal trade; days and times when a pub is closed are also listed.

○ Bar food (and restaurant) times: these denote when food is served in the bar (and restaurant, if there is one).

○ Children: often children are allowed in a family room or eating area of a pub, but not in the main bar area. Any restrictions on children are listed.

○ Car park: if a pub has its own car park, this is noted.

○ Wheelchair access: this means that the proprietor has confirmed that the entrance to the bar/dining-room is at least 80cm wide and passages at least 120cm across – the Royal Association for Disability and Rehabilitation (RADAR) recommendations. If 'also WC' is given, it means that the proprietor has told us that the toilet facilities are suitable for disabled people.

○ Garden/patio: this is noted for pubs with outside seating areas. If a pub has a children's play area or another interesting feature – e.g. a boules pitch – this is mentioned in the text.

○ Smoking: restrictions on smoking or special areas designated for non-smokers are noted.

○ Music: if background or live music is ever played, or if a pub has a jukebox, this is stated.

○ Dogs: any restrictions on dogs *inside* the pub are listed. Most pubs will allow dogs in their gardens. Guide dogs are normally exempt from restrictions, although it is best to check beforehand if you have special requirements.

○ Cards: major credit and debit cards are listed if a pub accepts these as a means of payment. Note that this service may apply only to restaurant meals and/or accommodation. If a pub does not accept cards, we note this.

○ Accommodation: if a pub offers overnight accommodation, the number of bedrooms and a range of B&B prices – from the lowest you can expect to pay for a single room (or single occupancy of a twin/double) to the most you are likely to pay for a twin/double – are listed. Pub bedrooms have not been officially inspected for this guide.

Report forms

At the very back of the book are report forms which you may use to recount your pub-going experiences. The address is FREEPOST, so no stamp is necessary (full details on the report forms). Because *The Which? Guide to Country Pubs*, like its sister publication *The Good Food Guide*, relies to a great extent on unsolicited feedback from readers, your comments are invaluable to us and will form a major part of our research when we prepare future editions.

The top-rated pubs

❀ ❀ indicates a pub where the quality of the bar food is comparable to that of a 'serious' restaurant – i.e. ingredients are consistently first class, and imagination, skill and an individual style are hallmarks of the kitchen.

ENGLAND
Cambridgeshire
Pheasant Inn, Keyston
Three Horseshoes, Madingley
Cumbria
Punch Bowl Inn, Crosthwaite
Devon
Drewe Arms, Broadhembury
Essex
White Hart, Great Yeldham
Gloucestershire
Churchill Arms, Paxford
Village Pub, Barnsley
Greater Manchester
White Hart, Lydgate

Herefordshire
Stagg Inn, Titley
North Yorkshire
Angel Inn, Hetton
Blue Lion, East Witton
Crab & Lobster, Asenby
Star Inn, Harome
Yorke Arms, Ramsgill
Oxfordshire
Sir Charles Napier, Chinnor
Shropshire
Waterdine, Llanfair Waterdine
Wiltshire
George & Dragon, Rowde

 indicates a pub offering distinctly above-average bar food that shows ambition and good ideas, or simple pub fare prepared particularly well.

ENGLAND
Berkshire
Dundas Arms, Kintbury
Harrow Inn, West Ilsley
Royal Oak, Yattendon
Buckinghamshire
Chequers Inn, Wooburn Common
Crooked Billet, Newton Longville
Cambridgeshire
Anchor Inn, Sutton Gault
Old Bridge Hotel, Huntingdon
Co Durham
Rose and Crown, Romaldkirk
Cumbria
Bay Horse Hotel, Ulverston
Queens Head Hotel, Troutbeck
Snooty Fox Tavern, Kirkby
　　Lonsdale
Derbyshire
Red Lion, Hognaston
Devon
Arundell Arms, Lifton
Dartmoor Inn, Lydford

Jack in the Green, Rockbeare
Nobody Inn, Doddiscombsleigh
Peter Tavy Inn, Peter Tavy
White Hart, Dartington
Dorset
Fox Inn, Corscombe
Shave Cross Inn, Shave Cross
East Riding of Yorkshire
Wellington Inn, Lund
East Sussex
Griffin Inn, Fletching
Jolly Sportsman, East Chiltington
Tiger Inn, East Dean
Essex
Bell Inn, Horndon on the Hill
Gloucestershire
Eagle and Child, Stow-on-the-
　　Wold
Fox Inn, Lower Oddington
Hare & Hounds, Foss Cross
New Inn, Coln St Aldwyns
Yew Tree Inn, Clifford's Mesne

Hampshire
East End Arms, East End
Red House, Whitchurch
Herefordshire
Roebuck Inn, Brimfield
Kent
Dove, Dargate
Harrow Inn, Ightham
Kentish Horse, Markbeech
Sportsman, Seasalter
Lancashire
Bay Horse Inn, Forton
Mulberry Tree, Wrightington
Leicestershire
Berkeley Arms, Wymondham
Norfolk
Hoste Arms, Burnham Market
Three Horseshoes, Warham All
   Saints
Northamptonshire
Falcon Inn, Fotheringhay
Northumberland
Cook and Barker Inn, Newton-on-
   the-Moor
General Havelock Inn, Haydon
   Bridge
Manor House Inn, Carterway
   Heads
Queens Head Inn, Great
   Whittington
North Yorkshire
Black Bull Inn, Moulton
Fox and Hounds, Sinnington
General Tarleton, Ferrensby
Plough Inn, Saxton
Sandpiper Inn, Leyburn
Sportsman's Arms, Wath-in-
   Nidderdale
Nottinghamshire
Martins Arms, Colston Bassett
Oxfordshire
Bell, Standlake
Greyhound, Rotherfield Peppard
Lamb at Buckland, Buckland
Trout at Tadpole Bridge, Tadpole
   Bridge
Rutland
Olive Branch, Clipsham
Shropshire
Hundred House Hotel, Norton
Somerset
Three Horseshoes, Batcombe

Suffolk
Cornwallis, Brome
Warwickshire
Howard Arms, Ilmington
Kings Head, Aston Cantlow
West Sussex
Horse Guards Inn, Tillington
King's Arms, Fernhurst
Lickfold Inn, Lickfold
West Yorkshire
Millbank, Millbank
Ring O'Bells, Thornton
Three Acres Inn, Roydhouse
Wiltshire
Angel, Heytesbury
Bell, Ramsbury
Grosvenor Arms, Hindon
Pear Tree, Whitley
Seven Stars, Bottlesford
Tollgate Inn, Holt
Worcestershire
Walter de Cantelupe Inn,
   Kempsey

SCOTLAND
Argyll & Bute
Crinan Hotel, Crinan
Borders
Wheatsheaf, Swinton

WALES
Carmarthenshire
Salutation, Pontargothi
Conwy
Queen's Head, Glanwydden
Gwynedd
Penhelig Arms Hotel, Aberdovey
Isle of Anglesey
Ye Olde Bulls Head, Beaumaris
Monmouthshire
Clytha Arms, Clytha
Pembrokeshire
The Wolfe, Wolf's Castle
Powys
Bear Hotel, Crickhowell
Nantyffin Cider Mill Inn,
   Crickhowell
Red Lion Inn, Llanfihangel-nant-
   Melan
Seland Newydd, Pwllgloyw
Wynnstay Hotel, Machynlleth

Pubs serving exceptional draught beers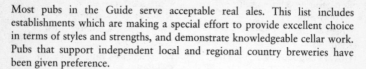

Most pubs in the Guide serve acceptable real ales. This list includes establishments which are making a special effort to provide excellent choice in terms of styles and strengths, and demonstrate knowledgeable cellar work. Pubs that support independent local and regional country breweries have been given preference.

ENGLAND
Berkshire
Bell Inn, Aldworth
Dundas Arms, Kintbury
Buckinghamshire
Crooked Billet, Newton Longville
Lions of Bledlow, Bledlow
Red Lion, Chenies
Cambridgeshire
Anchor Inn, Sutton Gault
Cheshire
Bhurtpore Inn, Aston
Dog Inn, Over Peover
Grosvenor Arms, Aldford
Cornwall
Maltsters Arms, Chapel Amble
Royal Oak, Lostwithiel
Trengilly Wartha Inn, Constantine
Cumbria
Britannia Inn, Elterwater
Drunken Duck Inn, Ambleside
Masons Arms, Cartmel Fell
Old Crown, Hesket Newmarket
Queens Head, Tirril
Queens Head Hotel, Troutbeck
Shepherds Inn, Melmerby
Derbyshire
Three Stags Heads, Wardlow Mires
Devon
Anchor Inn, Cockwood
Drewe Arms, Broadhembury
Duke of York, Iddesleigh
Hoops Inn, Horn's Cross
Jack in the Green, Rockbeare
Langton Arms, Tarrant Monkton
Malsters' Arms, Tuckenhay
Masons Arms, Branscombe
Nobody Inn, Doddiscombsleigh
Peter Tavy Inn, Peter Tavy
Tower Inn, Slapton
Union Inn, Dolton

Dorset
Bottle, Marshwood
Fox Inn, Corscombe
Langton Arms, Tarrant Monkton
East Sussex
Griffin Inn, Fletching
Jolly Sportsman, East Chiltington
Essex
Bell Inn, Horndon on the Hill
Cap & Feathers, Tillingham
Gloucestershire
Kings Arms Inn, Didmarton
Kings Head, Bledington
New Inn, Coln St Aldwyns
Hampshire
Flower Pots Inn, Cheriton
Hawkley Inn, Hawkley
John of Gaunt, Horsebridge
Peat Spade, Longstock
Sun, Bentworth
Herefordshire
Riverside Inn, Aymestrey
Stagg Inn, Titley
Kent
Bell Inn, Smarden
Gate Inn, Marshside
Hare, Langton Green
Kentish Horse, Markbeech
Shipwrights Arms, Oare
Three Chimneys, Biddenden
Lancashire
Eagle & Child, Bispham Green
New Inn, Yealand Conyers
Leicestershire
Bell Inn, East Langton
Old Crown, Cavendish Bridge
Norfolk
Darby, Swanton Morley
Fishermans Return, Winterton-on-Sea
Jolly Sailors, Brancaster Staithe

Red Lion, Stiffkey
Lord Nelson, Burnham Thorpe
Three Horseshoes, Warham All
  Saints
Northumberland
Dipton Mill, Hexham
Feathers Inn, Hedley on the Hill
Queens Head Inn, Great
  Whittington
North Yorkshire
Buck Inn, Thornton Watlass
Malt Shovel, Brearton
Peacock, Forhill
Nottinghamshire
Martins Arms, Colston Bassett
Oxfordshire
Falkland Arms, Great Tew
Royal Oak, Ramsden
Tite Inn, Chadlington
Shropshire
Burlton Inn, Burlton
Crown, Munslow
Dog Inn, Worfield
George & Dragon, Much Wenlock
Hundred House Hotel, Norton
Three Tuns, Bishop's Castle
Waterdine, Llanfair Waterdine
Somerset
Horse & Groom, East Woodlands
Royal Oak of Luxborough,
  Luxborough
Suffolk
Angel, Lavenham
Crown, Westleton
De La Pole Arms, Wingfield
Froize Inn, Chillesford
Moon & Mushroom Inn, Swilland
Surrey
The Hankley, Tilford
Plough Inn, Coldharbour
Warwickshire
Fox & Hounds Inn, Great Wolford
West Sussex
Black Horse, Nuthurst

The Fox Goes Free, Charlton
Halfway Bridge Inn, Halfway Bridge
King's Arms, Fernhurst
Lickfold Inn, Lickfold
Three Horseshoes, Elsted
West Yorkshire
Old Bridge Inn, Ripponden
Wiltshire
Dove Inn, Corton
George & Dragon, Rowde
Lamb at Hindon, Hindon
Tollgate Inn, Holt
Worcestershire
Peacock, Forhill
Talbot, Knightwick

SCOTLAND
Borders
Traquair Arms, Innerleithen
Dumfries & Galloway
Creebridge House Hotel, Minnigaff
Fife
Ship Inn, Limekilns
Stirling
Clachan Inn, Drymen

WALES
Gwynedd
Harp Inn, Llandwrog
Isle of Anglesey
Ship Inn, Red Wharf Bay
Monmouthshire
Boat Inn, Penallt
Clytha Arms, Clytha
Red Hart, Llanvapley
Pembrokeshire
Nag's Head Inn, Abercynch
Powys
Nantyffin Cider Mill Inn,
  Crickhowell
Vale of Glamorgan
Plough and Harrow, Monknash
Wrexham
Pant-yr-Ochain, Gresford

Pubs serving better-than-average wine 🍇

This award goes to pubs where wines have been chosen with imagination and in keeping with the dishes on offer; where there is good global choice (from easy-drinking house wines to classics) at fair prices; where the lists themselves give useful information to aid choice; and where there is at least a good handful available by the glass. Judging has been stricter for this edition of the Guide, as wines in country pubs continue to improve; as a result, some wine-award winners in the previous edition are not in the list below.

ENGLAND

Bedfordshire
Knife & Cleaver, Houghton Conquest

Berkshire
Bird in Hand, Knowl Hill

Buckinghamshire
Bull and Butcher, Turville
Chequers Inn, Wooburn Common
Crooked Billet, Newton Longville
Five Arrows Hotel, Waddesdon

Cambridgeshire
Anchor Inn, Sutton Gault
Chequers, Fowlmere
Old Bridge Hotel, Huntingdon
Pheasant Inn, Keyston
Three Horseshoes, Madingley

Cornwall
Pandora Inn, Mylor Bridge
Rising Sun, St Mawes
Trengilly Wartha Inn, Constantine

Co Durham
Morritt Arms, Greta Bridge
Rose and Crown, Romaldkirk

Cumbria
Bay Horse Hotel, Ulverston
Drunken Duck Inn, Ambleside
Pheasant Inn, Casterton

Devon
Anchor Inn, Cockwood
Arundell Arms, Lifton
Cott Inn, Dartington
Drewe Arms, Broadhembury
Jack in the Green, Rockbeare
Kings Arms Inn, Stockland
New Inn, Coleford
Nobody Inn, Doddiscombsleigh
Masons Arms, Branscombe
Old Rydon Inn, Kingsteighnton
Sloop Inn, Bantham
White Hart, Dartington

East Riding of Yorkshire
Wellington Inn, Lund

East Sussex
Griffin Inn, Fletching
Jolly Sportsman, East Chiltington

Essex
Bell Inn, Horndon on the Hill
White Hart, Great Yeldham

Gloucestershire
Kings Arms Inn, Didmarton
Kings Head, Bledington
New Inn, Coln St Aldwyns
Village Pub, Barnsley

Greater Manchester
White Hart, Lydgate

Herefordshire
Roebuck Inn, Brimfield
Stagg Inn, Titley

Kent
Dering Arms, Pluckley
Griffins Head, Chillenden

Lancashire
Forest Inn, Fence
Inn at Whitewell, Whitewell

Lincolnshire
Black Horse Inn, Grimsthorpe

Norfolk
Hoste Arms, Burnham Market
White Horse, Brancaster Staithe

Northamptonshire
Falcon Inn, Fotheringhay

Northumberland
Cook and Barker Inn, Newton-on-the-Moor

North Yorkshire
Abbey Inn, Byland Abbey
Angel Inn, Hetton
Blue Lion, East Witton
Buck Inn, Buckden
Fox and Hounds, Carthorpe
General Tarleton, Ferrensby

Nag's Head, Pickhill
Plough Inn, Saxton
Red Lion, Burnsall
Sportsman Arms, Wath-in-
 Nidderdale
Star Inn, Harome
White Swan, Pickering
Yorke Arms, Ramsgill
Oxfordshire
Bird in Hand, Hailey
Boar's Head, Ardington
Lamb at Buckland, Buckland
Lamb Inn, Burford
Sir Charles Napier, Chinnor
Rutland
Olive Branch, Clipsham
Shropshire
Crown Inn, Hopton Wafers
Waterdine, Llanfair Waterdine
Somerset
Blue Ball Inn, Triscombe
Crown Hotel, Exford
Haselbury Inn, Haselbury Plucknett
Three Horseshores, Batcombe
Suffolk
Angel, Lavenham
Cornwallis, Brome
Surrey
Old School House, Ockley
West Yorkshire
Kaye Arms, Grange Moor
Old Bridge Inn, Ripponden

Ring O'Bells, Thornton
Wiltshire
Angel, Heytesbury
Angel Inn, Upton Scudamore
Bell, Ramsbury
George & Dragon, Rowde
Lamb at Hindon, Hindon
Seven Stars, Bottlesford
Three Crowns, Brinkworth

SCOTLAND
Borders
Burts Hotel, Melrose
Wheatsheaf, Swinton
Midlothian
The Howgate, Howgate

WALES
Carmarthenshire
Salutation, Pontargothi
Gwynedd
Penhelig Arms Hotel, Aberdovey
Monmouthshire
Clytha Arms, Clytha
Pembrokeshire
The Wolfe, Wolf's Castle
Powys
Bear Hotel, Crickhowell
Nantyffin Cider Mill Inn,
 Crickhowell
Wynnstay Hotel, Machynlleth

New entries

The following pubs did not appear as main entries in the previous edition of the Guide, although some have been in the Out and About section, or may have appeared as main entries in previous editions.

ENGLAND
Bedfordshire
Chequers Inn, Keysoe
Berkshire
Red House, Marsh Benham
Swan Inn, Inkpen
Buckinghamshire
Crooked Billet, Newton Longville
Crown, Cuddington
Lone Tree, Thornborough
Rising Sun, Little Hampden
White Hart, Preston Bissett
Cambridgeshire
Black Horse, Elton
Old Bridge Hotel, Huntingdon
Cornwall
Gurnard's Head Hotel, Treen
Rising Sun, St Mawes
Roseland Inn, Philleigh
Cumbria
Mill Inn, Mungrisdale
Old Crown, Hesket Newmarket
Three Shires Inn, Little Langdale
Derbyshire
Black Swan, Idridgehay
Devon
Anchor Inn, Cockwood
Cadeleigh Arms, Cadeleigh
Drewe Arms, Drewsteignton
Golden Lion Inn, Tipton St John
Rising Sun, Umberleigh
Tradesman's Arms, Stokenham
Dorset
Cock & Bottle, Morden
Fox Inn, Ansty
Shaves Cross Inn, Shave Cross
East Sussex
Sussex Oak, Blackham
Essex
Bull, Blackmore End
Cap & Feathers, Tillingham
Swan Inn, Chappel
Gloucestershire
Eagle and Child, Stow-on-the-Wold
Gumstool Inn, Tetbury

Kings Arms Inn, Didmarton
Queens Arms, Ashleworth
Village Pub, Barnsley
Wyndham Arms, Clearwell
Yew Tree Inn, Clifford's Mesne
Hampshire
Clump Inn, Chilworth
Fox & Hounds, Crawley
Star Inn, East Tytherley
White Hart, Cadnam
Herefordshire
Ancient Camp Inn, Eaton Bishop
Stagg Inn, Titley
Three Crowns Inn, Ullingswick
Kent
Chequers Inn, Smarden
Griffins Head, Chillenden
Green Cross Inn, Goudhurst
Kentish Horse, Markbeech
Sportsman, Seasalter
Lancashire
Bay Horse Inn, Forton
Forest Inn, Fence
Mulberry Tree, Wrightington
Leicestershire
Berkeley Arms, Wymondham
Old Crown, Cavendish Bridge
Lincolnshire
Bell Inn, Coleby
Norfolk
Crown Hotel, Mundford
George & Dragon, Newton
Hoste Arms, Burnham Market
Jolly Sailors, Brancaster Staithe
Kings Arms, Shouldham
Lord Nelson, Burnham Market
Ostrich Inn, Castle Acre
Spread Eagle, Barton Bendish
White Horse, Brancaster Staithe
Northumberland
Feathers Inn, Hedley on the Hill
North Yorkshire
Hare Inn, Scawton
Plough, Fadmoor
Red Lion, Burnsall

Sandpiper Inn, Leyburn
Nottinghamshire
King's Head, Collingham
Oxfordshire
Greyhound, Rotherfield Peppard
Moody Cow at the Wykham Arms,
  Sibford Gower
Royal Oak, Ramsden
Trout at Tadpole Bridge, Tadpole
  Bridge
Rutland
Olive Branch, Clipsham
Shropshire
Burlton Inn, Burlton
Dog Inn, Worfield
George & Dragon, Much Wenlock
Waterdine, Llanfair Waterdine
Somerset
Blue Ball Inn, Triscombe
Kingsdon Inn, Kingsdon
Montague Inn, Shepton Montague
Three Horseshoes, Batcombe
Suffolk
Bull, Cavendish
Moon & Mushroom Inn, Swilland
Queen's Head, Bramfield
Surrey
Crown Inn, Chiddingfold
The Hankley, Tilford
Warwickshire
Kings Head, Aston Cantlow
Three Horseshoes, Wixford
West Yorkshire
Millbank, Millbank

Wiltshire
Angel, Heytesbury
Angel Inn, Upton Scudamore
Beckford Arms, Fonthill Gifford
Bell, Ramsbury
Pear Tree Inn, Whitley
Tollgate Inn, Holt
Worcestershire
Crown & Sandys Arms, Ombersley
Horse & Jockey, Far Forest
Peacock, Forhill

SCOTLAND
Argyll & Bute
Crinan Hotel, Crinan

WALES
Caerphilly
Hollybush Inn, Draethen
Carmarthenshire
Salutation, Pontargothi
Isle of Anglesey
Ye Olde Bulls Head, Beaumaris
Pembrokeshire
Nag's Head Inn, Abercynch
Powys
Felin Fach Griffin, Felin Fach
Wynnstay Hotel, Machynlleth
Vale of Glamorgan
Plough and Harrow, Monknash
Wrexham
Pant-yr-Ochain, Gresford

About the editor

Andrew Turvil is head of the research and inspection programme for Britain's most prestigious guide to restaurants, *The Good Food Guide,* and has had many years' experience of inspecting and writing about pubs and restaurants.

Introduction

Everyone has an idea of what makes the perfect country pub. Some will wax lyrical about the little thatched place they came across on holiday, while others have adored their local for as long as they can remember and judge all others against it. Among the hostelries in Britain's villages and country towns there is something for everyone, and the very best can be found in the pages of this Guide.

Twenty-first-century blues
The pub does not hold the same position it had in society as it did, say, at the beginning of the twentieth century. Even the name 'public house' is something of an anachronism these days. That term made more sense when a pub's main purpose was to provide a place (perhaps the only place) where people in a community could meet socially. Now, the scene has changed enormously. The twenty-first-century pub has to compete with the very best, and worst, that a modern industrialised country has to offer: shopping centres, leisure complexes, multi-channel TV, computer games, theme parks, chain restaurants. . . . Is it really any wonder that the number of pubs is declining, unable to compete? Many are snapped up as private houses, or bought by large corporations to become 'themed venues' – a theme worse than death.

The pub, even now, is often at the physical centre of a village, but unfortunately the number which really are at the heart of the community is declining. Six pubs a week, according to the Campaign for Real Ale (CAMRA), are closing, and are probably gone forever.

Pubs have been set a challenge as never before, and many – certainly those listed in these pages – have responded with imagination and dedication. There has been a phenomenal diversification into the selling of food (a trend that was triggered partially by the introduction of drink-driving laws and is now well established). The British now spend over £3 billion a year on pub food, and in many pubs food represents about 60–70 per cent of turnover. Standards are rising all the time and the number of pubs in this Guide awarded special mention for outstanding food has been creeping upwards over the years (over 100 in this edition), and the number of those that are maintaining high standards, but are not singled out for awards, is also rising. No secret formula exists for becoming a successful food pub; but good sense tells us that the answer does not lie in having a vast menu (as some publicans and pub-owning companies seem to believe). A large menu is usually a giveaway in itself, suggesting that the pub relies on bought-in, frozen, multi-portion meals. A focus on fresh ingredients, cooked to order, is the common theme that links all good food pubs.

Making use of local producers also helps give a pub a sense of identity and place. Whether making the most of local vegetables and meats, or finding the best supplier for a particular cheese, a pub's dedication to good sourcing demonstrates that the quality of the ingredients is as important as the ability to cook them. Many of the pubs in these pages make it their business to search out the best, demonstrating commitment to quality and seasonality.

We are also delighted to note that, not before time, the quality of wine is improving in many pubs. Accordingly, we have devoted more time than in previous editions to assessing the better-than-average wine lists in order to determine which pubs should receive a wine award, indicated by the bunch-of-grapes symbol at the top of entries. All the award-winners are listed on pages 14-15. It is not enough nowadays merely to offer a selection of reasonably priced wines from the New and Old Worlds. Those wines must be imaginatively chosen too, with an awareness of what is on the menu. Details on vintages and growers should appear on wine lists, for the benefit of today's more knowledgeable wine-drinkers.

Price has been a consideration too: some pubs with excellent, restaurant-standard lists have failed to win an award because, simply, their wines are pitched chiefly at customers with very deep pockets. Therefore, our wine award has gone to pubs offering a good global selection of well-priced wines – from easy-drinking house wines to admirable classics – plus a good handful by the glass. (As far as wines by the glass are concerned, the Crooked Billet in Newton Longville is way ahead of the field, with all 250 wines available.) Our stricter criteria for wine mean that some pubs which received an award in the previous edition of this Guide have not done so this time.

A brief word about . . . wines by the glass. Surely it is not asking too much in this day and age to provide a selection of, say, half a dozen or so wines in a variety of styles, rather than the all too common 'house red', 'house dry white' and 'house medium white'. A huge range of good-value wines is now available (check any supermarket), and there is no longer any excuse for bog-standard choices.

While researching this edition our inspectors have eaten in hundreds of pubs around Britain, and have found that the very best places can stand shoulder-to-shoulder with many fine restaurants in terms of quality of food. But that is not the norm. Take pot luck when selecting a pub and you are likely to be disappointed. We found many pubs that have not only failed to rise to the challenge of providing the food and drink that increasingly discerning customers demand, but also seem oblivious to the fact that their futures are at risk. Pubs that are unfriendly, shabby, offering indifferent beer and poor food are not hard to find. It will be no coincidence if those pubs are the ones that don't survive. And once a pub has been turned into a private house or restaurant, it is unlikely to revert to its former function, and the numbers will continue to dwindle.

'We can't get the staff'

The difficulty of recruiting catering staff is one of the problems cited by people in the hospitality industry, and it is a genuine one. The growth in the demand for kitchen and waiting staff throughout Britain has been enormous, and the shortage of well-trained chefs and servers is felt everywhere, but particularly in rural areas. We have had many a pub meal prepared by a poorly trained teenager, whose role as 'chef' involves learning how to use the microwave and putting some garnish on the side of the plate. Poor food is still being turned out by the truckload. A menu of bought-in dishes can be prepared by a small, unqualified team, certainly, but alternatively a short menu of simply prepared but fresh dishes is another way of coping with staff shortages.

A brief word about . . . garnish. Does the customer really want – *whatever* has been ordered – some limp lettuce, unripe tomatoes and raw onion on the plate? Chefs would do well to spend a few minutes to think up something appropriate for each dish, and not to bother using it if it isn't ripe or fresh.

This is for real

The sales of real ales have been in decline for the past few decades, owing to a number of reasons – not least the continued rise of mass-produced pressurised lagers and nitro-keg beers. Real beers have a taste, individuality and tradition that cannot be matched by their 'long-life' rivals, and good country pubs do their best to support the (mostly) independent breweries that produce them, thus keeping choice alive and well for the consumer.

The fact that three companies – Scottish & Newcastle, Carlsberg-Tetley and Interbrew – produce 80 per cent of all beer brewed in the UK must be a factor in the continued move away from real ale. These major companies are the main producers of nitro-keg ales and pressurised lagers. That leaves 20 per cent of beer production in the hands of the independents. The major brewers have the upper hand when it comes to sales and marketing, and their products are often aimed at young adults. The lagers and nitro-kegs are the fast food of the brewing industry – easier to keep and distribute in vast quantities and highly advertised. The relentless campaigning of organisations such as CAMRA and Cask Marque – the latter awards plaques to pubs that serve well-kept real beers – is flying the flag for real ale, but it is an uphill battle.

In this Guide we list the ales available in each pub, and it is disturbing to see what a limited and often predictable range is served in many of them, even in pubs with high standards in other areas. Traditionally the freehouse has most flexibility when it comes to supporting the smaller brewers, and it is important that they stock local ale rather than just selling the big brands. Where we have found a pub offering a really good range of real ales, we have given it a beer award, indicated by the jug symbol at the top of the entry. Award-winners are listed on pages 12-13.

Today we are mostly owned by . . .
Every day, somewhere in the UK, a pub is put under threat. The newspapers are full of stories about some big brewer or other buying up some smaller brewer, or a pub-owning company putting its pubs up for sale. The numbers involved are sometimes huge – as the Guide went to press Whitbread (owned by Interbrew) was looking for buyers for its 3,000 pubs. This is business, of course, and each company has to please its shareholders, but the effect on those who actually run the pubs, and their customers, can be enormous. Who is to say how many of the properties will remain pubs? How many communities will lose their friendly local and gain instead a chain restaurant or 'themed' venue or just another executive 'des res'?

We have spoken to pub staff who are not actually sure who owns the place any more. Some establishments have the names of long-since-defunct companies still emblazoned above the door. This insecurity is not good for the managed or tied houses, where a landlord is likely to be less inclined to give his all for a company if he thinks his loyalty is not worth anything. Several hundred tied, managed and leased houses appear in this Guide, and some brewers, clearly, are giving their landlords the opportunity to be creative and imaginative with the food they serve. But not everyone is that lucky. The most successful pubs in a portfolio are likely to be ones that will prove to be the most attractive to potential buyers – not all of which will wish to keep them operating as pubs.

Establishments that have lacked investment, or are in need of refurbishment, or a new licensee to inject a little inspiration, are probably the ones most in danger of being changed utterly as the big pub-owning chains saturate the country with their brands, turning traditional inns into chain restaurants or fast-food joints.

Vive la difference
Although horse-brasses, low beams and open fires are features common to a vast number of traditional country pubs, many that incorporate these still manage to have a style that is all their own. There are 110 new entries in this edition (a list of them appears on pages 16-17), and they include some wonderfully individual and quirky places. It is good to see some young teams – not to discriminate against the not-young, but the industry needs young blood if it is to prosper – taking over average pubs and really turning them around. Many have the wit and wisdom to convert the pubs with a sensitive eye and maintain the pub-like environment, retain the friendly atmosphere, yet bring the pub up to date. Although the majority of the pubs in this Guide are freehouses, a number of those owned by breweries and pub companies are nurturing progressive chefs. Pubs provide a good opportunity for a chef to run his/her own kitchen without personally bearing the risk of starting up a restaurant.

We are not arguing that every pub need compete at the highest culinary levels, although we have tried to ensure that all main entries in the Guide serve food of a good standard. For many people, however, it will be the pub's range of real ales that is the main attraction. The Out and About section towards the back of the book is the place to find characterful pubs that don't necessarily put food first, or indeed offer any food at all. They might offer well-kept beers from local micro-breweries, be in a fantastic old building in a superb location, or just exude atmosphere. These pubs are all valued for what they offer the pub-lover. It would be a great shame if the character of these places were changed in the name of progress.

A brief word about . . . soft drinks. The typical soft drinks available in most pubs are the usual leading brands (often bearing an astounding mark-up). Even some of the good food pubs do not expand on these, but the best offer home-made lemonade or ginger beer, fresh fruit juices or cocktails. Some imagination is always appreciated by the consumer, particularly the one who has to drive home afterwards.

Post code lottery

Our researchers have travelled the length and breadth of Britain, and visited pubs in all parts of the land. It is a simple fact that some areas have better pubs than others. Sometimes the reasons are obvious – tourist hot-spots, for example, are bound to attract enterprise – but in some areas it is a bit of a mystery. We are looking at a high standard, so it is not fair to conclude that any pub not listed is necessarily bad, but the dearth of really good pubs in certain counties is very disappointing.

The high-fliers are North Yorkshire with 11 rosette winners (plus lots of other great entries), Devon 7, Gloucestershire 7, Oxfordshire 5, Powys 5 and Wiltshire 7. Buckinghamshire can hold its head up high, as can Sussex, Kent, Cornwall, Dorset, Herefordshire, Suffolk and Norfolk. Visit any of these counties and you won't have to travel very far to find a first-class pub, with great food, excellent beer and a pleasant atmosphere (see pages 10-11 for a list of our top-rated pubs). We wish the same could be said of Bedfordshire, Hertfordshire, Staffordshire and Lincolnshire.

Let's look at Hertfordshire, for example. Not famous for tourism, certainly, but it is a fairly prosperous county with some attractive countryside. Where are the outstanding pubs? Although there are plenty of pubs in the county and some of them are very pleasant, we cannot single any of them out for outstanding food, although many are acceptable. But you won't be excited, amazed and wowed in Hertfordshire.

Scotland is unlike the rest of Britain as far as pubs are concerned. The number of Scottish entries in this Guide is not high, particularly given the size of the country, and many of those listed are located in hotels rather than are pubs *per se*. We have included them none the less because they are useful stops on a journey. Real ale is not that easy to come by in Scotland, either, despite the fact that some good independent breweries exist; we have found some pubs that stock them and you'll find them among the main entries and in the Out and About section.

A brief word about . . . chicken nuggets. Children can be demanding, certainly, but the best pubs do not try to palm them off with unimaginative processed meals. A child-focused menu can still include good-quality ingredients and real flavours.

When is a pub not a pub?

When it is a restaurant. Every year we drop a number of establishments from the Guide because we feel they can no longer be classified as pubs. That is usually because they have become restaurants instead, although the division is not always black and white. Some establishments do not consider themselves to be pubs any more and have been gradually evolving into restaurants – greeting customers at the door, shrinking the bar area, and no longer selling real ales. Welcoming – not just accepting – customers who want to drink but not eat is one of the most important criteria for being a pub. Many of the pubs in the Guide have separate restaurants, usually providing a more formal environment with waiter service and often more complex dishes, but to be featured in these pages they must demonstrate a commitment to the pub side of the business as well. Hence, the Angel in Long Crendon, the Goose at Britwell Salome, the Walnut Tree in Fawley, the Olive Branch in Marsden and the White Hart in Nayland may be good places in which to eat, but no longer feature in this guide.

Room for a little one?

The presence of children in pubs has always been a contentious issue. Many people think the pub is the domain of the adult and that the presence of children is distracting and spoils the atmosphere. The introduction in the mid-1990s of 'children's certificates' in England and Wales (Scotland had them earlier) had a negligible effect on how pubs conduct their business. The uptake of certificates has been low, and things are pretty much carrying on as before. The upshot is that in most cases children are allowed in areas where food is consumed. To exclude children completely is to deprive them of a civilising experience, and Britain is the only country in the world in which you will find food-serving establishments that ban children.

Of course, parents need to play their part, and make sure that their children's behaviour does not annoy the other customers. We have all seen the look of anxiety on the faces of other diners when a nearby table is occupied by a family with small children. They expect the worst. But in our experience you are just as likely to sit next to a group of adults who are obnoxious as you are a group of badly behaved children. In each main entry in the Guide we have made it clear whether children are welcome, and try to mention in the text if there are special facilities, such as play areas in the garden or children's menus.

Reports, please

This Guide is a compendium of shared experiences. We have followed up as many as possible of the recommendations you have sent us, despatching our inspectors to hundreds of pubs throughout Britain. Thank you for taking the time to put pen to paper, or finger to keyboard, and communicating your enthusiasm. Please keep your comments coming for the next edition (see the report forms at the back of the book for postal and email addresses).

Many of your reports confirmed our findings in the previous Guide, some disagreed with us or noted changes, while others alerted us to pubs we had not heard about. Whether pro, con or neutral, all your feedback is positively welcomed. Please let us know if you are aware of the arrival of new licensees or chefs, closures, or any other significant changes.

We hope the Guide leads you to the discovery of a new favourite pub.

Andrew Timm

ALDBURY   Hertfordshire   map 3

Valiant Trooper

Trooper Road, Aldbury HP23 5RW   TEL: (01442) 851203
off A41, 1½m E of Tring

Aldbury really is the archetypal picture-postcard village, complete
with duck pond. Its history goes back to Saxon times, but the village
inn is much younger, dating from the mid-eighteenth century. Inside,
it has bags of character in the shape of beams, low ceiling, flagged
floors and so on. Bar food is not complex but is served in generous
measure and is well presented. Snacks include jacket potatoes, open
sandwiches, ploughman's and filled ciabatta, while those looking for
something more substantial might opt for moules marinière followed
by steak au poivre, tarragon and honey-glazed chicken breast, or
smoked haddock thermidor, with Mississippi mud pie, or bread-and-
butter pudding to finish. The restaurant is in an old stable block;
here, a wide-ranging menu deals in the likes of prawn and scallop
pesto, Thai chicken with noodles, local wild pigeon braised in red
wine, and lambs' kidneys in a brandy, paprika and cream sauce.
Fuller's London Pride and John Smith's are supplemented by three
guest ales, which have included beers from Timothy Taylor, Ridleys
and Ash Vine. A list of around 20 wines includes nine by the large
glass; bottle prices start at £8.50. SAMPLE DISHES: chicken liver pâté
and toast £3.50; steak and kidney pie £7.50; chocolate roulade £3.

Licensee Timothy O'Gorman (freehouse)
Open *11.30 to 11, Sun 12 to 10.30; bar food and restaurant all week 12 to 2
(2.30 Sun; restaurant closed Mon), Tue to Sat 6.30 to 9.15; closed 25 and 26
Dec*
Details *Children welcome in eating areas   Car park   Wheelchair access (also
WC)   Garden and patio   No-smoking area in bar   Background music   Dogs
welcome in bar only   Delta, MasterCard, Switch, Visa*

ALDERMINSTER   Warwickshire   map 5

▲ *Bell*

Shipston Road, Alderminster CV37 8NY   TEL: (01789) 450414
WEB SITE: www.thebellald.co.uk
on A3400, 4m S of Stratford-upon-Avon

If the tourist crowds at Stratford-upon-Avon become a little overbearing, it may well be worth taking a short hop south to
Alderminster. There, this former coaching inn is well placed to cater
for at least some of the overspill. A conservatory extension affords
views of the Stour Valley as well as of the inn's own courtyard

garden, while the main room retains many of its original features, such as flagstones and wall and ceiling timbers. A range of bistro-type favourites is offered on the main menu, taking in field mush-rooms with garlic and herbs en croûte, king prawn kebab with a spicy dip, and main courses such as lamb rogan josh with spiced rice and sambals, a mixed dish of barbecued cuts of chicken, pork and lamb with chips, or seafood and shellfish casserole. The extensive pudding list features chocolate, brandy and almond mocha torte, lemon posset with blackcurrant compote, and peach and almond tart with frozen almond cream. Greene King IPA and Old Speckled Hen are on handpump, and there are ten wines to be had by the glass on the 50-strong list. Wine lovers also have a selection of bin-ends, special wines and a connoisseur's corner to browse through – the emphasis is on France. SAMPLE DISHES: seared scallops with warm potato salad with crème fraîche and pesto £6.75; pan-fried lambs' liver with crispy bacon, caramelised onions, bubble and squeak and port gravy £9; Lottie's poached pears in elderflower syrup with ginger Chantilly cream and home-made shortbread £4.

Licensee Keith Brewer (freehouse)
Open *12 to 2.30, 7 to 11 (10.30 Sun); bar food and restaurant 12 to 2, 7 to 9.30; closed evenings 24 to 26 Dec and 1 Jan*
Details *Children welcome   Car park   Wheelchair access (not WC)   Garden   No smoking in dining room   Occasional live music   No dogs   Amex, Diners, MasterCard, Switch, Visa   Accommodation: 5 rooms, B&B £25 to £65*

ALDFORD   Cheshire   map 7

Grosvenor Arms

Chester Road, Aldford CH3 6HJ
TEL: (01244) 620228
just off B5130, 5m S of Chester

It may seem to defy current fashion to have no separate restaurant in this large, imposing, red-brick building apparently built as a pub for the nearby estate of the Duke of Westminster. There is something of the country house about it, an impression reinforced by furniture and décor redolent of the first half of the twentieth century, and it is all admirably suited to its upmarket Cheshire location. The large conservatory is a non-smoking area, with blackboards that repeat the printed menu. Among sandwiches are poached salmon with crème fraîche, and open prawn and Marie Rose on walnut bread, while ploughman's offers a choice of two out of four cheeses. To start, you might consider Caesar salad with air-dried Cheshire ham, or smoked salmon on vegetable salsa with Cheshire cider dressing. Sophisticated main dishes display modern touches: pork fillet wrapped in bacon comes on creamed leeks and fondant potatoes with prune and Armagnac sauce, for example, or grilled fresh trout with rosemary butter, spinach and butter beans. A vegetarian option might be Stilton, leek and asparagus quiche with potato salad and coleslaw, and for pudding there's hot waffle with vanilla ice cream and fruits of the forest berries. Five real ales are served, including Boddingtons Bitter and Flowers IPA plus guests from the local Beartown Brewery, but pride of place goes to whisky, including more than 100 malts, 30 Irish and 35 bourbons. Almost all of the 20 wines on the reasonably priced list are offered by both bottle and glass. SAMPLE DISHES: chicken liver parfait with red onion chutney £5; 8oz steakburger with Gruyère topping and chips £8; blackberry frangipane with sauce Anglaise £4.

Licensees R.G. Kidd and D.J. Brunning (freehouse)
Open *11.30 to 11, Sun 12 to 10.30; closed 25 Dec evening; bar food 12 to 10*
Details *Children welcome Car park Wheelchair access (also WC) Garden and patio No smoking in conservatory No music Dogs welcome in 1 bar only Amex, Delta, MasterCard, Switch, Visa*

ALDWORTH Berkshire map 2

Bell Inn

Aldworth RG8 9SE TEL: (01635) 578272
on B4009, 3m W of Streatley

In one visitor's view, the Bell is 'an example of what pubs used to look like 50 years ago or more'. It has been in the hands of the Macaulay family for over 200 years; it has been a pub for 400, and the building is even older. Comfort then and now are different, so hard wooden chairs, narrow benches and odd tables are what you get – along with a modern note in the *Country Life* magazines on a window ledge. It stands opposite the old village well, and the garden and back field are edged by farms and woodlands. Beer is the main focus here, and the pub stocks a decent selection of well-kept ales, among them West Berkshire Maggs Magnificent Mild, Old Tyler Bitter, Arkell's 3B, Kingsdown Ale and Crouch Vale Best Bitter. Wine hardly counts – although Berry Bros' Good Ordinary Claret, one of three house wines sold by the glass, is decent enough. Food in the bar (there is no restaurant) is limited to home-made soup, rolls with generous and good-quality hot fillings, ploughman's, and a dish of the day, which might be pasta. Neither canned music nor gaming machines disturb the peace of the Bell's customers. SAMPLE DISHES: hot and crusty mature Cheddar roll £1.50; sausage hotpot £5; sponge pudding with treacle £2.50.

Licensee H.E. Macaulay (freehouse)
Open *Tue to Sat and bank hol Mon 11 to 3, 6 to 11, Sun 12 to 3, 7 to 10.30;
bar food 11 to 2.45, 6 to 10.45, Sun 12 to 2.45, 7 to 10.15; closed 25 Dec*
Details *Children welcome in family room Car park Wheelchair access (not
WC) Garden No music Dogs on leads welcome   No cards*

ALNMOUTH   Northumberland   map 10

▲ *Saddle Hotel*

24/25 Northumberland Street, Alnmouth NE66 2RA
TEL: (01665) 830476
*from A1, take Alnwick turn-off, then Alnmouth exit at mini-round-
about*

Fear not the savage winds from the North Sea, for all the houses in
this main street turn their backs on the beach, and in any case this
'simple, untrendy' local provides a warm and cosy atmosphere.
Think of all the pub snacks you can, and you will almost certainly
find them on the menu here, plus the occasional surprise. For example, Northumbrian stottie bread is the basis not only of sandwiches
but also of the Saddle pizza, which like many dishes is offered in full
portions or, at reduced prices, for 'La' – little appetite – rations.
Craster kipper, Northumberland sausage, Barnsley lamb chops, large
Yorkshire pudding filled with sausage or roast of the day, and fried
North Sea cod, prized by locals, are a reminder to visitors of just
where they are. Reasonably priced two- or three-course meals are
offered in the restaurant in the evenings. Old Speckled Hen and
Theakston Cool Cask are the real ales on offer, and three house
wines are available by the glass. SAMPLE DISHES: savoury mushrooms
£4; gammon grill £9 (or 'La' £4.50); profiteroles with chocolate
sauce £2.50 ('La' £1.50).

Licensee Michael McMonagle (freehouse)
Open *11 to 3, 6 to 11 (10.30 winter), Sun 12 to 3, 6 to 10.30; bar food 12
to 2, 6 to 9; restaurant all week D only 6 to 8.30*
Details *Children welcome in eating areas Wheelchair access (no WC) No
smoking in dining room Background music Dogs welcome Delta, Diners,
MasterCard, Switch, Visa Accommodation: 8 rooms, B&B £30 to £60*

---

*After the main section of the Guide is the special 'Out and about'
section listing additional pubs that are well worth a visit. Reports on
these entries are most welcome.*

ALRESFORD Hampshire map 2

Globe on the Lake

The Soke, Alresford SO24 9DB TEL: (01962) 732294
on lower end of Broad Street on B3046 Basingstoke road

A delightful location at one end of Alresford's main street makes the Globe a much-sought-after summer destination. It sits by the side of the village lake, where ducks and swans provide serene distraction for outdoor drinkers and diners. Inside, log fires, low beams and traditional dark wooden tables together with a settee next to an inglenook lend an air of cosiness. Above the fireplace, the daily-changing blackboard menu entices with the likes of smoked mackerel pâté, or grilled goats' cheese en croûte to start, followed by a good range of fish – perhaps herb-crusted cod with sun-dried tomato sauce, or spiced salmon with mango salsa – and cosmopolitan meat dishes such as chilli beef burrito with salsa and guacamole. Steaks are classically done with brandy and pepper sauce and chips, and to finish there is peach melba or, more fashionably, figs and mascarpone. A generous 17 wines by the glass kicks off a well-pitched and priced list, with both Old and New World classics coming in well under the £20 mark. Real ale drinkers are looked after, too, with Wadworth 6X, Brakspear Bitter, and Courage Best and Directors all on tap. SAMPLE DISHES: home-made hummus with crusty bread £4; pork tenderloin with cider sauce £8.50; vanilla terrine with raspberries and blackcurrant coulis £4.

Licensees Marc Conway and Emma Duveen (Entrepreneur Pubs)
Open *11 to 3, 6 to 11, Sun 12 to 3, 7 to 10.30; bar food and restaurant 12 to 2, 6.30 to 9, Sun 12.30 to 2, 7.30 to 9*
Details *Children welcome in dining room Wheelchair access (not WC) Garden No smoking in dining room No music Dogs by arrangement Amex, Delta, MasterCard, Switch, Visa*

AMBLESIDE Cumbria map 8

▲ *Drunken Duck Inn*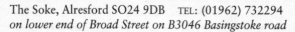

Barngates, Ambleside LA22 0NG TEL: (015394) 36347
WEB SITE: www.drunkenduckinn.co.uk
off B5286, between Ambleside and Hawkshead, 3m S of Ambleside

Real ale fans will be glad to find Cracker Ale, Tag Lag, and Chester's Strong & Ugly from the pub's own brewery, Barngates, as well as Jennings Bitter on handpump, plus bottled beers, including 12 from Belgium, as well as Thatcher's ciders. These still leave room for 50-odd wines set out on a nicely presented list that offers essential guidance for food-matching in its chatty, informative tasting notes. The range is wide, with plenty of options under £15 and with 12 or so wines available by the glass. So there's no shortage of choice of what to drink while enjoying the views of Lakeland or the bar's log fire, multitude of pictures on walls, and relaxed atmosphere. And you may have plenty of time to appreciate them because this perpetually full place can't always provide fast service, although it's very friendly. Menus include such unusual couplings as fried whitebait with salade niçoise and Cumberland whole-grain mustard dressing, grilled mallard breast on olive mash with baby fennel and basil dressing, and pear Condé tart with grilled marzipan. Dishes might be as simple as smoked bacon chop, or slow-roast duck leg, or as imaginative as grilled salmon fillet with shrimps. SAMPLE DISHES: langoustines poached with lemon, garlic and coriander £7; fell-bred beef fillet on roast tomatoes, peppers, olives and garlic with sweet chilli dressing £15; chocolate crème brûlée £4.75.

Licensee Stephanie Barton (freehouse)
Open *11.30 to 11, Sun 12 to 10.30; closed 25 Dec; bar food and restaurant 12 to 2.30, 6 to 9*
Details *Children welcome   Car park   Wheelchair access (also WC)   Patio No smoking in dining room   No music   Dogs welcome exc in restaurant Amex, Delta, MasterCard, Switch, Visa   Accommodation: 11 rooms, B&B £50 to £140*

ANSTY   **Dorset**   map 2

▲ *Fox Inn*   NEW ENTRY

Ansty DT2 7PN   TEL: (01258) 880328
WEB SITE: www.fox-inn-ansty.co.uk
from A35 Bere Regis to Dorchester, take Northbrook junction and follow directions to Piddlehinton; approx 200yds from this junction follow signs to Cheselbourne and follow road to Ansty

Steep roofs with pointed finials give a slightly Gothic impression to this pub, reinforced inside by high ceilings, brown wallpaper with a floral print and zoological relics that include stuffed foxes and a pheasant as well as a collection of goats' horns and a glass case containing a manikin of a huntsman. Badger Dorset Best and Tanglefoot are on draught, and ten wines, listed on a blackboard, are sold by the glass, with the full list running to nearly 40 decently priced bottles. The restaurant menu, also available in the bar, is priced according to the number of courses taken, and includes such modern starters as marinated pigeon with orange and star anise dressing, and red mullet escabèche with chard and saffron-roasted peppers. Among main courses, a tad more traditional, might be roast rump of lamb with caramelised shallots, plum tomatoes and oregano pan jus, and roast fillet of cod with wilted spinach. In the bar, baguettes are served until 6.30, and the full menu here encompasses a casserole of salmon, cod, mussels and leeks; and lime-marinated escalopes of pork with stir-fried vegetables; while one of the daily specials might turn up risotto of local crab and wild mushrooms. SAMPLE DISHES: salad of chicken, Parmesan and crisp smoked bacon £4.50; beer-battered fried cod with chips £9; warm blueberry English muffin £4.

Licensees Phillip and Shirley Scott (freehouse)
Open *9am to 11pm (10.30pm Sun); bar food and restaurant 12 to 3, 6.30 to 9.30*
Details *Children welcome in eating areas Car park Wheelchair access (also WC) Garden and patio No-smoking area in bar, no smoking in dining room Occasional background music Dogs welcome Amex, Delta, MasterCard, Switch, Visa Accommodation: 14 rooms, B&B £40 to £175*

APPLEBY   Cumbria   map 10

▲ *Royal Oak Inn*

Bongate, Appleby CA16 6UN   TEL: (017683) 51463
just off A66 at S edge of Appleby, 12m SE of Penrith

A short drive from Appleby, in virtually any direction, brings you to glorious countryside. Bongate is the oldest part of Appleby, and this medieval coaching inn dominates the main street. Inside are homely bars and a more formal restaurant, with interchangeable menus. Lunchtime snacks take in the usual sandwiches, jacket potatoes and salads, while among light bites nachos with melted cheese, salsa and sour cream find their place alongside Thai fishcakes, and Whitby scampi with chips. Blackboard specials might include haggis with mustard sauce, a dish an inspector found 'tasty and smooth with a good hot, gritty tang', or game pie. Bongate lamb pudding, or baked fillet of cod with pancetta might be on the printed menu, with a ring of choux pastry filled with bananas in Mars bar sauce among puddings. Other temptations could be little brown shrimps, or smoked salmon with balsamic-roasted asparagus followed by home-made lasagne, or teriyaki-style salmon with sweet cucumber salad. Beer drinkers can choose from Black Sheep Best Bitter, John Smith's, Bass, Worthington, and Yates plus a guest such as Marston's Pedigree, and malt whisky lovers from around 30. At least seven wines are offered by the glass from a short, fairly priced list. SAMPLE DISHES: Royal Oak smoky £5; blackeye bean and asparagus tacos £8; treacle tart £3.

Licensee E. McCauley (Mortal Man Inns)
Open *11 to 11, Sun 12 to 10.30; bar food and restaurant 12 to 2.30, 6 to 9 (9.30 Fri and Sat)*
Details *Children welcome in lounge and dining room   Car park   Wheelchair access (also WC)   Patio   No smoking in dining room   No music   Dogs welcome in taproom   Amex, Delta, MasterCard, Switch, Visa*
Accommodation: 9 rooms, B&B £37 to £90

APPLEY   Somerset   map 2

Globe Inn

Appley TA21 0HJ   TEL: (01823) 672327
from M5 junction 26 take A38 W for 3m; turn right to Greenham and after 1m turn right at T-junction, signposted Stawley; pub further ½m on left

Hidden away in a secluded hamlet surrounded by unspoilt rolling countryside, this rambling 500-year-old pub is reached along narrow, winding country lanes that seem to go on for ever. Despite the isolated location, it is a popular place, both with travellers stopping for refreshment (it is not far off the A38) and with locals out for a meal. Four rustic but comfortable rooms – one decorated with prints of liners, another with pictures of magpies – radiate off a narrow, flagstoned central passageway, where you will find the serving hatch. Menus offer extensive choice, mostly traditional pub fare with plenty of fish dishes, such as smoked haddock and bacon chowder, seafood pancake, and battered scampi. Various steak options include bookmaker's sandwich (4oz fillet steak in a toasted roll) or a 12oz sirloin, and there might also be lamb curry, and venison pie. Beers on handpump include Cotleigh Tawny from the highly rated Cotleigh Brewery in nearby Wiveliscombe, plus a guest such as Butcombe Gold or Teignworthy Reel Ale. Four wines are sold by the glass from a list that runs to 20-plus bottles. SAMPLE DISHES: chicken liver pâté £4.75; grilled fillet of Scottish salmon with chive, white wine and cream sauce £9.50; hot Toblerone crêpes £4.50.

Licensees A.W. and E.J. Burt (freehouse)
Open *Tue to Sat and bank hol Mon 11 to 3, 6.30 to 11, Sun 12 to 3, 7 to 10.30; bar food Tue to Sun 12 to 1.45, 7 to 9.45; restaurant Tue to Sat 7 to 9.45, Sun 12 to 1.45*
Details *Children welcome in eating areas   Car park   Garden   No smoking in dining room   No music   No dogs   Delta, MasterCard, Switch, Visa*

Recommendations for good country pubs will be very welcome.

ARDELEY   Hertfordshire   map 3

Jolly Waggoner

Ardeley SG2 7AH   TEL: (01438) 861350
off B1037 at Cromer, 5m E of Stevenage

One of the requirements of the quintessential country pub experience, thought a reporter, is that it should be reached down single-
track lanes, and in this the Jolly Waggoner does not disappoint. It is
an attractive cottagey inn with benches outside for summer eating,
which probably doubles the numbers catered for, as the interior is
fairly small. Horse brasses and wooden beams set the tone well,
although a collection of empty champagne bottles hints at the lush
life as well. Bar snacks include salads of various descriptions (chicken
and cashew nut, smoked salmon, stir-fried vegetables with garlic and
ginger), as well as home-made soups and sandwiches, while more
substantial dishes encompass chicken cooked in wine and cream with
mushrooms, onions and garlic, or locally made sausages. Look at the
board for puddings, which might include strawberry and mango
pavlova, or fruit brûlée. Next door, a slightly smarter restaurant,
Rose Cottage, seems almost like the dining room of a private house,
and serves a more elaborate menu. Greene King IPA and Abbot Ale
are on tap, and the wine list offers a compact selection, with just
house red and white by the glass. SAMPLE DISHES: fried goats'-cheese
and tomato salad £5.25; steak and kidney pie £9; bread-and-butter
pudding £3.50.

Licensee D.J. Perkins (Greene King)
Open *Tue to Sat (and bank hol Mon lunchtime) 12 to 2.30, 6.30 to 11, Sun
12 to 3, 7 to 10.30; bar food Tue to Sun (and bank hol Mon) 12 to 2, Tue to
Sat 6.30 to 9; restaurant Tue to Sat 6.30 to 9.30; closed Tue after bank hol
Mon*
Details *No children under 7   Car park   Wheelchair access (not WC)   Garden
and patio   Background music   No dogs   Delta, MasterCard, Switch, Visa*

ARDINGTON   Oxfordshire   map 2

Boar's Head 🍇

Church Street, Ardington OX12 8QA   TEL: (01235) 833254
off A417, 2m E of Wantage

A watering hole for Ridgeway walkers, this mainly nineteenth-
century pub is leased from the Victorian model estate which owns
much of the prosperous village, and its location next to the church
suggests a rustic idyll. However, its restaurant is decorated in a light,
airy style, with vineyard maps on the sunny-coloured walls, and the

style of cooking is just as sophisticated and metropolitan. Typical starters are crab with lime mayonnaise and guacamole, or a salad of shredded duck, apricots and toasted rice, while main dishes might include saddle of venison with red cabbage and ginger glaze, or roast monkfish with pommes pistou and pancetta. More traditional pub-style décor in the bars is in tune with a blackboard menu on which you might find Oxford bangers and mustard mash, or grilled lambs' liver. Desserts such as gâteau opera, figs on toasted panettone with mascarpone, or tarte Tatin with its own sorbet also show ambition soaring above the usual pub level. Ales on draught are Shepherd Neame Spitfire, Brakspear Bitter and Arkells 3B. The list of over 40 wines, with seven by the glass, is chosen with an enthusiast's palate, and the notes are unusually interesting. Trendy Bonny Doon vineyard (California) and Argentinian Malbec make an appearance, and there are some classics too – see the brief bin end selection of old vintages. SAMPLE DISHES: spaghetti with seafood £4.50; angler's pie £7; pear frangipane tart £4.50.

Licensee Mark Stott (freehouse)
Open *Tue to Sun (exc Sun evening) 12 to 3, 6.30 to 11; bar food and restaurant 12 to 2.15, 7 to 9.15*
Details *Children welcome   Car park   Wheelchair access (not WC)   Patio No smoking in dining room   Background music   Dogs welcome   Amex, Delta, MasterCard, Switch, Visa*

ARKESDEN   Essex   map 3

Axe and Compasses
Arkesden CB11 4EX   TEL: (01799) 550272
off B1038, 1m N of Clavering

Themis Christou brings the warmth of his Mediterranean origin to this pub, an appealing part-thatched building. A tiny stream runs through the pretty village of just 300 inhabitants, some of whom cross it by little footbridges to reach their thatched cottages. Set right in the centre, the Axe dates from 1650, the thatched roof indicating the original part of the brick building. The interior is very traditional, with pub games in the public bar, and more comfort in the other rooms, the lounge furnished with easy chairs, settees and antiques. The menus, the same throughout, don't stray far from conventional pub fare, such as pâté on redcurrant and port coulis, or grilled Mediterranean prawns with garlic butter, although starters may also include focaccia with red onions and Stilton, or julienne of lambs' liver and bacon with red wine in puff pastry. Pan-fried duck breast with Grand Marnier, and chicken breast with a port and Stilton sauce are typical of main dishes, with fish options of perhaps trout fillets sprinkled with cumin cooked with capers and prawns in brown butter. The bar menu might offer grilled sardines, leek and bacon crumble, or grilled polenta with stir-fried vegetables on a croûton with melted cheese. Desserts come on a trolley. Drink Greene King IPA or Old Speckled Hen or one of the three-monthly-changing guest beers – or one of ten wines by the glass from a well-balanced list. SAMPLE DISHES: selection of seafood with lemon and parsley mayonnaise £6; halibut steak on leek sauce £9.75; pork loin on Stilton and mushroom sauce £7.25.

Licensee Themis Christou (Greene King)
Open *11 to 2.30, 6 to 11, Sun 12 to 3, 7 to 10.30; bar food and restaurant 12 to 2, 6.45 to 9.30; restaurant closed Sun evening winter*
Details *Children welcome in dining room   Car park   Patio   No smoking in dining room   No music   No dogs   Delta, MasterCard, Switch, Visa*

ARLINGTON   East Sussex   map 3

Old Oak

Arlington BN26 6SJ   TEL: (01323) 482072
off A22, 4m SW of Hailsham, outside village of Arlington

Although this fine eighteenth-century white-painted brick pub is 'rather in the middle of nowhere', it has the Abbot's Wood Nature Reserve just opposite, and from the back there are fine views over the South Downs. Inside is a congenial, well-patronised bar and a rather more formal restaurant. The menus are generally not inter-changeable, and the lunchtime bar blackboard offers conventional snacks, such as filled baked potatoes, salads and baguettes, as well as hot dishes, including pasta, ham, egg and chips, a curry, and steak and ale pie. The daily specials board might list turkey and ham pie or fresh cod, while seasonally changed puddings could be banoffi pie, spotted dick, or home-made apple and blackberry pie. Restaurant dishes usually include a choice of fish, a roast, and various char-grilled steaks. From barrels in full view are drawn Badger Dorset Best Bitter and local Harveys Sussex Best, and there is a weekly-changing guest ale too, among them perhaps Morrells' Oxford Bitter or Fuller's London Pride. Three wines are served by the glass from a short list. SAMPLE DISHES: ploughman's £4.75; steak and kidney pudding £5; treacle sponge £3.

Licensee Ian Nicoll (freehouse)
Open *11 to 3, 6 to 11, Sun 12 to 3, 7 to 10.30; bar food and restaurant (exc Sun and Mon evenings) 12 to 2, 7 to 9; closed evening 25 Dec, 26 Dec*
Details *Children welcome in dining room   Car park   Wheelchair access (not WC)   Garden   Occasional background music   Dogs welcome in bar   Amex, Delta, MasterCard, Switch, Visa*

Duke's Head Hotel

Armathwaite CA4 9PB   TEL: (016974) 72226
off A6, between Carlisle and Penrith

The name of this sleepy hamlet means 'hermit's clearing', and it is
not hard to see why the hermit chose this location: it is right in the
heart of the beautiful Eden Valley, a paradise for bird-watchers and
walkers. The friendly, family-run village inn is a well-proportioned
whitewashed building in the centre of the village. Inside, there are
two bar areas, one a slightly austere room with table skittles, the
other a comfortable, homely lounge with chintzy cushions on chairs
and settees; beyond the lounge is the dining room, where you can
book a table. One menu is served throughout, offering a generous
range of mostly traditional pub fare, such as prawn cocktail, steak in
brandy, cream and peppercorn sauce, or home-boiled ham with salad
and fried potatoes. More interesting are the blackboard specials,
which might feature braised lamb shank in a rosemary and red wine
jus, or baked sea bass fillet with Noilly Prat and leeks. Tetley Bitter is
always available, while the guest ale might be Castle Eden or
Marston's Pedigree. A list of New and Old World wines includes
four by the glass. SAMPLE DISHES: smoked salmon and prawns £4.25;
braised pieces of chicken with sun-dried tomatoes, chorizo and Rioja
sauce £8.25; ginger, date and walnut sponge £3.25.

Licensee Henry Lynch (Pubmaster)
Open *11.30 to 3, 5.30 to 11; bar food and restaurant 12 to 1.45, 6.15 to 9;
closed 25 Dec*
Details *Children welcome   Car park   Wheelchair access (not WC)   Garden
No smoking in dining room   Background music   Dogs welcome in 1 bar
Delta, Diners, MasterCard, Switch, Visa   Accommodation: 5 rooms, B&B
£28.50 to £48.50*

▲ *Crab & Lobster* 🏵 🏵

Dishforth Road, Asenby YO7 3QL   TEL: (01845) 577286
WEB SITE: www.crabandlobster.co.uk
off A168, between A19 and A1

Having celebrated its tenth birthday in 2000, the Crab & Lobster is
all set for another dynamic decade, its sphere of operations now
extending to a hotel, Crab Manor. The pub itself is quite enough of
a cabinet of curiosities to be going on with. Hundreds of peculiar
objects, from drums to parasols, are suspended above the smartly set

tables in the dining area. As well as a choice of real ales including Theakston, Black Sheep and Worthington, David Barnard also prides himself on running a wine list of considerable discernment, with no fewer than 14 available by the glass. The cooking has an 'eclectic' slant to it: begin perhaps with monkfish tortillas with chilli salsa and sour cream, or foie gras parfait with a pickle of Granny Smiths and vanilla, before proceeding to Moroccan lamb tagine with couscous, or Goan fish curry with coconut rice and raita. King scallops with tomato chutney on an onion pancake were perfectly timed at one spring lunch, while summer pudding a little later in the year was a well-made dessert. Theme evenings, such as blues suppers and jazz dinner-dances, seem to take place most weeks. SAMPLE DISHES: crispy duck, chorizo, pancetta, mango and coriander salad £6; bouillabaisse with saffron potatoes and rouille £13.50; raspberry brûlée cheese-cake £4.50.

Licensee David Barnard (freehouse)
Open *11.30 to 3, 6.30 to 11, Sun 12 to 11; bar food and restaurant 12 to 2.30, 6.30 to 10, Sun 12 to 10*
Details *Children welcome in eating areas   Car park   Garden and patio   No smoking in dining room   Occasional live or background music   Dogs welcome   Amex, MasterCard, Switch, Visa   Accommodation: 12 rooms, B&B £80 to £140*

ASHLEWORTH   Gloucestershire   map 5

Queens Arms   NEW ENTRY

Ashleworth GL19 4HT   TEL: (01452) 700395
village signposted off A417 Gloucester to Ledbury road at Hartpury

Outside this cottage-style pub are two magnificent clipped yew trees, 200 years old. The sensitively modernised interior preserves the beams and iron fireplace, and the spacious lounge is homely yet bright, with Tiffany-style lamps in an otherwise conventionally deco-rated room. Clues to Tony and Gill Burreddu's background are a prominently displayed South African flag and the menu's bobotie, described as spicy minced beef topped with savoury egg custard, raisins and almonds. They call the Queens Arms a 'village pub and restaurant', and despite the emphasis on food three well-kept beers are on offer from a list that includes Timothy Taylor Landlord plus perhaps Young's Bitter or Special, Donnington BB, Shepherd Neame Spitfire and Marston's Pedigree. The wine list, modest in length and prices, is strong on South African bottles; six wines are sold by the glass. The menu includes sherried kidneys in a thick, rich, herby gravy, and tasty roast tomato and pesto soup. Follow them with a main course of perhaps chicken, ham and leek pie, salmon fillet with a creamy white wine and lemon sauce, or roast pheasant with a game and bitter chocolate sauce. Vegetables are fresh and properly cooked, and among desserts might be Cape brandy pudding, or apple, pineapple and date flan. SAMPLE DISHES: Brie and Stilton croquettes £4.50; roast cod topped with mozzarella with a dressing of basil, balsamic vinegar and olive oil £11; lemon cheesecake £3.75.

Licensees Tony and Gill Burreddu (freehouse)
Open *12 to 3, 7 to 11 (10.30 Sun); bar food and restaurant 12 to 2, 7 to 9 (10 Fri and Sat); closed 25 Dec*
Details *Children welcome   Car park   Wheelchair access (not WC)   Garden and patio   No smoking in dining room   Background music   No dogs   Delta, MasterCard, Switch, Visa*

ASHPRINGTON   Devon   map 1

▲ *Durant Arms*

Ashprington TQ9 7UP   TEL: (01803) 732240
off A381 Totnes to Kingsbridge road, 2m SE of Totnes

Dating from the eighteenth century, the Durant Arms is at the centre of the South Hams village of Ashprington. Both the interior décor and the hospitality of Graham and Eileen Ellis create a homely and welcoming atmosphere. Menus are supplemented by blackboard specials and offer almost entirely traditional English fare using produce from local sources, all freshly cooked to order. On the specials board are usually seven starters, twelve meat courses, six of fish and eight desserts. These might include home-made soups, pork tenderloin, chicken suprême, steaks, and home-made puddings along the lines of treacle tart and crème brûlée. Theme nights are a frequent occurrence. Flowers IPA and Wadworth 6X will keep beer drinkers happy, and Old Pig Squeal, a local still cider from the flagon, will cheer cider drinkers. Equally local is English wine from Sharpham: the Estate Reserve is one of seven bottles (out of around 25) also offered by the glass, all at modest prices. SAMPLE DISHES: creamy garlic mushrooms £4; Barbary duck breast £12.25; blackberry and apple pie £3.25.

Licensees Graham and Eileen Ellis (freehouse)
Open *11.30 to 2.30, 6 (6.30 winter) to 11, Sun 12 to 2.30, 7 to 10.30; bar food and restaurant 11.30 to 2, 6 (7 Sun) to 9; closed evenings 25 and 26 Dec*
Details *Children welcome   Car park   Wheelchair access (also WC)   Patio No smoking in dining room   Occasional live and background music   Dogs welcome   MasterCard, Switch, Visa   Accommodation: 6 rooms, B&B £30 to £50*

▲ *Waterman's Arms*

Bow Bridge, Ashprington TQ9 7EG
TEL: (01803) 732214

This large stone-built pub stands by Bow Bridge, and it has extended across the road with chairs and tables by the river. An inspector found it 'a bit shambolic' inside though cosy too, with a welcoming atmosphere; one wall is covered with old fob watches and there is a hotchpotch of pictures and photographs on the others. It's not too fancy, and locals gather round the log fire in winter to read the papers and chat with relaxed and friendly staff. Food may be rather pricey, but it is imaginative and portions are generous. Sandwiches include crab with salad, or smoked salmon with cream cheese. Among light snacks are warm broccoli and feta tart, pork, apple and calvados pâté, and a platter of cold bites – Parma ham, salami, rollmops, buffalo mozzarella and marinated vegetables. Lunchtime specials might run to farmhouse sausages on herb mash, or deep-fried cod with peas and chips, while the restaurant menu takes in seafood platters, Cajun steak topped with Stilton, and fruit-stuffed Gressingham duck breast. Beers on handpump are Bass, Bow Bridge Bitter, and Theakston XB, and cider lovers will be pleased to find Ruddy Turnstones on tap plus, for the stout-hearted, Pig Squeal and Shag. The reasonably priced wine list offers six house wines by the glass. SAMPLE DISHES: mussels marinière £6; Thai green chicken curry £8; bread-and-butter pudding £3.95.

Licensee Steven Simmons (Eldridge Pope)
Open *11 to 11, Sun 12 to 10.30; bar food and restaurant 12 to 2.30, 6.30 to 9.30*
Details *Children welcome   Car park   Wheelchair access (also WC)   Garden and patio   No-smoking area in bar, no smoking in dining room   Live or background music   Dogs welcome   Delta, MasterCard, Switch, Visa Accommodation: 15 rooms, B&B £54 to £79*

ASKRIGG   **North Yorkshire**   **map 8**

Kings Arms

HERRIOT COUNTRY

Askrigg DL8 3HQ   TEL: (01969) 650817
off A684 Sedburgh to Bedale road, ½m N of Bainbridge

The Kings Arms, which in *All Creatures Great and Small* became the Drover's, is on the main street of a pretty Dales village. Sit outside in the small back courtyard or go inside, where all is clean and rustic and has been virtually unchanged for years. Although the pub has no car park, there is limited parking on the roadside and a public car park nearby. A huge stone fireplace warms one bar, horses' harnesses hang from the ceiling in another, and there is much James Herriot decorative crockery. It's a relaxed, casual place, with staff who warmly welcome locals, visitors and walkers alike. Theakston XB, John Smith's Best and Black Sheep Best Bitter are the real ales on draught, plus a guest in summer, along with Scrumpy Jack cider, and eight wines are served by the glass from a carefully chosen list of over 50 bottles. The Silks Room restaurant, 'where Wensleydale meets the Orient' as the pub's own literature puts it, offers a taste of the exotic, from chicken satay to fillet of sea bass with plum and black-bean sauce. Other menus are on blackboards, with another for Sunday lunch, from which a couple relished tender and tasty roast beef and lamb, both accompanied by 'very good' Yorkshire pudding and 'carefully cooked' vegetables. Dinner might include avocado and smoked bacon salad, or spicy salmon fishcake followed by skate sautéed with capers, oranges and cider, or courgette and aubergine casserole with spicy couscous. SAMPLE DISHES: trio of breaded Wensleydale cheeses with crab apple jelly £4; Cajun chicken with pineapple and sweet pepper sauce £8; lemon tart with raspberry coulis £4.

Licensee Graham Turner (freehouse)
Open *11 to 11 (11 to 3, 6 to 11 winter), Sun 12 to 10.30; bar food 12 to 2, 6.30 to 9; restaurant Fri and Sat 7 to 9*
Details *Children welcome Wheelchair access (not WC) Patio No-smoking area in bar, no smoking in dining room Occasional background music Dogs welcome Delta, MasterCard, Switch, Visa*

ASTON   **Cheshire**   map 7

Bhurtpore Inn 🍺

Wrenbury Road, Aston CW5 8DQ
TEL: (01270) 780917
off A530, 5m S of Nantwich

WHISKY

This unpretentious yet comfortable village pub has a lot going for it on several fronts, good food and drink, and a colourful history among them. The Indian connection goes much deeper than the pub's name, which commemorates a successful siege by a local landowner. Anglo-Indian culture is embodied not just in pictures and sculptures but also in the special menu board, which includes half a dozen home-made curries and baltis: the latter served with naan instead of rice. Also on the board might be smoked salmon pâté with a herb and nut coating, or chicken breast on creamed leeks with Shropshire blue cheese sauce. More conventional pub food is there, too, in the form of mushrooms in cream, garlic and horseradish followed perhaps by steak, kidney and real ale pie. Vegetarians have around four main courses to choose from, and desserts run to lemon brûlée and sticky toffee pudding. But an inn's – and particularly this inn's – *raison d'être* is to provide liquid refreshment. Real beers here are a choice from Hanby Drawwell Bitter or nine frequently changing guest brews from small independent breweries. In addition, there are about 180 Belgian and German bottled beers, 120 whiskies and a farmhouse cider. The very modestly priced wine list, with a distinct focus on modern, fruity styles, begins with house red and white at £7.95, proceeding to fine wines and champagnes all under £35. With the latter you're given a longer tasting note to explain exactly why you pay more. Eight wines are served by the glass. SAMPLE DISHES: mini Indian savouries with mango chutney and mini naan bread £4; rabbit casseroled in red wine with bacon and thyme £8; warm chocolate fudge cake with ice cream £3.

Licensees Simon and Nicky George (freehouse)
Open *12 to 2.30, 6.30 to 11, Sun 12 to 3, 7 to 10.30; closed 25 Dec; bar food and restaurant 12 to 2, 7 to 9.30, Sun 12 to 2.30, 7 to 9*
Details *Children welcome in eating areas L and before 8 evenings Car park Wheelchair access (also WC) Garden and patio No smoking in 1 bar area and dining room Occasional live music Dogs welcome in games room only No cards*

ASTON CANTLOW   **Warwickshire**   map 5

Kings Head ✿   NEW ENTRY

FISH

Aston Cantlow B95 6HY   TEL: (01789) 488242
village signposted off A3400 NW of Stratford or off A46 Stratford to Alcester road

---

Standing opposite the magnificent early-sixteenth-century guild house is the equally impressive timber-framed and creeper-clad Kings Head. The pub's main claim to fame is that it was supposedly the venue for the wedding breakfast of John Shakespeare and Mary Arden (William's parents) after they made their vows in the thirteenth-century church next door. In the bar the decorative theme is tasteful rustic simplicity – huge polished flagstones, original beams, scrubbed pine tables, and scatter cushions on pews and old settles – while the light and airy rear dining room has more of a metropolitan feel. A visitor found the atmosphere throughout 'great'. One menu serves both areas, a printed card supplemented by a daily-changing list of fish specials, which might include 'beautifully cooked' whole sea bass drizzled with puttanesca butter, or a simple plate of smoked salmon with saffron mayonnaise. Generally the cooking avoids old-fashioned pub grub type dishes, though some old favourites are done up in a modern style: salmon and coriander fishcakes, or chargrilled calf's liver with mustard mash and red onion jam, for example. Otherwise expect things like bruschetta of roast field mushrooms with Roquefort, and risotto verde with shaved Pecorino. A regular fixture is 'the famous Kings Head duck supper'. Greene King Abbott Ale is on tap plus a guest such as Fuller's London Pride, while wine drinkers are offered a selection of more than 30, including six by the glass. SAMPLE DISHES: grilled sardines with pesto £5; suprême of salmon with gazpacho sauce and deep-fried basil £11.75; chocolate fudge brownie £4.50.

Licensee Paul Hales (Classic Country Pub Co)
Open *Mon to Fri 11 to 3, 5.30 to 11, Sat 11 to 11, Sun 12 to 10.30; bar food and restaurant 12 to 2.30, 7 to 10, Sun 12 to 3, 7 to 9; no food 25 Dec*
Details *Children welcome   Car park   Wheelchair access (also WC)   Garden and patio   No-smoking area in 1 area of bar   Occasional background music   Dogs welcome exc in the restaurant unless guide dogs   Amex, Delta, MasterCard, Switch, Visa*

ASWARBY   Lincolnshire   map 6

▲ *Tally Ho Inn*

Aswarby NG34 8SA   TEL: (01529) 455205
on A15 Peterborough to Lincoln road, 5m S of Sleaford

The décor's hunting theme is appropriate to the name of this inn, established over a hundred years ago in what had been a farmhouse in the eighteenth century. Friendly customers and a warm greeting from staff have been appreciated, and children are welcome. The restaurant has its own menu of mainly quite straightforward dishes, from garlic mushrooms to flash-fried beef fillet in pink peppercorn sauce, although there may also be ham rolls stuffed with spinach and cheese, or grilled salmon fillet in cream and dill sauce with mussels, prawns and cockles. The bar menu and bar specials board deliver baguettes and ploughman's, Lincolnshire sausage with chips, and wild boar sausages with apple mash. Others are more unusual: salmon and spinach fishcakes, venison and cranberry casserole, and rump steak with onion and mushrooms soaked in Bateman ale and topped with Lincolnshire Poacher cheese. Among desserts you might find pear and toffee crumble tart, or apple and calvados pancakes. Bateman XB and Bass, plus guest beers, are on handpump, and three wines are sold by the glass. SAMPLE DISHES: goujons of plaice and scampi £6.25; tuna steak with hot pepper salsa £7.50; banana cream pie £2.75.

Licensee Christine Shepherdson (freehouse)
Open *12 to 3, 6 to 11, Sun 12 to 3, 7 to 10.30; bar food 12 to 2.30, 6.30 to 10; restaurant Mon to Sat 7 to 9.30, Sun 12 to 2*
Details *Children welcome   Car park   Garden   No smoking in dining room Background music   Dogs welcome   Delta, MasterCard, Switch, Visa Accommodation: 6 rooms, B&B £35 to £50*

A W R E   **Gloucestershire**   **map 2**

▲ *Red Hart Inn*

Awre GL14 1EW   TEL: (01594) 510220
off A48 Newnham to Chepstow road, 2m S of Newnham

A table in the beer garden outside this fifteenth-century inn at the height of summer would be an enviable prospect. The pub is not far from the River Severn in a very becoming little Gloucestershire village found along narrow lanes. Dried hop flowers covering dark oak beams and a collection of beer mats attract the eye on entering the L-shaped bar, which gives on to a more formal dining area at one end. Chicken liver pâté with Cumberland sauce, home-cured gravad lax, beef bourguignon, and chargrilled steaks (are you hungry enough for a 16oz piece of rump?) are all there, but one or two more novel ideas might show up in, for example, oat-coated venison stuffed with apple and Stilton on a port glaze, or cheesy chicken filled with smoked bacon and asparagus mousse on a red wine sauce. Vegetarians have their own options, and desserts bring on the likes of meringue nest filled with summer fruits, and sticky toffee pudding with toffee sauce. Fuller's London Pride, draught Bass and Freeminer Speculation Ale will impress the real ale enthusiasts, as might one of the regularly changing guest beers from Bath Ales and SP Sporting Ales. A wide-ranging and fairly priced wine list includes two house wines by the glass. SAMPLE DISHES: grilled anchovies on toasted brioche with lemon chutney £4.25; lamb Wellington £10.50; home-made Malteser cheesecake £3.25.

Licensee Jerry Bedwell (freehouse)
Open *Tue to Sun 12 to 3, all week 6.30 to 11 (10.30 Sun); bar food and restaurant (exc Mon lunchtime and Sun evening) 12 to 2, 6.45 to 9; closed 25 Dec and 1 Jan*
Details *Children welcome   Car park   Wheelchair access (also WC)   Garden No-smoking area in bar, no smoking in dining room   Background music   No dogs   Amex, Delta, MasterCard, Switch, Visa   Accommodation: 2 rooms, B&B £50 to £55*

🍇 *indicates a pub serving better-than-average wine, including good choice by the glass.*

AXFORD   Wiltshire   map 2

Red Lion

FISH

Axford SN8 2HA   TEL: (01672) 520271
off A4, 3m E of Marlborough, between Mildenhall and Ramsbury

On the outskirts of a village overlooking the Itchen valley, the Red
Lion is a red-brick and flint building with a small conservatory
entrance. Agar Fisheries of Marlborough supply the fresh fish, and
you can eat it either in the lounge, set out for casual dining, or in the
main restaurant, which has more formal settings. Walls are hung
with small watercolours by local artists, while ceramic pint pots and
china jugs adorn the bar. The bar menu encompasses the likes of
pork and leek sausages with mash; steak and kidney pie; and
battered fillet of haddock with chips or sauté potatoes. Fish is the
focus, however, on the restaurant menu (also available in the bar),
and one visitor enjoyed three plump scallops in a shell with a light
cream sauce, and then thick wing of skate ('oozing with sweet sea
savour') served with capers, deep-fried new potatoes and vegetables.
Lemon sole is poached in Chardonnay, baked halibut comes with a
citrus sauce, and creamy tagliatelle is the medium for smoked
salmon. Meat eaters might opt for roast rack of lamb with redcurrants and rosemary, or half a Gressingham duck finished with
Cointreau and orange. Hook Norton Best Bitter, Flowers Original
and Wadworth 6X are on tap, and there is a commendably extensive
wine list, including a few fine wines, with 13 by the glass. SAMPLE
DISHES: chicken liver and brandy pâté £4.25; mixed seafood pan-
fried with garlic £15; Mississippi mud pie £3.75.

Licensees Melvyn and Daphne Evans (freehouse)
Open *11.30 to 3, 6.30 to 11, Sun 12 to 3, 7 to 10.30; bar food and
restaurant 12 to 2, 6.30 to 9.30; closed 25 Dec*
Details *Children welcome   Car park   Wheelchair access (not WC)   Garden
and patio   No smoking in dining room   Background music   No dogs   Delta,
MasterCard, Switch, Visa*

AYMESTREY   Herefordshire   map 5

▲ *Riverside Inn* 🍺

Aymestrey HR6 9ST   TEL: (01568) 708440
WEB SITE: www.theriversideinn.net
on A4110, 6m NW of Leominster

This half-timbered inn is a long, narrow, tall building on the A4110
near the bridge over the River Lugg. It sits on steeply rising ground,
with trestle tables near the water's edge, and secluded, leafy spots for

al fresco eating higher up the hill. Inside, the bar and an ancillary dining area with spindle-backed chairs and brightly patterned carpet are on the ground-floor level, while the main dining room, otherwise known as the Barn Restaurant, is downstairs. Beams, bare wooden tables and decorative dried hops contribute to the simple country atmosphere. The Riverside has always been proud of its food suppliers, and they are given judicious credit in the preface to the menu. New chef Mark Flello follows the lead set by his predecessors on turning this premium produce into some imaginative dishes. You might start with rillettes of duck with spring onions served with marrow and ginger jam, or pigeon breast with a sauce of juniper, cinnamon and hazelnut, before proceeding to monkfish on braised fennel with sweet carrot sauce, or rack of nicely pink Marches lamb with an impressive stock-based tarragon-scented sauce. Steak, kidney and Kingfisher pie does not, be assured, contain the brightly coloured bird but rather nearby Woodhampton brewery's beer of that name. The selection of English and Welsh cheeses from the Mousetrap in Leominster is not to be missed. Apart from Kingfisher, other ornithologically named beers on draught include Red Kite, Jack Snipe and Wagtail, and there is Weston's cider. Whiskies and brandies are well chosen, and there are half a dozen wines (including two champagnes) by the glass. SAMPLE DISHES: Cornish crab salad £6; woodland venison with damson sauce £15; home-made ice creams and sorbets £3.50.

Licensees Val and Steve Bowen (freehouse)
Open *11 (or earlier) to 11 (10.30 Sun); bar food and restaurant 12 to 2.30, 6.30 to 9.30; closed 25 Dec*
Details *Children welcome in bar eating area   Car park   Wheelchair access (not WC)   Garden   No smoking in dining room   No music   Dogs welcome Delta, MasterCard, Switch, Visa   Accommodation: 5 rooms, B&B £25 to £70*

BALLINGER COMMON   **Buckinghamshire**   map 3

Pheasant

Ballinger Common HP16 9LF   TEL: (01494) 837236
WEB SITE: www.pheasantdining.co.uk
off A413 at Great Missenden, 3m W of Chesham

The sign outside may say 'Eating House', but drinkers, one visitor noted, receive just as warm a welcome. Opposite the cricket pitch and a children's playground, the Pheasant is in fine walking country that also happens to be less than an hour's drive out of London. A patio garden has picnic benches and an assortment of shrubs and pot plants, and, inside, the genuinely homely atmosphere is what lures people in. Fish is a strong point among the frequently changing blackboard specials – perhaps a fillet of cod, sensitively cooked and served with prawns in a dill sauce – or there may be best end of lamb, pork fillet, or duck breast with an orange and ginger sauce. The mainstays of the printed menus are such items as mushrooms with Stilton and port, calf's liver and bacon, and salade niçoise. Treacle, chocolate and toffee make up a large part of the dessert range, but there is always the possibility of some kind of fruit tart too. Adnams Best Bitter is on draught, as is Stowford Press cider, and the short wine list offers three by the glass. SAMPLE DISHES: whitebait served with granary bread £5; herb-crusted rack of lamb with port sauce £14.75; Austrian chocolate cake £4.50.

Licensee Nigel Wimpenny-Smith (freehouse)
Open *Tue to Sun 12 to 3, Tue to Sat 6.30 to 11; bar food 12 to 2.15, 6.45 to 9.15*
Details *Children welcome in bar eating area   Car park   Wheelchair access (also WC)   Garden   No smoking in dining room   Occasional background music   No dogs   Amex, Delta, Diners, MasterCard, Switch, Visa*

BANTHAM   Devon   map 1

▲ *Sloop Inn* 🍇

Bantham TQ7 3AJ   TEL: (01548) 560489
off A379, 4m W of Kingsbridge

Among the former owners of this sixteenth-century pub, set in the unspoilt South Hams area, has been John Whiddon, who achieved infamy for his smuggling and wrecking activities. Nowadays you are more likely to see walkers, boating enthusiasts and surfers than smugglers, thanks to the proximity of the Coast Path, the Avon Estuary, and a wonderful sandy beach about 300 yards away over sand dunes. There is a nautical feel to the interior, a series of connected rooms with a welcoming atmosphere and a décor of sloping panelled walls, bar counters made from old boat timbers, pictures of the sea and old photographs of the village. The sea theme continues on the daily specials blackboards, which specialises in fish and shellfish: for example, deep-fried squat lobster with lemon and tarragon mayonnaise, steamed sea bass with spring onions, lemon grass and ginger, and brochette of monkfish and scallops with bacon and red wine risotto. A printed menu offers standard pub fare, such as hearty salads, basket meals, and pasties, and drinking options are just as wide and varied: beers are draught Bass, Dartmoor IPA and Palmers IPA, and Luscombe Devon Cider is also available, as well as 20 malt whiskies, several Belgian bottled beers and local organic soft drinks, including ginger beer. The wine list is helpfully divided up by style – crisp dry whites, elegant middleweight reds, etc. – and has some interesting, well-priced choices, not least in the selection of wines from Devon which gets its own page. Only one wine breaks the £17 threshold (a celebratory magnum of Château Lestage Simon at a good-value £36), and ten wines are available by the glass. SAMPLE DISHES: fresh local crab £5; pan-fried halibut with saffron and chives £11.50; summer pudding with clotted cream £3.25.

Licensee Neil Girling (freehouse)
Open *11 to 2.30, 6 to 11, Sun 12 to 2.30, 6.30 (7 winter) to 10.30; bar food and restaurant 12 to 2, 7 to 10; closed evenings 25 and 26 Dec*
Details *Children welcome in eating areas Car park Wheelchair access (not WC) Patio No cigars/pipes Background music Dogs welcome Delta, Switch Accommodation: 5 rooms, B&B £31 to £66*

BARNARD GATE Oxfordshire map 2

Boot Inn

Barnard Gate OX8 6XE TEL: (01865) 881231
off A40, between Witney and Oxford

How the Boot got its name is a matter for the history books, but it continues to deserve it thanks to its ever-growing collection of footwear donated by celebrities as diverse as the Bee Gees and Jeremy Paxman. The mellow Cotswold-stone pub is a popular dining venue just off the A40 – far away enough not to be troubled by traffic noise but close enough to attract passing trade as well as locals, giving it a lively atmosphere. Inside, it has a smart but relaxed feel, the spacious main bar sporting a quarry-tiled floor and a log fire, while rustic stone and terracotta is the theme in the two dining areas. Over the fireplace is a specials board, perhaps listing tomato and tarragon soup, smoked duck salad, and roast cod in a herb crust with tartare sauce. This is offered in addition to a brasserie-style menu that gives plenty enough choice by itself, from game casserole to red Thai chicken curry. The lunchtime version also includes light meals and sandwiches. Hook Norton Best Bitter plus a monthly-changing guest such as Wychwood Hobgoblin are the real ales. For wine drinkers, no fewer than ten are sold by the glass. SAMPLE DISHES: king prawns with garlic bread and lemon mayonnaise £6; crispy duck breast with spicy noodles and prune and ginger jus £13; raspberry crème brûlée £4.25.

Licensee Andrew Lund-Yates (freehouse)
Open *11 to 3, 5 to 11, Sun 11 to 3, 7 to 11; bar food and restaurant 12 to 2.30, 7 to 9.30*
Details *Children welcome Car park Wheelchair access (not WC) Garden No smoking in dining room Live music No dogs Amex, Delta, MasterCard, Switch, Visa*

BARNSLEY   Gloucestershire   map 2

▲ *Village Pub* 🍷🍷🍇   NEW ENTRY

Barnsley GL7 5EF   TEL: (01285) 740421
WEB SITE: www.thevillagepub.co.uk
on B4425, 4m NE of Cirencester

In case the road sign should make you think for a moment you'd
missed a turning and ended up in Yorkshire, this particular Barnsley
is a quiet, small village on a B-road leading north-east from
Cirencester. This inn-with-rooms is smack in the centre of the
village, diagonally opposite Rosemary Verey's Barnsley House
gardens, as horticultural enthusiasts will be delighted to hear. The
pub itself has no garden, but does have a well-designed brick patio
for outdoor eating, while the redecorations within have created an
inviting mix of the trendy and the traditional, with botanical prints
and faux bookcases contributing to the genteel feel. No distinction is
made between the various eating areas in a warren of little rooms,
and the same menu is offered throughout. The cooking is ambitious
and makes good use of some excellent raw materials, as in starters of
rare seared tuna with black-bean sauce and 'Asian slaw', or grilled
mackerel with truffled potato salad and chive crème fraîche. Follow
that perhaps with roasted salmon with curried lentils and cucumber
salad, organic pork chop with butternut gnocchi, Parmesan and sage,
or ribeye steak with a red wine sauce, braised chicory and a side
plate of chips, and finish with sticky toffee pudding, or banana and
rum crème brûlée. To drink are draught Stowford Press Scrumpy
Supreme, bottled Hereford cider, and local apple juice, and for devotees of the grain Hook Norton Best and Wadworth 6X are on tap
while Shepherd Neame Spitfire makes a guest appearance from time
to time. The enterprising wine list is longer on reds than whites but
offers a generous 14 wines by the glass, either 175 or 250ml (a third
of a bottle!). SAMPLE DISHES: steamed mussels and clams with lemon
and garlic £5.50; poached lamb knuckle with spiced pumpkin,
tomato and pesto £11; pear and almond tart £4.

Licensees Tim Haigh and Rupert Pendered (freehouse)
Open *Mon to Fri 11 to 3.30, 6 to 11, Sat 11 to 4, 6 to 11, Sun 12 to 4, 7 to
10.30; bar food 12 to 2.30 (3 Sat and Sun), 7 to 9.30 (10 Fri and Sat); closed
25 Dec*
Details *Children welcome Car park Patio No-smoking area in bar No
music Dogs welcome Delta, MasterCard, Switch, Visa Accommodation: 6
rooms, B&B £55 to £145*

---

*If you disagree with any assessment made in the Guide, write to tell
us why -- The Which? Guide to Country Pubs, FREEPOST, 2
Marylebone Road, London NW1 4DF.*

BARNSTON   Merseyside   map 7

Fox & Hounds

Barnston CH61 1BW   TEL: (0151) 648 1323
WEB SITE: www.the-fox-hounds.co.uk
off A551, 1¼m N of Heswall

The present Fox & Hounds was built in 1911 on the site of a much older pub with the same name. It was mainly used as a tea room in the 1930s, and the 'new' bar was domestic accommodation until the mid-1980s – that is when the present owners converted the premises, though they retained much of the original woodwork, doors and leaded windows that give the place its character. Daily blackboard specials depend partly on supplies, partly on the mood of the chef: fish pie, sausage and mash, lamb hotpot, or baked salmon with whole-grain mustard and honey sauce are typical. There is also a printed menu offering a range of platters, including Neptune (tuna, prawns, and smoked salmon) and Barnston (ham, beef, and chicken with chutney), plus various open sandwiches (the roast beef version has been recommended). Note that food is available only at lunchtime. Webster's Yorkshire Bitter and Theakston Best, Old Peculier and Cool Cask are supplemented by two guest ales. A brief list of wines offers three by the small or large glass as well as by the litre or half-litre. SAMPLE DISHES: prawn cocktail £2.75; Somerset pork chop in cider sauce £5.50; apple pie £2.50.

Licensee Ralph Leech (freehouse)
Open *11 to 11, Sun 12 to 10.30; bar food 12 to 2*
Details *Children welcome in family room   Car park   Wheelchair access (not WC)   Garden and patio   No music   Dogs welcome exc at food times   No cards*

BARTON BENDISH   Norfolk   map 6

▲ Spread Eagle   NEW ENTRY

ECCENTRIC

Church Road, Barton Bendish PE33 9DP
TEL: (01366) 347295
pub signposted off A1122 between Swaffham and Downham Market

With its cream walls and grey slate roof, the Spread Eagle, like most of the village, has, according to a reporter, 'a well-manicured kind of prettiness, not what you would call rustic'. Inside, the main bar area is an Aladdin's cave, with an amazing quantity and variety of stuff, most of it for sale, ranging from a string of onions to a set of jockey's silks. There are two dining rooms, one chintzy, the other split-level with black and white photographs of local life on its exposed-stone walls and more bric-à-brac. A blackboard of specials supplements printed menus that offer traditional pub food. In keeping with its idiosyncratic style, the inn, while including chicken Kiev and Barnsley chop as main courses, also lists under the heading of 'Foreign Meals' such dishes as chilli con carne, spaghetti bolognese, and chicken tikka masala. Two real ales are on tap, including regular Greene King IPA plus a guest brew – maybe Old Speckled Hen or Marston's Pedigree. SAMPLE DISHES: broccoli and Stilton soup £3; baked whole plaice with chips £7; pancakes £3.25.

Licensees Carole and Lucie Gransden (freehouse)
Open *Wed to Sun 12 to 2.30 (3 Sun), all week 7 to 11 (10.30 Sun); bar food and restaurant 12 to 2.15, 7 to 9.30*
Details *Children welcome in dining room   Car park   Wheelchair access (also WC)   Garden   No smoking in dining room   No music   No dogs   Amex, Delta, MasterCard, Switch, Visa   Accommodation: 4 rooms, B&B £20 to £45*

BATCOMBE   Somerset   map 2

Three Horseshoes 🏵 🍇   NEW ENTRY

Batcombe BA4 6HE   TEL: (01749) 850359
off A359 between Bruton and Frome, 3m N of Bruton

The sleepy village of Batcombe may be difficult to find, reached by a web of country lanes, but it is worth making the effort to seek out this old honey-coloured stone pub next to the church. At the rear is a terrace with picnic benches and a children's play area. Inside, the long, low-ceilinged main bar has a relaxing atmosphere and a warm and tasteful décor, its terracotta walls hung with various paintings, and features a stone inglenook with a wood-burning stove. The dining room is in a stone-walled converted barn adjacent to the main bar. Blackboard menus offer a large choice, the main board offering such dishes as calf's liver with bacon and onion, Caesar salad, and steak and Guinness pie. These are supplemented by daily specials, such as venison steak with port jus, or 'squeaky-fresh' grilled cod with sun-blushed tomatoes and pine nut butter. Several reporters have commented that food is big both on flavour and portion-size. Beers come from Butcombe, Adnams and Wadworth. Nine house wines by the large glass (£2.75) or bottle (£11) head up a list that is predominantly French but also includes good choice from the New World. As well as some luxurious offerings from Bordeaux and beyond, there's plenty to entertain the palate at affordable prices. SAMPLE DISHES: avocado and bacon salad £4.75; pan-fried chicken with pasta in Thai cream sauce £10; chocolate bread-and-butter pudding £3.50.

Licensees Tony and Sarah Lethbridge (freehouse)
Open *12 to 3, 6.30 to 11, Sun 12 to 3, 7 to 10.30; bar food and restaurant 12 to 2 (2.30 Sat and Sun), 7 to 9.30 (10 Fri and Sat)*
Details *Children welcome   Car park   Wheelchair access (also WC)   Garden and patio   No-smoking area in bar   No music   Dogs welcome   Delta, MasterCard, Switch, Visa*

BEELEY   Derbyshire   map 9

Devonshire Arms

Beeley DE4 2NR   TEL: (01629) 733259
off B6102, 5m N of Matlock

The Devonshire started life as three cottages in the early part of the eighteenth century and was converted to a hostelry barely 20 years later. Once a busy coaching inn on the Bakewell to Matlock run, it is now in prime position to serve visitors to nearby Chatsworth House and Haddon Hall, or indeed Peak District hikers. A warren of little rooms is found within, some carpeted, some flagstoned, and the full rural ambience of roaring fires and cushioned settles prevails. Food is available throughout the day, seven days a week, taking in devilled whitebait, smoked chicken and bacon salad, or grilled goats' cheese to start, followed by fillet of salmon with hollandaise, Cumberland sausage, or Barnsley lamb chop with mint jelly. Finish with bread-and-butter or hot Bakewell puddings. Cask ales are Black Sheep Best Bitter and Special Ale, as well as Theakston XB and Old Peculier, and the wine list is short but serviceable, with four bottles sold by the glass. SAMPLE DISHES: avocado and prawn cocktail £5.75; sirloin steak au poivre £12.50; chocolate ice cream £3.

Licensee John Grosvenor (freehouse)
Open *11 to 11, Sun 12 to 10.30; bar food and restaurant 12 to 9.30; closed 25 Dec*
Details *Children welcome   Car park   Wheelchair access (not WC)   Patio No-smoking area in bar, no smoking in dining room   No music   No dogs MasterCard, Switch, Visa*

BEETHAM   Cumbria   map 8

▲ *Wheatsheaf*

Beetham LA7 7AL   TEL: (015395) 62123
just off A6, 5m N of Carnforth

Dogs, walkers in muddy boots and drinkers are welcome at this sixteenth-century inn by the river and opposite the church in a quiet hamlet – but only in the taproom. Here, three ales from Jennings, the well-respected Lakeland brewer, are served, plus winter and summer guest beers. The rest of the pub is given over to diners, and the feel is more that of a restaurant. Orders are taken at the tables, which are set with fresh flowers and candles, and bookings, although not generally necessary, are accepted (and may be advisable at busy times). One menu serves throughout, offering modern cooking with a global scope: lamb kofta appears next to moules marinière and tandoori chicken among starters, while mains range from Cajun salmon to grilled pork loin with apple crisps and a sage and cider gravy, via baked aubergine with Puy lentils and goats' cheese. Aside from the main menu, eating options take in a good-value mini-menu and a set-price three-course dinner. An attractive, 20-strong wine selection won't break the bank as it stays below the £20 mark. Nine are available by the half-bottle and six by the small or large glass, from £1.95. Cookery classes are held regularly. SAMPLE DISHES: spicy fishcakes with basil and tomato sauce £5.25; wild mushroom risotto £9; Earl Grey and prune parfait £4.75.

Licensee Diane Munro (Manna Houses Ltd)
Open *11 to 3, 6 to 11, Sun 12 to 3, 7 to 10.30; bar food and restaurant 12 to 2, 6 (7 Sun) to 9*
Details *Children welcome in bar eating areas   Car park   Wheelchair access (not WC)   Patio   No smoking in dining areas   Background music   Dogs welcome in bar only   Delta, MasterCard, Switch, Visa   Accommodation: 5 rooms, B&B £55 to £70*

BENTWORTH   Hampshire   map 2

Sun 🍺

Sun Hill, Bentworth GU34 5JT   TEL: (01420) 562338
off A339, 3m W of Alton

Originally a pair of seventeenth-century cottages, this peacefully situated and attractive pub is on a narrow lane just south of the village of Bentworth. Tubs and hanging baskets provide a wealth of colour in the summer, best enjoyed from the wooden picnic tables at the front. Low-slung beams with settles and open fires add to the charm of the interior. An enterprising range of draught ales take in Ringwood Best, Stonehenge Pigswill, Badger Champion Ale and Cheriton Best plus regularly changing guests, while half a dozen wines may be had by the glass. Food is served throughout the pub, and is advertised on a blackboard menu that deals in homely (and entirely home-made) country cooking. That means hearty soups, such as leek and potato or mushroom with pork, with a choice of steak and kidney pie, Cumberland sausage with mash and onion gravy, or chicken curry to follow. The odd foray is made into unfamiliar territory, perhaps for pheasant with pickled walnuts, or spicy vegetarian fajitas, but old-school puddings bring you back home with rhubarb and pear crumble, or treacle tart. SAMPLE DISHES: courgette and red pepper soup £2.50; venison in Guinness £8.25; country apple pudding £3.

Licensee Mary Holmes (freehouse)
Open *12 to 3, 6 to 11, Sun 12 to 10.30; bar food 12 to 2, 7 to 9.30; closed evenings 25 and 26 Dec*
Details *Children welcome in family room   Car park   Wheelchair access (not WC)   Garden and patio   No music   Dogs welcome   Delta, MasterCard, Switch, Visa*

BERWICK   East Sussex   map 3

Cricketers Arms

Berwick Village, BN26 6SP   TEL: (01323) 870469
WEB SITE: www.cricketersberwick.co.uk
just off A27 Lewes to Polegate road

The Cricketers is an attractive flint-faced building with a red-tiled roof and cottagey windows. A mature garden at the front, with wooden bench tables, is a pleasant place for fine-weather eating. Inside, the cricket theme is enthusiastically pursued, with cricket bats on the beams and walls, and with pictures of the sport going back to the nineteenth century. The large public bar with its beamed ceilings, robust pine tables, quarry-tiled floors and log fires manages to be both 'pubby' and smart at the same time. There is also a family room, plus another small cosy room with a fireplace, though no separately designated dining room. The short printed bar menu, available all day at weekends, is supplemented by blackboard specials, which might offer soup, pâté, pie and fish of the day as well as vegetarian dishes. Specials which pleased a reporter were smoked haddock Mornay and good, chunky chips; and a large slice of chicken, leek and bacon pie which came with a jacket potato 'properly baked in the oven'. Light dishes might include deep-fried Camembert with cranberry sauce, and hot creamy garlic mushrooms.

This is a Harveys of Lewes pub, and the brewery's Best Bitter and seasonal brews are served straight from the cask. Wines of the month are chalked on a blackboard, and ten wines are served by the glass. SAMPLE DISHES: pan-fried king tiger prawns £5.50; sea bass steaks with salad and chips or new potatoes £7.50; treacle sponge £3.25.

Licensee Peter Brown (Harveys)
Open *summer Mon to Fri 11 to 3, 6 to 11, Sat 11 to 11, Sun 12 to 10.30; winter Mon to Sat 11 to 3, 6 to 11, Sun 12 to 6; bar food summer Mon to Fri 12 to 2.15, 6.30 to 9, Sat and Sun 12 to 9.30; winter Mon to Sat 12 to 2.15, Sun 12 to 5; closed 25 Dec*
Details *Children welcome in bar eating area   Car park   Garden   No music Dogs welcome   Delta, MasterCard, Switch, Visa*

BIDDENDEN　　Kent　　　　　　　　　　　map 3

Three Chimneys 🍺

Hareplain Road, Biddenden TN27 8LW　　TEL: (01580) 291472
on A262, 2m W of Biddenden

A short way back from a three-road junction, this quintessentially Kentish pub has a well-maintained beer garden to the rear and a stylish front courtyard for open-air eating in clement weather. Step down from the front door into a tiny bar area, with an open fire when the weather isn't so clement, and on into a series of interlinked rooms with endearingly mismatched furniture and a predominantly ochre colour scheme. Blackboard menus are transported to the table for closer perusal, and might offer starters such as crab cakes with chilli and a mango and coriander salsa, or pan-fried king scallops with whole-grain mustard mash, and main courses of roast cod topped with a poached egg and Parmesan shavings on bubble and squeak with a mustard cream sauce, or loin of venison on a caramelised onion tartlet with carrot and swede mash and a port jus. You might opt to finish with a pancake filled with caramelised bananas, or lemon brûlée with plum compote. The choice for real beer fans encompasses Adnams Best Bitter; Spitfire Premium Ale, Master Brew and seasonal ales from Shepherd Neame; and Flowers Original – all drawn straight from the barrel – while the wine list deals mainly in France and the southern hemisphere, with seven offered by the glass. To complete the premium drinking, there is an extensive collection of malt whiskies and, naturally enough, Biddenden cider. SAMPLE DISHES: spicy sweet potato and coconut soup £3.25; pan-fried chicken on Parmesan roast new potatoes with a wild mushroom sauce £12; chocolate rum and raisin torte with praline ice cream £4.50.

Licensee Craig Smith (freehouse)
Open *11.30 to 3, 6 to 11, Sun and bank hols 12 to 3, 7 to 11; bar food and restaurant 12 to 2, 6.30 to 9.45 (9 Sun)*
Details *Children welcome in dining room   Car park   Wheelchair access (not WC)   Garden and patio   No music   Dogs welcome   Delta, MasterCard, Switch, Visa*

BIRCHOVER   Derbyshire

map 5

Druid Inn

Main Street, Birchover DE4 2BL   TEL: (01629) 650302
from A6 near Haddon Hall take B5056; Birchover signposted on left after 2m

A pleasant, unassuming pub in ravishing Peak District countryside, the creeper-covered Druid Inn was built 400 years ago of local stone. A tripartite extension has provided a further series of rooms on different levels, ranging from the small, beamed and quaintly traditional, warmed by open fires, to a pair of formal dining rooms with tablecloths and flowers on the tables. A sheltered outside terrace is popular with walkers, who make up a significant part of the clientele. For drinkers, Marston's Pedigree and beers from the Mansfield brewery over the border in Nottinghamshire are on handpump, as well as guests in summer, there is a large selection of whiskies, and three house wines may be had by the glass from the predominantly French list. For those who wish to eat – and most who come here do – a huge blackboard menu offers wide choice. Among starters might be sweet and spicy Szechuan spare ribs, various pâtés with toast, and prawns with apple and celery in garlic butter, and for mains steamed salmon with cranberry and orange sauce, poached chicken with chorizo and peppercorn sauce, or Hungarian lamb stew with sour cream, dark beer and mustard. A number of Indian and Far Eastern dishes are included, and vegetarians are spoilt for choice: from casseroles (getting a special thumbs-up was one made of beans, pulses and vegetables in white wine, with herb dumplings) to curries, pastas and paella. Puddings extend to hot Bakewell tart (the regional speciality) and death by chocolate. Booking is advisable at weekends. SAMPLE DISHES: New Zealand mussels on the half-shell with cream, garlic and onion £5; vegetable soochow with spicy sauce and rice £7.50; sherry trifle £3.

Licensee Brian Bunce (freehouse)
Open *12 to 3, 7 to 11; bar food and restaurant 12 to 2, 7 to 9*
Details *Children welcome   Car park   Wheelchair access (not WC)   Garden No-smoking area in bar, no smoking in dining room   Background music   No dogs   Amex, Delta, Diners, MasterCard, Switch, Visa*

BIRCH VALE Derbyshire map 8

▲ *Waltzing Weasel*

New Mills Road, Birch Vale SK22 1BT TEL: (01663) 743402
WEB SITE: www.w-weasel.co.uk
on A6015, ½m W of Hayfield

Not only does the Weasel waltz: it also plays the fiddle, if the pub's logo is anything to go by. The stone-built inn, in a Peak District village south of Glossop, has a horseshoe-shaped bar, with tapestry-covered chairs, a splendid dresser, a longcase clock and a partly exposed slate floor. The traditional atmosphere is such that no music disturbs the scene, and neither do games machines or mobile phones (switch it off if you have one). The restaurant enjoys a pretty view on to a terrace and shrubbery and offers slightly more elaborate food than the dishes available in the bar, although starters are common to both menus. These include salmon fishcakes, fried sardines, and duck pâté. Bar diners then go on to mixed bean chilli, Barnsley chop, or fish of the day, which might be Arctic char with lemon butter, while the restaurant crowd choose from chicken Marengo with rice, sirloin steak with mushrooms and tomatoes, or seasonal game, such as pheasant, partridge or hare. Sunday lunch brings on roast beef and Yorkshire pudding. Treacle tart has been pronounced excellent, with 'light, buttery pastry and a really gooey filling', and there is also fruit crumble or ice cream. Marston's Best is on handpump plus a guest – often Timothy Taylor Landlord – and there is a selection of malt whiskies. The fully annotated wine list offers plenty of reasonably priced choice, with half a dozen by the glass. SAMPLE DISHES: gravad lax £6.25; duck and cherry pie £9.50; bread-and-butter pudding £3.75.

Licensee Michael Atkinson (freehouse)
Open *12 to 3, 5.30 to 11; bar food 12 to 2, 7 to 9; restaurant 7 to 9 (8.30 Sun)*
Details *Children welcome Car park Wheelchair access (not WC) Garden and patio No smoking in dining room No music Dogs welcome Amex, Delta, MasterCard, Switch, Visa Accommodation: 8 rooms, B&B £39 to £99*

BISHOP'S CASTLE   Shropshire   map 5

▲ *Three Tuns* 🍺

Salop Street, Bishop's Castle SY9 5BW   TEL: (01588) 638797
WEB SITE: www.thethreetunsinn.co.uk
off B4385, just off A488, 8m NW of Craven Arms

Beer is taken seriously at this old inn close to the Welsh border: so
seriously, in fact, that it runs its own nineteenth-century tower brewery on a spot across the yard where beer has been brewed since the
1600s. The cask and bottled beers produced are served in the pub
(and a few other outlets) and include XXX Bitter, Sexton, Offa's Ale,
Clerics Cure, Bellringer and the seasonal Old Scrooge. For aficionados
there is also a museum dedicated to the history of beer and brewing.
In the pub, large spaces sparsely dotted with tables beneath heavy-
beamed ceilings, with some old sepia-tinted vintage photographs on
the walls, set the scene for dining as well as drinking. Order your food
at the bar and it will be brought to you by friendly, forthcoming staff.
The style of cooking is as unpretentious and uncluttered as the
surroundings, offering dishes such as home-made pâtés, toasted goats'-
cheese salad, game pie in season, and a good range of fresh fish and
organic meats. Vegetables and bread, too, are organic, and the kitchen
aims to make everything in-house. Finish with a home-made pie or
crumble, or something light like a syllabub. Four wines are served by
the glass. SAMPLE DISHES: rich fish soup £3.50; beef in a Three Tuns
ale £7.50; sticky toffee pudding £3.25.

Licensee Janet Cross (freehouse)
Open *Mon to Thur 12 to 3, 5 to 11, Fri to Sun 12 to 11; bar food and
restaurant 12 to 2.30 (3.30 Sun), 7 to 9.30; open 25 Dec 12 to 2 only, closed
Sun evening winter*
Details *Children welcome   Car park   Wheelchair access (not WC)   Garden
and patio   No smoking in dining room   Occasional live music   Dogs
welcome   Delta, MasterCard, Switch, Visa   Accommodation: 4 rooms, B&B
£35 to £75*

BISPHAM GREEN   Lancashire   map 8

Eagle & Child 🍺

Malt Kiln Lane, Bispham Green L40 3SG   TEL: (01257) 462297
*from M6 junction 27, take A5209 over Parbold Hill, right on B5246,
fourth left signposted Bispham Green; pub is ½m on right*

An outstanding range of fine real ales and out-of-the-ordinary food
make this rural pub well worth a visit. It is in a conservation area in a
very attractive part of Lancashire, and inside are two suitably rustic

bar areas, with coal fires and hop-garlanded beams setting the tone. The printed menu is mostly standard pub fare, such as steak and ale pie, plus a couple of less familiar items: smoked fish and bacon in a rustic roll, for example. Most interesting is the daily specials board, where the kitchen's inventive streak is given full rein. Expect dishes like confit of beef with couscous and tomato sauce, and king scallops with mango and sweet potato, though you may also find Cumberland sausage with mash, or roast lamb with mint sauce. Desserts can be equally creative: strawberry crumble, for example. Regular theme nights (curries, for instance) are also held. Two regular beers, Thwaites Best Bitter and Moorhouses Black Cat, are joined by five changing guest ales, plus Belgian fruit beers and a decent selection of ciders. Besides the house selections listed on the menu, there is also a list of over 30 wines, including seven by the glass. At the rear of the pub is a bowling green, a popular summer attraction. SAMPLE DISHES: deep-fried goats' cheese with caponata £4.50; pan-fried chicken breast with tomatoes, Jack Daniel's and cream £10; chocolate mousse £3.50.

Licensee John Mansfield (freehouse)
Open *12 to 3, 5.30 to 11, Sun 12 to 10.30; bar food 12 to 2, 6 to 8.30 (9 Fri and Sat), Sun 12 to 8.30; closed evening 25 Dec*
Details *Children welcome in family room   Car park   Wheelchair access (not WC)   Garden and patio   No smoking in 1 room   Occasional live or background music   No dogs   Delta, MasterCard, Switch, Visa*

BLACKBOYS   **East Sussex**   **map 3**

Blackboys Inn

Lewes Road, Blackboys TN22 5LG   TEL: (01825) 890283
on B2192, 3m E of Uckfield

Set slightly back from the main road through the village, behind its own parking space and small patches of green, the inn is a large, convivial place. To one side is the public bar and games room, and to the other is a series of interconnecting rooms leading to a plush, carpeted space with cloths on the tables. You can eat just about anywhere, and the range of menus encompasses a large carte, a bar snack menu, a separate vegetarian list and a range of specials chalked on a blackboard above the bar. Well-kept Harveys Sussex Best Bitter and Pale Ale, plus seasonal ales, head up the beer selection, with Scrumpy Jack cider and half a dozen wines by the glass in support. The main wine list is fairly priced and offers reasonable choice. The cooking tends to the rich and weighty in style, with enormous portions (especially of vegetables). Gratinated crab and Gruyère tart is one way to start, and might be followed by roast lamb fillet on fried potatoes, or a large piece of steak in one of the classic sauces. Fish and seafood are plentiful: perhaps grilled lobster with garlic prawns, scallops and mussels, or poached salmon fillet with an asparagus and basil sauce. Finish with banoffi pie, or a raspberry-stuffed white chocolate mousse with Cointreau sauce. Staff are cheery and keen to help. SAMPLE DISHES: home-cured salmon with lime and coriander dressing £5; roast confit of goose leg salad with hoisin dressing £10.25; crème brûlée £3.50.

Licensees Edward and Claire Molesworth (Harveys)
Open *11 to 3, 6 to 11, Sun 12 to 3, 7 to 10.30; bar food and restaurant 12 to 2.15, 6.30 to 9.30; closed 25 Dec, 1 Jan*
Details *Children welcome in dining room   Car park   Garden and patio   No smoking in dining room   Jukebox   Dogs welcome exc in dining room   Delta, MasterCard, Switch, Visa*

BLACKHAM   East Sussex   map 3

Sussex Oak   NEW ENTRY

Blackham TN3 9UA   TEL: (01892) 740273
on A264 about 5m W of Royal Tunbridge Wells

The external red house-colours of Shepherd Neame's pubs are warm and welcoming, but to keep the warmth inside in winter, customers must use a side entrance because the front door admits unwelcome draughts. Draughts that are allowed are Shepherd Neame Master Brew, Spitfire and Best Bitter in the long, narrow bar with a log fire, hop garlands, copper hunting horns, Guinness-inspired pictures, and a small television. As the Guide went to press the restaurant was open only on Friday and Saturday evenings. Called the Flambé, its menu specialises in that technique of finishing dishes – but fire has reached bar desserts, too, such as banana flambé and crêpes suzette. From the short bar menu you might choose 'smooth and wobbly' Stilton terrine with Guinness, or authentic vegetable samosas with mango chutney and mint yoghurt. Main dishes include Caribbean pork in Malibu sauce, and the signature dish of chicken masala with basmati rice and naan. Its rich, powerful flavours confirmed to a reporter that 'Vijay knows his spices' and is equally at home with penne with tomato, garlic and basil sauce. About 30 wines feature on the list, with house wines available by the glass. SAMPLE DISHES: avocado with garlic mushrooms and croûtons on salad £4.50; cod and chips £7; cinnamon and plum pudding £3.75.

Licensee Vijay Shukla (Shepherd Neame)
Open *summer 11 to 11, Sun 12 to 10.30; winter 10.30 to 3, 6 to 11, Sun 12 to 5; bar food 11 to 3, 6 to 9.45, Sun 12 to 4, 6 to 9.45; restaurant Fri and Sat 7 to 9.45; closed evenings 25 and 26 Dec*
Details *Children welcome   Car park   Wheelchair access (also WC)   Garden Background music   Dogs welcome   Delta, MasterCard, Switch, Visa*

BLACKMORE END   Essex   map 3

Bull   NEW ENTRY

Blackmore End CM7 4DD   TEL: (01371) 851037
between A1017 and B1053, 6m N of Braintree

Even on quiet days the atmosphere is friendly and warm at this traditional village pub, which is surrounded by rolling fields in the heart of Constable country. Although it is somewhat plain-looking on the outside, the interior's livelier décor compensates, with plenty of horse brasses adorning the gnarled and twisted beams and standing timbers, colourful floral curtains, and shelves laden with books. Straightforward pub fare is the order of the day on the printed menu card, including a wide selection of hot or cold sandwiches, such as minute steak in a crusty baguette accompanied by crisps and home-made coleslaw. The smarter dining area at one end of the main bar has its own, more ambitious menu, though this is available throughout the pub: start perhaps with scallops served in a shell with a wine and mushroom sauce, followed by rack of lamb baked in herbs with redcurrant sauce. To drink there are well-kept beers from Adnams and Greene King, plus a guest such as Old Speckled Hen, and a selection of European and New World wines that include five by the glass. SAMPLE DISHES: moules marinière £6.25; medallions of beef glazed with Stilton on ratatouille £12.75; crème brûlée £4.50.

Licensee Sydney Morris (freehouse)
Open *11.30 to 3, 6 to 12, Sun 12 to 11.30; bar food and restaurant 12.30 to 2.30 (3 Sun), 7 to 9.45*
Details *Children welcome in eating areas   Car park   Wheelchair access (not WC)   Garden and patio   Background music   Dogs welcome   Delta, MasterCard, Switch, Visa*

BLAKENEY   Norfolk   map 6

▲ *White Horse Hotel*

4 High Street, Blakeney NR25 7AL   TEL: (01263) 740574
on A149, 5m W of Holt

Just a stone's throw from the sea, on the narrow High Street, is Blakeney's oldest hotel, which dates from the seventeenth century and still looks very much as it did in its earliest days as a coaching inn. The well-maintained bar is decorated with works by local artists depicting nearby scenes, and many are for sale. As befits the coastal location, fish features prominently on the bar menu: deep-fried herring roes on toast, cod or plaice in beer batter, and fisherman's pie topped with flaky pastry are typical offerings from the printed list, while the blackboard of daily specials might feature mussels marinière, and grilled salmon with salsa verde. For meat eaters there might be steak and kidney pudding. The menu in the restaurant, which is in a converted stable block overlooking the walled garden and courtyard, goes in more for meat and game: perhaps pigeon, rabbit and pistachio terrine, and roast rack of lamb with mustard and lentil sauce. Beers are from Adnams, Bass and Woodforde's, and a succinct wine list offers nine by the glass and eight by the half-bottle, chosen with an eye to modern fruitiness and traditional complexity alike. SAMPLE DISHES: deep-fried local whitebait £4; dressed local crab salad £7; pear and almond tart £3.

Licensee Daniel Rees (freehouse)
Open *11 to 3, 5.30 (6 winter) to 11, Sun 12 to 3, 7 to 10.30; bar food 12 to 2, 6 to 9; restaurant Tue to Sat 7 to 9; closed 2 weeks Jan*
Details *Children welcome in family room   Car park   Wheelchair access (not WC)   Garden   No-smoking area in bar   No music   No dogs   Amex, Delta, MasterCard, Switch, Visa   Accommodation: 10 rooms, B&B £30 to £90*

BLEDINGTON   Gloucestershire   map 5

▲ *Kings Head* 🍺 🍇

The Green, Bledington OX7 6XQ   TEL: (01608) 658365
on B4450 4m SE of Stow-on-the-Wold

Smack on the Gloucestershire–Oxfordshire border stands this fine fifteenth-century stone-built inn, next to a babbling brook complete with ducks. The village itself is a quintessential Cotswold jumble of cottages built of mellow-hued local stone, all clustering towards the church. A recent extension to the rear of the Kings Head houses six guest rooms, and there is a terrace and garden at the back, too. The weathered interior is low-ceilinged and welcoming. Eating takes place anywhere you like, although there is the option of a separate dining area with high-backed settles and traditional pub tables. The style of the cooking can be trendily old-fashioned, offering homemade lentil and ham broth, chicken liver and cranberry pâté, breast of duck with braised red cabbage, and hearty lamb shank with a thick, warming stew of winter root vegetables and roasted new potatoes. That said, a more experimental streak brings on black pudding with maple syrup and pesto crostini, perhaps followed by grilled salmon on bok choy and spring onions with a red wine and thyme sauce, and then chocolate chip and banana sponge pudding. More mainstream desserts include sticky treacle pudding, or cherry and almond tart served with lemon sorbet. Real beer lovers will find joining regulars Wadsworth 6X and Hook Norton are weekly-changing guests such as Wychwood ales, Hampshire Pride of Romsey and Shepherd Neame Spitfire. Stowford Press cider and a wide selection of gins are also available, and ten wines by the glass head up an enterprising list that shows considerable ambition. Everything's there from appealing Pask's Sauvignon (from New Zealand) to the illustrious Château Patache d'Aux (Bordeaux), and most of the wines come in at under £20. SAMPLE DISHES: warm salad of bacon, black pudding and sauté potatoes with a poached egg £6; rack of lamb with oregano, garlic butter and red chard £16; banoffi pie £3.25.

Licensee Archie Orr-Ewing (freehouse)
Open *11 to 2.30, 6 to 11, Sun 12 to 2.30, 6.30 to 10.30; bar food and restaurant 12 to 2, 7 to 9.30; closed 25 and 26 Dec*
Details *Children welcome in family room   Car park   Wheelchair access (not WC)   Garden and patio   No-smoking area in dining room   Occasional background music   Dogs welcome exc in dining room   Amex, Delta, MasterCard, Switch, Visa   Accommodation: 12 rooms, B&B £45 to £90*

BLEDLOW   Buckinghamshire   map 3

Lions of Bledlow 🍺

Church End, Bledlow HP27 9PE   TEL: (01844) 343345
off B4009, 2m SW of Princes Risborough; take West Lane, not Bledlow Ridge turning

Just outside the village, in a pretty location at the end of a single-track road, this is very much the traditional village pub: equally welcoming whether you are a local dropping in for a pint or a walker stopping off for sustenance. In summer, picnic benches in the garden make al fresco eating an appealing possibility; otherwise sit in the low-beamed bar (tall people beware!), which has a real pubby feel due in part to the horse brasses and glass tankards about the place, or in the slightly smarter dining room, where tables are adorned with fresh flowers. One compact menu is available throughout, offering snacks (baguettes, salads, ploughman's) and straightforward dishes along the lines of avocado with crab, steak and Guinness pie, or chicken tikka masala, with deep-fried breaded lobster tails one of the more unusual items. Daily blackboard specials might include fishcakes, roast chicken, or hot smoked mackerel; one visitor commended the quality of the main ingredients in honey-glazed lamb cutlets and Cajun-spiced salmon. There's a children's menu of the fish fingers sort, or an extra plate will cheerfully be provided for children to share an adult's order. As well as the usual line-up of Marston's Pedigree, Wadworth 6X, Brakspear Bitter and Courage Best, there is a guest ale, usually from a local brewery such as Rebellion or Vale. Wines are a concise selection, the majority under £12, and eight are available by the glass from £1.50. SAMPLE DISHES: broccoli in Stilton sauce £3.50; pork fillet in cream and mushroom sauce £7.50; chocolate torte £3.25.

Licensee Mark McKeown (freehouse)
Open *11.30 to 3, 6 to 11, Sun 12 to 4, 7 to 10.30; bar food and restaurant
12 to 2.30, 7 to 9.30*
Details *Children welcome in eating areas   Car park   Garden and patio   No
smoking in dining room   No music   Dogs welcome   Amex, Delta, Diners,
MasterCard, Switch, Visa*

BOOTHSDALE   Cheshire   map 7

Boot Inn

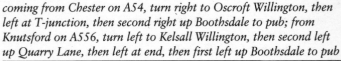

Boothsdale, Willington CW6 0NH
TEL: (01829) 751375
*coming from Chester on A54, turn right to Oscroft Willington, then
left at T-junction, then second right up Boothsdale to pub; from
Knutsford on A556, turn left to Kelsall Willington, then second left
up Quarry Lane, then left at end, then first left up Boothsdale to pub*

On the edge of the area known locally as Little Switzerland, the Boot
has produced its own guide to walks – from one mile to eight – that
begin and end at this traditional inn. The absence of music
contributes to the relaxed atmosphere in rooms that are warm and
comfortable, one furnished with church pews. What might have a
place on the restaurant menu (also available for those eating in the
bar) is spicy marinated chicken in a poppadom basket with coconut
and coriander soured cream, followed by a casserole of partridge,
pheasant and mallard, or grilled lemon sole with anchovies, prawns,
capers and lemon butter. Many bar dishes are traditional – for example, devilled kidneys, or garlic prawns, then liver and bacon, or
breaded plaice with tartare sauce – while interesting vegetarian
choices may include asparagus and Brie bake, or stir-fried pepper
satay with sesame seeds and mushrooms. Greenalls Bitter and Cains
Formidable Ale are on tap, plus guests such as Flowers Original or a
brew from local Weetwood Ales. The short, fairly priced wine list is
divided between Europe and the New World, with four by the glass
from France, and malt whisky fans will find 30 to choose from.
SAMPLE DISHES: nut-roasted Brie with Cumberland and port sauce
£5.50; Barnsley chops with minted gravy £8.50; 'rich and wicked'
chocolate truffle with cream £3.50.

Licensee Mike Gollings (Inn Partnership)
Open *Mon to Fri 11 to 3, 6 to 11, Sat 11 to 11, Sun 11 to 10.30; bar food
and restaurant Mon to Fri 11 to 2.30, 6 to 9.30; Sat, Sun and bank hols 11 to
9.30; closed 25 Dec*
Details *Children welcome in snug and restaurant   Car park   Garden and
patio   No smoking in dining room   No music   No dogs   Amex, Delta,
Diners, MasterCard, Switch, Visa*

BORASTON   Shropshire   map 5

Peacock Inn

Worcester Road, Boraston WR15 8LL   TEL: (01584) 810506
WEB SITE: www.thepeacockinn.com
on A456, 1¼m E of Tenbury Wells

Despite being on an A-road, this large white-painted pub is in an isolated position looking over fields. Flower-filled hanging baskets and tubs brighten up the paved patio, with its trestle tables, to the front, while the interior is dominated by wooden panelling, two large embroideries, each depicting a peacock, adding decoration. Most of the space is given over to eating, and the same menus are served throughout, with the addition of sandwiches at lunchtimes. On offer might be marinated aubergine with buffalo mozzarella, or a generous helping of fresh-tasting beer-battered coconut prawns with a honey and mustard dressing, followed by Gressingham duck breast with wild mushrooms and green peppercorn sauce, sea bass on basil mash with beurre blanc, or a pasta: perhaps penne al arrabbiata with smoked chicken and bacon. Real ales include Hook Norton Best Bitter, Hobson's Choice, Burton and Tetley Bitter. Thirty-five wines are listed, of which six are house wines by the glass or bottle, the rest selected with a keen eye for quality to tempt those willing to spend over £20 or even £30 a bottle. SAMPLE DISHES: broccoli and Stilton soup £3.50; game pie £8.50; apple and calvados pie £4.50.

Licensees James and Alice Vidler (freehouse)
Open *12 to 3, 6 to 11 (10.30 Sun); bar food and restaurant 12 to 2.30, 6 to 9.30*
Details *Children welcome   Car park   Garden   No-smoking area in dining room   Background music   Dogs welcome exc in dining areas   Delta, MasterCard, Switch, Visa   Accommodation: 3 rooms, B&B £40 to £65*

BOTTLESFORD   Wiltshire   map 3

Seven Stars

Bottlesford SN9 6LU   TEL: (01672) 851325
off A345 at mini-roundabout at North Newnton; follow signs for Woodborough then Bottlesford

Wish upon a star to be in this pretty, old thatched pub, set in nine acres of grounds in the Vale of Pewsey. Wish upon six more and the pub's landlord will be a cheerful Frenchman bringing more than a touch of his homeland to its food. The rambling interior is full of dark wood, carved panelling and doors, open fires, benches, settles and banquettes, and lots of dining tables. Snacks along the lines of croque monsieur, sandwiches, salads and omelettes are served in the bar at lunchtime, while the deliciously Franglais restaurant menu changes daily and is available throughout. On it you might find Sandridge sausages with garlic mash and onion gravy, or seafood pot-au-feu, with modern touches extending to fried pigeon breasts with mango and salad. An inspector found crab cakes Creole 'all crab meat and crab flavour' and approved whole pan-fried plaice with a 'light, properly made beurre blanc'. Game is served in season, and a blackboard lists desserts of perhaps raspberry crème brûlée, or treacle sponge. The cross-Channel *entente* extends to drinks, which take in Badger Dorset Best, Wadworth 6X, one of three alternating Stonehenge ales, local organic cider, and a serious wine list. Eight wines are sold by the small and large glass (starting at £1.90 and £2.95, respectively), while the main list focuses on France. Some very smart names crop up – Chassagne-Montrachet, Auxey-Duresses to name two – but better prices are available if you make your choice from farther shores. SAMPLE DISHES: home-smoked salmon and langoustine salad £6; coquilles St Jacques normande £12.75; chocolate fondant £4.

Licensees Philippe Cheminade and Kate Lister (freehouse)
Open *Tue to Sat 11 to 3, 6 to 11, Sun 12 to 3; bar food and restaurant 12 to 2, 7 to 9.30; also open bank hol Mon lunchtime, closed Tue following*
Details *Children welcome in dining room Car park Wheelchair access (not WC) Garden and patio No smoking in 1 dining room Background music Dogs by arrangement Delta, MasterCard, Switch, Visa*

BRAMDEAN Hampshire   map 2

Fox Inn

Bramdean SO24 0LP   TEL: (01962) 771363
on A272 Winchester to Petersfield road, 3m SE of New Alresford

This white-weatherboarded, 400-year-old pub is set back from the main road in the heart of the village. On an outside wall is an oak carving of the Prince of Wales' feathers commemorating the occasion on which George IV, while still heir to the throne, visited the pub for refreshment. The interior has been comfortably modernised, with terracotta walls, attractive lamps and good tables, to make a dining pub without a separate restaurant but with a relaxed and civilised atmosphere. The one real ale on tap is Greene King Abbott Ale, and there are some 30 modestly priced wines on the list, with six by the glass. On daily-changing blackboard menus are sandwiches and other bar snacks as well as traditional starters and a good range of interestingly sauced meat and fresh fish dishes. On offer might be broccoli and Stilton soup, poached pear with blue cheese and bacon, or wild boar pâté (said by a reader to be 'home-made, with a good texture and rich flavour'), followed perhaps by monkfish italienne, pork fillet with Stilton and brandy, or 'meaty, fresh and well-cooked' grilled halibut with tarragon sauce. Among the home-made puddings is 'forgotten lemon heaven' (lemon mousse cheesecake made with cottage cheese). Service is friendly, and food is delivered to the table by efficient kitchen staff. SAMPLE DISHES: deep-fried whitebait £5; chicken breast with almond and sherry sauce £9; sticky toffee pudding £4.

Licenses Jane and Ian Inder (Greene King)
Open *11 to 3, 6 (6.30 winter) to 11, Sun 12 to 3, 7 to 11; bar food 12 to 2, 7 to 9; closed Mon evenings Jan and Feb; no food Sun evenings Jan and Feb*
Details *No children   Car park   Garden and patio   No-smoking area in bar Background music   Dogs welcome   Amex, Delta, MasterCard, Switch, Visa*

BRAMFIELD   **Suffolk**   map 6

Queen's Head   NEW ENTRY

The Street, Bramfield IP19 9HT   TEL: (01986) 784214
off A144, 3m S of Halesworth

Right in the village look for the crinkle-crankle wall: the pub is opposite. Half of it is non-smoking, and all of it is free of music. It has no restaurant, but the landlord, doubling as chef, describes it as a 'dining pub'. Above all, we are told that the Queen's Head is the first pub outside London to offer certified organic dishes. The organic section of the menu lists four starters, including a reader's happy choice of tasty, smooth chicken liver and brandy pâté with 'ambrosial' Cumberland sauce. Then he enjoyed chicken, leek and tarragon bake with bacon crumble topping, followed by 'gorgeous' praline ice cream. More organic ingredients are used in the rest of the menu, taking in 'beautifully fresh' fried plaice in a dry, light batter, or Thai-style free-range chicken curry. Stir-fried vegetables are another popular feature. On draught are Adnams Best Bitter and Broadside, plus Crones organic cider and local organic apple juices. Some 20 wines include a couple of organics, and five house wines are offered by the glass. SAMPLE DISHES: potted salmon and smoked trout £5; pork chop braised in organic cider £7; pavlova with banana, mango sauce and toasted coconut £3.50.

Licensees Mark and Amanda Corcoran (Adnams)
Open *11.45 to 2.30, 6.30 (7 Mon) to 11, Sun 12 to 3, 7 to 10.30; bar food 12 to 2, 6.30 (7 Sun and Mon) to 10 (9 Sun); closed evening 25 Dec and all day 26 Dec*
Details *Children welcome   Car park   Wheelchair access (not WC)   Garden and patio   No-smoking area in bar   No music   Dogs welcome   Amex, Delta, Diners, MasterCard, Switch, Visa*

BRANCASTER STAITHE   Norfolk   map 6

Jolly Sailors 🍺 NEW ENTRY

Main Road, Brancaster Staithe PE31 8BJ   TEL: (01485) 210314
WEB SITE: www.the-jolly-sailors.co.uk
on A149, between Hunstanton and Wells-next-the-Sea

The atmosphere at this rustic-looking white-painted cottage is very
much that of a traditional village pub, with a real sense of community. Notices on the walls advertise local events and the pub's own
entertainments, which include regular live music and quiz nights.
Two small bar areas cater for drinkers, one a cosy room with sofas;
behind them is the main bar with its whitewashed rough walls of
rough stone and crackling log fire, and décor of rare albino birds in
display cases and old and new photos of the village. Food is served
all day, and various eating options take in bar snacks (sandwiches,
steak and kidney pie, burgers, etc.), and daily specials on blackboards, which might include plaice with prawns and tarragon. There
is also the restaurant menu, which serves the dining room at the rear
of the pub and offers things like roast beef with Yorkshire pudding,
chicken curry with rice, and tuna steak with roasted lemon. Beer
drinkers are well served, the fine range comprising ales from Greene
King and Adnams, and local brews such as Woodeforde's Wherry
and Iceni Fine Soft Day, as well as a guest; the short wine list
includes three by the glass. SAMPLE DISHES: deep-fried Brie £4; cod in
beer batter with chips and peas £8; apple crumble £3.25.

Licensees Darren Humphrey and Wendy Darrington (freehouse)
Open *10 (11 for alcohol) to 11, Sun 10 (12 for alcohol) to 10.30; bar food
and restaurant 10 to 9 (10 in holiday season); closed 25 Dec after 4*
Details *Children welcome   Car park   Wheelchair access (not WC)   Garden
and patio   No smoking in dining room   Occasional live or background music
Dogs welcome exc in restaurant   Delta, MasterCard, Switch, Visa*

▲ White Horse 🍇 NEW ENTRY

VIEWS

Main Road, Brancaster Staithe PE31 8BW
TEL: (01485) 210262
WEB SITE: www.whitehorsebrancaster.co.uk

From the front, on the main road, this looks an uninspiring modern
building, but go inside and you will be treated to one of the finest
views in Norfolk. The conservatory restaurant at the rear makes the
most of the vista across marshland to the coast and Scolt Head
Island; this room opens on to a terrace for summer use. The bar area
at the front doesn't have the view but is attractively decorated in a
smart, modern style, with a tiled floor, pine furniture, and pale
yellow walls hung with old photographs. The menu also has an up-

to-date feel, with things like chilli and coriander pork belly with fried noodles and plum sauce, and lamb with tomato cassoulet and crisp sage. At lunchtimes there is also a list of lighter dishes, such as salt-cod with mango dressing, or pork and leek sausages with tagliatelle and sun-dried tomatoes, and blackboards list filled ciabattas and children's dishes. Local mussels, cooked in a cream and white wine sauce, are a seasonal treat. Beers are from East Anglian brewers Greene King and Adnams; Stowford Press cider is also served. Every effort has gone into selecting the succinct 50-bottle wine list, which leads with 12 by the glass. There are also seven half-bottles and eight Owners Reserve wines to choose from, not to mention some off-beat names and unusual grapes. Digging deep for the £42 Meursault isn't necessary when there's plenty under £20 on offer, but it's always a nice option. SAMPLE DISHES: grilled sardines on bean sprout salad £5.50; confit duck leg with roast new potatoes and garlic cream £8.25; sticky toffee pudding £3.50.

Licensees Cliff Nye and Kevin Nobes (freehouse)
Open *11.30 to 11 (11.30 to 3, 6.30 to 11 winter), Sun 12 to 3, 7 to 10.30;*
bar food and restaurant 12 to 2.30, 6.45 to 9.30; closed evening 25 Dec
Details *Children welcome   Car park   Wheelchair access (not WC)   Patio*
No smoking in dining room   Live or background music   Dogs welcome
Amex, Delta, Diners, MasterCard, Switch, Visa   Accommodation: 8 rooms,
B&B £50 to £90

BRANSCOMBE   Devon   map 2

▲ *Masons Arms* 🍺 🍇

Branscombe EX12 3DJ   TEL: (01297) 680300
WEB SITE: www.masonsarms.co.uk
off A3052, 5m E of Sidmouth

Although Andy and Paula Painter arrived in spring 1998 to take over day-to-day running of the pub, Murray Inglis, who has owned the Masons Arms for close on 30 of its 600 years, remains very much involved. During the daytime, the pleasant walk from the picturesque village through the valley, or to the beach, will help build up appetites. Back inside the neat and well-maintained pub, a simple and traditional feel is created by polished stone floors and by a large inglenook in the public bar, and on fine days it is possible to sit outside under thatched parasols. A laminated menu card lists various baguettes, sandwiches and ploughman's at lunchtime, as well as starters/light meals such as baked Brie with peach compote, and main dishes of lamb casserole, or deep-fried cod in beer batter. The set-price restaurant menu (dinner only, also available in the bar) offers more sophistication along the lines of roast duck breast with

Cointreau and orange sauce, and spit roasts are a feature of Sunday and Tuesday lunch and Friday dinner. Alongside regulars Otter Bitter and Masons Ale (brewed for the pub by Otter), three weekly-changing guests might include Badger Tanglefoot and beers from Church End Brewery. Lyme Bay cider is also served. Wines by the glass, small or large, start at £1.90 and focus on fruity varietal grape flavours – there are six red and six white. There's a very French feel to the rest of the list and prices stay under the £20 mark, except for a few indulgent Burgundian classics which might find their way to the bottom of the enthusiast's wallet. SAMPLE DISHES: grilled goats' cheese with Mediterranean vegetables £3.75; whole black bream with sun-dried tomatoes and garlic £10.50; peach and apricot crumble £3.10.

Licensees Andy Painter and Murray Inglis (freehouse)
Open *Mon to Fri 11 to 3, 6 to 11 (11 to 11 July and Aug), Sat 11 to 11, Sun 12 to 10.30; bar food 12 to 2, 7 to 9; restaurant 7 to 8.45*
Details *Children welcome Car park Patio No-smoking area in bar, no smoking in dining room Occasional live music Dogs welcome exc in restaurant Delta, MasterCard, Switch, Visa Accommodation: 22 rooms, B&B £24 to £150*

BRASSINGTON Derbyshire map 5

Ye Olde Gate Inne

Well Street, Brassington DE4 4HJ TEL: (01629) 540448
just off B3035 Ashbourne to Wirksworth road, 4m W of Wirksworth

It's difficult to imagine a more welcoming place in late autumn than this small stone pub, when the Virginia creeper covering its walls has turned fiery red and the spectacular kitchen range is in full blaze. Beams, flagstone floors, copper bed pans, brasses and rush-seated chairs add to the atmosphere of this early-seventeenth-century building. Another fire blazes in a second, plainer bar, and the panelled dining room, with a window overlooking the large garden, is a light and pleasant room. A reporter noted the friendliness of the locals, which confirmed the inn's pride in its tradition of conversation. Some of the blackboard menu is as English as potted shrimps, venison rump steak, or an inspector's 'delicious' cottage pie with 'obviously home-made, creamy potatoes' covering full-flavoured beef. More exotic palates may be tempted by French onion soup, lamb tagine, or Thai green chicken curry. In the summer there are barbecues in the garden. Marston's Pedigree and Head Brewer's Choice are on handpump, along with Scrumpy Jack cider, and three wines are served by the glass. SAMPLE DISHES: Orkney crab pâté £4.25; game pie £11; warm pecan fudge brownie with vanilla ice cream £3.25.

Licensees Paul and Evie Burlinson (Wolverhampton & Dudley)
Open *Mon to Thur 12 to 2.30, 6 to 11, Fri and Sat 12 to 3, 6 to 11, Sun 12
to 3, 7 to 10.30; bar food Mon to Thur 12 to 1.45, 7 to 8.45, Fri and Sat 12
to 2, 7 to 9, Sun 12 to 2, 7 to 8.30; closed Mon lunchtime winter*
Details *No children under 10   Car park   Wheelchair access (also WC)
Garden   No smoking in dining room   Occasional live music   Dogs welcome
No cards*

BREARTON   North Yorkshire   map 9

Malt Shovel 🍺

Brearton HG3 3BX   TEL: (01423) 862929
off A61 and B6165, 2m E of Ripley

'This feels like the ultimate local: comfortable but unpretentious; full
of character without being twee; friendly but not overbearing' was
how one pub-goer described a much-enjoyed visit to the Malt
Shovel. The interior is divided into two areas, with low ceilings, a
real fire, pewter tankards, old bottles and brasses all adding to the
homely atmosphere. It can get crowded, and as bookings aren't
taken, it's best to arrive early. Local beers are a strong suit, and
include Daleside Nightjar, Black Sheep and Theakston, along with a
couple of frequently changing guests: perhaps Durham Magus,
Rudgate Battleaxe, or Moorhouses Pendle Witches Brew. There is
also real cider from La Cantina, and around 30 malt whiskies, plus a
wine list of around 20 that runs the gamut from New Zealand
Sauvignon to Montepulciano d'Abruzzo; all the wines on the list are
served by the glass, from £1.65. The cooking is properly homely too,
making use of decent ingredients that are treated with skill by an on-
the-ball kitchen. Twenty or so main-course specials of the day
chalked up on the board take in the likes of tangy goats'-cheese and
leek tart in crisp pastry, 'soft-as-butter' liver and bacon with black
pudding, roast pork, lamb casserole cooked in white wine with 'delicious herby juices', or haddock pan-fried in Cajun spices. Vegetarians
get a fair look-in too: maybe spinach and mushroom lasagne, or
potato and tomato curry with Basmati rice and salad. Most dishes
can also be ordered in smaller versions suitable for children or as
starters. Vegetables are competently cooked, and puddings too get
the thumbs-up: for example generously sized apple and blackberry
crumble, or bread-and-butter pudding with rum and raisins. SAMPLE
DISHES: mussels steamed in white wine with garlic, herbs and tomatoes £4; game pie £6.50; fresh fruit brûlée £2.50.

Licensee Les V. Mitchell (freehouse)
Open *Tue to Sun 12 to 2.30, 6.45 to 11 (10.30 Sun); bar food Tue to Sun 12
to 2, Tue to Sat 7 to 9*
Details *Children welcome   Car park   Wheelchair access (not WC)   Patio
No music   Dogs welcome   No cards*

▲ *Roebuck Inn* 🏵 ❦

LOCAL PRODUCE

Brimfield SY8 4NE   TEL: (01584) 711230
WEB SITE: www.roebuckinn.demon.co.uk
just off A49 Leominster to Ludlow road, 4m W of Tenbury Wells

The atmosphere in the bars, especially the snug where locals play cribbage and dominoes, is that of a lively pub, and the dining room, in a modern extension, is comfortable and bright, with cane furniture and parquet flooring. Everything is made in the kitchen, from bread to petits fours, and the frequently changing menus, available throughout the pub, make a point of focusing on local, seasonal ingredients. They offer eight starters, among them a 'soup of the moment' – seafood chowder, say – and perhaps Mediterranean mixed salad with herb-infused olive oil. Then consider 'our famous fish pie', which a reader dubbed 'excellent': salmon, cod and prawns topped with cheese-glazed leek mash. Specials, mainly fish and game, might be seared scallops with chorizo and an orange, vanilla and cardamom dressing, followed by partridge stuffed with herbs in pear sauce, or crisply grilled fillet of sea bass on a risotto of brown shrimps and basil. Most of the cheeses on the board are local, including Hereford Hop, Ragstone and Finn. Real ales stocked are Morland Old Speckled Hen, Tetley Bitter and Wood Parish Bitter, and there are local ciders and home-made fruit gins too. The 40-strong wine list is organised into styles – and possible food matches – with plenty to choose from France and the New World. Prices are pitched well-below the £15 mark (with the odd treasure a little higher, such as Meursault at £37.50). Eight wines are offered by the glass and six by the half-bottle. SAMPLE DISHES: moules marinière tartlet £5; roast rump of lamb on black pudding and apple rösti £13; citrus meringue pie £4.

Licensee David Willson-Lloyd (freehouse)
Open *11.30 (12 winter) to 3, 6.30 (7 winter) to 11, Sun 12 to 3, 7 to 10.30; bar food and restaurant 12 to 2.30, 7 to 9.30; closed 25 Dec*
Details *Children welcome in bar eating area and dining room   Car park Wheelchair access (not WC)   Patio   No smoking in dining room   No music Dogs welcome in snug bar   Delta, MasterCard, Switch, Visa Accommodation: 3 rooms, B&B £45 to £60*

If you visit any pubs that you think should appear in the Guide, write to tell us -- The Which? Guide to Country Pubs, FREEPOST, 2 Marylebone Road, London NW1 4DF.

BRINKWORTH   Wiltshire   map 2

Three Crowns 🍇

Brinkworth SN15 5AF   TEL: (01666) 510366
WEB SITE: www.threecrowns.co.uk
on B4042 Malmesbury to Wootton Bassett road

This is an attractive, stone-built old inn with an ivy-clad brick extension to one side and a huge conservatory dining room at the back. In
the main bar, real fires blaze, the lighting is gentle, there is a curiosity
of a table made out of giant bellows, and only the piped pop music
strikes an untraditional note. A large blackboard above the fire lists
lunchtime snacks, such as jacket potatoes, sausages of various descriptions, ploughman's and heftily filled rolls. In the conservatory,
another board announces more elaborate cooking, encompassing no
starters but a range of generously portioned main courses. These
might be fillet of sea bass in garlic butter with scampi and prawns;
veal pie using local meat cooked in sweet cider, white wine and
tarragon under a lid of buttery puff pastry; or duck breast with
Marsala cream sauce garnished with sauté foie gras. If you have room
for a pudding, there is summer fruit meringue gâteau, strawberry and
Grand Marnier cheesecake, or apple and rhubarb crumble. Archers
Village Bitter, Castle Eden, Fuller's London Pride, and Wadworth 6X
are the handpumped beers, and there is a highly commendable,
comprehensive wine list, with at least ten dispensed by the glass.
Many wines come in below the £20 mark, but those that don't are
classics that the connoisseur will be glad of the opportunity to sample.
SAMPLE DISHES: ploughman's lunch with roast chicken £7; gratinated
fillet of cod with leek and tomato in cream sauce £15; lemon and
Cointreau mousse with passion-fruit sauce £4.75.

Licensee Anthony Windle (Whitbread)
Open *11 to 3, 6 to 11; bar food 12 to 2, 6.15 to 9.30; closed 25 Dec*
Details *Children welcome   Car park   Wheelchair access (also WC)   Garden
No smoking in dining room   Background music   Dogs welcome in bar
Amex, Delta, Diners, MasterCard, Switch, Visa*

BROADHEMBURY   Devon   map 2

Drewe Arms 😊 😊 🍺 🍇

Broadhembury EX14 3NF   TEL: (01404) 841267
off A373, between Cullompton and Honiton

Despite being only a few minutes from the M5, Broadhembury is a
peaceful, quintessentially English village with thatched, whitewashed

cottages. The Drewe Arms is a large, immaculately maintained fifteenth-century building, with custard-coloured walls, next to the church. Inside, there are lots of quirky, artistic touches to the décor, such as colourful William Morris-print oilcloths on the tables, bunches of posies in glass vases, and a teetering ceramic clock by a local artist on the mantelpiece. Walls are packed with prints on a fishy theme, which is entirely appropriate given the menu of almost exclusively fish and seafood dishes (with a couple of token meat offerings). Descriptions are simple, avoiding flowery menu-speak, and when the food arrives it turns out to be prepared with an equally straightforward approach. The uncomplicated treatments are none the less interesting, ranging from traditional lemon sole with herb butter, or mussels steamed with garlic and herbs to the occasional modern idea, such as fillet of brill with horseradish hollandaise. The main menu is supplemented by a list of open sandwiches with various toppings; the gangplank version comes with prawns, gravlax, beef and Brie. There is also a three-course fixed-price menu. Beers, served under gravity direct from the cask, are the full range from the Otter Brewery, in nearby Honiton. For those who like to follow their grapes, the wine list is full of affordable treasures. With around a dozen half-bottles, six wines by the glass, and a stunning cache of house specials, there is plenty of choice. SAMPLE DISHES: spicy tomato soup £5; skate wing with black butter and capers £11; hazelnut parfait £4.50.

Licensees Kerstin and Nigel Burge (freehouse)
Open *11 to 3 (2.30 winter), 6 to 11 (7 to 10.30 Sun); bar food and restaurant 12 to 2, 7 to 9.30; closed Sun evening winter, 25 and 31 Dec*
Details *Children welcome in eating areas   Car park   Wheelchair access (also WC)   Garden   No smoking in dining room   No music   Dogs by arrangement Delta, MasterCard, Switch, Visa*

BROME   Suffolk   map 6

▲ *Cornwallis* ♀ ♥

Brome IP23 8AJ   TEL: (01379) 870326
WEB SITE: www.thecornwallis.com
at junction of A140 and B1077, midway between Norwich and Ipswich

This rather grand country hotel, restaurant and bar stands in extensive grounds, with parkland, a pond, a walled garden and an avenue of impressive trees, not far from the attractive town of Eye. Stripped-wood tables and a glassed-over well are the principal features of the comfortable, beamed bar, and there is some rather serious cooking going on, as befits the surroundings. Starters, or 'Quick Bites', include poached salmon and prawns in a seasoned bun with tomato and horseradish mayonnaise, or club sandwich which is substantial enough to share. Braised shoulder of lamb with sweet red cabbage and flageolet beans was enjoyed by one visitor, or there might be grilled chicken breast with smoked bacon; pesto linguine and sage cream; or fish and chips with minted mushy peas. End with lemon tart with peach sauce or an imaginative selection of farmhouse cheeses. If you can find a corner for them, pieces of vanilla fudge come with coffee. A fine and extensive wine list contains plenty to chew over, including some witty wine quotations, and ten offerings by the glass. Prices are reasonable considering some of the wines are very fine indeed (e.g. Château d'Yqem 1970 at £580). But there's plenty around the £15 mark, and a nice selection of Alsace wines shows the owners know what they're doing when it comes to matching with food. St Peters Best Bitter and Adnams Best and Broadside are on handpump. SAMPLE DISHES: tomato and basil soup with chorizo and tapénade £4.25; hoisin-basted duck breast with sauté bok choy and passion-fruit dressing £11; poached pear with hazelnut praline, caramel sauce and vanilla ice cream £4.

Licensees Jeffrey Ward and Richard Leslie (freehouse)
Open 11 to 11; bar food and restaurant 11 to 3, 5 to 9.45
Details Children welcome Car park Wheelchair access (also WC) Garden and patio No-smoking area in bar, no smoking in dining room Background music Dogs welcome exc in dining areas Delta, MasterCard, Switch, Visa Accommodation: 16 rooms, B&B £72.50 to £125

BUCKDEN   North Yorkshire   map 8

▲ *Buck Inn* 🌢

Buckden BD23 5JA   TEL: (01756) 760228
WEB SITE: www.thebuckinn.yorks.net
on B6160, between Kettleworth and West Burton

Creepers and hanging baskets soften the grey-stone frontage of this Georgian coaching inn on a village green in the great walking country of Upper Wharfedale. Regulars and tourists alike appreciate the comfortably modernised bars and the restaurant, which is in the courtyard where wool auctions were held long ago. The dishes on the restaurant and bar menus are virtually the same, but in the restaurant they are offered as a two- or three-course set-price meal. Fresh linguine in a rich sauce of cream, garlic, bacon and wild mushrooms, or chicken liver and foie gras parfait might precede something as simple as chargrilled lamb cutlets, or roast duck breast with stir-fried noodles and an oriental-style sauce. Vegetarian choices are available on request, and desserts might include lemon crème brûlée or home-made sorbets. At least four real ales are on draught, including Theakston

Best Bitter, John Smith's Cask Bitter, Old Peculier and Black Bull plus maybe a long-term guest such as Tetley Bitter. Of some 40 wines, only a Rioja Gran Reserva is over £20, and ten are offered by the glass. SAMPLE DISHES: sea bass and red pepper terrine £5.25; fillet of beef in a red wine and garlic sauce with creamed leeks and cheese mash £13; apple and blackberry crumble with crème anglaise £3.

Licensee Nigel Hayton (freehouse)
Open *11 to 11 (10.30 Sun); bar food and restaurant Mon to Sat 12 to 2, 6.30 to 9.30, Sun 12 to 5, 7 to 8.30*
Details *Children welcome   Car park   Patio   No smoking in dining room Occasional background music   Dogs welcome   Delta, MasterCard, Switch, Visa   Accommodation: 14 rooms, B&B £33 to £72*

BUCKLAND   Oxfordshire   map 2

▲ *Lamb at Buckland* 🏵 🍇

Lamb Lane, Buckland SN7 8QN   TEL: (01367) 870484
off A420, midway between Faringdon and Kingston Bagpuize

This eighteenth-century Cotswold-stone building in a cul-de-sac has a small, uncluttered bar, with – given the pub's name – sheep as a decorative theme throughout. The dining room is a different, more refined world of restful blue and yellow and tables with white linen cloths contrasting happily with low, beamed ceilings – and the only lamb in sight is roast. The menu, the same throughout the pub, changes with the seasons. Snacks range from ploughman's, black pudding or Welsh rarebit to attractive fishy options, such as sauté herring roes, or baked seafood pancake. A full meal might start with a salad of scallops with bacon and endive and proceed to a main course of game, perhaps saddle of hare, roast duck breast, or kedgeree. Ingredients are first class and are handled by the kitchen with skill. The ales on draught are usually Hook Norton Best Bitter and Wadworth 6X, but the pride of the Lamb is its long list of wines, with 12 by the glass. The list offers plenty to make you smile: from the amusing thirsty-sheep cartoon on the front page to the welcome selection of house wines starting at £10.25 (£1.90 the glass). Classics and new finds from South America make particularly interesting drinking. SAMPLE DISHES: scrambled eggs with smoked salmon and prawns £6; steak and kidney pie £11; junket £3.50.

Licensee Paul Barnard (freehouse)
Open *11 (12 Sun) to 11; bar food and restaurant 12 to 2, 7 to 9.30; no food 25 and 26 Dec*
Details *Children welcome   Car park   Wheelchair access (not WC)   Garden and patio   No smoking in dining room   Live or background music   No dogs Amex, Delta, MasterCard, Switch, Visa   Accommodation: 4 rooms, B&B £39 to £58*

Dysart Arms

Bowes Gate Road, Bunbury CW6 9PH   TEL: (01829) 260183
off A51, 5m NW of Nantwich

The Dysart Arms is opposite the church of St Boniface, parts of
which date from the fourteenth century and which contains a collection of carved alabaster and stone effigies that are worth a peek. The
pub itself is a red-brick building with a large garden and, within,
exposed brick walls and stone floors; towards the back is a more
formal carpeted dining area. Food is listed on both blackboard and
printed menus, with orders taken at the bar. Salmon and smoked
haddock fishcakes are mightily proportioned and served with lemon
mayonnaise, and soup of the day might be something a little out of
the ordinary, such as parsnip and apple. Bangers and mash, using
sausages from a local butcher, come highly recommended, and those
in the mood to branch out could go for seared salmon on tagliatelle
with Thai curry sauce, and vegetarians could try perhaps baked field
mushrooms stuffed with lentils on ratatouille. A range of fine farmhouse cheeses and Mövenpick ice creams and sorbets supplement
desserts such as Eve's pudding with custard. Timothy Taylor
Landlord and Boddingtons are on handpump, and the continually
changing guest beers are always worth investigating too. With
around a dozen wines by the glass from a fairly compact list, this is
clearly a place in which the casual drinker will feel as much at home
as the diner. SAMPLE DISHES: satay prawns with prawn crackers £6;
braised shoulder of lamb with redcurrant sauce £11; sticky toffee
pudding with butterscotch sauce £3.50.

Licensee Darren Snell (freehouse)
Open *11 to 11, Sun 12 to 10.30; bar food Mon to Fri 12 to 2.15, 6 to 9.30,
Sat 12 to 9.30, Sun 12 to 9*
Details *Children welcome; no under-10s after 6pm   Car park   Wheelchair
access (also WC)   Garden and patio   No smoking in dining room
Background music   Dogs welcome in bar   Amex, Delta, MasterCard, Switch,
Visa*

▲ *Lamb Inn* 🍇

Sheep Street, Burford OX18 4LR   TEL: (01993) 823155
from A40 take A361 N; in village take first left into Sheep Street

If it weren't so authentic, the Lamb might almost be a Hollywood
version of the English country inn. Built of mellow-hued Cotswold

stone and dating from the fifteenth century, it sits in a pleasant village not far from Oxford's dreaming spires. Inside, the stone-flagged floors, uneven beams and the gleam of pewter and brass remind you of the venerability of the place, but it has also been sensitively modernised in just the right places, so that the handsome pillared dining room with polished floorboards makes the right sort of backdrop for the ambitious modern cookery on offer there. Bar food is available at lunchtime only (not Sunday), and the range comprises spinach and Gorgonzola ravioli in tomato cream, pork tenderloin with sweet curry sauce and pilaff rice, and beef stroganoff with tagliatelle. In addition are sandwiches and baguettes filled perhaps with roast leg of lamb with minted mayonnaise, or prawns in Marie Rose sauce, while bar desserts might include crème brûlée or lemon tart. The fixed-price dinner menus in the restaurant (£22 for two courses and £27 for three) move up a few gears to embrace such dishes as feuilleté of lambs' sweetbreads with leeks and pink peppercorns in a Marsala cream sauce, followed perhaps by a whole grilled sole with seared scallops and prawns in lime butter, and then port and cranberry cheesecake with plum compote. A deeply classical and extensive wine list will make for much happy perusal among oenophiles (the by-the-glass choice extends to a dozen), while beer drinkers should seek out Hook Norton Best Bitter, Badger Dorset Best, and Wadworth 6X. There's also Stowford Press cider. SAMPLE DISHES: cream of lentil soup with bacon lardons £3.50; braised shank of lamb with a sage jus, dauphinois potatoes and vegetables £9; Grand Marnier and orange cheesecake £3.75.

Licensee Richard De Wolf (freehouse)
Open *11 to 2.30, 6 to 11, Sun 12 to 3, 7 to 10.30; bar food Mon to Sat 12 to 2; restaurant Sun 12 to 1.45, all week 7 to 9; closed 25 and 26 Dec*
Details *Children welcome   Garden   No smoking in dining room   No music Dogs welcome exc in restaurant   Delta, MasterCard, Switch, Visa Accommodation: 15 rooms, B&B £70 to £125*

BURLTON   Shropshire   map 7

▲ *Burlton Inn*   NEW ENTRY

Burlton SY4 5TB   TEL: (01939) 270284
WEB SITE: www.burltoninn.co.uk
on A528, 9m N of Shrewsbury

This eighteenth-century pub in a tiny village is notable for the flowers both outside and in, and for the warmth of the colour co-ordinated open-plan interior, with soft red-brick walls complemented by a deep-rose-pink décor. An inspector found it 'stylish and civilised without being the slightest bit pretentious'. The same menu is offered throughout, and food is served at tables decorated by more flowers and candles. Bar snacks are ciabatta rolls, ploughman's and jacket potatoes, while more adventurous starters or light lunches could see some exotic combinations of flavours, as in melon and crab salad with redcurrant and mint dressing, or a main course of grilled bacon chop topped with three-cheese butter. More conventional are Stilton-stuffed roast mushrooms, slow-cooked half-shoulder of lamb on potato and parsnip mash, and steaks from a local butcher. Imaginative puddings from a blackboard might be raspberry flummery, or pear and ginger crumble. Banks's Bitter is the regular ale, supplemented by three frequently changing guests, from a number of local and small breweries or from Greene King, Shepherd Neame or Charles Wells. The list of 20 modestly priced wines is unusual in not including a single bottle from France; five are sold by the glass. SAMPLE DISHES: cauliflower and Shropshire Blue soup £3.25; baked sea bass on a bed of tomatoes, courgettes and anchovies topped with red pepper butter £11; old-fashioned bread-and-butter pudding £3.25.

Licensees Gerald and Ann Bean (freehouse)
Open *11 to 3, 6 to 11, Sun 12 to 3, 7 to 10.30; bar food 12 to 2 (restricted menu Mon lunchtime), 6.30 to 9.45 (9.30 Sun); closed evening 25 Dec, 26 Dec, bank hol Mon lunchtimes*
Details *Children welcome in bar eating area   Car park   Wheelchair access (also WC)   Garden and patio   No music   Dogs by arrangement   Delta, MasterCard, Switch, Visa   Accommodation: 6 rooms, B&B £45 to £70*

BURNHAM MARKET   **Norfolk**   map 6

▲ *Hoste Arms* ♣   [NEW ENTRY]

The Green, Burnham Market PE31 8HD
TEL: (01328) 738777
WEB SITE: www.hostearms.co.uk
on B1155, 5m W of Wells-next-the-Sea

Looking like something out of a Jane Austen novel, this large, butter-cup-yellow seventeenth-century inn stands on the village green in the heart of affluent Burnham Market. It functions on several levels, primarily as a smart but informal country hotel with a restaurant, conference facilities and so on. At the front, however, is a very pubby wood-panelled bar where locals and hotel guests gather to sup regional brews from Woodforde's, Greene King and Adnams, though greater emphasis is placed on wines: the 'short' list is longer than the full list in most other pubs, and no fewer than 12 wines come by the glass. There is everything from Latour to Le Montrachet at the top end, but plenty else that's imaginative and affordable in every other style category. Food is served in an elegantly laid-up area off the bar, which operates the same menu as the restaurant, and the closest the cooking gets to traditional pub grub is beefburger with bacon, cheese and chips. Fish is the main concern, whether in simple dishes such as pan-fried squid on couscous, or more exotic treatments like pan-fried tuna with Asian stir-fry and hoisin sauce. Options for meat eaters might include pan-fried loin of pork with black pudding and a caper and black olive dressing, or roasted ham hock with rosemary jus. Or you could, if you wish, just stick to a sandwich at lunchtime. SAMPLE DISHES: smoked mackerel mousse with crème fraîche and red pepper dressing £5.75; baked cod with rösti, wilted spinach and white wine sauce £9.75; vanilla brûlée with shortbread £4.25.

Licensees Paul Whittome and Emma Tagg (freehouse)
Open *11 to 11, Sun 12 to 10.30; bar food and restaurant 12 to 2, 7 to 9*
Details *Children welcome in eating areas   Car park   Wheelchair access (also WC)   Garden and patio   No-smoking area in dining room   Occasional music No dogs   Delta, MasterCard, Switch, Visa   Accommodation: 28 rooms, B&B £66 to £86*

▲ Lord Nelson   NEW ENTRY

Creake Road, Burnham Market PE31 8EN
TEL: (01328) 738321

Not to be confused with the pub of the same name in the neighbouring village of Burnham Thorpe (see entry), this tribute to Norfolk's favourite son is a relatively recent arrival on the pub dining scene. A large public bar caters for those who just want to have a drink, while diners can eat in the lounge, which is decked out with Nelson memorabilia, or in the small restaurant at the back. The standard bar menu includes all the old favourites, but the restaurant menu, also chalked on a blackboard, is where the real interest lies. Typical of the style are grilled goats' cheese with artichoke hearts; Brancaster mussels with lemon, garlic, parsley and butter; lamb and leek pie; and salmon and cod fishcakes with prawn and parsley sauce. Among dishes to receive praise have been pork and cider pie – a 'high-quality stew' of lean and tender meat in tangy gravy with a puff pastry lid – and sticky gingerbread pudding with ginger wine and brandy sauce. Value for money is also commended. Real ales are from Greene King and Bass, and the short wine list includes three by the glass. SAMPLE DISHES: Thai prawns with coriander and lime mayonnaise £4.50; game pie £8.25; tiramisù £3.50.

Licensees Richard and Paula Ayres (Unique Pub Company)
Open *11 to 3, 6 (6.30 winter) to 11, Sun 12 to 3, 7 to 10.30; bar food and restaurant 12 to 2.15, 6.30 to 9.30*
Details *Children welcome in eating areas   Car park   Wheelchair access (also WC)   Garden and patio   No smoking in dining room   Occasional live music; jukebox   Dogs welcome   MasterCard, Switch, Visa   Accommodation: 2 rooms, B&B £25 to £60*

BURNHAM THORPE   **Norfolk**   map 6

Lord Nelson

Walsingham Road, Burnham Thorpe PE31 8HN
TEL: (01328) 738241
off B1155/B1355, 2m S of Burnham Market

The name of this flint and brick pub is dedicated to the village's most famous son, and indeed the pub has been around long enough to have hosted the farewell party held by its namesake before he joined his new ship in 1793. In those days it was called the Plough, but was renamed shortly after Nelson's death. Apart from that, and the abundant Nelson memorabilia that adorn the walls, it remains largely unchanged since his day. Unusually, the pub has no bar counter, so orders are taken at table and beers are tapped direct from the cask in the taproom at the back. These include local brews such as Nelson's Revenge from Woodforde's, and Abbot Ale and IPA from Greene King. A printed menu offers a range of snacks, sandwiches, baguettes, ploughman's and breakfasts, plus main dishes such as deep-fried Whitby scampi, or a substantial mixed grill. There is also a blackboard of daily specials: game terrine with red onion chutney, perhaps, or Brancaster mussels poached in a dill and celery sauce, followed by grilled fillets of red mullet with red wine gravy, or braised duck legs in port sauce with new potatoes roasted with rosemary. From October to May, live music is performed here on the first Friday of the month, and there is a play area for children in the garden. SAMPLE DISHES: cauliflower and blue cheese soup £3.25; grilled lamb chops with red wine and rosemary sauce £8.75; apple pie £3.25.

Licensee L.A. Stafford (Greene King)
Open *11 to 3, 6 to 11 (10.30 Sun); winter opening hours may vary: phone to check; bar food 12 to 2, 7 to 9*
Details *Children welcome in eating areas   Car park   Wheelchair access (also WC)   Garden   No-smoking area in bar, no smoking in dining room
Occasional live music   Dogs welcome exc in dining room   Delta, Switch*

BURNSALL   **North Yorkshire**   map 8

▲ *Red Lion*   NEW ENTRY

RIVERSIDE

Burnsall BD23 6BU   TEL: (01756) 720204
WEB SITE: www.redlion.co.uk
on B6160 N of Bolton Bridge

Look for Burnsall's bridge – you can't miss it. It's a magnificent five-arched affair over the River Wharfe, with the Red Lion positioned right next to it. Fashioned from a terraced row of old stone cottages, it has a cosy, low-ceilinged bar with a real fire and a congregation of stuffed foxes and deer. Beyond the bar is a separate, more formal restaurant with linen-covered tables. Several menus are in operation, all available throughout: a light-lunch listing of cold items such as sandwiches and salads, a carte, a specials board and a fixed-price 'Taste of Wharfedale' menu. The carte is particularly ambitious, offering a choice of timbale of blue cheese with curly kale and celeriac chips, dill-cured salmon with avocado and lemon and coriander dressing, or terrine of pork and rabbit with toasted brioche and cranberry sauce among the starters. Follow those with something like pot-roast Gloucester Old Spot pork with roasted shallots, apple sauce and rösti, or confit of lamb with potato gratin and a chutney made with aubergine, tomatoes and sultanas. A couple of vegetarian options are offered too: perhaps leek and goats'-cheese tart with rocket salad. Puddings include crème brûlée with raspberries and blackberries, or dark treacle tart with honeycomb ice cream, or you could opt for a selection of cheeses that celebrates Yorkshire's (and Ireland's) finest. On handpump are well-kept beers from Theakston, along with Old Speckled Hen, John Smith's Smooth and Timothy Taylor's Best Bitter. Bordeaux and Burgundy are great strengths on the restaurant wine list (available in the bar on request), but there's also an imaginative selection from the rest of the world. Prices are reasonable, full tasting notes let you know just what you'll be getting, and there is a handy range of half-bottles. Around 15 wines are sold by the glass from £2.30. SAMPLE DISHES: smoked haddock fishcakes with braised chicory and green tomato chutney £6; venison with pan-fried polenta, wild mushrooms, and green peppercorn sauce £12.75; chocolate and prune terrine with redcurrant compote £6.50.

Licensee Elizabeth Grayshon (freehouse)
Open *11.30 to 11.30, Sun 12 to 10.30; bar food 12 to 2.30, 6 to 9.30; Sun 12 to 3, 6.30 to 9.30; restaurant 12 to 2.30, 7 to 9.30*
Details *Children welcome   Car park   Wheelchair access (not WC)   Garden No-smoking area in bar, no smoking in dining room   No music   Dogs welcome   Amex, Delta, Diners, MasterCard, Switch, Visa   Accommodation: 11 rooms, B&B £48 to £120*

BURPHAM   West Sussex   map 3

George and Dragon

Burpham BN18 9RR   TEL: (01903) 883131
2½m up single-track, no-through road signposted Warningcamp off A27, 1m E of Arundel

---

The road to the pretty village is a cul-de-sac, and the pub is tucked away between the church and a playing field. Although the inn dates from the early eighteenth century, with black-beamed low ceilings, cream-painted walls hung with floral prints, and a coal-effect gas fire, the ambience is slightly suburban in feel. Bar food is conventional in scope, but fine cooking lifts it out of the ordinary. There is a wide choice of baguettes, sandwiches and jacket potatoes, as well as Parma ham with mozzarella, and smoked duck salad. Daily specials might be venison sausages with juniper sauce, skate wing and capers, or redcurrant-glazed calf's liver. In the restaurant, a starter such as assiette of smoked duck breast with tarragon and orange dressing, followed by pavé of sea bass with a compote of creamed leeks and red wine jus might feature on the monthly-changing four-course promotional menu. Well-kept Burpham Best Bitter and Harveys Sussex Best Bitter are the regulars on tap, plus a weekly-changing guest from Timothy Taylor or the Hop Back Brewery. Around 40 reasonably priced wines are listed, with six by the glass. The selection starts with a special page of French reds, but turn over and there are one or two choices from just about every wine producing country you could name. SAMPLE DISHES: moules marinière £5; chicken and asparagus pie £6.25; apricot pithiviers £4.

Licensees Kate Holle and James Rose (freehouse)
Open 11 to 2.30, 6 to 11, Sun 12 to 3, 7 to 10.30; bar food (exc Sun evening end Aug to Easter) 12 to 2, 7 to 9.30; restaurant Mon to Sat 7 to 9.30, Sun 12 to 2; closed 25 Dec
Details No children Car park Wheelchair access (also WC) Patio No pipes Background music No dogs Amex, Delta, Diners, MasterCard, Switch, Visa

BUTLEY Suffolk

map 6

Oyster Inn

Butley IP12 3NZ   TEL: (01394) 450790
on B1084, 4m W of Orford

The garden is a lovely place in which to eat in fine weather; otherwise, you will probably agree with a reader who found the pub thoroughly comforting inside, with coal fires in antique black grates, cushioned settles, pine tables and a variety of pictures on the walls. A mixture of locals and weekenders appreciate the quiet ambience, except for conversation and occasional live folk music or jazz. The blackboard menu offers a decent choice, from half a roast duck, described as 'perfectly moist, with the skin beautifully crisp', or pink roast rack of lamb accompanied by 'superb' potatoes cooked in cream with garlic, to home-made pies such as gobble grunt (game). Starters range from deep-fried potato skins with a dip, to well-timed moules marinière, or chicken liver pâté. This is an Adnams pub, with up to five of the brewery's ales on draught. All ten wines listed are available by the glass. SAMPLE DISHES: home-made soup £3.50; three-cheese and pasta bake £6; blueberry sponge with vanilla sauce £3.25.

Licensees Carol and Mike Hanlon (Adnams)
Open *Mon to Fri 11.30 to 3, 6 to 11, Sat 11.30 to 11, Sun 12 to 3, 7 to 10.30; bar food 12 to 2, 7 to 9*
Details *Children welcome   Car park   Wheelchair access (not WC)   Garden and patio   Occasional live music   Dogs welcome   MasterCard, Switch, Visa*

BUTTERTON   Staffordshire   map 5

▲ *Black Lion Inn*

Butterton ST13 7SP   TEL: (01538) 304232
WEB SITE: www.theblacklion.clara.net
just off B5053, 6m E of Leek

Walkers and enthusiasts for other outdoor pursuits appreciate this cottagey-looking old stone inn, which dates from 1782. It has a prime position opposite the church in this small village on the edge of the Manifold Valley, and enjoys excellent views over the Peak District. Inside, a large collection of whisky jugs hangs from the exposed beams, on the stone walls and over the open fireplaces. As well as sandwiches, baguettes and salads, the printed bar menu lists things such as hot mozzarella melts, Goan chicken curry and steak Diane. In addition, daily blackboard specials might include rabbit pie with herbed suet crust, and oatcake stuffed with smoked haddock, mushrooms and tomato in cheese sauce. The restaurant at the rear of the pub has its own menu, typically offering hot sweet-and-sour prawns, followed by chicken stuffed with sage, mascarpone and dolcelatte and wrapped in Parma ham. Beers include Hartington Bitter from the Whim brewery, only a few miles away, Theakston Best Bitter and Marston's Pedigree, plus guests such as Wells Bombardier. Fifteen international wines are offered, starting at £7.50 and all, except sparkling, under £12; four are available by the glass. SAMPLE DISHES: creamy garlic mushrooms £3; lamb shank with port and rosemary sauce £9.75; lemon sponge with lemon sauce £2.50.

Licensee Tim Lowes (freehouse)
Open *Tue to Sun 12 to 2.30 (3 Sat and Sun), all week 7 to 11 (10.30 Sun); bar food 12 to 2, 7 to 8.45; restaurant Fri and Sat 7 to 9.30, Sun 12 to 2; closed 25 Dec*
Details *Children welcome in bar eating area   Car park   Wheelchair access (not WC)   Garden and patio   Live or background music   Dogs welcome in bar   MasterCard, Switch, Visa   Accommodation: 3 rooms, B&B £35 to £55*

BYLAND ABBEY   North Yorkshire   map 9

▲ *Abbey Inn* ❦

Byland Abbey YO61 4BD   TEL: (01347) 868204
WEB SITE: www.bylandabbeyinn.co.uk
off A170, between Thirsk and Helmsley, 2m W of Ampleforth

The Abbey Inn enjoys an isolated rural position off the main Thirsk
to Helmsley road (from which it is signposted), and is so named
because it stands close to the remains of twelfth-century Byland
Abbey. Only one end wall of the abbey is just about still standing,
but the two-storey, creeper-clad inn is in much better shape. Martin
and Jane Nordli have been proprietors here since 1997, and they run
the place with a welcoming approach. Stuffed birds, tall candlesticks
and *objets d'art* of all kinds give the interiors a feeling of Victorian
exotic. This is a wine-lovers pub, with a commendable list that spans
a range from New Zealand's Cloudy Bay Chardonnay to Nekeas
Tempranillo from Navarra. The eight house wines, four of each
colour, are all sold at a uniform price of £11.50 the bottle, or £2 a
glass. Beer drinkers will find Black Sheep Best Bitter on draught, as
well as Tetley, and there is a small but enterprising range of speciality cognacs and armagnacs. The cooking shows evidence of an inven-
tiveness to match the wines, with Cajun chicken breast on apricot
and mint salsa, seared salmon with broad bean purée and lemon
sauce, and duck breast marinated in orange and jasmine with
Cumberland sauce among likely main courses. Starters may be a little
nearer the pub norm, taking in soups, pâtés and smoked salmon,
while simpler one-course lunches might include lamb rogan josh, or
wild boar sausages with cheese and chive mash. Finish with apple
and raisin crumble, or lemon posset. SAMPLE DISHES: pear, Stilton and
bacon salad £6; roast shoulder of lamb with mint and redcurrant
gravy £12.50; white chocolate crème brûlée £4.

Licensees Martin and Jane Nordli (freehouse)
Open *11 to 3, 6.30 to 11, Sun 12 to 6; bar food 12 to 2, 6.30 to 9, Sun 12 to
4; closed Mon lunchtime*
Details *Children welcome   Car park   Wheelchair access (also WC)   Garden
No smoking in 2 rooms   Background music   No dogs   Delta, MasterCard,
Switch, Visa   Accommodation: 3 rooms, B&B £40 to £110*

CADELEIGH   Devon   map 1

Cadeleigh Arms   NEW ENTRY

Cadeleigh EX16 8HP   TEL: (01884) 855238
village signposted off A3072 Crediton road at Bickleigh

In a small village high in the hills above the Exe Valley, this plain, cream-painted pub is the centre of the community and also attracts diners and walkers. The bar area, with its flagstone floor, settles, farmhouse chairs and an armchair with a throw-over cover, has a roaring log fire in winter. The inn is rustic but comfortable and welcoming. The pine-furnished dining room has views over rolling countryside, and another area is devoted to pool and games; there is also a skittle alley. Home-smoked guinea fowl, with 'delicious' chutney, also home-made, is what to expect among starters, with others perhaps oak-smoked Barbary duck breast, and tandoori chicken with salad and mango chutney. A note after the main courses mentions that additional fish dishes and curries are available, as well as pork fillet fried in butter with apple and cider sauce, prawn gumbo on tagliatelle, braised lamb shank on grain mustard mash, and steaks. Cotleigh Tawny Bitter and Pale are drawn straight from the cask, and four wines, including a local English dry white, are sold by the glass from a short, fairly priced list. SAMPLE DISHES: home-cured gravad lax with honey and mustard dressing £4.75; lamb and mint sausages £6; chocolate torte £3.50.

Licensees Alexander Sainthill and Ann Kurniak (freehouse)
Open *Mon to Sat 11 to 11 (winter 11 to 3, 5.30 to 11), Sun 12 to 3, 6.30 to 10.30; bar food and restaurant (exc Sun and Mon evenings) 12 to 2.30, 7 to 9.30*
Details *Children welcome in family and games rooms   Car park   Wheelchair access (also WC)   Garden   Jukebox   Dogs welcome   Switch, Visa*

CADNAM   Hampshire   map 2

White Hart   NEW ENTRY

Old Romsey Road, Cadnam SO40 2NP   TEL: (02380) 812277
1/3m off M27 junction 1

This old coaching inn on the edge of the New Forest traces its history back to 1448, when an even older building than the present one was a stopping place for the return to Winchester of the body of William Rufus. Softly lit rambling rooms, with exposed brickwork and open fires, are made very comfortable with a mixture of old and new furniture and New Forest mementoes, pictures and country prints. Most of the customers come to eat, but a hard core of locals drop in for Wadworth 6X, Old Speckled Hen and Ringwood Best Bitter. Five red and five white wines from the short list are offered by the glass to accompany the long menu on blackboards. One lists snacks, from sandwiches to omelettes, scampi, pasta and a curry of the day, while another offers a longer list of main dishes, mostly traditional with the odd incomer in the shape of perhaps chicken fajitas, or spicy duck breast with plum sauce. Pies might include mixed fish, game, or steak and kidney with Irish stout. The large garden to the side and rear, where there's a pond, makes a pleasant spot in good weather. SAMPLE DISHES: duck and port pâté £5; mixed grill £13; rhubarb crumble £4.

Licensee Peter Palmer (Whitbread)
Open *11 to 3, 5.30 to 11, Sun 12 to 3, 5.30 to 10.30; bar food 12 to 2, 6 to 9.30*
Details *Children welcome in bar eating area　Car park　Wheelchair access (not WC)　Garden and patio　No-smoking area in bar　Occasional background music　No dogs　Delta, MasterCard, Switch, Visa*

CARTERWAY HEADS　　Northumberland　　map 10

▲ *Manor House Inn* ❦

Carterway Heads, Shotley Bridge DH8 9LX
TEL: (01207) 255268
on A68, 3m W of Consett

The inn is a long, two-storey former farmhouse dating from the mid-eighteenth century, and it overlooks the rather majestic landscape of Pennine foothills and Derwent Reservoir. A fire in 1999 laid waste the bar areas and parts of the living quarters, but the Browns managed to bounce back, refurbishing the bars with new beams and wood panelling. The treasured collection of jugs that hang overhead appears to have been saved for the nation – or for Carterway Heads anyway. Tables with lacy cloths and candles give the dining room a homely feel, and the atmosphere is friendly and welcoming. Theakston Best, Ruddles Best and Courage Directors are among the real ales on offer, along with a guest such as Durham Green Goddess. There is also Weston's scrumpy as well as over five dozen malt whiskies for the connoisseur. The kitchen draws inspiration from far afield, producing dishes ranging from mussels in Thai curry sauce, via a Szechuan-style stir-fry of wild mushrooms and vegetables served in a filo basket, to sea bass stuffed with Italian vegetables. For meat eaters there's duck breast with orange and coriander, or medallions of beef with a Madeira tarragon sauce. Among desserts might be fig and almond cake with butterscotch sauce, or home-made ice cream served with shortbread, or choose regional cheeses, which come with biscuits and onion marmalade. A fairly lengthy and reasonably priced wine list draws from France, Spain, Italy and the southern hemisphere, and includes a selection of fine wines. Ten wines are available by the glass. SAMPLE DISHES: chicken liver pâté £4; baked salmon with crayfish, dill and lemon £11.50; double chocolate Amaretto truffle £3.25.

Licensees Chris and Moira Brown (freehouse)
Open *Mon to Fri 11 to 3, 5.30 to 11, Sat 11 to 11, Sun 12 to 3, 6 to 10.30; bar food and restaurant Sun to Fri 12 to 2.30, 6 (7 in restaurant) to 9.30, Sat 12 to 9.30; closed evening 25 Dec*
Details *Children welcome in dining room   Car park   Garden and patio   No smoking in dining room   Background music in bar   Dogs welcome   Amex, Delta, MasterCard, Switch, Visa   Accommodation: 4 rooms, B&B £33 to £63*

CARTHORPE   North Yorkshire   map 9

Fox and Hounds 🍇

Carthorpe DL8 2LG   TEL: (01845) 567433
off A1, 4m SE of Bedale

On the main street of a tiny village, this stone-built inn attracts both locals and people from further afield for the quality of its food. The home-like, cosy interior is decorated with blue and white plates and jugs, ceramic dogs, and furniture such as a lovely old dresser, with a washing bowl and jug, that stands by the bar. Stone fireplaces, mottled pink and green wallpaper, and maroon, cream and green carpeting complete the picture. Young staff serve attentively and pleasantly – but expect delays at busy times. Menus, common to all areas, include modestly priced midweek set dinners (Tuesday to Thursday), a carte, and blackboard specials. Mainly traditional dishes take in black pudding with caramelised apple and onion marmalade, grilled lamb cutlets with redcurrant gravy, steaks, and poached salmon with hollandaise. More exotic incomers are barbecued spare ribs, or mango-stuffed chicken breast in light curry sauce. Tender, carefully cooked beef with Yorkshire pudding, and roast lamb with rosemary stuffing at Sunday lunchtime have both come with excellent gravy and vegetables, and sticky ginger pudding with ginger wine, brandy sauce and cream moved a reader to vow to return. On draught are John Smith's Cask Bitter and Theakston Best Bitter as well as Stowford Press cider. Around a dozen of the very reasonably priced wines on offer (the majority of which are from the New World) are sold by the glass, and only one bottle exceeds £20. Choices are available by region, and careful notes and a style guide assist decision-making. SAMPLE DISHES: whole dressed Whitby crab £6; steak and kidney pie £8; iced apricot and pineapple soufflé £3.75.

Licensee Howard Fitzgerald (freehouse)
Open *Tue to Sun 12 to 3, 7 to 11 (10.30 Sun); bar food and restaurant 12 to 2, 7 to 9.30; closed first week Jan*
Details *Children welcome   Car park   Wheelchair access (also WC)   No smoking in dining room   Background music   No dogs   Delta, MasterCard, Switch, Visa*

CARTMEL FELL   Cumbria   map 8

Masons Arms

Strawberry Bank, Cartmel Fell LA11 6NW
TEL: (015395) 68486
WEB SITE: www.masonsarms.uk.com
going N on A5074 turn left at sign for Bowland Bridge, then 1m up hill

HOME BREW

To say that beer is taken seriously at this popular Lakeland pub is something of an understatement. The list of bottled beers is comparable in size and scope to many restaurant wine lists (with examples from as far afield as Kenya and Singapore), and, for those not too familiar with some of the more unusual brewing styles of other countries, it includes comprehensive tasting notes. The pub is also home to the Strawberry Bank Brewery, which produces a range of superb brews, including one flavoured with damsons; these are supplemented by regularly changing guest ales. Food is also taken seriously, though the style is wholesome and hearty rather than fine and fancy. Alongside familiar pies, casseroles, sandwiches, and salads are more inventive options such as a 'pile of ribs', or vegetable burritos. Extra choice is offered on a blackboard, with plenty of vegetarian dishes: Stilton and apple crêpes, parsnip-lovers' bake, or spinach and mushroom moussaka, for example. For meat and fish eaters there may be a casserole of pork, peaches and Stilton; chicken, bacon and onion bake; or baked Lakeland trout with pesto. Three wines of each colour are sold by the glass. The pub itself has an informal, rustic feel and plenty of character, and an added attraction is the wonderful view. SAMPLE DISHES: Morecambe Bay potted shrimps £5; beef, beer and bacon casserole £8; Bavarian apple flan £3.25.

Licensee Helen Stevenson (freehouse)
Open *summer 11.30 to 11; winter Mon to Thur 11.30 to 3, 6 to 11, Fri and Sat 11.30 to 10.30, Sun 12 to 10.30; bar food 12 to 2, 6 to 8.45; closed 25 and 26 Dec*
Details *Children welcome   Car park   Wheelchair access (not WC)   Patio No smoking in 1 eating area   Occasional live music   Dogs welcome exc during eating hours   Amex, Delta, MasterCard, Switch, Visa*

CASTERTON   Cumbria   map 8

▲ *Pheasant Inn* 🍇

Casterton, nr Kirkby Lonsdale LA6 2RX   TEL: (015242) 71230
WEB SITE: www.pheasantinn.co.uk
on A683, 1m N of junction with A65

Lying halfway between the Lakes and the Dales in a tiny hamlet, this
whitewashed eighteenth-century roadside inn makes a good base for
touring, as well as being the 'nineteenth hole' for golfers from the
local club. It has something of the air of a genteel country hotel, but
once you are past the reception area, the cosy bar with its low beams
and polished brass feels very much the traditional pub, though one
room is set aside for dining. If you are just popping in for a drink,
there are beers from Theakston, Dent and Black Sheep, plus 30 malt
whiskies and a wide-ranging, international wine list. With wine prices
starting at £9.50 a bottle, and an Amarone della Valpolicella appearing mid-way through at £24, this is a list that offers both good value
and good choice. Forty-five wines are on offer, seven by the half-
bottle and 12 by the glass. Those looking for something to eat are well
served by a large and varied menu that ranges from traditional prawn
cocktail to spicy chicken Madras, also taking in haddock and chips
with mushy peas, and various sandwiches. On top of this is an equally
diverse specials board that might offer a Mediterranean seafood salad
to start, followed by lamb and root vegetable casserole, and rice
pudding with raspberry compote to finish. SAMPLE DISHES: Waldorf
salad £4.25; rabbit pie with juniper berries £8; gooseberry and
nectarine crumble £3.25.

Licensees Melvin and May Mackie (freehouse)
Open *11 to 3, 6 to 11, Sun 11 to 3, 6 to 10.30; bar food and restaurant 12
to 2, 6.30 to 9 (9.30 Fri and Sat); restaurant closed Mon Apr to Oct, Sun Oct
to Mar*
Details *Children welcome Car park Wheelchair access (also WC) Garden
and patio No smoking in dining room and 1 area in bar Background music
Dogs welcome Delta, Diners, MasterCard, Switch, Visa Accommodation: 11
rooms, B&B £40 to £72*

CASTLE ACRE   Norfolk   map 6

▲ *Ostrich Inn*   NEW ENTRY

Stocks Green, Castle Acre PE32 2AE   TEL: (01760) 755398
just off A1065 Swaffham to Fakenham road, 4m N of Swaffham

No explanation is offered as to the origin of this old coaching inn's
unusual name, but it is none the less a welcome new main entry to

the Guide. It overlooks the tree-lined green in the centre of this small, quaint village, which is known for its ancient stone arch. Enter directly into the main bar area, which is as well maintained as the exterior and has as its major feature an inglenook housing large black iron cooking pots; a large hall-type room is up a few steps beyond at the back. Eating options comprise a laminated card of pub staples, although pizzas are made on the premises, and several blackboards over the bar counter advertise daily specials. As well as beef and ale pie, these feature some fairly unusual and imaginative dishes, such as spicy bean burgers with peach chutney – a pair of crisp burgers with a real chilli kick accompanied by a proper fruity chutney – or perhaps Jamaican jerk chicken, or even crispy salmon kebabs with Cajun dip. Desserts also include some exotic choices, like baklava. Greene King ales are on handpump to wash it all down with, alongside a short list of wines that include five by the glass. SAMPLE DISHES: Mexican chilli cheese combi £4.25; filo-wrapped king prawns with pineapple salsa £5.50; treacle roly-poly pudding £2.

Licensee Raymond Wakelen (Greene King)
Open *12 to 3, 7 to 11; bar food 12 to 2, 7 to 10; closed evening 25 Dec; no food 25 and 26 Dec*
Details *Children welcome in family room Car park Wheelchair access (not WC) Garden and patio Live or background music Dogs welcome Delta, MasterCard, Switch, Visa Accommodation: 2 rooms, B&B £15 to £30*

CAVENDISH Suffolk   map 6

Bull NEW ENTRY

High Street, Cavendish CO10 8AX   TEL: (01787) 280245
on A1092 through village

This ivy-covered pub on a wide stretch of road opposite the Sue Ryder Foundation Museum stretches back to a terrace with tables under a canvas awning, complete with outdoor gas heaters. Inside, it is clean and well maintained, with no effort to achieve 'period' character, although parts of the building date from the sixteenth century. The bar area, furnished with plush velour banquettes, is separated by a partition from the dining area and its more formally laid tables. The daily-changing menu is available throughout, and although some items are conventional enough – scampi, burgers and gammon with chips, for example – interesting ideas abound. Grilled flat mushrooms are topped with goats' cheese and red pesto, and an oriental influence shows itself in a salad of smoked duck breasts on crispy noodles with plum sauce. Main dishes include kidneys turbigo with onions, mushrooms and pork sausage, or lamb tavas (a big, tender shank in a rich herby wine-based sauce) served with rice and Greek salad. The Bull is an Adnams pub, with the brewery's Southwold Bitter and Broadside on tap regularly plus maybe a seasonal guest such as Fisherman. At least six wines are offered by the glass. SAMPLE DISHES: quick-fried squid with chilli and garlic £7; fried, grilled or steamed skate £8; lemon and ginger crunch £3.25.

Licensee Gavin Crocker (Adnams)
Open *11 to 11, Sun 12 to 3, 7 to 10.30; bar food and restaurant Tue to Sun 12 to 2, 6.30 to 9*
Details *Children welcome   Car park   Garden and patio   No music   Dogs welcome   Delta, MasterCard, Switch, Visa*

CAVENDISH BRIDGE   Leicestershire   map 5

▲ *Old Crown* 🍺 NEW ENTRY

Cavendish Bridge DE72 2HL   TEL: (01332) 792392
Cavendish Bridge signposted off A6 E of M1 junction 24

The peaceful hamlet, just a single line of houses, is dominated by this white-painted pebbledash pub concealing seventeenth-century origins. Inside, its age is more apparent, and every wall is covered with shipping, railway, brewery and Second World War posters, prints, advertisements and paintings. In the words of a reporter, it is all part of the charm of an 'incredibly warm and welcoming local' run by a landlord 'of great individuality and character, a quality he imparts to the pub'. There is no separate restaurant, but daily specials can be quite sophisticated. Rolled leg of Kingussie lamb is stuffed with onion, bacon and breadcrumbs, and stufato di manzo is diced beef casseroled with celery and wild mushrooms in rich red wine sauce. More conventional are baguettes with fillings as substantial as beef and Stilton; cod, plaice or haddock with chips; a seafood platter; 'really tasty' meat and potato pie; and vegetarian dishes, including cannelloni with ricotta and spinach. Bass and Marston's Pedigree are regular beers, and Bateman XXXB, Everards Tiger and Fuller's London Pride might be among four guests, along with beers from Shardlow just across the road (two of these are brewed exclusively for the pub). Four wines from a 30-strong list are sold by the glass. SAMPLE DISHES: Japanese prawns £4.50; guinea fowl and duck pie £6.25; treacle sponge £2.

Licensees Peter and Gillian Morton-Harrison (freehouse)
Open *11.30 to 3.30, 5 to 11; bar food 12 to 2.30 (4 Sun); closed evenings 25 and 26 Dec*
Details *Children welcome   Car park   Wheelchair access (also WC)   Garden and patio   No music   Dogs welcome   Delta, MasterCard, Switch, Visa Accommodation: 1 room, B&B £25 to £35*

CHADLINGTON   Oxfordshire   map 5

Tite Inn 🍺

Mill End, Chadlington OX7 3NY   TEL: (01608) 676475
WEB SITE: www.titeinn.co.uk
off A361, 2½m S of Chipping Norton

The small stone-built inn at the edge of a quiet rustic village is
modest compared with some of its Cotswold neighbours. It has a
family-run feeling, and neither the barely audible classical music nor
the ghost of an unidentified woman detract from the ambience of a
friendly, peaceful hostelry with fast and efficient service from the
landlord and landlady. Real ale fans will be glad to find on handpump Fuller's London Pride and two guests (often from local breweries) in addition to the Tite Inn Bitter brewed by Archers. Old Rosie
cider's on draught too. Main dishes on the lunch menu are inspired
by the cuisines of, among others, Mexico, India, and South Africa,
the last represented by bobotie, a sort of curried meat loaf. A reader
has reported favourably on coarse, garlicky pâté and 'gooey, dense,
rich' chocolate tart. The evening menu is more Anglo-French in
style, with choice ranging from deep-fried Brie to seafood salad as
starters, and from lambs' kidneys braised in red wine, via fillet of
salmon en croûte, to steak with garlic mushrooms as mains. Around
half a dozen wines are sold by the standard or large glass, from £2,
on a French-biased list of close to 20 bottles. SAMPLE DISHES: chipo-
lata sausages with Dijon mustard dip £2; chicken Caesar salad £8;
treacle tart £3.

Licensees Michael and Susan Willis (freehouse)
Open *Tue to Sat and bank hol Mon 12 to 2.30, 6.30 to 11, Sun 12 to 2.30, 7
to 10.30; bar food and restaurant 12 to 2 (2.30 Sun), 7 to 9; closed 25 and 26
Dec*
Details *Children welcome   Car park   Wheelchair access (also WC)   Garden
No smoking in dining room   Occasional background music   Dogs welcome
Delta, MasterCard, Switch, Visa*

CHALGROVE   Oxfordshire   map 2

Red Lion Inn

115 High Street, Chalgrove OX44 7SS   TEL: (01865) 890625
on B480, 4 miles NW of Watlington

Located on the high street, over a little stream that runs the street's
length, the Lion has an unfussy and uncluttered yet warm and
welcoming ambience about it. Parts of the building reputedly date
from the eleventh century; tables are well spaced under beamed ceil-

ings in the main room, with fireplaces at both ends. The back garden
has a children's play area, and menus offer children's portions.
Restaurant and bar menus include imaginatively employed European
and Asian ideas and ingredients. Pigeon breast piri-piri with pickled
ginger and lemon-grass salad, and casarecce pasta with ricotta, marinated artichoke hearts and rocket please lovers of the exotic, while
others might choose old Oxford sausages with spicy red cabbage and
mash, or cod, chips and mushy peas. A variety of sandwiches and
warm open baguettes is also available. Seasonal and guest beers joint
Brakespear Bitter and Fuller's London Pride. An interesting short
wine list keeps everything under £16 and invites you to ask about the
Landlord's Special Indulgence – some 'different and special' bottles.
Seven wines are served by the glass. Note that parking is across the
street. SAMPLE DISHES: baked sardines filled with crab and herbs £5;
bacon chop, mustard mash, baked red onions £8; steamed treacle
pudding and custard £3.50.

Licensees Jonathan and Maggi Hewitt (freehouse)
Open *12 to 3, 6 to 11, Sun 12 to 3, 7 to 11; closed for 1 or 2 days between*
Christmas and New Year; bar food and restaurant all week L 12 to 2, Mon to
Sat D 7 to 9.30
Details *Children welcome in eating areas   Wheelchair access (also WC)*
Garden and patio   No smoking in dining room   Occasional live or
background music   Dogs welcome dry and on leads only   Amex, Delta,
MasterCard, Switch, Visa

CHAPEL AMBLE   Cornwall   map 1

Maltsters Arms

Chapel Amble PL27 6EU   TEL: (01208) 812473
off A39, 2m N of Wadebridge

Hanging baskets and tubs of flowers add colour to the white-painted
stone walls and thatched porch of the Maltsters Arms, and the interior is equally bright and well maintained, with highly polished black
tables on the flagstone floor and nautically themed pictures on the
walls. On the bar menu are Devon blue cheese and pear salad with
toasted pine nuts among a handful of starters, to be followed by
smoked salmon and Cornish crab salad, or ham on a bubble and
squeak tower with two fried eggs. The restaurant-style carte might
feature a seafood platter, and then a main course of seared lambs'
liver on roasted haggis, or savoury bread-and-butter pudding. There
may be as many as four fish dishes on the menu, and another menu
of specials lists up to around six more. Sardines fried in garlic butter
can be a starter or a main course, and other mains might be steamed
brill on mushroom and garlic mash, or cod and prawn Mornay. West

Country farmhouse cheeses are another strength, with around half a dozen ranging from goats' to yarg. Sharp's Maltsters, specially brewed for the pub, heads up the real ales, and Sharp's Cornish Coaster is also kept, along with Greene King Abbott Ale and Bass. Over 20 wines are sold by the glass. SAMPLE DISHES: melon and prawns with a ginger and lemon mayonnaise £4.75; whole sea bass baked with herbs and lemon £14.25; chilled chocolate soufflé £3.25.

Licensees Alastair Gray and David Coles (freehouse)
Open *(exc Mon winter) 11.30 to 2.30, 5.30 (6 winter) to 11, Sun 12 to 2.30, 7 to 10.30; bar food and restaurant 12 to 2 (1.45 winter), 6.30 to 9.30 (9 winter); closed evening 25 Dec*
Details *Children welcome in family room   Car park   Wheelchair access (also WC)   Patio   No smoking in dining and family rooms   Background music No dogs   Delta, MasterCard, Switch, Visa*

CHAPPEL   Essex   map 6

Swan Inn   NEW ENTRY
Chappel CO6 2DD
TEL: (01787) 222353
take Great Tey turning off A1124 at Wakes Colne and cross River Colne to reach pub

Local landmarks that will help you to find this rambling old inn include an impressive Victorian viaduct that stretches for miles across the broad, shallow Colne Valley. And the River Colne itself runs past the pub's car park. Enter the pub via a small, covered, cobbled courtyard, which is used for al fresco dining. The main bar is somewhat dark, with many beams and standing timbers, dark wooden furniture and deep-red upholstered banquettes, and the 'olde worlde' feel is enhanced by a large inglenook where a log fire burns on cold days. On handpump are Greene King IPA and Abbot Ale, and three house wines are served by the glass from a short list. Two boards list the food offerings: one incorporates dishes such as chicken and mushroom pie, tomato and basil soup, large ribeye steak, and even lobster salad. The second is where you will find the pub's speciality: fish. The proprietors have their own fish supply business, bringing in daily deliveries from Billingsgate and Lowestoft. Simple treatments make the most of fine ingredients: a huge whole grilled plaice, for example, served with roes still attached, and the 'seafood special' is a selection of grilled, poached and fried fish. The restaurant, in a converted barn, has its own menu, also specialising in fish. At the rear of the garden is a well-equipped children's play area. SAMPLE DISHES: Danish herrings £5; poached Scottish salmon with hollandaise £8.50; chocolate and Bailey's meringue £3.

Licensee T.L.F. Martin (freehouse)
Open *Mon to Fri 11 to 3, 6 to 11, Sat 11 to 11, Sun 12 to 10.30; bar food and restaurant 12 to 2.30 (3 Sat and Sun), 7 to 10.30 (10 Sun); closed evenings 25 and 26 Dec*
Details *Children welcome in bar eating area Car park Wheelchair access (not WC) Garden and patio No-smoking area in bar Background music Dogs welcome Amex, Delta, MasterCard, Switch, Visa*

CHARLBURY   Oxfordshire   map 5

▲ *Bull Inn*

Sheep Street, Charlbury OX7 3RR   TEL: (01608) 810689
on B4026, 6 miles SE of Chipping Norton

Charlbury is a small market town somewhat to the north-west of Oxford, where you will find this large, rambling Cotswold-stone inn. It is originally sixteenth-century, although it has been much renovated over the years, and the interior has benefited from understated modern design in natural gentle wood shades. A long, narrow area that confronts you upon entering is where the bar food is served, and there is a more formal restaurant area on the other side of the bar itself. The menu changes daily, and might feature the likes of butterfly king prawns deep-fried and served with aïoli, sweet-cured herrings with sour cream and dill pickles, or crispy duck leg on a bed of leaves with plum and orange dressing to start, followed by rather elaborate main courses such as grilled sea bass stuffed with fennel, tomatoes and onions, flamed in Pernod and sauced with lemon butter, or oak-smoked chicken in a warm salad with bacon, avocado and croûtons, dressed in olive oil and balsamic vinegar. For dessert, there may be apple, raspberry and walnut crumble with custard, or marinated strawberries topped with a lemon and brandy syllabub. Greene King IPA and Abbot Ale are on tap, along with guest beers, and there is a good collection of malt whiskies. The southern hemisphere is well to the fore on the wine list, which includes about half a dozen that are served by the large glass at £2.75. SAMPLE DISHES: pork and chicken liver terrine with onion marmalade £5; herb-crusted rack of lamb with rosemary, redcurrant and red wine sauce £13.50; chocolate and brandy mousse with crème fraîche £4.

Licensee Roy Flynn (freehouse)
Open *Tue to Sun 12 to 2.30, Tue to Sat 7 to 11.30; bar food Tue to Sun 12 to 2, Tue to Sat 7 to 9 (9 .30 Fri and Sat); restaurant Tue to Fri 12 to 1.30, Tue to Sat 2 to 9 (9.30 Fri and Sat), Sun 12 to 2; closed 25 Dec and 1 Jan*
Details *Children over 5 welcome in bar eating area Car park Wheelchair access (not WC) Patio No smoking in dining room Occasional live or background music Guide dogs only Delta, MasterCard, Switch, Visa Accommodation: 3 rooms, B&B £50 to £60*

CHARLTON   West Sussex   map 3

▲ *The Fox Goes Free* 🍺

Charlton PO18 0HU   TEL: (01243) 811461
off A286 Chichester to Midhurst road, 1m E of Singleton

This is a 400-year-old flint building, handy for the racing at
Goodwood and not all that far from the coast. William III used to
stop off here for refreshments while out hunting (which is presum-
ably why the fox goes free). Inside, 'cosy' is indeed the right word to
describe low-beamed connecting rooms, blazing fires in winter, and a
couple of comfortable chairs (get there early to bag them) on either
side of one of the fireplaces. On handpump are Bass, Ringwood Best
and the pub's own 'Fox Goes Free', together with Addlestone cider,
while four different countries supply the quartet of house wines on a
short list, and eight are sold by the glass. Casseroles are something of
a feature: order in advance if there are at least four of you, and a
genuinely slow-cooked dish will come to your table straight from the
oven. Venison, juniper and port, or pheasant, apple, calvados and
cream are among the choices. Otherwise, you might opt for a salad
of smoked duck and Roquefort, or crab and asparagus bake to start,
and then move on to sea bream cooked in white wine, bacon and
cream, or lamb noisettes in whisky, honey and thyme. Brazil nut and
toffee pie, or perhaps raspberry cheesecake, awaits the sweet-
toothed. SAMPLE DISHES: game and port terrine £4.50; tuna steak
topped with pesto, peppers and tomato £9.50; peach and almond
tart £3.

Licensee O.S. Ligertwood (freehouse)
Open *summer Mon to Fri 11 to 3, 6 to 11, Sat and Sun 11 to 11; winter Mon
to Sat 11 to 3, 6 to 11, Sun 12 to 4, 7 to 10.30; bar food and restaurant 12 to
2.30, 6.30 to 10.30 (12 to 10.30 Sat and Sun Easter to end Sept); open 25
Dec 12 to 2 (no food), 26 Dec 11 to 3 (limited menu)*
Details *Children welcome in dining room   Car park   Wheelchair access (also
WC)   Garden and patio   Live or background music   Dogs welcome
MasterCard, Switch, Visa   Accommodation: 4 rooms, B&B £35 to £55*

CHENIES   Buckinghamshire   map 3

Red Lion 🍺

Chenies WD3 6ED   TEL: (01923) 282722
off A404, between Chorleywood and Little Chalfont

A roadside inn at the edge of a village with fields behind, the Red
Lion is a cheery, deservedly popular place with a loyal following
that by no means consists exclusively of locals. Inside, a relaxed

atmosphere prevails, with the beamed dining area accessed through the main bar, and a separate room that contains just one table for when only intimacy will do. This is a beer specialist's pub. The jewel in the crown among the range is Lion Pride, brewed especially for the house by the Rebellion Brewery of Marlow, and it may be joined by Notley Ale from the local Vale Brewery, Wadworth 6X and Benskins Best Bitter. Four wines by the glass head up a list that accords prominence to the New World. Food is ordered from the bar, and the printed menus are augmented by daily specials on the blackboard. Cold snacks and jacket potatoes will satisfy lighter appetites, while those in the market for three courses might choose starters of perhaps sardines marinated in lime and coriander with tomato and onion salad, or Mexican pork with herbed yoghurt in a taco shell. Then it might be beef stroganoff with rice, or baked chicken and avocado in a Neapolitan sauce, finishing with apple and raspberry pie, or chocolate custard tart. Staff set to with a will, and clearly take some pride in what is being served. SAMPLE DISHES: fried flat mushrooms with garlic, mint and chilli £5; curried steak and kidney with spinach and rice £8; marmalade and ginger pie £2.75.

Licensee Mike Norris (freehouse)
Open 11 to 2.30, 5.30 to 11 (10.30 Sun); bar food 12 to 2, 7 to 10 (9.30 Sun); closed 25 Dec
Details No children   Car park   Wheelchair access (also WC)   Garden   No music   Dogs welcome   Amex, Delta, Diners, MasterCard, Switch, Visa

---

CHERITON   Hampshire   map 2

▲ *Flower Pots Inn* 🍺

Cheriton SO24 0QQ   TEL: (01962) 771318
4m S of New Alresford, off B3046 in Cheriton

A converted barn across the car park from this solid-looking red-brick pub houses the Cheriton Brewhouse (tours by arrangement), whose beers are highly rated by real ale fans. Pots Ale, Cheriton Best Bitter and Diggers Gold are the regular line-up, served direct from casks behind the bar; the home-brewed Village Elder ale has also been recommended, but you will need to be careful with the rather potent cider. To enable drinkers to concentrate fully on the superb ales, food is kept simple: hotpots (lamb and apricot, or chilli con carne), sandwiches (toasted or plain), large baps (filled with things like pork steak with apple sauce, or coronation chicken), jacket potatoes and various ploughman's are the standard offerings. The setting is equally uncomplicated, with quarry-tiled floors, chunky furniture and a log fire creating a convivial atmosphere for locals and visitors alike. Wines are limited, but three are available by the glass. SAMPLE DISHES: toasted home-cooked ham sandwich £3; six-ounce ribeye steak and onions in a large bap £5.25; beef stew with crusty bread £4.75.

Licensees P.M. and J.M. Bartlett (Cheriton Brewhouse)
Open *12 to 2.30, 6 to 11, Sun 12 to 3, 7 to 10.30; bar food (exc Sun and bank hol Mon evenings) 12 to 2, 7 to 9*
Details *No children   Car park   Wheelchair access (not WC)   Garden   No music   Dogs welcome   No cards   Accommodation: 5 rooms, B&B £35 to £55*

CHIDDINGFOLD   Surrey   map 3

▲ *Crown Inn*   NEW ENTRY

The Green, Petworth Road, Chiddingfold GU8 4TX
TEL: (01428) 682255
WEB SITE: www.crowninn.net
on A283, 5m S of Milford

This magnificent wisteria-clad timber-framed building beside the extensive village green dates from 1285, when it was a rest-house for travelling Cistercian monks and pilgrims. A front terrace is furnished with tables and chairs, and just outside the bar the public telephone is housed in a sedan chair. The spacious bar area has dark ceiling beams, some carved, sturdy upholstered chairs, and a log fire in the huge stone fireplace. The same menus, simpler at lunchtime and more ambitious in the evening, apply throughout and offer mainly traditional dishes. Lunchtime sandwiches include an unusual warm chicken Caesar salad, and there are a couple of light bites as well as 'larger plates': fish and chips, and pan-fried lambs' liver with bacon, for instance. Evening starters take in feta and tomato salad, and grilled sardines with garlic butter, with main courses of roast rack of lamb with potato and celeriac mash, skate wing with black butter and capers, or monkfish and tiger prawns on tagliatelle with ginger and lime cream sauce. Everything is well presented and served politely and efficiently. Badger Best, Tanglefoot and IPA are on draught, and a handful of wines come by the glass. SAMPLE DISHES: moules marinière £7; roast breast of Barbary duck with sweet plum sauce £11; chocolate and Grand Marnier roulade £4.50.

Licensees Nigel and Bernadette Clarke (Hall & Woodhouse)
Open *11 to 11, Sun 12 to 10.30; bar food Mon to Fri 12 to 2.30, 6.30 to 9.30, Sat 12 to 9.30, Sun 12 to 9*
Details *Children welcome   Patio   No-smoking area in bar   Background music   Dogs welcome   Amex, Delta, Diners, MasterCard, Switch, Visa Accommodation: 8 rooms, B&B £57 to £110*

CHIDDINGLY   East Sussex   map 3

Six Bells

Chiddingly BN8 6HE   TEL: (01825) 872227
off A22 Uckfield to Eastbourne road at Golden Cross service station

Here is a pub that is very much at the heart of its community, indeed
the only watering hole hereabouts, standing at a fork in the two
roads that go through this tiny village. The impressively spired
church is worth a look, while the eighteenth-century pub itself
charms the eye in a simple way with its red-brick façade and blue inn
sign. The small bar within, complete with seated inglenook, piano
and a stuffed fox beadily watching over things, is a cosy place in
which to drink, while the main bar is festooned with vintage advertisements and chronicles of village life. Scrumpy Jack cider is on
draught alongside beers such as Courage Best and Directors and
Harveys Sussex Best Bitter. Wines are not a strong point. The cooking will warm the cockles of traditionalists' hearts, if what they want
is pukka steak and kidney under a puff pastry lid, ploughman's with
good-quality, thickly sliced ham cooked in-house, and baked jacket
potatoes filled with baked beans and topped with cheese. Chicken
curry and rice, cheesy cauliflower and broccoli bake with salad, and
tuna pasta bake are other options, and you can finish with the likes
of treacle tart with ice cream. Friendly and helpful service adds to
the appeal. SAMPLE DISHES: buttered crab with salad £3.50; chilli con
carne and rice £4; walnut surprise £2.50.

Licensees Paul Newman and Emma Bannister (freehouse)
Open *11 to 3, 6 to 11, Sun 12 to 10.30; bar food 11.30 to 2.30, 6 to 10, Sun
12 to 2.30 , 7 to 10*
Details *Children welcome in family room   Car park   Garden and patio
Jukebox   Dogs welcome   Delta, MasterCard, Switch, Visa*

CHILLENDEN   Kent   map 3

Griffins Head 🍇   NEW ENTRY

Chillenden CT3 1PS   TEL: (01304) 840325
*from A2\M2 take Nonnington turn-off; pub is 1m past Nonnington
on left-hand side*

Though not far from Canterbury, this beautiful rural pub, a Wealden
hall dating from the fourteenth century, feels remote – more so if
you take the scenic route. Inside, the dominating feature is an enormous log-burning fireplace; ceilings are low, there are beams and
timbers everywhere, and the atmosphere is warm and friendly. Most

of this area is given over to drinkers, while eating mainly goes on in the adjoining attractive and snug dining room (booking may be advisable as it is a popular venue). A blackboard in here lists the daily offerings, which are in the modern pub style, with game in season and various fish options: menus have included marinated anchovy fillets, steak and kidney pie, Barnsley chops, grilled sea bass with rosemary, and roast partridge with cranberry and red wine sauce. Accompanying vegetables have earned special praise for including 'the best sauté potatoes I've had in the longest time'. Wine is taken seriously too – one of the first things you see on entering is a blackboard listing various champagnes – and good choice (six) is offered by the glass. On the main list, once you've got beyond the extensive selection of sparkling wines and dragged yourself away from the impressive Port Cellar, there are over 50 nicely chosen bottles to choose from, with prices rarely topping £20. This is a Shepherd Neame pub and real ale aficionados will find that brewery's range on offer. SAMPLE DISHES: herring roes on toast with bacon £5; chicken breast stuffed with bacon, mushrooms and cream cheese £9; treacle sponge £3.25.

Licensee Mark Jeremy Copestake (Shepherd Neame)
Open *11 to 11; bar food and restaurant 12 to 2, 7 to 9.30; closed Sun evening winter*
Details *No children   Car park   Garden and patio   No music   Dogs welcome exc in dining room   Amex, Delta, MasterCard, Switch, Visa*

CHILLESFORD   Suffolk   map 6

▲ *Froize Inn* 🍺

The Street, Chillesford IP12 3PU
TEL: (01394) 450282
on B1084, 7m E of Woodbridge

Centuries ago, the Froize did a brisk trade selling pancakes locally known by that name ('froise') to passing pilgrims on their way to one of the nearby friaries. It is a red-brick building with outside tables and neat gardens, and, within, low, beamed ceilings, much exposed brickwork and a clay pipe collection. The Shaws have developed a reputation for their enthusiastic devotion to fish cookery, and those who share their passion can enrol for cookery classes. As would be expected, fish is much in evidence on the menus. Appetisers range from smoked scallop terrine with lobster oil dressing to stir-fried Thai-style mussels with lemon grass, chilli oil and saké, while mains include the house speciality of seafood froize in crab sauce. Specials are where the kitchen really lets rip, and you might find yourself tempted by roast haddock stuffed with prawns on chorizo mash, or baby monkfish wrapped in Parma ham with Mediterranean vegetables and pesto. For meat eaters there might be braised wild duck with redcurrant and thyme sauce, while deep-fried fish and chips are there for the less adventurous, as well as salads and brown rolls for lighter appetites. Finish with ginger pudding and custard, perhaps, or plum crème brûlée. A good range of real ales is supplied by East Anglian microbreweries, including Woodforde's, Mauldons, St Peter's and Tolly Cobbold, and the wide-ranging wine list offers a dozen by the glass. SAMPLE DISHES: Norfolk cockle pots with tarragon and garlic butter £5.25; baked skate with roasted shallots and smoked bacon on red wine jus £12; mango and papaya parfait £3.75.

Licensees Alistair and Joy Shaw (freehouse)
Open *Tue to Fri 12 to 3, 6 to 11, Sat 12 to 11, Sun 12 to 10.30; bar food and restaurant 12 to 2, 7 to 9; closed last week Sept, last week Feb, first 2 weeks Mar*
Details *Children welcome in eating areas Car park Wheelchair access (also WC) Garden No smoking in dining room Dogs welcome in bar No cards Accommodation: 2 rooms, B&B £32 to £65*

CHILWORTH   Hampshire   map 2

Clump Inn   NEW ENTRY

Chilworth Road, Chilworth SO16 7JZ   TEL: (02380) 766247
on A27, ½m W of A33/M3/M27 junction N of Southampton

Once an estate house, this tall red brick building is dramatically lit at night, and its large garden is seen from the back of the bar. The spacious interconnected seating areas around the central servery have high ceilings, and the suggestion of a Victorian public library seems confirmed by well-stocked bookcases in the main bar and the provision of newspapers. The warm ambience is physically aided by open fires and comfortable furniture, including huge dining tables, pine and dark wood chairs and, in one area, squashy sofas and easy chairs. All around are attractive paintings and out-of-the-ordinary *objets d'art*. A big bowl of mixed nuts with nutcrackers is set out for all to help themselves. Among dishes which have pleased reporters are mushroom melt, with bacon, onions and melted Cheddar on toast with chutney, and fishcakes with good flavour and texture enhanced by sour-cream cheese topped with sweet chilli dressing. Otherwise, there might be game pâté or shrimp salad, followed by fish of the day (check the specials boards), chicken pasta, or steak and mushroom pie. Friendly staff 'were really trying to please'. Boddingtons and Ringwood Best Bitter are regular ales, while guests might be Fuller's London Pride, Bass, Old Speckled Hen or Flowers IPA. All 16 wines listed, none priced over £14, are available by the glass. SAMPLE DISHES: chorizo salad on roasted vegetables £3.50; lamb's liver £6.75; mulled wine cheesecake £3.25.

Licensee Raymond McBain (Whitbread)
Open *11 to 11.30, Sun 12 to 10.30; bar food 11.30 to 9.30*
Details *Children welcome in dining room　Car park　Wheelchair access (also WC)　Garden　No-smoking area in dining room　Occasional background music　No dogs　MasterCard, Switch, Visa*

CHINNOR　　Oxfordshire

map 2

Sir Charles Napier 🏵️🏵️ 🍇

Sprigg's Alley, Chinnor OX9 4BX
TEL: (01494) 483011
take exit 6 from M40; at Chinnor roundabout turn right,
continue straight up hill; Sprigg's Alley is signposted

The Sir Charles is an interesting animal: something between pub and restaurant, with no bar menu, and no conventional pub food either. Instead, there are £15.50 lunches and dinners, two courses with three choices in each, plus an à la carte menu and daily specials. All are served in both dining rooms and the bar. The eccentricities start with the décor, which includes giant terracotta pots, unusual sculptures (all for sale) inside and in the garden, plus quirky objects such as the weighted frying pan used as a door stop. Motley furniture too contributes to the relaxed atmosphere, which sometimes encourages lunch customers to linger until sunset. Service is pleasant and unrushed despite crowds of customers, especially for Sunday lunch. Menus, mainly with a modern European slant, may include baked cod with aubergine, peppers and rouille; ribeye of beef with a confit of shallots and truffle jus; or a crème brulée of vegetables. Game is featured in season, and oriental influences show in curried coconut and chicken soup, and pork teriyaki with stir-fried vegetables. Generous portions may rule out desserts even as light and fruity as clafoutis of black plums, or peach tart Normande. A breathtaking list of wine-lovers' wines is suitable for pockets deep or shallow. The by-the-glass selection (eight wines) starts at £3.50 and includes some genuine treasures, while the main list takes in old vintages (Clos Vougeot 1990) and old-school (Cos, Pichon, Palmer from Bordeaux) but encourages those new to wine with a fair smattering priced under £15 and plenty of half-bottles. Wadworth 6X and IPA come straight from the wood. Note there is a 12.5 per cent suggested service charge. SAMPLE DISHES: tomato risotto with Gruyère £5.75; navarin of lamb £9.50; hot date cake and toffee sauce £6.

Licensee Julie Griffiths *(freehouse)*
Open *Tue to Sun 12 to 3.30, Tue to Sat 6.30 to 12.30; bar food and restaurant Tue to Sat 12 to 2.30, 7 to 10, Sun 12 to 3.30; closed 25 Dec*
Details *Children welcome at L, no children under 7 at D   Car park   Wheelchair access (not WC)   Garden   No-smoking areas   Occasional background music   No dogs   Amex, Delta, Diners, MasterCard, Switch, Visa*

CHOLMONDELEY   Cheshire   map 5

▲ *Cholmondeley Arms*

Cholmondeley SY14 8BT   TEL: (01829) 720300
WEB SITE: www.cholmondeleyarms.co.uk
on A49, 5½m N of Whitchurch

Just opposite the gates to Cholmondeley (say 'chumley') Castle is a red-brick Victorian building that was once the village school. The conversion to a pub, done in the late 1980s, was clever enough to retain something of the feeling of those dear old golden-rule days, with settles and pews to sit on and old school desks installed on a raised area above the bar. Huge windows and colossal radiators complete the scene, but you won't be required to recite your 12 times table. Just enjoy the Marston's Pedigree, Banks's and Adnams handpumped ales, or alternatively one of the distinguished wines collected from all over the globe; seven wines are sold by the glass. Printed menus backed up by blackboard specials offer smoked salmon cornet filled with prawns in mayonnaise, hot Madras beef curry with rice and chutneys, and chicken breast with a piri-piri sauce of red peppers, honey and chilli. Omelettes, stuffed pancakes, and sandwiches are available lunchtimes, and it's all served with cheer and alacrity in agreeable surroundings. SAMPLE DISHES: grilled lobster tail with garlic butter £5.75; chicken breast with mushroom, Dijon mustard and cream sauce £9.25; bread-and-butter pudding £4.25.

Licensees Guy and Carolyn Ross-Lowe *(freehouse)*
Open *11 to 3, 7 to 11; bar food 12 to 2.30, 7 to 10; closed 25 Dec*
Details *Children welcome   Car park   Wheelchair access (also WC)   Garden and patio   Occasional background music   Dogs welcome   MasterCard, Switch, Visa   Accommodation: 6 rooms, B&B £45 to £60*

Prices quoted in an entry are based on information supplied by the pub, rounded up to the nearest 25 pence. These prices may have changed since publication and are meant only as a guide.

CHURCHINFORD   Somerset   map 2

▲ *York Inn*

Honiton Road, Churchinford TA3 7RF   TEL: (01823) 601333
off B3170, 10m S of Taunton

Standing at a five-way junction in an unspoilt part of southern Somerset, this sixteenth-century inn is worth seeking out for its pleasant atmosphere and carefully prepared home cooking. The simply furnished public bar has darts and a pool table, while the comfortable, rustic dining areas have hop-strewn beams, a collection of brasses and jugs, and a wood-burning stove. Cooking is mostly traditional in style, and the menu is neatly divided into headed sections. For starters there may be black pudding with bacon, and under 'salads, pasta, risotto' you may find garlic-roasted seasonal vegetables with red pepper jus. Blackened chicken might be listed under 'grills', and the 'fish and seafood' section could include fish pie, and sea bass with fennel and lemon. 'Super steaks' come in various cuts and weights. Otter and Butcombe Breweries provide the regular real ales, and four wines are sold by the glass alongside a list of two dozen bottles. SAMPLE DISHES: grilled sardines with parsley butter £4.25; pan-fried calf's liver with bacon and lyonnaise potatoes £11.50; almond and apricot tart £4.

Licensee W.D. Ambrose (freehouse)
Open *summer 12 to 2.30 (3 Sat), 6 to 11, Sun 12 to 10.30; winter Tue to Sat 12 to 2.30 (3 Sat), Mon to Sat 6 to 11, Sun 12 to 4, 7 to 10.30; bar food and restaurant (exc Sun evening) 12.15 to 1.45 (2 Sun), 7 to 9.30*
Details *Children welcome in eating areas   Car park   Wheelchair access (not WC)   Patio   No smoking in dining room   Occasional background music and karaoke   Dogs welcome exc in dining room   Amex, Delta, MasterCard, Switch, Visa   Accommodation: 3 rooms, B&B £30 to £58*

CLAVERING   Essex   map 3

▲ *Cricketers*

Clavering CB11 4QT   TEL: (01799) 550442
WEB SITE: www.thecricketers.co.uk
on B1038, off M11, between Saffron Walden and Bishop's Stortford

If you happen to see a chef here, he or she will be fully dressed, although this was where Trevor and Sally Oliver introduced their famously naked son Jamie to the joys of the kitchen. The à la carte bar menu, like the restaurant's two- or three-course table d'hôte dinner, displays more than a nodding acquaintance with fashionable ingredients and assemblies. These might be a seared medallion of shark loin on chard, courgette and beetroot; filleted trout with crab-meat, prawn and ginger sauce; or spicy chargrilled suprême of chicken on noodles with Szechuan peppercorn sauce. There are daily specials too, and Tuesday is fish specials day when fresh crab and lobster may be included. One special is always a hot pudding. All this is in a pleasing white painted building, partly sixteenth century, with gardens at the front and side. Inside it is open plan, with standing timbers representing internal walls, so there is lots of light on the typical and comfortable pub furniture, pictures and ornaments. Draught ales include Adnams, Flowers and Tetleys. There are six wines by the glass, and over fifty altogether, of which only five, champagne excepted, go over £20. SAMPLE DISHES: confit duck, white haricot beans, bacon and asparagus salad £4.75; monkfish fillet on a light Thai curry sauce with fine vegetables £15.50; steamed sultana sponge pudding and custard £3.

Licensee Trevor Oliver (freehouse)
Open *10.30 to 2.30, 6 to 11; bar food and restaurant 12 to 2, 7 to 10; closed 25 and 26 Dec*
Details *Children welcome in eating areas and family room   Car park Wheelchair access (not WC)   Garden and patio   No-smoking area in bar Background music   No dogs   Amex, Delta, MasterCard, Switch, Visa Accommodation: 8 rooms, B&B £65 to £90*

CLEARWELL   **Gloucestershire**   **map 2**

===

▲ *Wyndham Arms*   NEW ENTRY
Clearwell GL16 8JT   TEL: (01594) 833666
off B4231, 2m S of Coleford, in centre of village

This whitewashed inn stands in its own grounds in the middle of the village with Clearwell Castle only a couple of hundred yards away, and close to the River Wye and the Forest of Dean. A family-run hotel popular with holiday visitors, it welcomes those dropping in for a pint of draught Bass or a glass of one of the ten or so wines sold by the glass (starting at £2.30) from a long, interesting list that also includes around two dozen half-bottles. The traditional décor includes a big open fireplace, beamed ceilings, stonework and red plush banquettes. The non-smoking restaurant, with its long menu, also offers a multi-choice set-price lunch or dinner. Snacks or starters in the bar and grillroom range from sandwiches to giant Yorkshire pudding with sausages, or deep-fried oysters. Main dishes take in rainbow trout with prawns and capers, kidneys stroganoff, and spinach and cheese roulade. Cowboy's breakfast, served at both lunchtime and in the evening, consists of bacon, sausage, hamburger, tomato, fried egg, fried bread, mushrooms, baked beans and chips.

SAMPLE DISHES: deep-fried soft herring roes £4; pork tenderloin vien-
noise £12; chocaholic sundae £3.

Licensee John Stanford (freehouse)
Open 10 (12 Sun) to 11; bar food and restaurant 12 to 2, 6.45 to 9.30 (9
Sun)
Details *Children welcome Car park Wheelchair access (also WC) Garden
and patio No smoking in dining room No music No dogs Delta,
MasterCard, Switch, Visa Accommodation: 18 rooms, B&B £52.50 to £105*

CLEY NEXT THE SEA   Norfolk   map 6

▲ *George & Dragon Hotel*

Cley next the Sea NR25 7RN   TEL: (01263) 740652
on A149 coast road, in centre of village

On a corner of the narrow main road through the village, this imposing late-Victorian pub is especially popular with bird-watchers: this
stretch of the coast offers plenty of opportunities for rare sightings,
which can be recorded in a large tome on display on a brass lectern
in the main bar. Other features include a brick hearth with a log-
effect gas fire, display cabinets filled with jars of home-made chutney
for sale, and stuffed birds in cases. The place has a timeworn feel but
is neat and clean. Menus feature a selection of fish dishes, such as
cider-pickled herrings with salad, or mixed deep-fried seafood with
tartare sauce, plus salads with Cley crab or Norfolk ham, while 'the
Dragon's specials' are things like steak, kidney, Guinness and mushroom pie. In the evening there is also a curry of the day, and a
specials board offers extra choices, such as roast Gressingham duck
breast with braised red cabbage and red wine jus. Greene King beers
are on handpump, and the short, varied wine list is supplemented by
wines of the month listed on a board behind the bar. The pub's
garden is a small patch of grass across the road, with neatly trimmed
conifers and picnic benches. SAMPLE DISHES: leek, onion and potato
soup £2.50; fricassee of grey mullet and salmon with salad £6.50;
marmalade sponge pudding with citrus sauce £3.

Licensee R. Sewell (freehouse)
Open 11 (11.30 winter) to 2.30, 6 (6.30 winter) to 11, Sun 12 to 2, 7 to
10.30; bar food 12 to 2, 7 to 8.45 (8.30 Sun); closed evening 25 Dec
Details *Children welcome in dining room Wheelchair access (also women's
WC) Garden No smoking in dining room Background music Dogs
welcome Amex, Delta, MasterCard, Switch, Visa Accommodation: 9 rooms,
B&B £32.50 to £72.50*

CLIFFE   Kent   map 3

Black Bull

FAR EASTERN

186 Church Street, Cliffe ME3 7QD
TEL: (01634) 220893
off B2000, 5m N of Rochester

Given its location, well off major routes in a sprawling village overlooking the Thames Estuary, much of the clientele at this smart,
well-maintained pub must be locals. However, for fans of excellent
oriental food it merits a detour, or even a journey for its own sake.
The main menu is dubbed the Malaysian menu, reflecting the nationality of the chatty, friendly landlady, but it also takes in Thai,
Chinese and Indian influences. Among starters, satay has received
special praise, while successful main courses have included Penang
pork in a rich, tangy sauce flavoured with lime leaves and lemon
grass, and beef rendang with tender meat in a spicy coconut gravy.
Portions are large, but the house speciality dessert is worth saving
room for: a green pancake with a jug of coconut cream and a scoop
of coconut ice cream. At the rear of the pub is the atmospheric
Tapestries restaurant, which has a similar menu and has an ancient
well. The pub also offers takeaway menus and runs regular theme
nights featuring different oriental cuisines. Real ales might include
Wadworth 6X, Wells Bombardier Premium Bitter, and the Shepherd
Neame range, and among bottled beers is Singha Tiger beer from
Singapore. Fans of pub games should note the collector's-item table
football in the bar area. SAMPLE DISHES: achar awak (hot and crunchy
vegetable salad with roasted peanuts and sesame seeds) £3.50; Thai
beef £7; kueh dada (Malaysian pancake with coconut filling and
coconut ice cream) £3.75.

Licensees Michael and Soh Pek Berry (freehouse)
Open *Mon to Sat (exc Mon evening) 12 to 2, 7 to 11.30, Sun 12 to 2.30, 7 to
10.30; bar food all week 12 to 2, Tue to Sat 7 to 11.30; restaurant Sun 12.30
to 2, Tue to Sat 7 to 10; open 25 Dec 12 to 2.30 (no food)*
Details *Children welcome   Car park   Wheelchair access (also WC)   Patio
No smoking in dining room   Jukebox   Dogs welcome   MasterCard, Switch,
Visa*

CLIFFORD'S MESNE   Gloucestershire   map 5

▲ *Yew Tree Inn* ✿   NEW ENTRY

Clifford's Mesne GL18 1JS   TEL: (01531) 820719
Clifford's Mesne signposted from Newent

The Yew Tree has taken root on a steep hillside, offering far-reaching views, a background of birdsong and (if you're lucky) the slow clopping of the odd shire carthorse passing by. It is a former cider mill, extensively modernised and exuberantly colourful with flower-filled hanging baskets, and with window boxes on the porch roof. Picnic tables on the patio in fine weather are a good vantage point to take in the views, and inside is a spacious L-shaped bar adorned with statuettes of dogs (and some real ones too) and a cheerfully patterned carpet, as well as a separate restaurant area. A pair of blackboards indicates a two-pronged approach to cooking. One, available at lunchtimes only, offers simple bar snacks along the lines of prawn and avocado platter, or salads such as smoked duck with quails' eggs. Some of the vegetable ingredients come from the kitchen garden, and the very good bread is baked in-house. For more formal restaurant meals (also available in the bar), there might be beetroot and smoked venison soup, or smoked chicken salad with pesto to start, before main courses of calf's liver sautéed with spring onions, potato, and smoked bacon, or best end of English lamb with spicy couscous. A reporter was well pleased with pink-cooked duck breast with orange and coriander sauce. Finish with apple crumble, or lemon- and cinnamon-flavoured crème brûlée. Handpumped regulars Shepherd Neame Spitfire and Wye Valley Butty Bach are joined by guests such as Pitchfork from RCH Brewery in Somerset and Fuller's London Pride to make for good drinking, as does the rather swish wine list, which opens with around a dozen house recommendations served by the glass and goes on to cover France's vinous territory in some depth. Classic grapes of the New World and the 'best of the rest; from Europe get a look-in too, with prices for the most part staying below £20. SAMPLE DISHES: oak-smoked salmon tartare £4.75; breast of corn-fed chicken with wild mushroom sauce £8.50; chocolate and coffee tartlet £3.50.

Licensee Paul Hackett (freehouse)
Open *Tue to Sun 12 to 3, 6.30 to 11; bar food and restaurant 12 to 3, 6.30 to 10*
Details *Children welcome   Car park   Garden and patio   No-smoking area in bar, no smoking in dining room   Background music   Dogs welcome   Delta, Diners, MasterCard, Switch, Visa   Accommodation: 2 rooms, B&B £40 to £60*

CLIFTON HAMPDEN   Oxfordshire   map 2

Plough Inn

Abingdon Road, Clifton Hampden OX14 3EG
TEL: (01865) 407811
WEB SITE: www.the-ploughinn.co.uk
S of A415 Clifton Hampden to Dorchester road

This attractive timber-framed, thatched traditional pub close to the
Thames, is run with enthusiasm and charm by the extremely
hospitable Mr and Mrs Bektas. It is easy to relax in the low-beamed
bar with its comfortable cushioned benches and settles, or in one of
the neatly laid-up dining rooms with their well-spaced tables. Another
plus for many visitors is that the whole pub is a smoke-free zone.
'Light menu' dishes might include slow-roast crispy duck salad, steak
and ale pie, and chicken curry, while a blackboard lists sandwiches
and specials. A la carte menu offerings run to baked field mushrooms
with roasted provençale vegetables and mozzarella, grilled salmon
fillet on spinach with lemon butter sauce, medallion of beef fillet with
wild mushrooms, or breast of chicken Zingara flamed with strega,
while the short pudding list includes ice creams and perhaps lemon
cheesecake. Ales stocked are John Smith's, Courage Best and
Directors. France is the focus of the wine list, with six to choose from
by the glass and five by the half-bottle. Glass prices start at £2.10 and
bottle at £8.95. SAMPLE DISHES: mushroom pâté £4.25; pasta boscalina
(vegetarian) £6.25 chocolate truffle torte £3.50.

Licensee Yuksel Bektas (freehouse)
Open *11am to midnight, Sun noon to 10.30; bar food and restaurant 11am
to midnight*
Details *Children welcome   Car park   Wheelchair access (also WC)   Garden
No smoking throughout pub   Occasional background music in restaurant
Guide dogs only   Amex, Delta, MasterCard, Switch, Visa   B&B £67.50 to
£82.50*

CLIPSHAM   Rutland   map 6

Olive Branch ✿ ❦   NEW ENTRY

Main Street, Clipsham LE15 7SH   TEL: (01780) 410355
2m off A1 at Ram Jam Inn junction, 10m N of Stamford

Clipsham is nothing more than a handful of pretty stone cottages
and houses, and the Olive Branch is one of the first buildings you
come to (assuming you've come from the A1). The owners have
made it a foodie place while retaining the essentials of a real pub.
The mixture of sisal matting and tiled flooring, together with plain

wooden tables and chairs, pews, pale pastel walls, log fires and lamp-light all blend in a tasteful jumble, creating a good, relaxed atmos-phere. Two house beers from the local Grainstore Brewery are Olive Oil and Ten Fifty, and a third is a guest from perhaps Fenland Brewery, Oakham Ales or Brewster's. Vintage rum and armagnac offer rare experiences, but wine most interests the owners, and blackboards listing them outnumber the boards listing food. On one board are six red and six white wines by the glass all at around the £2 mark (eight more come by the half-bottle). Then there are ten red and ten white house wines (nothing over £15); then another ten each of red and white speciality wines. This all makes for excellent price guidance and allows for some superb choices to be had – such as Schug California Pinot Noir, Guigal's Côte-Rôtie, and a range of top-flight clarets. More boards offer sandwiches, made with local Rearsby bread, and a set lunch. The reasonably priced, modern European carte might include sea bream with saffron tagliatelle and sweet pepper sauce, or honey-glazed duck leg confit, which an inspector found 'superb – crisp, and falling off the bone', with sweet-and-sour onion marmalade and 'properly dressed' salad. Fish might feature as baked cod fillet in a hummus crust, or pan-fried salmon niçoise, and sweet lovers could go for bread-and-butter or sticky toffee puddings. SAMPLE DISHES: tempura prawns with sweet chilli dip £5; game casserole with vegetables and gratin potato £8.25; toasted rice pudding with figs and raspberry sauce £4.50.

Licensees Ben Jones, Marcus Welford and Sean Hope (freehouse)
Open *Mon to Fri 12 to 3, 6 to 11, Sat 12 to 11, Sun 12 to 6; bar food and restaurant Tue to Sat 12 to 2, 7 to 9.30, Sun 12 to 3; closed Mon winter*
Details *Children welcome   Car park   Wheelchair access (also WC)   Garden and patio   No smoking in dining room   Occasional background music   Dogs welcome in bar   Delta, MasterCard, Switch, Visa*

COCKWOOD   Devon   map 1

Anchor Inn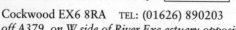

Cockwood EX6 8RA   TEL: (01626) 890203
off A379, on W side of River Exe estuary opposite Exmouth

This sixteenth-century inn on the Exe estuary has three cosy, pleas-antly pubby rooms, including a small no-smoking restaurant. (It can get very busy, and it is advisable to book.) From veranda tables it overlooks the harbour – appropriate as its enormous menu has a definite bias towards seafood. As well as listing 12 ways of preparing oysters and 30 ways with mussels, it includes 12 sorts of scallops, including scented with gin and dill, and a version (much enjoyed by a visitor) in cheese and asparagus sauce. There are single shellfish dishes, as well as amazingly generous selections, and many fish too, including plain grilled whole lemon sole with parsley butter. But carnivores are not neglected, and surfers and turfers might consider lamb with minted cockles, or pork steak stuffed with smoked salmon and crab. Vegetarians, too, get a look-in. Among desserts are 12 variations of treacle tart. Ales stocked are Bass, Fuller's London Pride, Wadworth 6X, Greene King Abbott Ale, Marston's Pedigree, Flowers Original and Brakspear plus two guests. A short list of 30 wines, with ten by the glass, is backed by a 'reserve list' of 300 more. Spelling may be decidedly erratic but that doesn't hide the fact that there are some marvellous wines available, and plenty of good-value choices that won't break the bank. There is ample choice of brandies and malt whiskies, too. SAMPLE DISHES: crab and brandy soup £3.50; shellfish selection £15; treacle tart with Amaretto £3.

Licensees Terry Morgan and Alison Sanders (Heavitree Brewery)
Open *11 to 11, Sun 12 to 10.30; bar food and restaurant 12 to 3, 6.30 to 10, Sun 12 to 2.30, 6.30 to 9.30; closed 25 Dec*
Details *Children welcome in eating areas　Car park　Wheelchair access (also WC)　Patio　No smoking in dining room　Background music　Dogs welcome on a lead　Amex, Delta, Diners, MasterCard, Switch, Visa*

COLDHARBOUR　Surrey　　　　　　　　　　　　　map 3

▲ *Plough Inn* 　　　　　　

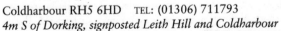

Coldharbour RH5 6HD　TEL: (01306) 711793
4m S of Dorking, signposted Leith Hill and Coldharbour

First-class beers are the primary attraction at this whitewashed roadside inn, which reputedly is also the highest in south-east England, being just below the top of Leith Hill. The Leith Hill Brewery on the premises supplies Crooked Furrow Bitter and Tallywhacker Porter, which head a large selection of fine real ales, including Ringwood Old Thumper, Badger Tanglefoot and Hogs Back TEA, plus Biddenden cider. The pub also offers simple but appealing home cooking, with menus listed on blackboards along the lines of warm blue cheese tartlet, skewered lamb fillet with rosemary and garlic, and pork fillet on walnut, apple and celery compote. Daily fish options might feature naturally poached smoked haddock with a poached egg on mashed potato, and to finish there may well be lemon pudding, or spotted dick. The varied clientele and friendly landlord give the place a welcoming atmosphere. From the pretty garden, with its lily pond, are fine views over the surrounding countryside, which provides excellent opportunities for walkers to build up an appetite before calling in for lunch. SAMPLE DISHES: black pudding with sauté apple and raspberry vinaigrette £6; chicken breast stuffed with garlic and sun-dried tomatoes wrapped in bacon £9; double chocolate pudding £3.50.

Licensees Richard and Anna Abrehart (freehouse)
Open *11.30 to 11, Sun 12 to 10.30; bar food and restaurant 12 to 2.30, 7 to 9*
Details *Children welcome in family room   Car park   Wheelchair access (also WC)   Garden and patio   No-smoking area in dining room   Occasional background music   Dogs welcome in designated areas   MasterCard, Switch, Visa   Accommodation: 5 rooms, B&B £40 to £75*

COLEBY   Lincolnshire   map 6

▲ *Bell Inn*   NEW ENTRY

3 Far Lane, Coleby LN5 0AH   TEL: (01522) 810240
on A607 from Grantham to Lincoln, take second left after Boothby Graffoe

Every inch a village local, the Bell has its own darts team, and in place of piped music you can enjoy the lively hubbub of people enjoying themselves. It is an attractive yellow-washed former cottage with a red pantiled roof, and, inside, the decorative theme is red carpets and plush red upholstery on dark wooden furniture. Though the feel is old-fashioned, the approach to food is serious and modern, as one glance at the menus will reveal – a printed list of bistro-style dishes and a blackboard of more inventive daily specials. Chef Troy Jeffery arrived at the Bell with experience at the highly regarded Sous le Nez en Ville restaurant in Leeds (of which licensee Richard Chamberlain is co-proprietor). His creative approach typically produces pan-fried duck breast on orange and sweet potato salsa, deep-fried Brie with pepper and mango chutney, or fillet of halibut with lightly curried tomatoes and a sesame and coriander crust. Draught Bass and Bateman XB are provided for real ale drinkers, and the short wine list offers good value, with several half-bottles and four by the glass. SAMPLE DISHES: fishcake with parsley sauce £3.75; braised lamb shoulder on butter bean mash £7; chocolate fondant £3.50.

Licensees Claire Charlesworth and Robert Chamberlain (Pubmaster)
Open *11.30 to 3, 5.30 to 11, Sun 12 to 10.30; bar food Tue to Sat 12 to 2.30, 5.30 to 9.30, Sun 12 to 8*
Details *Children welcome in eating areas   Car park   Garden   No smoking in dining room   Background music   Dogs welcome   Delta, MasterCard, Switch, Visa   Accommodation: 3 rooms, room only £34.50*

COLEFORD   Devon   map 1

▲ *New Inn* ❦

Coleford EX17 5BZ   TEL: (01363) 84242
off A377 Exeter to Barnstaple road, 4m W of Crediton

In a charming village in the heart of rural Devon, this inn's white-washed façade and thatched roof fit in perfectly – and have done so since the thirteenth century. Beside a stream is a patio for outdoor drinking, while the rambling interior has heavy beams, open log fires and sturdy old furniture, with the welcome from the proprietors matched by that from Captain, the resident chatty parrot. The spacious restaurant, in an extension created from some old barns, offers an imaginative menu (not available in the bar). You might choose cream of fennel and potato soup, whole baked John Dory with orange and chicory compote, then summer pudding. Bar food, prepared with equal care, could include warm chicken liver and smoked bacon salad, fish soup, beef curry, and a platter of fresh and smoked seafood. Four real ales are on draught, including regulars from Badger and Otter, plus guests which might be Exmoor Ale, Fuller's London Pride or Shepherd Neame Spitfire. There are seven wines by the glass from an impressive list of 50, almost all under £17 a bottle, including Down St Mary Bubbly from just down the road. Helpful style categories guide choice. SAMPLE DISHES: pasta with mushrooms and Stilton sauce £5; whole grilled plaice with chips and salad £11; local Langage Farm ice cream £3.

Licensee Paul Butt (freehouse)
Open *12 to 2.30, 6 to 11, Sun 12 to 2.30, 7 to 10.30; bar food and restaurant 12 to 2, 7 to 10 (9.30 Sun)*
Details *Children welcome   Car park   Wheelchair access (not WC)   Garden and patio   No smoking in dining room   Background music   Dogs welcome exc in dining room   Amex, Delta, Diners, MasterCard, Switch, Visa Accommodation: 6 rooms, B&B £50 to £75*

COLESHILL   Buckinghamshire   map 3

Red Lion

Village Road, Coleshill HP7 0LN   TEL: (01494) 727020
off A355 Amersham to Beaconsfield road

At night, red lights outline the roof of this white-pebbledash and timber-framed building, which has no pretension to be anything other than an old-fashioned village pub – and has no intention of being anything less. It is the local centre for darts, crib and quizzes (but no one even expects to become a millionaire), and village events are announced on notices in the entrance porch. There is no restaurant, just a few tables in the bar, which can be reserved, and a few more in the pleasant little garden. The regular printed bar menu is just that, though extends to creamed sardines on toast. More substantial, and sometimes more modern, dishes are listed on blackboards: perhaps prawn and pasta salad, liver and bacon, and beef casserole with lean meat in rich gravy with 'excellent al dente' vegetables. Greene King IPA, Fuller's London Pride, Rebellion IPA and Smuggler, and Vale Brewery's Wychert are on tap, and three wines are sold by the glass. SAMPLE DISHES: egg mayonnaise £3.95; lamb cutlets £8; apple pie £3.

Licensees John and Christine Ullman (Innspired Pubs)
Open *Mon to Fri 11 to 3, 5.30 to 11, Sat 11 to 11, Sun 12 to 4.30, 7 to 10.30; bar food (exc Sun evening) 12 to 2 (2.30 Sun), 7 to 9*
Details *Children welcome   Car park   Wheelchair access (not WC)   Garden and patio   No music   Dogs welcome   No cards*

COLLINGHAM   Nottinghamshire   map 5

King's Head   NEW ENTRY

6 High Street, Collingham NG23 7LA   TEL: (01636) 892341
on A1133 N of Newark-on-Trent

'Less a pub, more a bistro with beer and victuals', thought one visitor to this refurbished old inn. A cool and airy décor of white walls, terracotta-coloured tiled floors and a brushed aluminium bar counter give a contemporary and minimalist feel, and though real ales are served at the bar, eating is the main business. Chef-owner Jamie Matts has had plenty of experience at well-respected restaurants, and his menu offers a wide range of dishes, from traditional English to oriental. Old-fashioned pub staples, such as chargrilled steak with peppercorn sauce and chips, contrast with inventive modern dishes like pan-fried trout fillet with fennel risotto and herb sauce. Alongside the main menu is a list of lunchtime bar snacks and a specials board that might feature breast of pheasant and partridge with bubble and squeak and Stilton sauce. For beer drinkers, regular Timothy Taylor Landlord is supplemented by at least one seasonal ale: local Broadstone War Horse, for example. A short, annotated wine list opens with four house selections also available in two sizes of glass. Events include live jazz once a month. SAMPLE DISHES: smoked haddock and Scotch egg with curried mayonnaise £4; griddled lamb leg steak with fondant potatoes and a rosemary garlic sauce £9.50; toffee and Tia Maria cheesecake £2.75.

Licensee Jamie Matts (freehouse)
Open *Mon to Fri 12 to 2, 6 to 11, Sat 12 to 11, Sun 12 to 6; bar food and restaurant Mon to Fri 12 to 2, 6 to 9, Sat 12 to 9, Sun 12 to 4*
Details *Children welcome   Car park   Wheelchair access (not WC)   Patio No smoking in dining room   Occasional live and background music   Dogs welcome in bar   Delta, MasterCard, Switch, Visa*

COLN ST ALDWYNS   **Gloucestershire**   **map 2**

▲ *New Inn* 🏵 🍺 🍇

Coln St Aldwyns GL7 5AN   TEL: (01285) 750651
WEB SITE: www.new-inn.co.uk
off B4425, Cirencester to Burford road, 2m SW of Bibury

Queen Elizabeth I decreed that there should be a coaching inn within a day's travel of all main centres of population: thus did the New Inn come about. It is, you will have gathered, not so new, but the Evanses know how to run as hospitable a pub as any of their forerunners did. Exposed-stone walls and beamed ceilings set the tone, and the comfortable dining room is not without a certain chic. Handpumped ales, including Hook Norton Best Bitter, Butcombe Bitter and Wadworth 6X, are one of the strengths of the operation, as is a wine list that sources some of the best modern flavours from around the world and offers eight of its selections by the glass. Prices are kept nice and low (eight by the glass start at £1.90), and there's a short range of classics (Chambolle-Musigny, Ch. Gruaud-Larose) for special occasions. The cooking, too, is pretty much up to the minute. The Courtyard Bar menu runs to salmon kedgeree; peppered mackerel with a salad of avocado, orange and chicory; slow-roast belly of pork with an oriental stir-fry; and scallops with tagliatelle, nut butter and Parmesan. A fixed-price menu operates in the separate restaurant, with such dishes as chorizo and bacon risotto with chilli oil, and Scottish-inspired rib of beef with rösti and haggis and a whisky cream sauce. Desserts might be warm rice pudding with poached pears in mulled cider served with vanilla ice cream, or a trio of lemon variations. Vegetarians have their own menu, and children's meals are available too. SAMPLE DISHES: Caesar salad with seared swordfish £5; duck casseroled with olives, thyme and white wine with sun-dried tomato mash £11; blackberry and mint crème brûlée with yoghurt sorbet £4.50.

Licensee Brian Evans (freehouse)
Open *11 to 11 (11 to 2.30, 5.30 to 11 winter), Sun 12 to 10.30; bar food and restaurant 12 to 2 (2.30 Sun), 7 to 9 (9.30 Fri and Sat)*
Details *Children welcome in bar eating area; no children under 10 in dining room   Car park   Wheelchair access (also WC)   Patio   No smoking in dining room   No music   Dogs welcome   Amex, Delta, MasterCard, Switch, Visa Accommodation: 14 rooms, B&B £68 to £115*

COLSTON BASSETT Nottinghamshire map 5

▲ *Martins Arms* ✿ 🍺

School Lane, Colston Bassett NG12 3FD   TEL: (01949) 81361
off A46 Leicester to Newark road, 4m S of Bingham

Having sold the Crown at Old Dalby in the summer of 1999, the owners now focus all their efforts on this elegant Jacobean inn in the heart of the Vale of Belvoir. These efforts have included thorough refurbishment and redecoration, which have enhanced the country-house feel, as well as the addition of conference and wedding facilities and the opening of an antiques and interiors shop in a converted stable block. Colston Bassett Stilton appears with another local delicacy, Melton Mowbray pork pie, in the ploughman's lunch, as well as in rarebit with watercress, apple and grapes. But there is no shortage of choice on the ambitious menu that serves both the comfortable bar and the antique-furnished restaurant, and the scope of the cooking is wide, with homely steak and kidney pie appearing next to more exotic options such as five-spice duck with sweet potato pancake and tamarind sauce. Various sandwiches, salads and pasta dishes are also offered. Although the emphasis is on food, drinkers are welcome in the bar to partake of the fine real ales: Taylor Landlord, Batemans XXXB, Castle Rock IPA, Black Sheep Best Bitter and Marston's Pedigree are among the names to be seen adorning handpumps on the bar. The wine list takes you round the world in 40, with around six wines offered by the glass. Prices are very reasonable (starting at £12) and the short tasting notes offer good guidance as to style. SAMPLE DISHES: smoked haddock croquettes with tomato salsa £8; rack of lamb with bean and garlic purée and thyme jus £16; white chocolate marquise with praline crisp £5.

Licensees Lynne Strafford Bryan and Salvatore Inguanta (freehouse)
Open *12 to 3, 6 to 11, Sun 12 to 3, 7 to 10.30; bar food and restaurant 12 to 2, 6 to 10, Sun 12 to 2; closed evening 25 Dec*
Details *No children under 14 in bar, children welcome in dining room and family room   Car park   Wheelchair access (also WC)   Garden   No music No dogs   Delta, MasterCard, Switch, Visa   Accommodation: 2 rooms, B&B £35 to £65*

COMPTON MARTIN Bath & N.E. Somerset map 2

Ring o' Bells

Main Street, Compton Martin BS40 6JE   TEL: (01761) 221284
on A368, between Weston-super-Mare and Bath

A sprawling, whitewashed stone building in the middle of a Mendip village contains a stone-flagged bar, carpeted eating area and a family room where Disney characters adorn the walls. Food centres on the kinds of pub favourites that everyone, including the kids, will expect to see. Snacks such as half-pints of prawns with marie-rose dressing, or baked jacket potatoes filled with coronation chicken are on offer, while the main menu, which runs from Stilton mushrooms, or deep-fried Brie, through chilli con carne and lasagne, to Toblerone torte, is gently priced. Real ale drinkers will be tempted by Butcombe Bitter, Butcombe Gold and Wadworth 6X plus a guest such as Shepherd Neame Spitfire or Fuller's London Pride, and the weekly-changing guest wines are headed up by a range of five served by the glass. SAMPLE DISHES: mushrooms in garlic butter £3; Cajun-spiced chicken breast with salad and potatoes £6.75; Dorset apple cake £2.25.

Licensees Roger and Jackie Owen (freehouse)
Open *11.30 to 2.30, 6.30 to 11, Sun 12 to 3, 7 to 10.30; bar food 11.30 to 2, 6.30 to 9.30 (10 Fri and Sat, 9 Sun)*
Details *Children welcome in family room Car park Wheelchair access (not WC) Garden No smoking in family room No music Dogs welcome exc in dining area Delta, MasterCard, Switch, Visa*

CONSTANTINE   Cornwall   map 1

▲ *Trengilly Wartha Inn*

Nancenoy, Constantine TR11 5RP
TEL: (01326) 340332
WEB SITE: www.trengilly.co.uk
off A394 Falmouth to Helston road, between Constantine and Gweek

Readers' reports agree that it's well worth the effort to find this large, traditional and very popular inn, which 'appears to be miles from anywhere', down a steep hill along a single-track road. Inside are pubby bars with settles in seating stalls and old beams lined with beer mats, plus a separate restaurant. Except for fresh fish, bar and restaurant menus are not interchangeable, but even in the bar the choice is wide. Care is taken in the preparation and execution of such dishes as Devon blue cheese and walnut pâté, king prawns in beer batter, and, from the blackboard specials, oaky smoked duck stir-fried with mange-tout, ginger and soy served on basmati rice. Fish might include baked cod on caramelised onions, or steamed fillets of John Dory with a tomato and spinach sauce, and pasta and squash bake may be among vegetarian choices. Ploughman's and local smoked ham are available lunchtimes, served with home-made bread. The restaurant menu offers such treats as a terrine of langoustines and monkfish wrapped in sole, and beef fillet topped with a wild mushroom and tarragon mousse. Well-kept ales from the cask include Sharp's Cornish Coaster,

Skinner's Cornish Knocker Ale and guests from small West Country breweries. There are 50 malt whiskies, and if the nearly 300-strong wine list looks intimidating, there's a short list of top wines from the main categories for quick perusal – these are all reasonably priced, under £17. Twenty are available by the glass (two sizes) and extra accessibility is granted by a star-system indicating ready-to-drink vintages. France features strongly, the Australian list is good too, and a local Cornish wine makes a welcome appearance. SAMPLE DISHES: smoked fish platter £7.50; crab cakes with white wine sauce £10.50; pear and almond tart £3.50.

Licensees Michael Maguire and Nigel Logan (freehouse)
Open *11 to 3, 6.30 to 11, Sun 12 to 3, 7 to 10.30; bar food 12 to 2.15, 6.30 to 9.30, Sun 12 to 2, 7 to 9.30; restaurant 7.30 to 9.30; bar open 11 to 1.30 25 Dec (no food)*
Details *Children welcome   Car park   Wheelchair access (not WC)   Garden and patio   No-smoking area in bar, no smoking in dining room   No music Dogs welcome   Amex, Delta, Diners, MasterCard, Switch, Visa Accommodation: 8 rooms, B&B £40 to £85*

COOKHAM DEAN   Berkshire   map 3

▲ *Inn on the Green*

The Old Cricket Common, Cookham Dean SL6 9NZ
TEL: (01628) 482638
WEB SITE: www.theinnonthegreen.com
off A404, S of M40 junction 4

From the outside the inn appears much like any other rambling suburban house, but once inside you can't fail to be struck by its atmosphere and décor. Much effort and money have been lavished on the mock-Tudor interior to create a tastefully romantic setting, even in the bar area, and the sumptuous dining room features tables with damask napkins, quality glassware, candles and flowers that give any meal here a sense of occasion. The menu is also stylish, with plenty of modern ideas. Smoked quail with toasted pistachio salad and balsamic vinaigrette with candied ginger is a typically inventive starter. To follow there might be pan-seared monkfish on truffled mash, beef tournedos with béarnaise, or rack of lamb in a herb crust with rosemary cream. While chargrilled pineapple with coconut ice cream and toasted coconut shavings may sound the more exotic, bread-and-butter pudding was the real star dessert of one meal, being full of rum-soaked fruits with a rich butterscotch sauce. Al fresco eating is also an option in the courtyard, which is protected from sudden downpours by a retractable canopy. Brakspear Bitter and Fuller's London Pride are on handpump for real ale drinkers, and eight wines – four red and four white – are served by the glass.

SAMPLE DISHES: oriental-spiced sweet potato soup £4; poached salmon with passion-fruit hollandaise £14; lemon crème brûlée with orange tuile £4.

Licensees Tim Wilson and Andy Taylor (freehouse)
Open *12 to 3, 6 to 11, Sun 12 to 3, 7 to 10.30; bar food and restaurant 12 to 2.30, 7 to 10; closed evenings 25 and 26 Dec, first week Jan*
Details *Children welcome   Car park   Wheelchair access (also WC)   Garden No music   Dogs welcome exc in dining room   Amex, Delta, MasterCard, Switch, Visa   Accommodation: 8 rooms, B&B £60 to £110*

Jolly Farmer

Church Road, Cookham Dean SL6 9PD   TEL: (01628) 482905

Faced with the threat of losing a favourite watering hole, the villagers of Cookham Dean took over ownership of this homely eighteenth-century pub in the late 1980s. It is in the centre of the village opposite the church, and the two small, simply furnished bar areas have a lively atmosphere; refurbishment was on the cards as the Guide went to press. The adjacent dining room is more formally laid out and has its own menu of things such as Thai-spiced crab cake, and half a roast duck with orange sauce. For those eating in the bar, the menu is likely to offer toasted goats' cheese to start, followed by steak and kidney pudding, or poached salmon in white wine and dill sauce. Courage Best is the regular real ale; the two guest beers might be Brakspear Bitter and Wells Bombardier Premium Bitter. Three house wines are offered by the glass from a list of around 30 bottles. SAMPLE DISHES: deep-fried potato skins £4.50; warm smoked chicken, bacon and avocado salad £8; apple and sultana crumble £3.25.

Licensee Simon Peach (freehouse)
Open *11 to 3, 5.30 to 11, Sun 12 to 4, 7 to 10.30; bar food and restaurant (exc Sun evening) 12 to 2 (2.30 Sun), 7 to 9.30; closed evening 25 Dec*
Details *Children welcome   Car park   Wheelchair access (not WC)   Garden and patio   No music   Dogs welcome exc in dining room   Delta, MasterCard, Switch, Visa*

CORSCOMBE   Dorset   map 2

▲ Fox Inn ✿ 🍺

Corscombe DT2 0NS   TEL: (01935) 891330
WEB SITE: www.fox-inn.co.uk
off A356, 6m SE of Crewkerne

The thatched roof of this white-painted building, a seventeenth-century cottage extended in various directions, is set off by the green of creepers and, in summer, the colours of their flowers, while the surrounding country garden pleases gardeners and non-gardeners alike. The equally attractive interior with stone floors, pine furniture and blue-check tablecloths fully justifies the words 'a real country pub' on the Fox's postcards. The 'little bar', the stables, the conservatory and country kitchen dining room offer a choice of settings for serious diners, who can also eat in the bar. Here the restaurant's long menu is supplemented by blackboards listing a score of daily specials, with fish a mainstay. Many of the chef's ideas come from the East: Thai-style salmon salad, Szechuan peppered squid, or Kerala fish curry, for example. But meat eaters are not neglected, and might find Barbary Duck Leg with Puy lentils and red cabbage, Burmese beef curry, or New Orleans rabbit with Béarnaise sauce. Vegetarian options figure too: perhaps vegetable Moroccan tagine with couscous. More homely, and sometimes classic, influences appear in wild garlic soup; salmon with sorrel sauce; or gratin of crab, cod and monkfish. Exmoor Ale, Exmoor Fox, Fuller's London Pride, and Stowford Press cider are regularly served, bottled beers include Bitburger Drive, and the carefully chosen wine list covers just about everything and everywhere while keeping prices very reasonable. A separate fine wine listing includes some top Burgundy and Bordeaux (also modestly priced), and there are 11 wines by the half-bottle, though only four house wines are available by the (small) glass. Tasting notes are helpful aids to choice. Those with even more rarefied tastes can enjoy homemade damson vodka, sloe gin and non-alcoholic elderflower cordial. SAMPLE DISHES: fish soup with cod, mussels and prawns £5.50; beef braised with bacon, mushrooms and red wine £8; vanilla cream terrine with redcurrant coulis £3.25.

Licensees Martyn and Susie Lee (freehouse)
Open *12 to 3, 7 to 11, Sun 12 to 4, 7 to 10.30; bar food and restaurant 12 to 2, 7 to 9 (9.30 Fri and Sat)*
Details *Children welcome   Car park   Wheelchair access (not WC)   Garden No smoking in dining room   Occasional live music   No dogs   Amex, Delta, MasterCard, Switch, Visa   Accommodation: 3 rooms, B&B £50 to £70*

CORTON   Wiltshire   map 2

▲ *Dove Inn* 🍺

Corton BA12 0SZ   TEL: (01985) 850109
WEB SITE: www.thedove.co.uk
off A36, 5m from Warminster

This pretty, much-extended dining pub dating from the mid-nineteenth century is attractively set in a secluded courtyard in a small village near the River Wylye. Inside, the atmosphere is unpretentious and welcoming, and refurbishment since the Guide's last edition has added a polished oak floor, candelabra and non-smoking conservatory as part of the restaurant. 'We do not have a separate bar menu,' they tell us – though baguettes and ploughman's are available at lunchtime – with the kitchen geared to providing attractive and sometimes complex dishes. These might take the form of hare fillet on sauté wild mushrooms drizzled with port jus, chicken breast stuffed with haggis and pigeon, or braised Wiltshire lamb shank accompanied by butter beans and a rich thyme sauce. Local trout might turn up smoked with basil dressing (a starter), or grilled with fresh spinach and roasted tomato sauce (a main dish), and seared tuna comes with crisp seaweed and a red pepper dressing. Ales are a strong point here, with Oakhill Bitter the regular joined by two guests in winter, three in summer, which might be Brakspear Bitter, Fuller's London Pride or others. Ten well-priced house wines are all available by the glass (around the £3 mark), but the real fun starts on the main list, where 20 wines span the globe, from Chilean Chardonnay to Chassagne-Montrachet. Lovers of French classics will not be disappointed. SAMPLE DISHES: smoked duck with kumquat chutney £6.75; veal au gratin £13.25; hot chocolate puddle pudding with chocolate sauce £4.

Licensee William Harrison-Allan (freehouse)
Open *12 to 3.30, 6.30 to 11, Sun 12 to 4, 7 to 10.30; bar food and restaurant 12 to 2.30, 7 to 9.30 (9 Sun); closed evening 25 Dec*
Details *Children welcome   Car park   Wheelchair access (also WC)   Garden No-smoking area in dining room   Occasional background music   Dogs welcome exc in dining room   Delta, MasterCard, Switch, Visa Accommodation: 5 rooms, B&B £45 to £90*

COTTON   **Suffolk**   map 6

Trowel & Hammer

Mill Road, Cotton IP14 4QL   TEL: (01449) 781234
6m N of Stowmarket, just off the B1113

There is an upmarket feel about this white-painted inn on the outskirts of the village, though it also manages to keep to its country-pub roots, with its attractive dark panelled bars, French windows leading to the garden for outdoor eating, and a good selection of real ales. Its comfortable restaurant, lit by candles, offers the same menu as in the bar, but the service is a little more formal and tables need to be pre-booked. The cooking is modern enough to incorporate filo of prawns and lobster tails with seafood mayonnaise, or deep-fried Brie with Cumberland sauce as starters. Main dishes are basically classic with intriguing tweaks, such as barbecue sauce and red onion rice with a pork steak, or wild cherry and orange sauce with roast duck breast. Marlin makes a rare appearance, seared, and set on Thai noodles with spicy tomato sauce. In a more straightforward vein are lasagne with chips or salad, and fish pie, while imaginative desserts include apricot and Cointreau crème brulée, and mango and lime syllabub. Adnams, Greene King IPA and Abbott Ale are supported by guests, usually from Mauldons or Nethergate, and stronger tipples include absinthe and out-of-the-ordinary vodkas. Four or five wines are offered by the glass from the 30-strong list, which favours France but touches down in Italy and the New World too. SAMPLE DISHES: half-pint of shell-on prawns with Thai dipping sauce £4.25; chicken, bacon and garlic in puff pastry with sage gravy £8; pancakes with apples and calvados £3.50.

Licensees Simon and Jonathan Piers-Hall (freehouse)
Open *Mon to Fri 11.30 to 3, 6 to 11, Sat 11.30 to 11, Sun 12 to 10.30; bar food and restaurant 11.30 to 2, 6 to 9.30 (10 Fri and Sat)*
Details *Children welcome   Car park   Wheelchair access (also WC)   Garden Occasional live or background music   Dogs welcome   Delta, MasterCard, Switch, Visa*

COXWOLD   **North Yorkshire**   map 9

▲ *Fauconberg Arms*

Coxwold YO61 4AD   TEL: (01347) 868214
WEB SITE: www.fauconberg.co.uk
off A19 7m S of Thirsk; pub on main street in middle of village

The carefully cleaned and restored yellowish-stone houses of this very old village suggest the Cotswolds rather than Yorkshire, and the pub stands solidly at the centre. The interior is dominated, in season, by an enormous wood-burning fire powerful enough to heat two rooms and to make those close thankful for a pint of Tetley Bitter, John Smith's or Theakston, which are the real ales on offer. Around the fireplace is a collection of brass, including warming pans and pokers; in one corner is a spinning wheel, and oak furniture, of various ages, displays the marks of local carvers. The restaurant, with a large oak dresser, runs from the front to the back of the building. The bar offers luxurious sandwiches, including roast pork and apple, and in both areas you can choose starters such as mousse of salmon and oak-roast sea trout, or smoked haddock and spinach pastry parcels. Rump steak casseroled in red wine with mushrooms and peppers might be among main courses, with something like spinach, feta and tomato tart among vegetarian choices. Sunday lunch brings on traditional roasts with all the trimmings. Ten wines are sold by the glass, and house wines are about £10. SAMPLE DISHES: griddled bacon and fried egg baguette £3.75; roast salmon fillet stuffed with fennel and lemon £8.25; banana brioche-and-butter pudding £3.50.

Licensees Robin and Nicky Jaques (freehouse)
Open *11 to 3 (2.30 winter), 6 (6.30 winter) to 11, Sun 12 to 3, 7 to 10.30; bar food and restaurant (exc Mon evening in winter) 12 to 2, 7 to 9*
Details *Children welcome Car park Patio No-smoking area in dining room Background music No dogs Delta, MasterCard, Switch, Visa Accommodation: 4 rooms, B&B £35 to £60*

CRANMORE Somerset map 2

Strode Arms

Cranmore BA4 4QJ TEL: (01749) 880450
just S of A361, 4m E of Shepton Mallet

The comforting solidity of the Strode Arms starts with the large, dark grey stone exterior of the building, originally a farmhouse dating from the late fifteenth century, standing opposite the village pond. The impression is strengthened within by traditional wooden furniture, a rustic décor, a peaceful non-musical background, and pleasant, professional service. Dishes rarely stray beyond the traditional; an oriental influence, for instance, is limited to mild chicken curry. 'Egg mayonnaise Strode' is generously garnished with prawns, capers, smoked trout, anchovy and asparagus, but more typical starters are smoked Dorset trout, duck liver terrine, or florentine pancake stuffed with spinach in cheese sauce. Main dishes include steaks, both beef and wild boar, home-made pies, and a trio of country sausages comprising pheasant, venison and wild boar. Desserts range from full-bodied bread-and-butter or sticky toffee puddings to more delicate lime and ginger crunch flan. Flowers IPA, Marston's Pedigree and Oakhill Best Bitter are normally available, and the guest ale changes monthly; there is Wilkins cider too. Forty-odd wines, plus eight by the glass or bottle, provide a wide choice and are reasonably priced, mostly under £20. SAMPLE DISHES: salmon, prawn and smoked trout terrine £5.25; stuffed lambs' hearts £8: pear and almond tart £3.50.

Licensees Rodney and Dora Phelps (freehouse)
Open *11.30 to 2.30, 6.30 to 11 (10.30 Sun); bar food and restaurant 12 to 2, 7 to 9.30 (10 Fri and Sat); closed Sun evening Oct to end Mar*
Details *Children welcome in dining room Car park Wheelchair access (not WC) Garden and patio No music Dogs welcome exc in dining room Delta, MasterCard, Switch, Visa*

Recommendations for good country pubs will be very welcome.

CRAWLEY   **Hampshire**   map 2

Fox & Hounds   NEW ENTRY

Crawley SO21 2PR   TEL: (01962) 776006
Crawley signposted off A272 NW of Winchester

After a spell as a French restaurant, the Fox & Hounds has reopened
with its original name under the same ownership as the Plough at
Sparsholt (see entry). Like much of the charming village, the red-
brick, timbered building, with a fine overhanging façade and bow
windows, is only a hundred or so years old. Although the open-plan
interior is light and airy, the traditional décor includes hunting prints
and wooden tables of various sizes. Blackboard menus operate
throughout, with starters including perhaps vegetable and herb soup,
or artichoke, goats' cheese and rocket salad (which one reporter gave
a definite thumbs-up), followed by something along the lines of
'beautifully presented' salmon and smoked haddock stew, chicken
breast with a banana and red onion compote and rice, or pork
tenderloin wrapped in Parma ham with calvados sauce. Regular
draught ales are Wadworth 6X and Henry's Original IPA, with
Butcombe Bitter and Wadworth seasonal brews among the guests.
Around ten wines, from a list that approaches 20 bottles, are sold by
the glass. SAMPLE DISHES: smoked salmon and crab parcels £6; Thai
chicken and king prawn curry £8.50; chocolate and nut ganache £4.

Licensees Ashley Carkeet and Richard Crawford (freehouse)
Open *11 to 3, 6 to 11, Sun 12 to 3, 6 to 10.30; bar food 12 to 2, 6 to 9
(9.30 Fri and Sat, 8.30 Sun); open 11 to 1 25 Dec (no food)*
Details *Children welcome in dining room   Car park   Wheelchair access (not
WC)   No smoking in dining room   No music   Dogs welcome   MasterCard,
Switch, Visa*

CRAZIES HILL   **Berkshire**   map 3

Horns

Crazies Hill RG10 8LY   TEL: (01189) 401416
off A4 at Kiln Green, 3m N of Twyford

The oldest part of the pub was a Tudor hunting lodge, and extensions respect that heritage. The cosy, low-ceilinged bar in the original area leads to an eighteenth-century barn, now the restaurant,
with scrubbed pine tables and chairs on its quarry-tiled floor. Dried
flowers hang from the beams and eponymous stags' horns are
mounted on the walls. On the menu is a wide selection of first and
main courses, ranging from soup of the day (such as hearty roast
pepper and sweet potato), and Thai crab cakes, to traditional pork

and leek sausages with mash, and roast chicken breast with sherry and tarragon sauce. Fresh fish is on offer too, and other specials of the day might take in roast partridge with a red wine, mushroom and bacon sauce. At lunchtime only, baguettes – from cheese and pickle to hot roast beef, lamb or pork with appropriate relishes – are also available. Sunday lunch specials extend to duck breast, baked sea bass, and pasta as well as a choice of roasts. Theme nights are a regular feature. Beers kept are Brakspear Bitter and Special and seasonal ales such as Leaf Fall and Three Sheets. The short but varied wine list offers seven by the glass. SAMPLE DISHES: breaded prawns with garlic mayonnaise £6; beef, mushroom and Guinness pie £8; plum frangipane £4.

Licensee Andrew Hearn (Brakspear)
Open *11.30 to 2.30, 6 to 11, Sun 12 to 6; bar food and restaurant 12 to 2 (3.30 Sun), 7 to 9.30; closed 25 and 26 Dec, evening 1 Jan*
Details *Children welcome in dining room lunchtime and early evening   Car park   Wheelchair access (also WC)   Garden   No music   Dogs by arrangement   Delta, Diners, MasterCard, Switch, Visa*

CROSLAND HILL   West Yorkshire   map 8

Sands House

Blackmoorfoot Road, Crosland Hill HD4 7AE
TEL: (01484) 654478
off A62, 2m SW of Huddersfield town centre

It's a busy place, filled with drinkers in the bar and relaxed parties of every sort in the animated dining areas. The keynote is robust, hearty food, but that doesn't exclude some imaginative touches on the menu. Start perhaps with potted cheese rolled in walnuts, or chilli meatballs with tomato and garlic sauce, and continue with gammon steak, venison medallions on caramelised onions with blue cheese butter, or a vegetarian dish such as oriental spring roll with black-bean sauce. Those with old-fashioned Yorkshire appetites may be able to cope with rice pudding, or chocolate and orange tart. It's a pleasant place, and not quite what might be expected on the outskirts of Huddersfield, where town and moorland meet. The pub is owned by the Unique Pub Company, a name to some extent justified by the collection of clocks inside, and veteran traffic lights, telephone boxes and the like in the children's play area outside. Old Speckled Hen, Boddingtons Bitter, John Smith's, Tetley Bitter and a guest ale are all available. SAMPLE DISHES: 'Po Boy' sandwich (hot beef, fried onions and American mustard on French bread) £2.50; sea bass on salad with sweet pepper salsa £7.25; lemon and walnut meringue £2.75.

Licensee Bob Buckley (Unique Pub Company)
Open *11.30 to 11, Sun 12 to 10.30; bar food and restaurant 11.30 to 9.30*
Details *Children welcome in bar eating area   Car park   Garden   No smoking in dining room   Background music   No dogs   Amex, Delta, Diners, MasterCard, Switch, Visa*

CROSTHWAITE   Cumbria   map 8

▲ *Punch Bowl Inn* ❀❀

Crosthwaite LA8 8HR   TEL: (015395) 68237
WEB SITE: www.punchbowl.fsnet.co.uk
off A5074, 3m S of Windermere

Not many pubs can boast a chef with past experience of leading the kitchen at one of the world's finest restaurants, but the Punch Bowl Inn is just such a place: licensee Steven Doherty's former life was as head chef at Le Gavroche in London. He has sold his second pub, the Spread Eagle in Sawley, and the Punch Bowl is once again his main focus. Despite the emphasis on food, this seventeenth-century inn in the Lyth Valley remains a traditional pub at heart, serving Theakston ales in an informal setting with lots of atmosphere. Cooking, too, maintains the balance between the quality you would expect from a top chef and the lack of pretension you would hope for in a pub; excellent local ingredients also help. Lunchtime menus feature straightforward dishes such as carrot and coriander soup followed by baked ham with mash and grain mustard sauce, with Crosthwaite damson pancake, or Shorrocks traditional crumbly Lancashire farmhouse cheese to finish. The style is equally down to earth on dinner menus, though wider influences appear along with occasional dishes from the classical French repertoire. Starters might be penne pasta in creamy tomato and basil sauce, or a plate of charcuterie (including Cumbrian air-dried ham), while main courses run to confit duck legs on spinach with red wine jus; roast leg and best end of Cumbrian fell-bred lamb; or chargrilled tuna with sweet pepper, lime and ginger sauce and pickled vegetables. With around a dozen half-bottles to choose from on the succinct and imaginative wine list, and another dozen wines by the glass, diners will find ample choice for matching wine with food. SAMPLE DISHES: baked goats'-cheese niçoise £5.75; baked sea bass fillet with sauce anti-boise £11.25; peach poached in red wine with orange and amaretti cream £4.25.

Licensees Steven and Marjorie Doherty (freehouse)
Open *11 to 11, Sun 12 to 10.30; bar food and restaurant 12 to 2 (2.30 Sun winter), 6 to 9; closed Sun and Mon evenings winter, 25 Dec, 2 weeks Nov*
Details *Children welcome   Car park   Garden andpatio   No-smoking area in bar, no smoking in dining room   No music   No dogs   MasterCard, Switch, Visa   Accommodation: 3 rooms, B&B £37.50 to £55*

CUDDINGTON   **Buckinghamshire**   map 2

Crown   NEW ENTRY

Aylesbury Road, Cuddington HP18 0BB   TEL: (01844) 292222
WEB SITE: www.thecrowncuddington.co.uk
off A418, 4½m W of Aylesbury

The Berry family are doing Cuddington proud. Having successfully run Annie Bailey's for a number of years, they have now taken over the village's other main pub, the Crown, and the previous premises are now their family home. This one, on a prime corner site, is a thatched building with whitewashed walls and a pair of bay trees guarding the entrance. The bar area along the front retains its popularity among locals, while three interconnecting rooms for diners have tiled floors, lots of mirrors and old prints on the walls, and an intimate, candlelit atmosphere. Fuller's is the landlord, so there is London Pride on draught alongside Chiswick Bitter and a guest such as ESB. The wine list confines itself to just a dozen bottles, with five wines sold by the glass. Thursday night is curry night, when a range of Indian and Thai dishes are advertised on portable blackboards. Otherwise, the printed menus offer the likes of warm smoked bacon and pine kernel salad, black pudding with red cabbage, or aubergine, goats' cheese and tomato gâteau with garlic salsa as starters or light snacks, and then main courses that take in beer-battered cod with chips and mushy peas, and slow-roasted ham shank with bubble and squeak. Pasta dishes such as penne with mushrooms and bacon in a cream sauce are carefully cooked, and puddings will satisfy too: lemon tart, and apple pie with cinnamon have been praised. SAMPLE DISHES: fishcake with tartare sauce £5; cushion of lamb with sweet potato and cardamom mash £11.50; sherry and Drambuie syllabub £4.

Licensee David Berry (Fuller's)
Open *12 to 3, 6 to 11, Sun 12 to 3, 7 to 10.30; bar food and restaurant 12 to 2.30, 6.30 to 10, Sun 12 to 3, 7 to 9.30*
Details *Children welcome in dining room   Car park   Wheelchair access (not WC)   Patio   No-smoking area in dining room   Background music   No dogs   Delta, MasterCard, Switch, Visa*

DARGATE   Kent   map 3

Dove

Plum Pudding Lane, Dargate ME13 9HB   TEL: (01227) 751360
signposted off A299, 4m SW of Whitstable

A solid-looking late-Victorian pub covered in climbing plants, the
Dove is a vision of English pastoral in the summer, with the beer
garden to the rear full of flowering shrubs. Inside, an unfussy atmosphere prevails, with bare-boarded floors, foursquare wooden furniture, and photographs showing the locality at various stages of its
history. Do not expect, however, typical pub fare, for the cooking is
far more enterprising than that. First courses of terrine of foie gras
with tomato and apple chutney, or warm Bayonne ham tart with
rocket and Parmesan salad, might be followed by confit leg of duck
with bacon and button mushrooms, salt cod with chorizo and flageolet beans, or a main-course salad of roasted scallops and prawns
flavoured with pickled ginger. Good desserts have included apple
and almond tart with ice cream, and passion-fruit and orange crème
brûlée. Fine local produce is enthusiastically used throughout.
Shepherd Neame is the tied brewery, which means Master Brew
Bitter is probably the ale to go for, and a reasonable wine list
includes eight by the glass. SAMPLE DISHES: grilled goats' cheese on
tomato and onion salad £5; fillet of halibut with braised leeks and
ceps £15; baked chocolate pudding with crème anglaise £4.

Licensees Nigel and Bridget Morris (Shepherd Neame)
Open *all week (exc Mon lunchtime) 11.30 to 3, 6 to 11; bar food Tue to Sun
12 to 2, Wed to Sat 7 to 9*
Details *Children welcome in family room   Car park   Garden   Background
music   Dogs welcome   Delta, MasterCard, Switch, Visa*

DARTINGTON   Devon   map 1

▲ *Cott Inn* 🍇
HISTORY

Dartington TQ9 6HE   TEL: (01803) 863777
WEB SITE: www.oldenglish.co.uk
S of A385, 2m NW of Totnes

This splendid fourteenth-century whitewashed stone and cob inn has
held a licence continuously since 1320. What also might be a record
is its thatched roof, at 183 feet one of the longest in Britain. Outside,
it is as pretty as a picture, and benches in the neat garden give visitors the chance to enjoy the setting. Inside, the tidy, carpeted bar,
with open fires and a wealth of beams, is furnished with comfortable

antiques and adorned with various prints and brass artefacts. A range of real ales includes Wells Bombardier Premium Bitter and Theakston Old Peculier. Food appears in two very different guises. At lunchtime a buffet operates in the dining room, with casseroles, pies, quiche and salads the order of the day. In the evening the operation becomes more of a restaurant, with full table service and a menu that goes in for things like pan-fried turbot with Devon crab and tarragon sauce, braised lamb in an apricot, Madeira and rosemary sauce, steak and kidney pie, and oriental-style grilled red mullet. No one could quibble with the reasonably priced wine list, which in around 30 wines covers just about every wine-producing country. Nine wines are served by the glass, and there's a blackboard of bin ends available for those who want to try something new. SAMPLE DISHES: chorizo, tomato, mozzarella and black olive platter £5; shoulder of pork slow-roasted in hoisin and plum sauce £8; double chocolate cream pots £3.50.

Licensees Adrian and Jan Skinner (Old English Inns)
Open *11 to 11, Sun 12 to 10.30; bar food 12 to 2.30; restaurant 6.30 to 9.30*
Details *Children welcome in bar eating area   Car park   Garden and patio No-smoking area in bar, no smoking in dining room   Occasional live music Dogs welcome   Amex, Delta, MasterCard, Switch, Visa   Accommodation: 6 rooms, B&B £55 to £65*

▲ *White Hart* ♣ 🍇

ORGANIC

Dartington Hall, Dartington TQ9 6EL
TEL: (01803) 847111
from A384 follow signs for Dartington and then to Dartington Hall

The White Hart occupies what were originally the kitchens of magnificent fourteenth-century Dartington Hall – you will find the pub at one end of the Great Hall, its entrance leading off the courtyard. The age of the building shows in stone walls and floors, and a log fire burns in a tall fireplace, but simple, light oak furniture adds a modern touch. The hall stands in 1,200 acres of farm and parkland, and much of the produce used in the kitchen is farmed organically on the estate; what the estate can't provide comes from local suppliers. At lunchtime, a short card lists things like bacon and avocado salad, poached Scottish salmon steak, or bangers and mash, plus a selection of filled baguettes. In the evening, the cooking style is more involved, typically producing smoked duck on spiced orange with Cointreau and orange zest dressing, pan-fried scallops with sauté potatoes and lardons, seared tuna steak with sesame seeds and a lemon butter sauce, or lamb cutlets with onion marmalade and rosemary-roasted garlic and a cranberry and red wine jus. A blackboard offers daily specials. Real ale drinkers will appreciate the range offered, which includes Butcombe Bitter, plus Dartmoor IPA and Jail

Ale from the Princetown Brewery. Organic drinks include apple juice, ginger beer, and Sam Smith Best Organic Ale (bottled). There's a relatively short (30 wines) but imaginatively chosen wine list which includes a couple of English bottlings and 'Miami Mist', a Canadian Pinot Gris. Every effort has been made to keep bottle prices under £20, and ten by the glass also reflect a will to make wine as accessible as possible. SAMPLE DISHES: smoked salmon and scrambled egg £5.25; baked chicken breast stuffed with prawn mousseline with mixed berry sauce and parsnip crisps £9; West Country cheeses £4.25.

Licensees Paul Haresnape and Nick Edwards (freehouse)
Open *11 to 11, Sun 12 to 10.30; bar food 12 to 2.30, 6 to 9; closed Christmas to New Year*
Details *Children welcome in dining room   Car park   Wheelchair access (also WC)   Garden   No smoking in dining room   Occasional background music   No dogs   Delta, MasterCard, Switch, Visa   Accommodation: 50 rooms, B&B £37 to £90*

DIDMARTON   Gloucestershire   map 2

▲ *Kings Arms Inn* 🍺 🍇   NEW ENTRY

The Street, Didmarton GL9 1DT   TEL: (01454) 238245
on A433 SW of Tetbury

Though it may seem a little plain on the outside, what lies inside this seventeenth-century Cotswolds coaching inn makes it a welcome new addition to the Guide. Sensitively restored by the current owners – the two bar areas now have green wood panelling, cream walls, sporting prints and garlands of hops to go with the old beams and stone fireplace – the inn is clearly a popular hub of local life, and the lovingly tended garden, with lawns, dry-stone walls, apple trees, and a boules pitch, simply adds to its attractions. The restaurant menu, also available in the bar, offers varied and interesting choice without being overlong, typically taking in Roquefort soufflé on apple and celery salad, and a trio of smoked oysters, mussels and scallops with orange and dill dressing, followed by venison medallion with poached pears and redcurrant sauce, and pan-fried monkfish with a provençale breadcrumb topping and a mussel and saffron sauce. This is supplemented in the bar by a blackboard of things like hop and pork sausages with onion gravy and mash, haddock in beer batter with chips, or salmon and cod fishcakes with lime mayonnaise, plus a selection of baguettes. Though this is principally a dining pub, beers are a strong suit: four real ales are on offer at a time, regulars Uley Bitter and John Smith's being supplemented by fortnightly-changing guests. The list of around 30 wines includes some very fine French options – Brouilly, Chassagne-Montrachet and Saint-Julien cleverly chosen from some less well-known names. Six house wines are sold by the glass (two sizes), with prices starting at £2.60, and careful thought overall is given to pleasing both the modern and traditional palate. SAMPLE DISHES: pork and green peppercorn terrine with tomato chutney £4; grilled minted lamb steak with salad and sauté potatoes £8; tarte Tatin with apricot coulis £4.

Licensees Nigel and Jane Worrall (freehouse)
Open *12 to 3, 6 to 11, Sun 12 to 3, 7 to 10.30; bar food and restaurant 12 to 1.45, 7 to 9.45 (restaurant closed Sun evening); closed evening 25 Dec*
Details *Children welcome in eating areas   Car park   Wheelchair access (not WC)   Garden   No smoking in dining room   Occasional live or background music   Dogs welcome exc in dining room   Delta, MasterCard, Switch, Visa Accommodation: 4 rooms, B&B £40 to £65*

DODDISCOMBSLEIGH   Devon   map 1

▲ *Nobody Inn* ✿ 🍺 🍇

Doddiscombsleigh EX6 7PS   TEL: (01647) 252394
3m W of A38, Haldon Racecourse exit

'I've been coming here for over eight years, and it hasn't changed a bit,' reads one reporter's testimony to the consistency that Nick Borst-Smith has brought to this much-praised venue over past the 30 years. The operation embraces a serious wine business, and the 700-strong list indeed is probably unrivalled by any other in the Guide, with around 40 being offered by the glass. Some 250 whiskies of various descriptions are kept, as are some fine cask-conditioned ales, including the proprietary Nobody's Bitter from Branscombe Vale, along with Brimblecombe Farm cider. The place itself is low, white and beamed, dating from the fifteenth century, complete with dark interiors full of 'lots of quiet corners for romantic trysts'. Crisp linen and big gleaming glasses adorn the dining-room, but the atmosphere is anything but stuffy. Denhay air-dried ham with melon and a tomato and ginger chutney is a good way to start, or there may be snails with garlic butter, or 'fish fingers' – a layered terrine of smoked salmon and white fish with a sauce of white vermouth. Classic main courses take in rainbow trout with almonds, grilled beef sirloin with shallots and mushrooms on a red wine sauce, or lamb's liver sautéed with onion, garlic and thyme, but there are more novel dishes too: ostrich fillet garnished with ox tongue, gherkins and cranberries. Puddings include the likes of top-notch raspberry frangipane tart with 'amazing' local clotted cream, but the star of the show at meal's end is the superb selection of dozens of farmhouse English cheeses, majoring of course in Devon's finest. SAMPLE DISHES: roasted salmon on brioche with roasted red peppers and a light citrus sauce £4; sliced fillet of beef with creamy tarragon sauce £11.50; blackcurrant and summer berry cheesecake £4.

Licensee N.F. Borst-Smith (freehouse)
Open 12 to 2.30, 6 to 11, Sun 12 to 3, 7 to 10.30; bar food 12 to 2, 7 to 10; restaurant Tue to Sat and bank hol Mons 7.30 to 9.15; closed 25, 26 and 31 Dec and 1 Jan
Details No children Car park Garden and patio No smoking in dining room No music Guide dogs only Delta, MasterCard, Switch, Visa
Accommodation: 7 rooms, B&B £23 to £70

DOLTON   Devon   map 1

▲ *Union Inn* 🍺

Dolton EX19 8QH   TEL: (01805) 804633
WEB SITE: www.unioninndolton.co.uk
on B3217, 7m S of Great Torrington

Dolton is on the Tarka Trail, along which walkers may be enjoyably distracted by buzzards and badgers before arriving at this popular dining pub. Originally built as a Devon longhouse of traditional cob construction, the Union became a hotel around 200 years ago. The interior is as home from home as you could wish for, with a squashy old chesterfield, cushioned window seats, oak settles and sturdy wooden tables. The pub serves an enterprising slate of real ales, including St Austell Hicks Special Draught, Exmoor Ale, Clearwater Beggars Tipple and Cavalier, and Sharp's Doom Bar Bitter. The short but wine list has half a dozen by the glass from a selection supplied by local merchants Christopher Piper Wines. Full-on New World flavours from Australia and Chile feature highly, and there are half-bottles to choose from too. Hot bar snacks such as omelettes, sausages with bubble and squeak, or a quarter-pound lamb burger supplement the main menu. The latter offers tempura-battered prawns with a sweet chilli dip, chicken breast with creamy mushroom sauce, and various steaks. Look to the blackboard for specials such as a warm salad of cured ham and roast vegetables, or seared scallops with red pepper vinaigrette. Luxurious desserts include rum-spiked chocolate truffle torte, or a top-drawer version of bread-and-butter pudding. SAMPLE DISHES: garlic mushrooms £4; whole sea bass grilled with herbs and garlic £12.50; banana and rum crème brûlée £3.25.

Licensee Ian Fisher (freehouse)
Open Thur to Tue 12 to 2.30, 6 to 11, Sun 12 to 2.30, 7 to 10.30; bar food and restaurant 12 to 2, 7 to 9; closed first 2 weeks Feb
Details No children Car park Wheelchair access (not WC) Garden No smoking in dining room Occasional background music Dogs welcome exc in dining room Delta, MasterCard, Switch, Visa Accommodation: 3 rooms, B&B £45 to £60

DOWNHAM Lancashire map 8

Assheton Arms

Downham BB7 4BJ TEL: (01200) 441227
off A59, 3m NE of Clitheroe

Very little has changed in this village since the Assheton family
bought it in 1558, though the traditional, stone-built inn, which is
next to the church and surrounded by charming cottages, has been
adapted and modernised over the years. Inside, the low-ceilinged
rooms are furnished with solid oak tables and wing-back settles,
and a coal-effect gas fire blazes in the massive central fireplace. The
pub is popular and often busy with drinkers and those who come to
eat. While not as old-fashioned as the setting, the printed menu
goes in for tried and tested favourites, such as steak and kidney pie,
deep-fried haddock with tartare sauce, and chicken Kiev. More
interesting specials listed on the blackboard might include deep-
fried squid with garlic mayonnaise, lobster thermidor, and lamb
balti. Castle Eden and Boddingtons are the real ales served, and the
list of around 20 wines includes a handful by the glass. SAMPLE
DISHES: grilled queen scallops with garlic butter and Gruyère £6.50;
venison, bacon and cranberry casserole £8; Lancashire cheese and
biscuits £3.25.

Licensees David and Wendy Busby (Whitbread)
Open 12 to 3, 7 to 11 (10.30 Sun); bar food 12 to 2 (2.30 Sun), 7 to 10
Details *Children welcome Car park Wheelchair access (also WC) Patio
No-smoking area in bar Background music Dogs welcome Amex, Delta,
Diners, MasterCard, Switch, Visa*

DREWSTEIGNTON Devon map 1

▲ Drewe Arms NEW ENTRY

Drewsteignton EX6 6QN TEL: (01647) 281224
2m S of A30, 8m W of Exeter

A long, low, thatched pub tucked away next to the church in an
attractive village high above the wooded slopes of the Teign Valley,
close to Dartmoor and just a mile away from the National Trust
property Castle Drogo. These formidable attributes once paled into
insignificance when the place was run by the legendary Mabel
Mudge, who retired as Britain's longest-serving landlady in 1996, at
the age of 99, after a stint of some 75 years. Colin and Janice Sparks
ensure that Mabel's influence lives on, in the small restaurant that
bears her name and retains her old cooking range, as well as the orig-

inal dresser and cupboards. The cooking has moved on a league or two, now offering the likes of grilled New Zealand mussels topped with garlic butter and Stilton, or sun-dried tomato bruschetta, perhaps followed by Barbary duck breast glazed with strawberries and honey, or bacon-wrapped pheasant breast stuffed with apricots and sauced with port and juniper. Consult the blackboard for fish dishes and other daily specials. Puddings deal in riches such as banana and butterscotch pavlova, or Devonshire junket. Real ales include Bass, Gale's HSB and Old Speckled Hen, and a wide range of around 20 wines is available by the glass. SAMPLE DISHES: smoked chicken and pickled walnut salad £4; rack of lamb with mash and roasted garlic and rosemary jus £12; local cheeses with biscuits £4. Note that some of the information below may not be accurate, as the pub opted not to supply current details.

Licensees Colin and Janice Sparks (Whitbread)
Open *11 to 2.30, 6 to 11, Sun 12 to 3, 7 to 10.30; bar food and restaurant 12 to 2, 7 to 9.30*
Details *Children welcome in dining room   Wheelchair access (also WC) Garden and patio   No smoking in dining room   Occasional live music   Dogs welcome in bar   MasterCard, Switch, Visa   Accommodation: 3 rooms, B&B £25 to £50*

DUNCTON   West Sussex   map 3

Cricketers

Duncton GU28 0LB [F6]   TEL: (01798) 342473
on A285, 3m S of Petworth

This old farmhouse situated at the foot of the South Downs, partially hidden from the road by a screen of venerable trees, is 'a refreshingly pubby pub', catering for those seeking an unpretentious establishment serving simple pub grub. The interior is just one big room with an old-world feel, thanks to old farm implements and sepia prints on the walls. A range of filled rolls is available for those after something light, while the full menu offers unpretentious modern dishes, starting perhaps with pan-fried duck livers with crisp pancetta, tomato and red onion salad with balsamic vinegar, followed by chargrilled tuna with warm mixed-bean salad, or twice-cooked belly of pork in Chinese marinade with coriander rice. The simple approach appears to work well, one reporter commending the 'juiciest, tastiest' hare and wild mushroom terrine, a generous portion of tender lamb chops with 'outstanding' vegetables, and walnut bread-and-butter pudding with 'excellent flavour'. Three real ales are usually on tap: Archers, Young's and a guest. Wines include a good selection of four by the glass served in generous measure. SAMPLE DISHES: calamari and tiger prawns with chilli jam and coriander crème fraîche £5; sauté breast of duck with boulangère potatoes, braised red cabbage and red wine jus £10, lemon posset £4.25.

Licensee Tamzin Corbett (freehouse)
Open *11 to 3, 6 to 11; bar food and restaurant 12 to 2.30, 6.30 to 9.30, Sun 12 to 3; closed Sun evening winter*
Details *Children welcome in dining room   Car park   Garden   Occasional live music   Dogs welcome exc in dining room   Delta, MasterCard, Switch, Visa*

DUNSFOLD   Surrey   map 3

)unsfold GU8 4LE   TEL: (01483) 200242
W of Cranleigh

dates from Georgian times, enjoys a tranquil setting common in this village near Guildford. The small racterised by low ceiling beams and pictures and walls. This is a popular place, and on busy days, ing, people can take their meals outside at picnic den. Blackboards list the daily specials. On Sundays onal roasts, maybe lamb or beef, and various sausage se, you might find things like baked avocado and followed by seared duck breast, or monkfish. There nu of staples such as ham, egg and chips. At any time are on tap, which might include Marston's Pedigree, King & Barnes Sussex and Friary Meux Best. Four wines are offered by the glass from a list of 30-odd bottles. SAMPLE DISHES: prawn and herb tagliatelle £5; lamb shank £9.50; lemon meringue pie £3.75.

Licensee Ian Greaves (Punch Taverns)
Open *11 to 3, 6 to 11, Sun 12 to 3, 7 to 10.30; bar food 12 to 2.15, 7 to 10, Sun 12 to 2.30, 7 to 9.30*
Details *Children welcome in eating areas   Car park   Wheelchair access (not WC)   Garden   Occasional live music   Dogs welcome   Delta, MasterCard, Switch, Visa*

DUNWICH   Suffolk   map 6

▲ *Ship Inn*

SEASIDE

St James Street, Dunwich IP17 3DT
TEL: (01728) 648219
off B1125, 4m SW of Southwold

In medieval times Dunwich was one of the busiest ports on the east
coast. Since then, much of the old town has been lost to the sea, but
it remains a most attractive place. At its heart is this old inn, once
popular with smugglers but now attracting a much more desirable
clientele of holidaymakers and locals. Lunchtime bar food is typically
hearty fare, taking in soup, ploughman's, salad platters, and fish (cod
or plaice) and chips, as well as a meat dish such as pork and bean
stew, and a vegetarian option. The menu expands in the evening to
add such things as fish crumble, herby sausages on onion gravy, or
lamb chops with redcurrant gravy, with perhaps curried mushrooms,
or whitebait for starters. Cooking is of a similar style in the Fo'c's'le
dining room, where fresh local fish is the speciality. Three house
wines at £9.25 per bottle, £4.75 for half a litre and £1.60 per glass
open a short but varied international list. The pub remains true to its
roots in the beer department, serving ales from Suffolk brewers
Adnams and Mauldons. SAMPLE DISHES: Caesar salad £4.75; chicken
and cider pie £5.75; peppered sirloin steak £9.95.

Licensees Stephen and Ann Marshlain (freehouse)
Open *11 to 3.30, 6 (7 winter) to 11 (10.30 Sun); bar food and restaurant 12
to 2, 7 to 9; closed evening 25 Dec*
Details *Children welcome exc in bar   Car park   Wheelchair access (not WC)
Garden and patio   No smoking in dining room   No music   Dogs welcome
exc in dining room   MasterCard, Switch, Visa   Accommodation: 3 rooms,
B&B £40 to £59*

EASINGTON   Buckinghamshire   map 2

Mole and Chicken

VIEWS

Easington HP18 9EY   TEL: (01844) 208387
WEB SITE: www.moleandchicken.co.uk
off B4011, 1m N of Long Crendon on Chilton road

A dining pub it may be, and the owner sometimes calls it a restaurant; but it's none the less a pub, offering hand-pulled ales and cider
to non-diners in the bar area. You can enjoy the pleasantly informal
ambience in any corner of the open-plan interior, or in the garden
with its expansive views over the Buckinghamshire/Oxfordshire
countryside. There are no bar snacks, and the à la carte menu is

modern, with a touch of the global about it: for example, starters of chicken satay, or 'secret recipe' fishcakes on a mild curry sauce, followed by Thai prawn curry, or duck and bacon salad with warm plum sauce. But tradition shows up in Gressingham duck with orange sauce, and steak, kidney and Guinness pie. Devoted carnivores may wish to note a rare delicacy, roasted pig cheeks on leek and potato mash, served with red wine and shallot sauce. Vegetarian, fish and pasta dishes are offered on specials boards. On draught are Greene King IPA, Old Speckled Hen and Hook Norton Best Bitter. Over 40 malt whiskies are available, and wines include six by the glass. SAMPLE DISHES: smoked chicken, avocado and crispy bacon salad £6; roast shoulder of lamb £13; Bramley apple and blackberry crumble £3.95.

Licensee Shane Ellis (freehouse)
Open *12 to 3, 6 to 12, Sun 11 to 9; bar food 12 to 2, 7 to 9.30, Sun 12 to 9; closed 25 Dec*
Details *Children welcome   Car park   Wheelchair access (not WC)   Garden and patio   No smoking in dining room   Background music   No dogs   Amex, Delta, MasterCard, Switch, Visa*

EAST CHILTINGTON   **East Sussex**   **map 3**

Jolly Sportsman 🏵 🍺 🍇

Chapel Lane, East Chiltington BN7 3BA   TEL: (01273) 890400
on B2116 E of Plumpton turn N signposted East Chiltington, continue approx 2m then first left (pub is signposted)

Standing a little back from a quiet lane, and with no immediate neighbours, the Sportsman still manages to be Jolly in its isolation. It is a partly tiled, partly weatherboarded pub with garden tables to the front and at the back, where there is also a children's climbing frame. A small, atmospheric public bar with dark floors and exposed brick walls painted a mellow yellow contains a blackboard menu, and a separate dining room is set out with solid wooden tables. The same menus are offered throughout, and the drill is quite relaxed. Food is taken seriously, though: excellent breads and olives start a meal off, preparing the appetite for such starters as curried celery and apple soup, or a salad of grilled goats' cheese, artichoke and red peppers. Main courses that have met with approval include loosely textured fishcakes made with a mix of tuna and white fish, and roast breast of guinea fowl on the bone with slow-cooked potatoes and buttered spinach with almonds. Herb-crusted hake, or Moroccan-style lamb brochette with basmati rice might be other examples of the cosmopolitan range. Traditional desserts, whether chocolate pudding with matching sauce, or blackberry and apple crumble, are a strong point. Sunday lunch is a fixed-price affair, and there is also the option of a set-price two-course lunch from Tuesday to Saturday. Constantly changing brews from microbreweries and local beers from Rectory and Harveys will keep real ale fans happy. Backing these up is an exemplary wine list of reach and discernment. There may be only half a dozen by the glass (from £1.85), but the choice of half-bottles is very fine indeed. Bottle prices start at £9.75, with most of the list remaining well under £20. The odd price exception for the likes of, for example, Château Gruaud-Larose (at £50) is forgivable and relatively reasonable. Real lemonade and ginger beer a good choices for drivers and children. SAMPLE DISHES: crab, shrimp and papaya salad £5.25; crisp duck confit on Puy lentils £10.50; roast nectarine with honey and brandy ice cream £5.

Licensees Bruce and Gwyneth Wass (freehouse)
Open *Tue to Sat and bank hol Mon 12 to 2.30, 6 to 11, Sun 12 to 4; bar food and restaurant 12.30 to 2 (3 Sun), 7 to 10; closed 4 days Christmas*
Details *Children welcome   Car park   Wheelchair access (also WC)   Garden No-smoking area in bar   No music   Dogs welcome   Delta, MasterCard, Switch, Visa*

EAST DEAN   East Sussex   map 3

Tiger Inn ✿

The Green, East Dean BN20 0DA   TEL: (01323) 423209
off A269 Seaford to Eastbourne road, 4m W of Eastbourne

The Tiger Inn nestles in a little hollow at the centre of this attractive village a short way out of Eastbourne. Tables opposite the village green will entice the summer visitor, while the flickering gas fire and snug, low-ceilinged rooms within are a tonic on a winter's night. Stuffed birds and even a stuffed fox in glass cases provide plenty of distraction for the eye. Food and wines are all displayed on boards, the latter a concise but distinguished listing, including at least nine by the glass. The cooking deals largely in quintessential country-pub fare, but the quality of the ingredients and the careful presentation lift it above the norm. Texas-style chilli con carne that comes with baked potato wedges has been well seasoned and generous, fishcakes made of smoked haddock and leeks look like giant Scotch eggs and are full of flavour, and steak and ale pie is made with Harveys bitter. Desserts are of the indulgent variety, such as sticky pecan tart, or chocolate and cream roulade. Handpumped ales consist of Harveys Sussex Best Bitter, Adnams Best Bitter, Flowers Original and Old Speckled Hen. SAMPLE DISHES: smoked salmon £5; fish pie £11; French lemon tart £3.

Licensee Nicholas Denyer (freehouse)
Open *Mon to Fri 11 to 3, 6 to 11, Sat 11 to 11, Sun 12 to 10.30; bar food 12 to 2, 6.30 to 9 (9.30 Fri and Sat)*
Details *No children   Car park   Patio   Occasional live music   Dogs welcome No cards*

EAST END   Hampshire   **map 2**

East End Arms 🏵

East End SO41 5SY   TEL: (01590) 626223
off B3054, 2m E of Lymington; follow signs for Isle of Wight ferry and continue 2m

---

This charming, unpretentious pub on the edge of the New Forest, near the Solent Way, appears well supported by local folk. Its proprietor, John Illsley, a founder member of the group Dire Straits, bought the premises to save them from the theme-pub fate. Sturdy tables, attractive prints and inviting furnishings enhance the sense of home comforts, and a large stone pig lounges in front of the open fire. The local micro-brewery is Ringwood, and its Fortyniner and Old Thumper beers are on offer here. So, too, is Thatcher's cider and a short, serviceable wine list (although only two wines are available by the glass). The cooking is generally highly praised, and seems proficient across the range, from filling lunchtime snacks to a full-scale restaurant menu. The former take in a range of freshly baked baguettes and ciabatta filled with rare roast beef and local chutney, or goats' cheese, red onion, aubergine, tomato and basil, while evening diners might be drawn by the choice of fresh fish, such as turbot, hake or brill, perhaps roasted and served with a lavender velouté sauce. An even more exotic offering has been roast Gressingham duck breast with spiced poppadoms and a banana and courgette bhajia. Among puddings is black and blue tart (denoting blackcurrants and blueberries rather than rough treatment). SAMPLE DISHES: devilled lambs' kidneys £4; pan-fried ribeye steak with Stilton butter and chips £12; lime and passion-fruit cheesecake £3.75.

Licensees P.J. and J.L. Sykes and J. Willcock (freehouse)
Open *11.30 to 3, 6 to 11, Sun 12 to 9; bar food and restaurant Tue to Sun 12 to 2, Tue to Sat 7 to 9; closed Mon evening Oct to Easter*
Details *Children welcome before 8pm   Car park   Wheelchair access (also WC)   Garden   Background music or occasional live music   Dogs welcome in bar only   Amex, Diners, MasterCard, Switch, Visa*

EAST LANGTON   Leicestershire   map 5

▲ *Bell Inn* 🍺

Main Street, East Langton LE16 7TW
TEL: (01858) 545278
WEB SITE: www.thebellinn.co.uk
just off B6047, 4m N of Market Harborough

The professionalism of landlord Alistair Chapman shows in the
warm, friendly atmosphere at this listed sixteenth-century pub,
sympathetically modernised since he took over in 1995. The pride of
the inn is its Langton Brewery next door, where Caudle Bitter and
the stronger Bowler are brewed and offered at the pub along with
regulars Greene King IPA and Abbot Ale plus guest beers, many
served straight from the wood. At lunchtime a range of sandwiches,
baguettes and bagels is on offer, as well as such dishes as Greek
salad, chicken satay kebabs and sweet-and-sour vegetables. Both
lunchtime and evening menus provide good choice: from traditional
steaks or gammon to chicken breast stuffed with chestnuts, beef and
black-bean stir-fry, or salmon suprême with a crunchy cheese and
herb topping. Finish with something like raspberry and marshmallow
cheesecake, or chocolate roulade. Half a dozen wines are sold by the
glass from the short but international list. SAMPLE DISHES: smoked
salmon croûte with Boursin £5; turkey, ham and sweetcorn pie
£8.75; bread-and-butter pudding £3.25.

Licensee Alistair Chapman (freehouse)
Open *Mon to Sat 11.30 to 2.30, 7 (6 Fri and Sat) to 11, Sun 12 to 3.30, 7 to
10.30; bar food Mon to Sat 12 to 2, 7 to 10, Sun 12 and 2 (2 sittings), 7 to
9.30*
Details *Children welcome   Car park   Wheelchair access (not WC)   Garden
No smoking in dining room   No music   Dogs welcome exc in dining room
Delta, Diners, MasterCard, Switch, Visa   Accommodation: 2 rooms, B&B
£39.50 to £55*

EAST TYTHERLEY   Hampshire   map 2

▲ *Star Inn*   NEW ENTRY

East Tytherley SO51 0LW   TEL: (01794) 340225
WEB SITE: www.starinn-uk.com
off B3084 Romsey road, N of Lockerley

Although mainly a dining destination, this attractive brick-built
sixteenth-century former coaching inn maintains a pub atmosphere.
It stands on a quiet lane overlooking the village cricket field, and a
terrace at the front allows customers to watch games in summer.

Inside, the comfortable and welcoming main bar is divided into a small seating area and, next to it, a skittle alley; there is also a carpeted dining area furnished in traditional pub style with dark wood furniture and plush banquettes. The clientele are mainly locals who come for good-value snacks and bar meals, as well as a more adventurous and elaborate blackboard menu. At the simple end of the scale might be something old-fashioned such as liver and bacon, while more inventive options have included sea bass with purple potatoes (with cabbage) and citrus vinaigrette, and red pesto and goats'-cheese cappelletti. In summer a changing guest ale joins the regular real ale line-up of Gales HSB and Ringwood Best. Around 30 wines are offered, of which around a dozen are available by the glass; prices start at £9.50 a bottle (£2.50 a glass). SAMPLE DISHES: tiger prawn and scallop risotto £5; hot and spicy pork fillet with mustard and saffron rice £12.50; chocolate and orange steamed pudding with white and dark chocolate sauce £5.

Licensees Paul and Sarah Bingham (freehouse)
Open *Mon to Fri 11 to 2.30, 6 to 11, Sat 11 to 11 (11 to 2.30, 6 to 11 winter), Sun 12 to 10.30 (12 to 2.30, 7 to 10.30 winter); bar food and restaurant 12 to 2, 7 to 9; closed evening 25 Dec and all day 26 Dec*
Details *Children welcome   Car park   Wheelchair access (also WC)   Garden and patio   No smoking in dining room   Background music   Dogs welcome exc in dining room   Delta, MasterCard, Switch, Visa   Accommodation: 3 rooms, B&B £45 to £60*

EAST WITTON   **North Yorkshire**   **map 8**

▲ *Blue Lion* 😊 😊 🍇

East Witton DL8 4SN   TEL: (01969) 624273
WEB SITE: www.thebluelion.co.uk
on A6108 Masham to Leyburn road, 2m SE of Middleham

Attractive in a plain sort of way, this unpretentious Dales coaching inn has been providing sustenance to travellers for more than 200 years. Its outward appearance has changed little in that time, and careful renovation has ensured that the features one might expect from a building of this age are all present and correct in the busy, friendly bar and in the candlelit dining room. But while the setting is steadfastly Georgian, the needs of a modern clientele are recognised by a bar menu that would not look out of place in a smart city brasserie. Influences come from Britain, France, Italy and occasionally further afield, but at the heart of the cooking is plenty of fine local produce, notably game. The result might be starters such as duck liver parfait with toasted brioche and piccalilli, or grouse terrine wrapped in bacon with a grain mustard sauce and tomato chutney, while main courses range from simple tagliatelle carbonara, or steak and kidney pudding, to roast halibut fillet with oysters and a red wine sauce, or chargrilled smoked beef with green bean salad and white pudding. Note that Sunday lunch is set-price only and offers more limited choice. The separate restaurant menu is similar in style, if slightly more elaborate, and vegetarians have their own well-considered menu. Beers are from Theakston and Black Sheep (brewed in the nearby village of Masham), and an extensive and clearly set out list usefully offers 12 wines not only by the glass but by the half-litre too. The full range spans the illustrious (Guigal's Hermitage, Château Beychevelle) and the eclectic (Argentinian Barbera) without neglecting those on a budget or food-lovers looking to match flavours on the restaurant menu. Bottle prices start at a very reasonable £9.95 for the house red and white. Service and accommodation are of as high a standard as everything else ('nothing is too much trouble,' noted a visitor). SAMPLE DISHES: sun-dried tomato risotto with toasted goats' cheese £4.75; chargrilled roe deer cutlet with juniper and red wine sauce £13.75; dark chocolate terrine with raspberry sorbet £4.25.

Licensee Paul Klein (freehouse)
Open *11 to 11; bar food and restaurant 12 to 2.15, 7 to 9.30; closed lunchtime 25 Dec*
Details *Children welcome in family room and bar eating area   Car park Wheelchair access (also WC)   Garden   No music   Dogs welcome   Delta, MasterCard, Switch, Visa   Accommodation: 12 rooms, B&B £53.50 to £89*

EAST WOODLANDS   Somerset   map 2

Horse & Groom 🍺

East Woodlands BA11 5LY   TEL: (01373) 462802
off A361, 2m S of Frome

In working-countryside of muddy lanes, farming equipment and stables, this pub felt like a home from home to a reader. The cosy lounge may be a little worn, but it's comfortable and clean, while the bar is more traditional, with a stone-flagged floor and a wood-burning fire. Customers are chatty, and staff couldn't be nicer. The light, sunny conservatory dining room and the bars look very different but share menus. The bar menu lists baguettes and ploughman's and goes through to lemon sole goujons Louisiana. Liver with onion gravy and bacon uses good-quality meat and comes with 'imaginative, nicely cooked' winter vegetables; it might be followed by apple and blackcurrant crumble with a 'good oaty topping'. Restaurant dishes include avocado with wild boar sausage and mayonnaise, and a main course of oriental savoury spring roll with sweet-and-sour beef noodles. Greene King IPA, Butcombe Bitter, Branscombe Vale

Branoc and Wadworth 6X are on handpump, and Stowford Press cider is also stocked. Half a dozen wines come by the glass from a modestly priced list of 25 bottles. SAMPLE DISHES: Stilton and asparagus tagliatelle £3.50; chicken curry on wild rice £6; steamed summer fruits pudding £3.50.

Licensee Kathy Barrett (freehouse)
Open *Tue to Sat 11.30 to 2.30, Mon to Sat 6.30 to 11, Sun 12 to 3, 7 to 10.30; bar food and restaurant 11.30 to 2 (2.30 Sun), 6.30 to 9*
Details *Children welcome in eating areas   Car park   Wheelchair access (also WC)   Garden   No smoking in dining room   Occasional live music   Dogs welcome exc in dining room   Delta, MasterCard, Visa*

EATON BISHOP   Herefordshire   map 5

▲ *Ancient Camp Inn* NEW ENTRY

Ruckhall, nr Eaton Bishop HR2 9QX
TEL: (01981) 250449
WEB SITE: www.theancientcampinn.co.uk
off A465 at Belmont Abbey, 4m W of Hereford

Fine views are a prime draw at this stone-built pub, perched on a hill above the River Wye. It is well worth making the journey down a long, winding, narrow road just to be able to sit on the terrace with a drink and enjoy the scenery. The pub's name comes from the fact that this was the site of an Iron Age hillfort, though the long, pale-green-painted building is of more recent origin. Enter into a carpeted lounge bar; the rest is all flagstone floors, stone walls and old wooden tables adorned with fresh flowers and candles: on the whole, the atmosphere is not in traditional pub vein. That said, a decent selection of real ales and ciders is served, including local brews Wye Valley Butty Bach and Dabinett and Bramley table cider. Bar food, available only at lunchtimes, mostly goes in for simple-sounding dishes such as tomato and mozzarella salad with pesto dressing, chicken and leek pie, or poached salmon salad, and one or two more complex offerings, such as turbot and basil terrine with shellfish dressing. The cooking style on the restaurant's dinner menu is more involved, with attractively presented dishes such as pan-fried Gressingham duck breasts on sweet potato mash with a lavender-scented jus and duck liver won ton. Wines run to over 50 bins, four of which are available by the glass. SAMPLE DISHES: glazed goats'-cheese salad with fresh figs and marinated tomatoes £5; spicy fish-cakes with parsley sauce £7; marinated double chop with creamed potatoes and lamb jus £7.25.

Licensees Ewan McKie and Lisa Eland (freehouse)
Open *Tue to Sun (exc Sun evening) 12 to 2.30, 7 to 11; bar food 12 to 1.45;*

restaurant 7 to 9; closed 2 weeks Jan
Details *No children   Car park   Wheelchair access (not WC)   Garden and patio   No smoking in dining room   Background music   No dogs   Delta, MasterCard, Switch, Visa   Accommodation: 5 rooms, B&B £45 to £70*

EGLINGHAM   Northumberland   map 10

Tankerville Arms

Eglingham NE66 2TX   TEL: (01665) 578444
on B6346, 6m N of Alnwick

Lining the main street of this delightful village are stone cottages, some Victorian, some older. Among them is this up-market dining pub, attractively decorated inside and divided into three areas: snug, main bar and dining area. Alongside a list of sandwiches and salads (melon, prawn and smoked trout with dill and lime mayonnaise, for example), the menu might offer local chicken and sage sausage with black pudding and mustard sauce, followed by roast salmon on fennel ragoût, steak and ale pie, or lambs' liver and bacon. Collops of venison with creamed peppercorn sauce, or pork fillet on caramelised onion and plum confit with sweet-and-sour sauce are more typical of the specials. Beers include Castles Bitter and Secret Kingdom from the solar-powered, ecologically sustainable North-umberland Brewery, as well as Ruddles Best and Shepherd Neame Spitfire. Just about every wine-producing country is represented on the short wine list. With nothing over £15.40, and plenty of fruit-first varietals to select from, this selection is nice and easy to get to grips with. Ten wines are available by the glass. SAMPLE DISHES: smoked haddock fishcake with Cajun sauce £4.25; roast cod on baked vegetables with smoked bacon and parsley sauce £7.50; lemon mousse gâteau £3.50.

Licensee John Blackmore (freehouse)
Open *12 to 3 (2 winter), 6 to 11; bar food 12 to 2, 6 to 9; closed 25 Dec*
Details *Children welcome   Car park   Wheelchair access (also WC)   Garden No smoking in dining room   Occasional background music   Dogs welcome exc in dining room   Amex, Delta, Diners, MasterCard, Switch, Visa*

ELSTEAD   Surrey   map 3

Woolpack

The Green, Elstead GU8 6HD   TEL: (01252) 703106
on B3001 Milford to Farnham road, 4m W of Godalming

This typical old pub by a small green in a prosperous-looking village
consists of white-plastered, low buildings. The interior is mainly
brown with touches of maroon, and there are local knick-knacks and
pictures, and wool-making paraphernalia. The long menu can take
time to absorb, with three blackboards to read. The style can be
described as modern eclectic, with shell-on prawns with lime, chilli
and coriander butter, and deep-fried calamari with garlic mayonnaise
among the starters. Mains take in Cajun chicken with a mango and
chilli dip, lamb curry, and cassoulet of duck and spicy sausage. More
homely notions are cod and prawn pie, or beef casseroled in ale.
Desserts along the lines of lemon meringue pie are displayed in a glass
cabinet. Fuller's London Pride and Greene King Abbot Ale are
dispensed straight from the cask, and 11 wines, almost half the list,
come by the glass. SAMPLE DISHES: mussels in herb and garlic butter
£4.50; Hawaiian chicken in rum, pineapple and peppers £8; pear and
chocolate chip pavlova £3.50.

Licensee S.A. Askew (Punch)
Open *11 to 2.30, 6 to 11, Sun 12 to 3, 7 to 10.30; bar food and restaurant
12 to 2, 7 to 9.45; closed evening 25 Dec, 26 Dec*
Details *Children welcome in family and dining rooms   Car park   Wheelchair
access (not WC)   Garden   No music   Dogs welcome in bar   Delta,
MasterCard, Switch, Visa*

ELSTED   West Sussex   map 3

Three Horseshoes 🍺

Elsted GU29 0JY   TEL: (01730) 825746
off A272, 3m W of Midhurst

Built in the sixteenth century as an alehouse for drovers, the Three
Horseshoes boasts among many attractions good views over the South
Downs. This is prime walking country, and Downs trekkers who have
worked up an appetite, or simply a thirst, will find this place about as
charming as country pubs get. A ragbag of antique furniture and old
framed photographs on the walls, as well as an inglenook, contribute
to the period detail, and the range of cask-conditioned ales serves
notice that this is still very much a beer lover's paradise: you are likely
to find Cheriton Pots Ale, Ballard's Best Bitter, Timothy Taylor
Landlord, Fuller's London Pride and numerous guest ales, particularly

in the summer. By contrast, wine drinkers are expected to take something of a back seat, with a modest list and just a couple of whites and one red available by the glass. The cooking, too, lives up to the bucolic surroundings, avoiding pretentiousness in favour of home-made soups, dressed crab and lobster from Selsey, and steak and kidney pie made with Murphy's stout. Finish with something indulgent such as treacle tart or banoffi pie. SAMPLE DISHES: baked Brie with cranberry sauce £4.95; braised lamb with apples and apricots and a tomato chutney sauce £9; blueberry crème brûlée £4.

Licensees Andrew and Sue Beavis (freehouse)
Open *11 to 2.30, 6 to 11, Sun 12 to 3, 7 to 10.30; bar food and restaurant 12 to 2, 6.45 to 9.30; closed Sun evenings winter*
Details *Children welcome   Car park   Garden   No music   Dogs welcome exc in dining room   Delta, MasterCard, Switch, Visa*

ELSTED MARSH   West Sussex   map 3

▲ *Elsted Inn*

Elsted Marsh GU29 0JT   TEL: (01730) 813662
off A272, 3m W of Midhurst and 1m N of Elsted

This unpretentious Victorian roadside pub used to stand beside a long-gone railway station, but it is still in perfect walking country next to a lane just north of the South Downs. The railway connection is maintained in the décor, with old railway prints and photographs in the two simple wooden-floored bars. Three open log fires add to the unspoilt atmosphere of a village local where traditional pub games and conversation triumph in the absence of piped music or electronic games. The friendly owners have kept up the tradition of using local produce in their home-made, mainly English food. Mushroom and Stilton soup, based on good stock, impressed a reader with its subtle cheese flavour, while freshly made salmon fishcakes with tartare sauce were also singled out. Other choices may include whole grilled plaice, pork in cider, cheesy fish pie, turkey and apricot casserole, and monkfish provençale. Fuller's London Pride and Ballard's Best are the real ales on tap, and six wines are offered by the glass or by the 250ml 'basin'. SAMPLE DISHES: salmon mousse £4.75; venison casserole £8; panettone and chocolate bread-and-butter pudding with vanilla ice cream £4.25.

Licensees Denny Baxter-Hill and Shelly Green (Enterprise Inns)
Open *11.30 to 3, 5.30 to 11, Sun 12 to 3, 6 to 10.30; bar food and restaurant 12 to 2.30 (3 Sun), 7 to 9.30*
Details *Children welcome in dining room   Car park   Wheelchair access (also WC)   Garden   No smoking in dining room   Occasional live music   Dogs welcome   Delta, MasterCard, Switch, Visa   Accommodation: 4 rooms, B&B £37.50 to £55*

ELTERWATER   Cumbria   map 8

▲ *Britannia Inn* 🍺

Elterwater LA22 9HP   TEL: (015394) 37210
WEB SITE: www.britinn.co.uk
off A593, 3m W of Ambleside

Fine real ales and a splendid location draw the crowds to this
Lakeland gem. Indeed, it is so popular that customers often spill out
of the pub on to the village green. Many of the clientele are walkers
– for this is prime hiking country – who call in to quench their thirst
with top-notch local brews Jennings Bitter, Coniston Bluebird, and
Dent Aviator, which are supplemented by guest ales such as
Hampshire Lionheart. For those who prefer grape to grain, there are
around 30 wines, three served by the glass, plus six country wines
from Lindisfarne. Food is simple but is not confined to traditional
English pub grub: main courses include rogan josh, albeit made with
Langdale Herdwick lamb. Cumberland pie and Waberthwaite
Cumberland sausage fly the local flag, and daily specials might
include beef stew with dumplings, or roast lamb in a crusty white
roll. The pub itself is an attractive whitewashed building in typical
Lakeland style, decked out with flower boxes and hanging baskets.
Inside, the bars have log fires and low oak beams, but the iron tables
and chairs on the patio in front have the best views of the wonderful
scenery. SAMPLE DISHES: cream of mushroom soup £2.25; Langdale
farmhouse pie £7; sticky toffee pudding with hot toffee sauce £3.25.

Licensees Judith Fry and Christopher Jones (freehouse)
Open *11 to 11, Sun 12 to 10.30; bar food 12 to 2, 6.30 to 9.30 (snacks
served 2 to 5.30); closed 25 Dec, and 26 Dec from 2.30*
Details *Children welcome   Patio   No smoking in dining room   No music
Dogs welcome   Amex, Delta, MasterCard, Switch, Visa   Accommodation: 13
rooms, B&B £24 to £78*

ELTON   Cambridgeshire   map 6

Black Horse   NEW ENTRY

14 Overend, Elton PE8 6RU   TEL: (01832) 280240
just off A605 2m W of A1

This small, seventeenth-century inn is 'full of old-world rustic
charm', writes a reporter, who described the service as 'very friendly,
careful, interested and efficient'. Open log fires, antique furnishings
and interesting artefacts, such as old Bakelite telephones and
Underwood typewriters, characterise the interior, and the rear
garden overlooks the church and open countryside. A set-price menu

offers plenty of choice, perhaps including a medley of seafood followed by roast pheasant with figs and apples, while on the carte zucchini niçoise, and mushroom stroganoff, might be among half a dozen or so vegetarian choices, with a kebab of monkfish and king prawns among fish. Bar snacks are also available, at lunchtime only. Draught Bass is the regular ale, while the two guests, which change almost daily, might be Caledonian Deuchars IPA or a seasonal Nethergate ale such as Vixen. Wines by the glass include 12 from the list of 50, plus four more bin-ends or specials. Mulled wine is always offered in winter. SAMPLE DISHES: brioche with wild mushrooms and watercress £5.25; salmon mille-feuille with shallot sauce £13; fruit cheesecake £4.25.

Licensee John Clennell (freehouse)
Open *11 (12 winter) to 3, 6 to 11; bar food 12 to 2, 6 to 10; closed Sun evening winter*
Details *Children welcome   Car park   Wheelchair access (also WC)   Garden No-smoking area in bar   No music   Dogs welcome   Amex, Delta, MasterCard, Switch, Visa*

ETTINGTON   Warwickshire   map 5

Chequers Inn

91 Banbury Road, Ettington CV37 7SR   TEL: (01789) 740387
off A422, 6m SE of Stratford-upon-Avon

Tranquillity reigns at the Chequers, owing in no small degree to the traffic-calming measures on the main road outside. It's a white-plastered, partly creeper-covered building, not large, on the edge of a quiet village, comprising just one L-shaped space divided between lounge and dining room. Although there is nothing immediately recognisable as a bar area, we retain its listing for its commitment to real ales, such as Hook Norton Best Bitter, Adnams and Fuller's London Pride. An ambitious wine list covers prestigious vinous territory, including New Zealand's celebrated Cloudy Bay, Ch. Musar from Lebanon and California's Opus One 1996 for a mere £165, although only four are served by the glass. The menu has a fashion-conscious slant. Bantry Bay mussels and bacon come in a creamy, garlicky Guinness sauce, salmon is marinated in lime and coriander and served with wilted spinach on a coulis of tomato and sweet pepper, and roast breast of Gressingham duck comes with baby vegetable 'fettucine' and a black cherry and brandy sauce. In this context, you wouldn't expect crème brûlée to be served *au naturel*, and indeed it turns out to be flavoured with passion fruit. Equally sharp flavours distinguish a citrus tart of lemon and lime, which comes with wild berry syrup. SAMPLE DISHES: warm salad of peppered mackerel with rocket, avocado and orange and cardamom oil £5.25; chargrilled Scottish ribeye steak with dauphinois potatoes and a red wine and pink peppercorn sauce £12.50; bread-and-butter pudding with orange custard £4.

Licensee Robert Russell (freehouse)
Open *all week (exc Sun evening) 12 to 2.30, 7 to 11; restaurant 12 to 2, 7 to 9 (9.30 Fri and Sat)*
Details *Children welcome Car park Garden and patio No smoking in dining room Background music No dogs Delta, MasterCard, Switch, Visa*

EVERSHOT Dorset map 2

▲ *Acorn Inn*

Fore Street, Evershot DT2 0JW TEL: (01935) 83228
WEB SITE: www.acorn-inn.co.uk
2m off A37 Yeovil to Dorchester road; 4m off A356 Crewkerne to Dorchester road

An inn called the Sow and Acorn, in a village renamed Evershed, featured in Hardy's *Tess of the d'Urbervilles*. This is it, a rough-stone, sixteenth-century coaching inn of great rustic appeal, a few yards down the road from the church in an unspoilt village. Exposed stone walls, a beamed ceiling, spindle-backed chairs and a skittle alley (but of course) imbue the place with period atmosphere, and there are two small dining rooms, one overlooked by a stuffed bird of prey in a glass case. The cooking is robust country-pub fare, ranging from starters such as a gratin of smoked fish, or warm pigeon breast salad, to main courses of the likes of wild boar and venison sausages with mash and onion gravy, or good old steak and kidney pie. Finish with bread-and-butter pudding, or apple crumble. Palmers IPA, Fuller's London Pride and Stowford Press cider are among the distinguished draught options, while home-made damson vodka and sloe gin offer fruity temptations. The wine list is a decent one, too, with four served by the glass, and a good spread of fairly priced bottles from France and the New World. SAMPLE DISHES: salmon and chive fish-cakes with gherkin mayonnaise £5.50; roast lamb with orange and redcurrant jus £16; chocolate terrine with cappuccino sauce £3.50.

Licensee Martyn Lee (freehouse)
Open *12 to 3, 6.30 to 11 (10.30 Sun); bar food and restaurant 12 to 2, 7 to 9 (9.30 Fri and Sat)*
Details *Children welcome Car park Wheelchair access (not WC) Patio No smoking in dining room Jukebox Dogs welcome in bar Amex, Delta, MasterCard, Switch, Visa Accommodation: 9 rooms, B&B £55 to £110*

EWEN   Gloucestershire   **map 2**

▲ *Wild Duck Inn*

Drakes Island, Ewen GL7 6BY   TEL: (01285) 770310
off A429 Cirencester to Malmesbury road, 3m SW of Cirencester

Waterfowl appear in the pub's name, in a draught ale, and seasonally
on the menu too. The linked group of Cotswold-stone buildings, with
an Elizabethan farm at its core, is well weathered and mossy, and the
well-tended garden, with a manicured lawn, matches the characterful
interior, with natural stone and deep-crimson walls bearing old
pictures and hunting trophies – and, yes, more ducks. Service by
young, bright and professional staff is another factor in what a reader
calls 'a glowing ambience'. The single printed menu, available
throughout, is sensibly short, with supplementary light meals at
lunchtimes, such as tuna burger with roast Mediterranean vegetables
and lime mayonnaise, or pork sausages with garlic mash. Ham
ploughman's is a generous portion of hand-cut, home-cooked meat
with apple wedges, pickled onions, chutney and salad with a good
vinaigrette. Main courses range from rare lamb fillet glazed with
honey and lavender to poached monkfish with prawns in a chilli and
coconut sauce. A pudding of marinated fruits with mascarpone and
cumin shortbread has been described as 'a perfect dish'. Beers on tap
are Theakston Best Bitter and Old Peculier, Smiles Best, and house
brew Duck Pond and Courage Directors – and are joined by guests
such as Wells Bombardier Premium Bitter. The 30-odd wines are well
assorted but only two are offered by the glass. SAMPLE DISHES: fried
squid with chorizo £5.75; smoked haddock topped with Welsh
rarebit on plum tomatoes £11; dark chocolate tart with raspberry
compote £4.

Licensees Dino and Tina Mussell (freehouse)
Open *11 to 11, Sun 12 to 10.30; bar food and restaurant 12 to 2 (2.30 Sun),
6.45 to 10*
Details *Children welcome in eating areas   Car park   Garden and patio
Background music   Dogs welcome exc in dining room   Amex, Delta,
MasterCard, Switch, Visa   Accommodation: 11 rooms, B&B £50 to £90*

EXFORD   Somerset   map 1

▲ *Crown Hotel* 🍇

Exford TA24 7PP   TEL: (01643) 831554
WEB SITE: www.gratton.co.uk/crown
on B3224, 9m SW of Minehead

The gabled second floor overhangs the entire frontage of this rather
grand village pub in Exmoor National Park. Guns, hunting trophies
and deer's antlers as candle holders confirm the impression of an up-
market, well-maintained hunting lodge. The restaurant offers a set-
price menu with around half a dozen choices at each course. Its
modern, mostly European starters include cappuccino of asparagus
and wild mushroom, or warm salad of pigeon with lime confit.
Follow perhaps with crispy aromatic duck accompanied by creamy
mustard onions and French beans. Bar food runs to such sophisticated starters as pressed game terrine with pear chutney, or curried
crab and mango salad with coriander yoghurt. More traditional
dishes of honey-glazed pork cutlet with parsnip purée, or pan-fried
calf's liver with lyonnaise potatoes and sage and onion dressing
might show up among main courses, with desserts of perhaps Jaffa
cake pudding with honeycomb ice cream and orange syrup. Exmoor
Ale, Exmoor Fox and Exmoor Gold are on the pumps. Of 12 house
wines offered by the glass, ten are French and the others Australian.
Prices are reasonable for mainly French classics, though the cost of
some bottles in a supplementary 'collection of fine and rare wines'
creeps up to three figures. On the whole, though, the list provides
plenty of interest at affordable prices. SAMPLE DISHES: confit duck leg
with cassoulet £6.25; tiger prawns sautéed in lemon and garlic butter
£11.75; white Valrhona chocolate mousse with honey and ginger ice
cream £4.50.

Licensees Michael Bradley and John Atkins (freehouse)
Open *11 (12 Sun) to 2.30, 6 to 11; bar food 12 to 2 (2.30 Sun), 6.30 to
9.30; restaurant Sun 12 to 2.30, all week 6.30 to 9.30*
Details *Children welcome in bar eating area   Car park   Garden   No-
smoking area in dining room   Occasional live music   Dogs welcome   Amex,
Delta, MasterCard, Switch, Visa   Accommodation: 17 rooms, B&B £47.50 to
£116*

FADMOOR   North Yorkshire   map 9

Plough   NEW ENTRY

Main Street, Fadmoor YO62 7HY   TEL: (01751) 431515
about 2m N of Kirkbymoorside, off A170

Fadmoor is a small village of stone houses. On the corner of its trian-
gular green stands the Plough, painted cream with green detailing
and a red wavy-tiled roof. Inside, the beams in the low ceilings are
hung with bunches of hops, the bar walls are yellow, and so are the
shades of the wall lights; there are also old paraffin lamps, now elec-
tric. A wood-burning range contributes to the warm glow. The
carpeted lounge is comfortable and homely, while the dining room is
a tad more formal. There are bar snacks, and blackboard menus offer
a generous choice of starters and main courses for dinner, a few less
at lunchtime. A reporter's verdict of 'a very high standard of home
cooking' is borne out by appealing dishes, perhaps including mussels,
or a salad of roasted red peppers, smoked salmon and Brie, followed
by roast herb-crusted cod on leek and cheese mash, or griddled lamb
steak with rosemary and redcurrant sauce. On draught is Black
Sheep Bitter, plus a guest in summer. A blackboard lists special
wines, supplementing the main list that includes about six by the
glass. SAMPLE DISHES: duck liver terrine with mandarin and brandy
chutney £4.50; steak and kidney suet pudding £8.75; almond
meringue roulade with fruit compote and cream £3.50.

Licensee Catherine Feather (Holf Leisure Ltd)
Open *Tue to Sat 12 to 2.30, 6.30 to 11, Sun 12 to 2.30, 7 to 10.30; bar food
and restaurant (exc Sun evening) 12 to 2, 6.30 to 9; closed 25 Dec*
Details *Children welcome   Car park   Garden and patio   No smokingin
dining room   Background music   No dogs   MasterCard, Switch, Visa*

FAR FOREST   Worcestershire   map 5

Horse & Jockey   NEW ENTRY

Far Forest DY14 9DX   TEL: (01299) 266239
*beside A4117 Ludlow road at Far Forest, between Bewdley and
Cleobury Mortimer*

This long, mellow-yellow-painted building with blackened red roof
tiles and brick chimneys re-opened in spring 1999 after being carefully restored and refurbished by its new owners. Side and rear
gardens make the most of views across the Wye Forest and Lem
Brook Valley. The interior has been tastefully decorated in open-plan
style, but with original beams, a huge inglenook, cushioned pew

benches and a window seat by the fire. The bar menu goes interestingly beyond the usual with such starters as whole roast quail with bacon and apricots; otherwise tradition rules, and you are encouraged to ask about daily varieties of sausage and mash. In the restaurant, open in the evenings, a more adventurous menu (also available in the bar) might offer venison and beetroot terrine, or deep-fried white pudding, to precede pork fillet rolled in hazelnuts, sage and Parma ham, or sweet potato and aubergine tortilla. A separate page lists six fresh fish dishes, with many more on Fridays: perhaps whole grey mullet roasted with chilli, mango and coriander. On Sundays three courses for £9.25 feature perhaps three roasts and a vegetarian dish among five main courses. On draught are Marston's Pedigree, Hobson's Best and Town Crier, plus a guest, as well as Stowford Press Cider. There are 30 wines with 12 by the glass, and a red and white of the month. SAMPLE DISHES: creamy olive and garlic mushrooms in a filo tulip £4; mighty mixed grill £13.25; pear and walnut strudel with elderflower cream £3.50.

Licensees Richard and Suzanne Smith (freehouse)
Open *12 to 3, 6 to 11, Sun 12 to 10.30; bar food 12 to 2.30, 6 to 9.30, Sun 12 to 8.30; restaurant Mon to Sat 6 to 9.30*
Details *Children welcome in eating areas   Car park   Wheelchair access (also WC)   Garden   No smoking in dining room   Occasional live or background music   No dogs   Delta, MasterCard, Switch, Visa*

FAVERSHAM   Kent   map 3

Albion

Front Brents, Faversham ME13 7DH   TEL: (01795) 591411
on Faversham Creek, near town centre; from Shepherd Neame Brewery take Bridge Road across creek and follow road round to right; pub car park is 150yds on right

Dating from 1750, this low, cottagey building is half a century younger than the Shepherd Neame Brewery, which is a short stone's throw from the pub on the other side of the creek. Naturally, the brewery's beers are served, including seasonal ales – the only surprise is that there is no direct pipeline from the brewery. A tree-lined towpath runs past the pub, with a jetty for those arriving by boat (possible only at high tide). Inside, the building's origin as a pair of cottages becomes apparent, and gnarled hop-garlanded beams betray its age. Two small areas are crammed with tables, and at times they can be busy – booking is recommended. The crowds come for the food, which has French influences, reflecting the landlord's nationality. Straightforward pub fare is offered on the printed menu; sausage and mash may not seem too ground-breaking, but the award-winning sausages are made by a local butcher. Otherwise, there is duck breast with port and mushrooms, or roast best end of lamb in a garlic and herb crust with redcurrant sauce. A blackboard lists daily specials, which might include pot-roast partridge and fish and seafood options. The short, varied wine list includes five by the glass. SAMPLE DISHES: smoked mackerel salad with hard-boiled eggs, cherry tomatoes and mustard dressing £4.25; baked chicken breast with a bacon, mushroom, tomato and wine sauce £9.25; coffee and hazelnut roulade £4.

Licensees Mr and Mrs Coevoet (Shepherd Neame)
Open *11.30 to 3, 6.30 (6 Fri and Sat) to 11, Sun 12 to 3, 7 to 10.30; bar food Mon to Thur 12 to 2, 6.30 to 9.30, Fri and Sat 12 to 2, 6.45 to 10, Sun 12 to 2, 7 to 9*
Details *Children welcome in bar eating area   Car park   Wheelchair access (also WC)   Garden and patio   Background music   No dogs   MasterCard, Switch, Visa*

F A W L E Y   **Buckinghamshire**   **map 2**

▲ *Walnut Tree*

Fawley RG9 6JE   TEL: (01491) 638360
off A4155 Henley to Marlow road, 4m N of Henley

'A friendly and welcoming pub for both the well-heeled younger set and serious walkers' was how one visitor summed up the atmosphere of this inn at the end of a seemingly interminable single-track road that passes through thick wooded areas. At the front is a raised patio with wrought-iron garden furniture, and to the side is a grassy area with picnic tables. Inside, you will find a small, cosy bar with a brick fireplace where a log fire burns on cold days; a second room is mainly used for overflow, and there are also a plainly decorated dining room and a conservatory. A simple but appealing bar menu offers things like local sausages with mash, and smoked salmon salad with new potatoes and lemon mayonnaise. This is supplemented by blackboard specials, such as moules marinière, or chargrilled grey mullet with bubble and squeak and ratatouille. The restaurant menu, also available in the bar, is similar in style: start perhaps with a filo parcel of crab with Gruyère, followed by rump steak in a port and Stilton sauce, or baked fillet of cod with basil sauce. The Walnut Tree is a Brakspear pub with the brewery's Bitter and Special on draught. The short wine list is pricey in places but includes several bottles under £15; 12 wines are sold by the glass. SAMPLE DISHES: salmon, asparagus and dill fishcakes with lime butter sauce £6.50; Mexican-spiced chicken with potato wedges and aïoli £9; braised shank of lamb with creamed potatoes and rosemary jus £11.75.

Licensee Adam Dutton (Brakspear)
Open *summer Mon to Fri 12 to 3, 6 to 11, Sat and Sun 12 to 11; winter Mon to Sat 12 to 3, 6 to 11, Sun 12 to 5; bar food and restaurant 12 to 2.30, 6 to 9.30*
Details *Children welcome   Car park   Wheelchair access (also WC)   Garden and patio   No smoking in dining room   Background music   Dogs welcome exc in dining room   Delta, MasterCard, Switch, Visa   Accommodation: 3 rooms, B&B £38.80 to £55*

FENCE   Lancashire   map 8

Forest Inn 🍇 [NEW ENTRY]

Cuckstool Lane, Fence BB12 9PA   TEL: (01282) 613641
WEB SITE: www.forestinn.co.uk
take Brierfield turning off A6068 outside Fence

This sturdy-looking stone building, on its own on a country lane surrounded by fields and sheep, looks like nothing out of the ordinary from the outside. Inside, the décor of the spacious, open-plan bar has a traditional and timeworn feel, with dark wooden panelling, a large stone fireplace and a stuffed owl sitting on a shelf; there is also a non-smoking conservatory extension. Despite the unassuming appearance, food rises above the run of the mill, and various eating options are offered. As well as the full menu, there is a range of interesting sandwiches at lunchtime, and blackboards list daily specials. Starters of toasted garlic ciabatta with tomato and coriander salsa, and Thai king prawns wrapped in filo with sweet chilli and balsamic dressing are typical of the kitchen's modern approach. Main courses are in similar vein: for example, crisp-roasted fillet of red snapper with crushed parsley potatoes and tomato, shallot and olive fondue, or braised shank of lamb with rösti and a stew of bacon, rosemary and red wine. Ruddles Best Bitter, Marston's Pedigree and Old Speckled Hen are on handpump, and there is something from just about everywhere on the 50-strong wine list, which is equipped with a numerical and alphabetical tasting guide to ensure you get the style of wine you want. Ten wines are available by the glass, and very little comes in at over £20 a bottle – the wines that do, an Amarone della Valpolicella and Jadot's Saint-Aubin, for example, are almost certainly worth the extra pounds. SAMPLE DISHES: crushed black pudding with sauté new potatoes, poached egg and Meaux mustard £5; fettucine of seafood with Parmesan and truffle oil £8; dark chocolate mousse with rum and raisin ice cream and Malibu crème anglaise £4.25.

Licensee C.W. Seedall (freehouse)
Open *12 to 11 (10.30 Sun); bar food and restaurant Mon to Sat 12 to 2.30,
5.30 to 9.30, Sun 12 to 9*
Details *Children welcome   Car park   Wheelchair access (also WC)   Garden
and patio   No smoking in dining room   Background music   No dogs   Amex,
Delta, MasterCard, Switch, Visa*

FENSTANTON   Cambridgeshire   map 6

▲ *King William IV*

High Street, Fenstanton PE18 9JF   TEL: (01480) 462467
WEB SITE: www.gallows-guest-house.co.uk
off A604, 5m SE of Huntingdon

Locals, business people and visitors use this relaxed, welcoming and
characterful pub, a row of seventeenth-century cottages in an attractive village. The rooms are mainly small, low-lit and unspoilt, but the
pleasant, no-smoking Garden Room is brighter, with modern abstract
prints themed on musical instruments. A light meals menu lists dishes
such as three-cheese ploughman's, or ham, egg and chips, plus a wide
variety of sandwiches and salads, while the main printed menu offers
something more substantial. Starters might include mushrooms café
de Paris (stuffed with Brie and baked in filo) – a dish one reporter
praised highly – or salmon and crab mousse, and main dishes range
from steak and kidney pudding to roast scallops with Thai curry sauce
and red pepper salsa. Blackboard specials increase the choice and
interest: uncomplicated but well-cooked and generously portioned
turkey à la king, and hake roasted with garlic, honey and ginger and a
chive rosotto cake with tomato sauce have both been specials enjoyed
by readers. Appealing desserts include fruits of the forest sablé with
iced raspberry parfait. On handpump are Greene King Abbott Ale and
IPA, plus a guest. Ten wines are sold by the litre or half-litre carafe as
well as by the bottle or glass, with another ten by the bottle, all at
friendly prices. Accommodation is offered in the pub's sister operation, Gallows Guest House, just down the street. SAMPLE DISHES: duck
liver parfait on red onion and black cherry confit £4.25; chicken and
mushroom roulade wrapped in bacon served on creamed leeks
£10.75; seasonal berry pudding £3.50.

Licensee Jeremy Schonfeldt (Greene King)
Open *11 to 3.30, 6 to 11.20, Sun 12 to 10.30; bar food and restaurant Mon
to Sat 12 to 2.15, 7 to 10, Sun 12 to 3.30; closed 25 Dec*
Details *Children welcome in eating areas   Car park   Wheelchair access (also
WC)   Patio   No smoking in dining room   Occasional live music   Dogs
welcome   Amex, Delta, MasterCard, Switch, Visa   Accommodation: 5 rooms,
B&B £45 to £50*

FERNHURST   West Sussex   map 3

King's Arms ✿ 🍺

Midhurst Road, Fernhurst GU27 3HA
TEL: (01428) 652005
on A256, 1m S of Fenhurst on sharp bend

A tiny seventeenth-century inn with a barn conversion (used for functions) sitting next to it, the King's Arms is very much in period-country-pub mould. Leather-upholstered chairs and settles, low beams (watch your head) and equestrian paraphernalia – from horse brasses to prints of polo ponies – are the decorative order of the day. Food is very much the hub here, though those who come for just a drink will not be disappointed, with five real ales to choose from – Timothy Taylor Landlord, Ventnor Golden, Comfortably Numb from Triple fff, Hogs Back TEA, as well as genuine Dublin-brewed Guinness. In addition to the printed lunch and dinner menu, black-board supplements and fish specials are displayed at table. Michael Hirst takes pride in offering the kind of food that is eaten in fashion-able metropolitan circles (indeed, the Hirsts used to run a place in London's Mayfair). That means squid ink risotto with lobster cream, marinated fillet of venison with warm Cumberland sauce, and main courses such as steamed breast of guinea fowl sauced with calvados and lime. Fish is imaginatively treated too, perhaps in the form of roasted monkfish with curried aubergine, spinach and red onions, while lighter lunchtime eaters might decide on a hot roast beef and horseradish sandwich. Puddings are a speciality and take in a wide range of steamed sponges, cheesecakes and ice creams, as well as the likes of chocolate and coffee mousse with mint anglaise. Half a dozen wines by the glass (around the £2.40 mark) head up an enter-prising list, helpfully grouped by style and with a slate of half-bottles too. An add-on list of odds and ends gives an opportunity for more adventurous choice. SAMPLE DISHES: salad of sesame-roasted duck with caramelised pear and a spring onion and ginger sauce £5.75; roasted cod fillet on creamed potatoes with pancetta, cabbage and peas £9; sticky toffee pudding with hot fudge sauce £4.25.

Licensees Michael and Annabel Hirst (freehouse)
Open *11.30 to 3, 5.30 (6.30 Sat) to 11, Sun 12 to 3; bar food and restaurant 12 to 2.30, 7 to 9.30; closed first 2 weeks Jan*
Details *Children welcome in eating areas lunchtimes, no children under 14 evenings Car park Garden No smoking in dining area No music Dogs welcome exc in dining room Delta, MasterCard, Switch, Visa*

Use the maps at the back of the book to plan your trip.

FERRENSBY   North Yorkshire   map 9

▲ *General Tarleton* ✿ ❦

Boroughbridge Road, Ferrensby HG5 0QB   TEL: (01423) 340284
WEB SITE: www.generaltarleton.co.uk
off A6065, 3m N of Knaresborough

This eighteenth-century coaching inn is more of a restaurant-with-rooms, but eating and drinking options are flexible and the beamed bar/brasserie still has enough of an informal, pubby feel to justify its inclusion in the Guide. The atmosphere in here is relaxed, helped along by a log-burning fireplace and cosy alcoves, and it is still possible to drop in just for a sandwich and a pint – beers come from Yorkshire brewers Timothy Taylor and Black Sheep – but it will be hard to resist the menu of ambitious modern brasserie fare. Typical options have included crisp tomato tart, provençale fish soup, risotto of Yorkshire ham and peas, slow-roast confit of lamb, and home-made black pudding with local sausages, mash and red wine gravy. Finish with lemon tart, sticky toffee pudding, or a selection of English farmhouse cheeses. The separate, more formal restaurant offers a fixed-price menu of three courses, with things like warm salt squid salad, or cappuccino of mushrooms to start, and seared monk-fish with mussels in a Thai curry sauce, or roast wood pigeon with foie gras on a potato galette to follow. With a highly impressive 22 wines by the glass, the imaginative list reflects the fact that the owners have their own wine importing company and so obviously take great care with their choices. There are some very smart Burgundies (Clos de Tart makes an appearance) and a selection of fine clarets too. Seekers of bargains will not be disappointed either. Ten house wines start at £10.95 a bottle, £1.95 the glass. SAMPLE DISHES: Bayonne ham and celeriac rémoulade £5; confit of roast duck on buttered bok choy with apricots and Agen prunes in a thyme and brandy sauce £11; chocolate marquise £4.50.

Licensees John Topham and Stephen Mannock (freehouse)
Open *summer 12 to 3, 6 to 11, Sun 12 to 3, 6 to 10.30; winter 12 to 2.30, 6 to 10.30 (11 Sat), Sun 12 to 3, 6 to 10.30; bar food 12 to 2.15, 6 to 9.30 (10 Sat, 9 winter), Sun 12 to 2.30, 6 to 8.30; restaurant Sun lunchtime and Mon to Sat evening, same hours; closed 25 Dec*
Details *Children welcome   Car park   Wheelchair access (not WC)   Garden No-smoking area in bar, no smoking in dining room   Occasional live or background music   Dogs welcome   Amex, Delta, MasterCard, Switch, Visa Accommodation: 14 rooms, B&B £65 to £84.90*

❦ *indicates a pub serving exceptional draught beers.*

FIR TREE Co Durham map 10

▲ *Duke of York*

Fir Tree DL15 8DG   TEL: (01388) 762848
on A68, 4m S of Tow Law

At the entrance to the Pennine valley of Weardale, this self-styled
'residential country inn and restaurant', licensed since 1760, was
once an important staging post. It has stood the test of time, remaining somewhere for weary travellers on the York to Edinburgh road
to rest and find sustenance, though nowadays the inn is the destination of most of the clientele rather than a stopping-off point; some
even come here to get married. Among interesting interior decorative features are bar fittings created by the famous craftsman
'Mouseman' Thompson. Daily-changing menus are listed on blackboards and local produce is to the fore – especially steaks.
Otherwise, you might find garlic mushrooms, followed by 'pork
Zaccharoff', with peach and brandy ice cream to finish. Black Sheep
Best Bitter is the only cask ale offered, though there are two further
Black Sheep bottled beers; wines are more numerous, the list
running to around 30 bins, with three by the glass. The pub has five
and a half acres of landscaped gardens, ideal for warm summer
evenings. SAMPLE DISHES: celery and Stilton soup £3.25; Arctic
chicken with prawns £13; sherry trifle £3.75.

Licensee G.R. Suggett (freehouse)
Open *11 to 3 (2.30 winter), 6.30 to 11 (10.30 winter); bar food and
restaurant 12 to 2, 6.30 to 9; closed 25 Dec*
Details *Children welcome   Car park   Wheelchair access (also WC)   Garden
Occasional background music   No dogs   Delta, Diners, MasterCard, Switch,
Visa   Accommodation: 5 rooms, B&B £52 to £69*

FLETCHING East Sussex map 3

▲ *Griffin Inn*

Fletching TN22 3SS   TEL: (01825) 722890
WEB SITE: www.thegriffininn.co.uk
off A272, between Maresfield and Newick, 3m NW of Uckfield

This Grade II listed inn, set in an impressively unspoiled village, has
been around since the sixteenth century and shows the signs of old
age in its bowed walls. Inside, it is classic old-style country pub, with
real fires and buckets of atmosphere. The two main bars – one a
public bar with pool table and a younger crowd – are always busy,
owing to the well-deserved reputation of the pub for excellent food
and drink. At the rear of the pub is the *Good Food Guide*-listed

restaurant, where Thursday night is fish night, but the bar offers an enticing alternative. Here the cooking is a blend of traditional and modern, local and international, fish and meat, and shows that a high degree of skill and intelligence is applied in the kitchen. Typical choices might include leeks and salmon in a wine and fennel jelly, bruschetta of pecorino with roasted red peppers and basil, pot-roast local pheasant with bacon, Puy lentils and roasted garlic, and pan-fried skate wing with chervil hollandaise. There are also hot ciabatta sandwiches, filled with things like Thai chicken, and, to finish, warm apricot with whisky cream, or upside-down pear and polenta cake with custard. To drink, Badger Tanglefoot joins fine local brews Harveys Sussex Best Bitter and Rother Valley Spirit Level. A clearly presented New World/Old World 80-strong wine list has been carefully assembled to accommodate bargain-hunters and connoisseurs alike (Cos d'Estournel, Léoville-Las-Cases and Nine Popes all make an appearance). Thirteen wines are available by the glass (between £2.50 and £3.20) and include some less usual Sicilian choices as well as familiar grape varietals and food-friendly favourites. Children have their own menu and are welcome to climb the trees in the large garden with its splendid views and explore the two acres of grounds. SAMPLE DISHES: home-cured gravad lax with dill mayonnaise £5.50; game pie of venison, pigeon and pheasant with juniper berries £8.50; rhubarb and ginger crumble £4.50.

Licensees Nigel and James Pullan, and John Gatti (freehouse)
Open *12 to 3, 6 to 11 (10.30 Sun); bar food and restaurant 12 to 2.30, 7 to 9.30; closed 25 Dec, restaurant closed Sun evening winter*
Details *Children welcome in eating areas Car park Wheelchair access (also WC) Garden and patio Occasional live music Dogs welcome exc in restaurant Amex, Delta, Diners, MasterCard, Switch, Visa Accommodation: 8 rooms, B&B £65 to £95*

FONTHILL GIFFORD Wiltshire   map 2

▲ *Beckford Arms* NEW ENTRY   LOCAL PRODUCE

Fonthill Gifford SP3 6PX TEL: (01747) 870385
take minor road off B3089 at Fonthill Bishop and follow signs to Fonthill Gifford

On a quiet country road adjoining the Fonthill Estate vineyard, this substantial eighteenth-century stone-built inn used to be just that. But Karen and Eddie Costello have transformed the décor and furnishings, the ambience, and the food and drink. Eddie's cooking, using fresh local produce, ranges from lunchtime sandwiches to such starters as Stilton parcels with port and onion dressing, or 'authentic, well-flavoured, hearty, warming' minestrone soup. Main dishes include roast Gressingham duck breast with wild berry jus, and a reader's choice from the specials board of a 'simple yet excellent' seafood grill comprising six langoustines and a tower of cod, salmon and red mullet. The flower- and shrub-filled garden is ideal for summer sipping. The conservatory is airy, while the bar and dining areas are tastefully rustic with lots of dark wood, huge candles, old prints and a log fire. Hop Back Best Bitter, from Salisbury, and Greene King Abbot Ale are always on tap, and two guests might be Hampshire Brewery's Pride of Romsey, Timothy Taylor Landlord or Shepherd Neame Spitfire. All five house wines, from a reasonably priced list, are sold by the glass. SAMPLE DISHES: pan-fried chicken livers with redcurrants and thyme £5; sauté Wiltshire pork medallions with pear and sage butter £9; treacle sponge pudding £3.50.

Licensees Karen and Eddie Costello (freehouse)
Open *11.45 to 11, Sun 12 to 10.30; bar food and restaurant 12 to 2.30, 7 to 9.30 (10 Fri and Sat, 9 Sun)*
Details *Children welcome in family room   Car park   Garden and patio Occasional background music   Dogs welcome   MasterCard, Switch, Visa Accommodation: 8 rooms, B&B £35 to £85*

FORD   Buckinghamshire   map 3

▲ *Dinton Hermit*

Water Lane, Ford HP17 8XH   TEL: (01296) 747473
off A418, 4m SW of Aylesbury

Set in the tiny village of Ford, this attractive stone building is reminiscent of a Cotswold pub from the outside. The interior is just as appealing, with beams, brick walls and cream and red paintwork; rural decorative touches are added in the shape of an antique milk churn and wooden barrels, as well as a portrait of the eponymous hermit, a man named John Bigg who lived in the 1600s – all of which give it a romantic charm. At one end of the pub is a formally set dining area. Food is mostly of the hearty and heartwarming variety – 'not gourmet but still a pleasure' – perhaps opening with celery and courgette soup, followed by roast pheasant with port gravy, or roast duck with dauphinoise potatoes. There is also a range of lighter bar meals such as ploughman's, various pasta dishes and open sandwiches. In winter there are two constantly changing real ales on offer – which might be from Hook Norton, Brakspear or Adnams – the range expanding in summer. The list of 30 wines includes own-label house wines and five by the glass. SAMPLE DISHES: avocado with grilled goats' cheese £5.50; beef stroganoff £11; chocolate torte £4.

Licensee John Chick (freehouse)
Open *Tue to Sat 11 to 11, Sun 12 to 3; bar food 12 to 2, 7 to 9.30, Sun 12 to 3; closed evening 24 Dec and all day 25 and 26 Dec*
Details *Children welcome in bar eating area   Car park   Wheelchair access (also WC)   Garden and patio   No music   Dogs welcome by arrangement in bar area only   Amex, Delta, MasterCard, Switch, Visa   Accommodation: 4 rooms, B&B £70 per room*

FORDHAM   Cambridgeshire   map 6

White Pheasant

Market Street, Fordham CB7 5LQ   TEL: (01638) 720414
on A142, 5m N of Newmarket

Set back a little from the main road, this large, white-painted seven-teenth-century inn is none the less easy for passing motorists to spot thanks to its prominent sign. Enter the light, airy main bar area, where tables are all laid for eating, hunting prints adorn the walls, and background music is likely to be Mozart: the atmosphere is somewhere between traditional pub and informal restaurant. Several blackboards are required to list the extensive daily food offerings, which feature plenty of local produce, including game, Norfolk chicken, and sausages from Newmarket. If prices seem higher than average, this is compensated for by generous portions and good-quality ingredients: one reporter's 'English lamb chops' comprised three 'huge', tender and flavoursome cutlets. At the rear of the pub is a restaurant with a décor of blue walls and tartan curtains, and a menu that runs to wild mushroom quiche, and Aylesbury duck breast on noodles with plum and spring onion sauce. Foresters IPA and Tolly Cobbold Original are the real ales served, and an extensive wine list offers no fewer than 23 by the glass, with a wide selection of English country wines. SAMPLE DISHES: smooth chicken liver pâté £3.75; lambs' liver and bacon with onion gravy £7.75; lemon and ginger crunch tart £4.

Licensee I.C. Hubbert (freehouse)
Open *12 to 2.30, 6 to 11, Sun 12 to 2.30, 7 to 9; bar food and restaurant 12 to 2.30, 6 to 10, Sun 12 to 2.30, 7 to 9*
Details *Children welcome   Car park   Wheelchair access (also WC)   Garden No-smoking area in dining room   Occasional background music   No dogs MasterCard, Switch, Visa*

FORDWICH   Kent   map 3

Fordwich Arms

King Street, Fordwich CT2 0DB   TEL: (01227) 710444
off A28, 3m NE of Canterbury

On the outskirts of Canterbury, Fordwich claims to be the smallest
town in the country. It even has a half-timbered sixteenth-century
town hall, which is opposite this large mock-Tudor pub. Inside, the
one large bar area is dominated by a central counter, and there are
log-burning fireplaces at either end of the room. The place is well
kept and attractively decorated, with floral wallpaper, dried flowers
and a collection of knick-knacks, and friendly staff set a cheerful
tone. There is also a separate dining room, though the same menu is
served both here and in the bar. The cooking style shows a wide
range of modern, international influences, starters encompassing
sesame prawn toasts, and home-smoked chicken with Caesar salad,
mains taking in fillet steak with caramelised mustard and brown
sugar, whole lemon sole with hazelnut butter, and honey-roasted
confit of duck with orange and walnut sauce. Beers include Flowers
Original and Shepherd Neame Master Brew, and eight wines are sold
by the glass. SAMPLE DISHES: Thai crab cakes £4.75; pork fillet with
apples and brandy £9.25; sticky toffee pudding £3.50.

Licensees Mr and Mrs Sean O'Donnell (Whitbread)
Open *11 to 11 (10.30 Sun); bar food and restaurant (exc Sun evening) 12 to
2.30, 6.30 to 10*
Details *No children   Car park   Wheelchair access (also WC)   Garden   No
smoking in dining room   Occasional background music   Dogs welcome exc in
dining room   Delta, MasterCard, Switch, Visa*

FORHILL   Worcestershire   map 5

Peacock 🍺 NEW ENTRY

Icknield Street, Forhill, King's Norton B38 0EH
TEL: (01564) 823232
*from M42 junction 3 take A435 towards Birmingham, pass Bekitts
Farm on left, then left at traffic island, then first left into Clewshaw
Lane and follow Picnic Spot signs; pub on right side of Picnic Spot*

Though you won't have too far to travel from Birmingham, Forhill is
very much out in the sticks. Sitting high on a hill, the Peacock is an
extended brick-built pub with garden seating at the front and a
terrace at the back with picnic benches. A genuine country atmosphere prevails in a rambling series of rooms with stripped tables,
pews, pine chairs and a wood-burning stove. The bar at the front is

full of people taking advantage of the real ales on offer: as this is a Scottish & Newcastle pub, these include up to eight beers from the parent company's brewery (Theakston Old Peculier, for example), which are joined by up to five guests (maybe Hobsons Best Bitter). Four house wines are sold by the glass. Both the bar and restaurant menus are served throughout the pub. The former offers straightforward one-plate meals such as chilli with rice and chips, bangers and mash, and vegetable risotto, together with soup and pâté. The restaurant menu spreads its wings a little for black pudding with sauté potatoes, crispy bacon and a poached egg as a trendy starter, followed maybe by duck breast with oriental sauce and noodles, or braised lamb with a mint and redcurrant jus. Fresh fish of the day is listed on a board, which also shows the puddings: perhaps spotted dick or chocolate torte. SAMPLE DISHES: Thai fishcakes £6; roast venison in red wine jus £10; crème brûlée £5.

Licensee Stephen Wakeman (Scottish & Newcastle)
Open *12 to 11 (10.30 Sun); bar food 12 to 6 (8 Sun); restaurant 12 to 10*
Details *Children welcome in eating areas   Car park   Wheelchair access (also WC)   Garden and patio   No smoking in dining room   Occasional live music   Dogs welcome in bar   Amex, Delta, Diners, MasterCard, Switch, Visa*

FORTON   Lancashire   map 8

Bay Horse Inn ☺ NEW ENTRY

Bay Horse, Forton LA2 0HR   TEL: (01524) 791204
WEB SITE: www.bayhorseinn.com
from M6 junction 33 take A6 towards Preston; take second left-hand turn; pub is on right

The Bay Horse is a black and white pub at a sharp bend in the road, with window boxes around the bay window. The roughcast walls inside are done in salmon-pink and hung with hunting prints. A separate room for dining is laid up a little more ornately than the rest, but this is essentially a pleasantly inviting, no-frills rural pub. Orders are taken at the bar, and the food on offer may raise some eyebrows if you're expecting standard pub fare. Salmon marinated in vodka and beetroot with pickled fennel and herb mayonnaise, Caesar salad with smoked duck, and the sensitively cooked scallops with smoked salmon in a sweet chilli sauce that were greatly enjoyed by an inspector crop up among first courses alone. After that, the choice extends from sea bass fillet with a risotto that might contain crab, saffron and vanilla, to meat dishes such as roast thick pork chop with black pudding mash, roast apple and a cider mustard sauce. However up to date the cooking sounds, portion sizes are very much of the old school (large, that is), but if you've left a spare corner for a pudding, try pear poached in red wine with vanilla ice cream, or crème brûlée.

Draught ales include Flowers IPA and Wadworth 6X. Three red and three white wines are served by the glass, and there are vintage ports and an expansive range of single malt Scotch to add interest. SAMPLE DISHES: pumpkin soup drizzled with truffle oil £3; slow-cooked Goosnargh duck, potato purée, elderberry wine and honey sauce £11; lemon tart with passion-fruit sorbet £4.

Licensee Brian Wilkinson (Mitchells)
Open *Tue to Sat 12 to 3, 6.30 to 11, Sun 12 to 5, 8 to 10.30; bar food and restaurant Tue to Sat 12 to 2, 7 to 9.30, Sun 12 to 4*
Details *Children welcome in dining room   Car park   Wheelchair access (also WC)   Garden and patio   No smoking in dining room   Background music No dogs   Amex, Delta, MasterCard, Switch, Visa*

FOSS CROSS   Gloucestershire   map 5

Hare & Hounds ✿

Foss Cross GL54 4NN   TEL: (01285) 720288
on A429, just S of Fossebridge, 6m N of Cirencester

Although this is an Arkell's pub, with the brewery's beers on draught, it bears the distinct stamp of its licensees, who also run a renowned restaurant in Moreton-in-Marsh and another pub, the Churchill Arms in Paxford (see entry). They have become more closely involved with the day-to-day running of the Hare & Hounds since the departure of their previous managers just as the Guide was going to press, and we expect the high standards to remain. The beamed bar is everything a traditional pub should be, with a warm, welcoming and lively atmosphere helped on cold days by a blazing log fire. Like its sister establishment, it manages to combine this informal, down-to-earth feel with a serious approach to food. Considerable efforts are made to seek out first-class ingredients, which are used to produce a daily-changing menu full of exciting modern ideas: for starters, duck confit comes with sauté cumin potatoes, sherry and shallots, while pigeon breast is partnered with local beetroot in a salad with a blue cheese dressing. Main courses are equally appealing inventions such as griddled tuna with bok choy, lemon grass, chilli and ginger, or breast of guinea fowl with butternut squash and a coconut, saffron, vanilla and tomato relish. Finish with something like lemon tart, or baked peach halves filled with frangipane and peach ice cream. A short, modestly priced list of wines includes no fewer than ten house offerings by two sizes of glass as well as by the bottle. SAMPLE DISHES: seafood risotto with saffron, basil and roast peppers £5; slow-braised lamb shank with celeriac and sage mash and thyme jus £10; sticky toffee pudding with butterscotch sauce and cream £4.

Licensees Sonya and Leo Brooke-Little (Arkell's)
Open *11 to 3, 6 to 11; bar food 12 to 2, 7 to 9; no food 25 Dec*
Details *Children welcome   Car park   Wheelchair access (also WC)   Garden*
No music   Dogs welcome   MasterCard, Switch, Visa

FOTHERINGHAY   **Northamptonshire**   map 6

Falcon Inn 🏵 🍇

Fotheringhay PE8 5HZ   TEL: (01832) 226254
off A605, 4m NE of Oundle

Fotheringhay, as one reporter puts it, 'packs a lot of history'. The magnificent church, which is well worth a look, has ancient royal connections, and it was in the now-ruined castle here that Richard III was born and Mary Queen of Scots was beheaded. That unlucky would-be monarch is represented in prints on the walls of this pretty country pub. Here, Windsor chairs, fresh flowers and discreet soft colours lend an air of modern comfort, and the main dining area is in a handsome conservatory extension. Ray Smikle cooks with an eye on developing round-the-world fashions without resorting to over-elaboration, delivering tuna carpaccio with lime and wasabi cream; Jamaican jerk chicken with a stew of sweet potato, plantain, okra and blackeye beans served with guacamole; and for one reporter a 'delicious' dish of partridge stuffed with cotechino sausage, ricotta and thyme. Fish might be red snapper, served with ratatouille and tapénade, and desserts take in panettone bread-and-butter pudding, or lemon and mascarpone tart with blueberry sauce. John Hoskins, Master of Wine and director of the Huntsbridge group, to which the Falcon belongs, has put together an extensive and inspired wine list, opening with eight whites and nine reds by the glass – 17 in total, from £1.90 to £3.75. The main list divides into bottles under £20 and a 'Top Class' selection of reds and whites: both sections have treats in store (for example, Langi Riesling from Australia at £17.50 and Le Cigare Volant from California's Bonny Doon at £26); there's also a nice group from Bordeaux (Langoa-Barton, Ducru Beaucaillou, etc.) Don't miss the fine selection of sweet wines. If it's proper beer you've come for, choose from Batemans Go for Gold, Elgood's Pageant Ale, or Adnams. SAMPLE DISHES: chilled tomato, fennel and garlic soup £4.50; butterflied leg of lamb with warm niçoise salad and basil oil £12.50; sticky toffee pudding with caramel sauce and rum and raisin ice cream £4.75.

Licensees Ray Smikle and John Hoskins (Huntsbridge Ltd)
Open *Tue to Sat 11.30 to 3, 6 to 11, Sun 12 to 3, 7 to 10.30; bar food and restaurant 12 to 2.15, 6.30 (7 Sun) to 9.30*
Details *Children welcome   Car park   Wheelchair access (also WC)   Garden and patio   No smoking in dining room   No music   No dogs   Amex, Diners, MasterCard, Switch, Visa*

FOWLMERE   Cambridgeshire   map 6

Chequers 🍷

High Street, Fowlmere SG8 7SR   TEL: (01763) 208369
off B1368, between A10 and A505, 5m NE of Royston

In 1660 Samuel Pepys spent a night at this sixteenth-century coaching inn, while, nearer the present day, pilots who flew from the
nearby airfield and who used the pub in both world wars have been
honoured in its sign. The same menu operates in the (non-smoking)
conservatory and in the bars. Although not overlong, it offers a taste
of the world with, for example, a warm salad of pancetta and prawns
with garlic bread, or roast salmon mousse on mint and cucumber
crème fraîche, followed by grilled plaice with lemon grass and chilli
paste with tomato and coriander salsa, saffron and cardamom rice.
Dover sole is plainly grilled, but steaks come with multi-ingredient
sauces and garnishes. There's plenty to choose from on the succinct
wine list, with France especially well represented, and a good selection from the New World too. Ten wines are available by the glass,
from £2.15. Except for a smattering, bottle prices on the main list
are mostly above £15, though house wines start at £8.50. Adnams
Best Bitter is the regular ale, and guests could be Black Sheep Best
Bitter, Timothy Taylor Landlord, or Gale's HSB. Of around thirty
malt whiskies, three are of cask strength – 60 per cent ABV or more.
SAMPLE DISHES: pea and chicken soup with mint and Parmesan £3;
seared tuna on salsa rossa with salad niçoise £9.75; pannacotta with
raspberries and grappa £4.25.

Licensees N.S. and P. Rushton (freehouse)
Open *11 to 2.30, 6 to 11, Sun 12 to 2.30, 7 to 10.30; bar food and
restaurant 12 to 2, 7 to 10, Sun 12 to 2.30, 7 to 9.30; closed 25 Dec*
Details *Children welcome   Car park   Wheelchair access (not WC)   Garden
No smoking in dining room and conservatory   No music   No dogs   Amex,
Delta, Diners, MasterCard, Switch, Visa*

GEDNEY DYKE   Lincolnshire   map 6

Chequers

Main Street, Gedney Dyke PE12 0AJ   TEL: (01406) 362666
WEB SITE: www.chequerspub.co.uk
just off B1359, from Gedney roundabout on A17, 3m E of Holbeach

The Chequers is a textbook Fenland country pub, painted white
beneath a red clay pantile roof, and looking suitably dazzling in
summer when the façade is hung with baskets of flowers. A garden
provides opportunities for outdoor eating and drinking. Heavy dark

wooden furniture, chintz curtains, a loudly patterned carpet and a profusion of bric-à-brac decorate the interior, and there is an open fire in winter. Dining is certainly a principal focus here: you may choose to eat in the bar, in the separate dining room or in the conservatory extension. Fresh fish features strongly, as do rare-breed cuts of meat, and there are good vegetarian options. Smoked fillet of lamb with a sweet mint 'pesto' makes an interesting starter, and there is a generous amount of filling in crab and Gruyère tartlet. Main courses run along classical lines, with steaks, lamb chop, and chicken breast in white wine and mushroom sauce to the fore, but Gloucester Old Spot pork with Cumberland sauce, or roast cod accompanied by scallops might also make an appearance. Midday visitors might lunch on something like a huge BLT sandwich. The sweet of tooth might go for baked lemon cheesecake with an apricot glaze, or banoffi pie with Chantilly cream. Real ales are Dixon's Old Honesty, locally brewed just for the pub, and Adnams Best Bitter and Greene King Abbot Ale. Ten wines by the glass head up a list that offers a sound international choice. SAMPLE DISHES: baked goats' cheese with raspberry vinaigrette £4.75; peppered venison on celeriac potato with Cumberland sauce £10.50; lemon sponge pudding with custard £3.50.

Licensees Simon and Linda Rattray (freehouse)
Open *12 to 2, 7 to 11 (10.30 Sun); bar food and restaurant 12 to 2, 7 to 9*
Details *Children welcome   Car park   Garden and patio   No smoking in dining room   Background music   No dogs   Amex, Delta, Diners, MasterCard, Switch, Visa*

GIBRALTAR   Buckinghamshire   **map 3**

Bottle and Glass

Gibraltar HP17 8TY   TEL: (01296) 748488
on A418, between Thame and Aylesbury

This very attractive sixteenth-century thatched inn, set a little way back from the main road in an unusually named village is, among other things, a tribute to somebody's green fingers. To sit at a trestle table at the front among flowering plants, some hanging and some in tubs, is a treat in summer. Inside, a cluster of alcoves and low-ceilinged rooms around a central bar continue the feeling of rustic charm. Separate menus operate for lunchtime and evening sessions, and although some traditional pub dishes are on offer, more modern cooking goes on alongside them. Fish and seafood are as enthusiastically celebrated as if the place were on the coast: perhaps a mixture cooked in a Normandy-style stew topped with collops of fresh lobster. Halibut fillet is roasted and served with a sauce of truffle, basil and pink peppercorns, while for those who can't choose between fish and meat, a pairing of king scallops with pork medallions in a seafood sauce might fit the bill – or choose lamb shank country style, or pasta with wild mushrooms, truffles, cream and herbs. Moules marinière, or perhaps a lamb kebab might start you off, and meals end with shortcake topped with exotic fruits with an apricot coulis, or lightly poached peach with Muscat and orange sorbet. The wine list is short and mostly French, with a handful served by the glass, while Morrells Oxford Bitter and Varsity are on handpump. SAMPLE DISHES: giant Mediterranean prawns with ginger mayonnaise £8.50; chargrilled tuna with wild mushroom sauce £10; profiteroles with Belgian chocolate sauce £5.

Licensee June Southwood (Morrells)
Open *11 to 3, 6 to 11, Sun 12 to 4; bar food and restaurant 12 to 2.30, 6.30 to 9.30 (10 Fri and Sat), Sun 12 to 4; closed 25 and 26 Dec*
Details *Children welcome   Car park   Wheelchair access (also WC)   Patio Background music   No dogs   Amex, Delta, Diners, MasterCard, Switch, Visa*

GOSFIELD   Essex   map 3

Green Man

The Street, Gosfield CO9 1TP   TEL: (01787) 472746
on A1017, 4m NE of Braintree

The Green Man is easy enough to find, being on the main road through the village, though perhaps it ought to be renamed the Pink Man in keeping with its exterior décor. The pub is divided into two parts with separate entrances. The public bar is a small, basically decorated room with a pool table where locals gather to drink; the saloon bar is in more traditional country-pub vein and has something of a rustic feel. This is a Greene King pub, serving that brewery's range of beers, and a list of 30-plus wines includes eight by the glass plus a special. Menus are displayed on boards and offer a varied range of dishes in modern and traditional styles. Starters might encompass oriental-style prawns in sweet-and-sour sauce as well as deep-fried Brie with garlic bread and port and cranberry sauce. To follow, you could choose from chicken curry, steak and kidney pudding, and pork chops with dill and a mustard sauce; fish options might take in grilled whole lemon sole, and at lunchtime a cold table operates, with a selection of meats, pies and salads. SAMPLE DISHES: crispy-coated garlic mushrooms with dips £3; half a roast duck with orange and red wine sauce £11; treacle tart £3.

Licensee Janet Harrington (Greene King)
Open *11 to 3, 6.15 to 11, Sun 12 to 3, 7 to 10.30; bar food (exc Sun evening) 12 to 2, 6.45 to 9*
Details *Children welcome   Car park   Wheelchair access (not WC)   Garden and patio   No smoking in dining room   Jukebox   Dogs welcome exc in eating area   Amex, Delta, MasterCard, Switch, Visa*

GOUDHURST   Kent   map 3

Green Cross Inn   NEW ENTRY

Station Road, Goudhurst TN17 1HA   TEL: (01580) 211200
on A262, 3m E of A21 and 1m from village of Goudhurst

The Lizzis took over this pub in June 2000, when it was in a somewhat bedraggled state. At the time of going to press, refurbishment
and redecoration had not yet commenced, but the pub is already
showing signs of a revival, pulling in a loyal following from the new
owners' previous pub in East Sussex as well as an increasing number
of locals. The main attraction is some first-class, straightforward pub
food; on the bar menu is a range of light dishes such as mussels and
chips; spaghetti with baby squid; sausage, bean and onion pie; and
Moroccan lamb on saffron rice. The restaurant menu, served in both
the bar and separate dining room, is more extensive but equally
unpretentious, and specialises in fish: maybe potted shrimps, or
smoked eel with horseradish to start, followed by poached turbot
with spinach and cheese sauce, or paella. Beers are a decent range
from Harveys, Shepherd Neame and the local small independent
brewer Larkins. House selections start at £9 on the list of around 50
wines; three wines are available by the glass. SAMPLE DISHES: queen
scallops with tagliatelle and a dry vermouth and tarragon cream
sauce £6.25; roasted breast and leg of local pheasant with wild
mushroom sauce £9.50; pannacotta with strawberry coulis £4.25.

Licensees Eleuterio and Caroline Lizzi (freehouse)
Open *11 to 3, 6 to 11; bar food and restaurant 12 to 2.30 (3 Sun), 7 to 10;
closed Sun evening winter*
Details *Children welcome   Car park   Garden   Background music   Dogs
welcome exc in dining room   MasterCard, Switch, Visa*

GRANGE MOOR   West Yorkshire   map 8

Kaye Arms 🍇

29 Wakefield Road, Grange Moor WF4 4BG   TEL: (01924) 848385
off A642 and B6118, 4m S of Dewsbury

The Kaye Arms styles itself as 'inn and brasserie' and combines a
modern approach to food with a traditional rural pub setting,
surrounded by nothing but countryside and farmland. The bar areas
are decorated as you might expect, with brasses adorning a brick fireplace, and various decorative plates and pictures on the walls. At
lunchtime, an informal menu offers a varied range of dishes: for
instance, mature Cheddar soufflé, steak sandwich, ploughman's, and
coq au vin. The evening menu is more extensive, with sections

devoted to fish and vegetarian options and highlighted recommendations. Start perhaps with warm smoked chicken breast on Caesar
salad, then move on to sauté monkfish in Parma ham with aubergine
confit, tomato fondue and roast new potatoes, or roast rack of lamb
with provençale vegetable stew and dauphinois potatoes. Desserts
feature a 'surprise trio' as well as a fruit tart or sticky toffee pudding.
Theakston Best Bitter is the only real ale offered; wine drinkers get a
much better deal. The neatly presented wine list numbers around 50
bottles, all under £20, with some great names cropping up – Guigal's
Côtes du Rhône, Rothbury Shiraz and Chateau de Tracy Pouilly-
Fumé. There's an add-on list of fine wines – Bordeaux and Burgundy
classics from some interesting past vintages – plus a selection of half-
bottles, and 12 wines by the glass (two sizes) beginning at £1.70.
SAMPLE DISHES: Cornish king crab cake £5.50; wild boar and Black
Sheep ale sausages £8; strawberry and chocolate meringue £3.50.

Licensees Brenda and Stuart Coldwell (freehouse)
Open *Tue to Sat 11.30 to 3, 7 (6.30 Sat) to 11, Sun 11.30 to 3, 7 to 10.30;
bar food 12 to 2, 7.15 (6.45 Sat) to 9.30 (10 Fri and Sat); closed 25 Dec to 2
Jan*
Details *Children welcome at lunchtime   Car park   Wheelchair access (also
WC)   No-smoking area in bar   Background music   No dogs   Delta,
MasterCard, Switch, Visa*

GRASMERE   Cumbria   **map 10**

▲ *Travellers Rest*

Grasmere LA22 9RR   TEL: (015394) 35604
WEB SITE: www.lakelandinns.com
just off A591 Keswick road, ½m N of Grasmere

A sixteenth-century former coaching inn, the Travellers Rest stands
out bright and white against rolling hills in the heart of the Lake
District, a little way out of Grasmere proper. This is Wordsworth
tourist country, and also walking country, and both constituencies
may be found ensconced in the cosy bar on a busy summer day.
Jennings Bitter is on handpump, as are Cumberland Ale and
Marston's Pedigree, and nearly all the major wine-producing countries are listed on the wine list, which offers three by the glass. Food
is served throughout the day for most of the year, mining a populist
seam with the likes of crunchy garlic mushrooms, smoked salmon
sandwiches, chargrilled steaks, scampi and chips, and chicken tikka
masala. For something a little more elaborate, try poached rainbow
trout stuffed with prawns and almonds in lemon and garlic butter, or
duck breast glazed with honey and rosemary. Puddings appear in the
form of chocolate melting cake, pear and ginger pudding with
custard, or a selection of ice creams. The owners have another

Lakeland place at St John's in the Vale, the King's Head. SAMPLE DISHES: celery and Stilton pâté with melba toast and salad £4; Cumberland sausage with onion gravy, mustard mash and mushy peas £7; lemon tart with lemon sorbet £3.25.

Licensees Graham and Derek Sweeney (freehouse)
Open *11 to 11 (10.30 Sun); bar food and restaurant 12 to 9.30 (exc 3 to 6 Sun to Fri Nov to Feb)*
Details *Children welcome   Car park   Wheelchair access (not WC)   Garden No smoking in dining room   Background music; jukebox   Dogs welcome exc in eating areas   Delta, MasterCard, Switch, Visa   Accommodation: 9 rooms, B&B £25 to £68*

GREAT HAMPDEN   Buckinghamshire   map 3

Hampden Arms

Great Hampden HP16 9RQ   TEL: (01494) 488255
off A4010 or A413, midway between Princes Risborough and Great Missenden

Terry and Barbara Matthews, who have been running the Hampden Arms for over a decade, number intrepid country walkers and cyclists among their clientele. The timber-framed pub has a large garden to the side and rear, and the sort of small-scale interior for which the word 'cosy' might have been coined. Wooden beams abound, and the wall decorations include the expected horse brasses, plus – less conventionally – a couple of old saws. Metal stoves are lit for warmth when the weather is cheerless, and a pint of Brakspear or Adnams will further lift the spirits. Addlestone's cider is also available. The printed and blackboard menus offer a wide range of food between them, with portion sizes to match. Steering a course through them might take you from devilled whitebait to beef stroganoff, or from lobster and prawn cocktail to the cheerily named merry berry duck. There's royal game pie when the season allows, and desserts look like a roll call of all-time favourites, with lemon meringue pie, sticky toffee pudding and apple and sultana crumble all making an appearance. Three wines are sold by the glass, and own-brand house wines are backed up by familiar French names such as Chablis, Muscadet and Fleurie. SAMPLE DISHES: deep-fried Brie £6; pork paprika £13; black cherry pancake £3.50.

Licensees Terry and Barbara Matthews (freehouse)
Open *Tue to Sun 12 to 2.30, 6.30 to 11; bar food 12 to 2, 6.30 to 9.30*
Details *Children welcome   Car park   Garden   No-smoking area   No music Dogs welcome by arrangement   Amex, Delta, Diners, MasterCard, Switch, Visa*

GREAT TEW   Oxfordshire   map 5

▲ *Falkland Arms* 🍺

Great Tew OX7 4DB   TEL: (01608) 683653
WEB SITE: www.banbury-cross.co.uk/falklandarms
off B4022, 5m E of Chipping Norton

The Falkland Arms is a two-storey inn of honey-coloured stone in
the kind of peaceful, timeless village the Cotswold district specialises
in. Viscount Falkland, after whom the inn is named and who once
lived nearby, was secretary of state to Charles I. The centuries-old
interiors have been superbly preserved, with oak settles, bench seating, flagstoned floors and wooden shutters at the windows, and a
varied collection of jugs and vessels hangs overhead. Another great
strength of the place is its commitment to real ales and ciders, with
eight normally on handpump including regulars Henry's Original
IPA, Badger Tanglefoot, Wadworth 6X and Inch's Harvest dry cider,
which are joined by guests ales such as Forest Gold (brewed by Red
Shoot). In addition, there are 14 conventional wines (half of which
are served by the glass), plus 16 traditional English country wines.
The cooking keeps things nice and simple, in harmony with the
surroundings, offering jacket potatoes, baguettes and such one-plate
meals as shepherd's pie or lasagne at lunchtime, and a more extensive daily-changing evening range. That might deliver carrot and
parsnip soup, king prawns in filo with a sweet chilli dip, chicken
breast with bacon and mushrooms in a Stilton cream sauce, or slow-
cooked lamb shank with mash and rosemary and garlic gravy. Finish
with sticky toffee pudding or tarte Tatin. Staff have been described
as friendly and chatty. SAMPLE DISHES: grilled goats'-cheese salad £4;
smoked haddock fishcake on chive butter sauce £7.50; banana and
walnut pancakes with toffee sauce and vanilla ice cream £4.25.

Licensee Paul Barlow-Heal (Wadworth)
Open *Mon to Fri 11.30 to 2.30, 6 to 11, Sat 11.30 to 11 (11.30 to 3, 6 to 11
winter), Sun 12 to 10.30 (12 to 3, 7 to 10.30 winter); bar food 12 to 2;
restaurant Mon to Sat 7 to 8; closed evenings 25 Dec and 1 Jan*
Details *Children welcome in dining room at lunchtime Wheelchair access
(not WC) Garden and patio No smoking in dining room Live music Dogs
welcome exc in dining room Amex, Delta, MasterCard, Switch, Visa
Accommodation: 6 rooms, B&B £40 to £80*

GREAT WHITTINGTON   Northumberland   map 10

Queens Head Inn 🏵 🍺

Great Whittington NE19 2HP   TEL: (01434) 672267
from A68 4m N of Corbridge turn E on B6318 at Stagshaw round-
about, then left to village

Dating from 1615, this pub in an out-of-the-way village overlooks lovely countryside. Although mainly devoted to dining, it stocks Queen's Head, Hambleton and Black Sheep bitters as well as Scrumpy Jack cider and more than 30 malt whiskies. The restaurant is a no-smoking zone, but there are 30 seats in the bar area, where, apart from sandwiches, the alternative to the main menu at lunchtime is a set-price two-course meal (three courses on Sundays). This might take in soup of the day, or pâté, followed by steak and ale pie, Cumberland sausage with Dijon mash, or lamb's liver and onions. The restaurant menu – also available in the bar – applies sophisticated modern ideas to such ingredients as fish from North Shields and local game and meat. Pot-roast guinea fowl comes with roasted vegetables and a sun-dried tomato and basil reduction, and seared salmon fillet is served on new potatoes and leeks with saffron and herb beurre blanc. Vegetarians can choose from vegetable tempura on noodles with sweet-and-sour sauce, baked vegetable gâteau, or mushroom and vegetable bolognese. Evening blackboard specials might include whole Dover sole with prawn and leek ragoût, lamb shank with Dijon mustard mash and provençale sauce, or fillet steak with mushroom and Stilton sabayon. Three wines come by the glass from a list of about 30 with a good range from the New World. SAMPLE DISHES: deep-fried black pudding with beetroot relish £5; pork tenderloin with apple tart and cider and ginger jus £11; duo of chocolate mousse £3.50.

Licensee Ian Scott (freehouse)
Open *Tue to Sat and bank hol Mon 12 to 2.30, 6 to 11, Sun 12 to 3, 7 to 10.30; bar food and restaurant Tue to Sun 12 to 2, 6.30 to 9*
Details *Children welcome in eating areas   Car park   Wheelchair access (also WC)   Garden   No smoking in dining room   Background music   No dogs Delta, MasterCard, Switch, Visa*

GREAT WOLFORD   Warwickshire   map 5

▲ *Fox & Hounds Inn* 🍺

Great Wolford CV36 5NQ   TEL: (01608) 674220
off A44, 3m NE of Moreton-in-Marsh

This honey-coloured Cotswold-stone pub, set in a pretty village of similar buildings, is an especially cosy place in the evening, when candlelight and easy-listening music set the tone. The welcome is warm and the service cheery. Traditional decorative features include a gleaming copper bar counter, dried hops strung along beams, and exposed stone walls. One of the primary attractions is what a reader has described as a 'smashing collection of beers', featuring well-respected names such as Hook Norton, Jennings, Black Sheep and others. There is also a large range of whiskies and a varied wine list, with six by the glass. On the food front, an unchanging printed menu of pub staples is enhanced by a blackboard of daily specials, which might include deep-fried black pudding with Cumberland sauce. As much effort is put into describing dishes as is put into their presentation: one reporter's 'local venison pan-seared and served with a gâteau of creamy dauphinois potatoes, with a tasty red wine, tarragon and sweet onion jus' arrived as slices of accurately cooked and tasty venison draped over a neat stack of potatoes and garnished with deep-fried shredded red cabbage and sprigs of thyme. SAMPLE DISHES: (prices and dessert list not available at time of going to press) smoked salmon cornets filled with prawns; Dover sole; roast shank of lamb.

Licensees Graham and Anne Seddon (freehouse)
Open *Tue to Sat 12 to 3, 7 to 11, Sun 12 to 3; bar food and restaurant Tue to Sat 12 to 2, 7 to 9.30, Sun 12 to 2.30*
Details *Children welcome in bar eating area   Car park   Wheelchair access (also WC)   Patio   No smoking in dining room   Background music   Dogs welcome   No cards   Accommodation: 4 rooms, room only £45*

GREAT YELDHAM   Essex   **map 6**

White Hart 🍷🍷 🍇

Poole Street, Great Yeldham CO9 4HJ   TEL: (01787) 237250
on A604 between Haverhill and Halstead, 6m NW of Halstead

No longer part of the Huntsbridge group (see Three Horseshoes, Madingley; Pheasant Inn, Keyston; and Old Bridge, Huntingdon), the White Hart has been taken over by John and Maria Dicken, who also own a highly rated restaurant in nearby Wethersfield. Their wealth of experience has ensured that this half-timbered Tudor pub has retained the high standards that have earned the place its reputation. Indeed, the flexible format has changed little under the Dickens' ownership, with the same menus whether you choose to eat in the bar or garden or the slightly more formal dining room. The 'light menu' goes in for snacky dishes like mozzarella, plum tomato and salami sandwich, or Thai chicken curry with cardamom rice. The full lunch menu might open with carrot and coriander soup, followed by duck and potato pie, or a simple dish of pasta with pesto. In the evening, the menu extends to around a dozen choices at each course. A number of dishes have a traditional feel – pan-fried sirloin steak with roasted new potatoes, calabrese and borde-laise sauce, for instance – while others are the result of distinctly modern ideas, as in roasted cod wrapped in pancetta with split-pea purée and a mint and mustard dressing. Although this is definitely a food pub, more than a token nod is given to beers. The house beer, Adnams Best Bitter, is joined by two regularly changing guests; there are also imported lagers, cider from Weston's, and a range of organic Suffolk fruit juices. The wine list is not the most pocket-friendly, but will satisfy anyone in pursuit of fine or unusual wine. At least nine wines are available by the glass, kicking off at £1.95, and the rest of the list is clearly divided into style categories, so whether you're looking for Latour, Puligny-Montrachet, or a simple, fruity Côte de Brouilly, you'll have no trouble finding them. SAMPLE DISHES: roasted pepper and Parmesan risotto £3.75; filet mignon of lamb on sauté salsify, button onions and bacon with dauphinois potatoes £13.75; baked apple and mincemeat tart with crème anglaise £4.50.

Licensees John and Maria Dicken (freehouse)
Open *11 to 3, 6 to 11, Sun and bank hols 12 to 3, 7 to 10.30; bar food and restaurant 12 to 2, 7 to 9.30*
Details *Children welcome   Car park   Wheelchair access (also WC)   Garden and patio   No smoking in dining room   No music   No dogs   Amex, Delta, Diners, MasterCard, Switch, Visa*

GRETA BRIDGE   Co Durham   map 10

▲ *Morritt Arms* 🍇
Greta Bridge DL12 9SE   TEL: (01833) 627232
off A66, 6m E of Bowes

A highly civilised stone-built coaching inn with a good bar, comfort-able beamed lounges and an elegant dining room, the Morritt stands by an old stone bridge and the entrance to Rokeby Park. Barnard Castle and Egglestone Abbey are nearby too, and the surrounding countryside is particularly fine, so there are reasons enough for a visit here. One Charles Dickens did just that in the 1830s while he was writing *Nicholas Nickleby*. Menus offer an interesting mix: 'towered seafood' turns out to be smoked trout, gravad lax and prawns on a tomato and saffron infusion, while salmon fishcakes are flavoured with basil and served with a sweet pepper coulis. Move on to seared strips of pork fillet on a cake of pineapple risotto, or peppered monkfish on wild mushroom rösti, before concluding with something such as almond and walnut tart with cappuccino ice cream, or a cheese selection. Real ales come in the form of Timothy Taylor Landlord, Theakston Cool Cask, Black Sheep and Tetley, and around 20 wines are available by the glass from an extensive list that is helpfully organised by grape and then country or region. Although only part of the list was available to the Guide before we went to press, it indicated that most tastes and pockets were well catered for. SAMPLE DISHES: smoked chicken Caesar salad £4.50; grilled sea bass on roast fennel mash with garlic and tomato coulis £10; sticky toffee pudding with toffee sauce £3.25.

Licensee Barbara Anne Johnson (freehouse)
Open *11 to 11, Sun 12 to 10.30; bar food and restaurant 11.30 to 2.30, 6 to 9.30*
Details *Children welcome   Car park   Wheelchair access (not WC)   Garden No smoking in dining room   Occasional background music   Dogs welcome Amex, Delta, Diners, MasterCard, Switch, Visa   Accommodation: 23 rooms, B&B £59.50 to £99.50*

GRIMSTHORPE   Lincolnshire   map 6

▲ *Black Horse Inn* 🍇

Grimsthorpe PE10 0LY   TEL: (01778) 591247
on A151, between A1 and A15, 4m NW of Bourne

In a small rural village in an attractive part of Lincolnshire, this old stone building dating from 1717 puts on a pretty face in summer with flower-filled hanging baskets. Enter the chintzy reception bar, where you will find big sofas and assorted books and games. Beyond it are two dining areas, which have the air of a well-established pub, where polished wooden tables are adorned with fresh flowers. Hands-on owners – Elaine is host, Brian runs the kitchen – guarantee a friendly atmosphere and good service, and the food is considered good value. An ambitious menu offers plenty of choice, starters ranging from chicken liver parfait with onion marmalade to risotto of spring onions, mascarpone and Parmesan, and main courses typically including Grassmere Farm Lincolnshire sausages with mash and shallot gravy, and roast salmon with noodles and a tomato and herb vinaigrette. These are supplemented by additional daily dishes, such as wild mallard with Puy lentils, spinach and red wine sauce, or red snapper fillet with tomato concassé and coriander cream sauce. The house beers are Black Horse Bitter and Grimsthorpe Bitter, brewed for the pub by the Oldershaw Brewery in Grantham. A very impressive, 180-strong wine list offers 12 by the glass, a page of half-bottles, and another of bin ends to boot. Bins are listed by style, from light, fruity whites to robust fruity reds, with classic clarets in between, and most purses and palates are catered for. Guest accom-

modation has been described as 'delightfully old worldy'. SAMPLE
DISHES: warm salad of crispy duck leg with red wine vinaigrette
£4.25; grilled calf's liver with shallot tarte Tatin, bacon and sage
£11; apple crumble with vanilla ice cream £4.

Licensees Brian and Elaine Rey (freehouse)
Open *11.30 to 2.30, 6.30 to 11, Sun 12 to 3, 7 to 10.30; bar food 12 to 2, 7
to 9.30; restaurant Tue to Sun (exc Sun evening) 12 to 2, 7 to 9.30*
Details *Children welcome   Car park   Garden and patio   No smoking in
dining room   Occasional background music   Dogs welcome in bar   Amex,
Delta, Diners, MasterCard, Switch, Visa   Accommodation: 6 rooms, B&B £45
to £95*

GUNWALLOE   Cornwall   **map 1**

▲ *Halzephron Inn*

Gunwalloe TR12 7QB   TEL: (01326) 240406
from A3083 4m S of Helston take small lane towards Church Cove

---

Located close to dramatic clifftops, this pub has its own smugglers'
tunnel leading to the beach. The weather can be dramatic, too, but
when waves are not breaking over the rocks there are great views of
the coast. Inside, the atmosphere is relaxed and cosy in the bar and
three dining areas, and children are welcome in the family room,
complete with play area. The menu is the same in all parts, but the
evening carte is longer than the one at lunchtime, which also offers
sandwiches. A list of daily specials complements the simpler dishes,
an unusual blackboard item being pancakes of the day. Evening
special starters might include bouillabaisse with garlic bread, or
seared scallops on olive polenta with tomato and white wine sauce,
and among main dishes might be lamb, lemon and honey tagine with
apricot and almond couscous, or guinea fowl on carrot and caraway
mash with bacon. All desserts, from summer pudding to lemon and
lime mousse, are home made. Real ales are Sharp's Cornish Coaster,
Doom Bar Bitter and Own; and six wines are served by the glass.
SAMPLE DISHES: grilled goats' cheese on garlic bread with salad £4.50;
grilled fillet of John Dory on seafood risotto £13.50; caramel walnut
brownie pie £3.50.

Licensee Angela Thomas (freehouse)
Open *11 to 2.30, 6 (6.30 winter) to 11 (10.30 Sun); bar food and restaurant
12 to 2, 7 to 9; closed 25 Dec*
Details *Children welcome in family room   Car park   Wheelchair access (not
WC)   Garden and patio   No smoking in dining room   Occasional live music
No dogs   Amex, Delta, MasterCard, Switch, Visa   Accommodation: 2 rooms,
B&B £38 to £68*

HAILEY   Oxfordshire   **map 5**

▲ *Bird in Hand* 🍇

Hailey OX8 5XP   TEL: (01993) 868321
WEB SITE: www.oxfordpages.co.uk/birdinhand
on B4022 Charlbury to Witney road; turn right ½m after Hailey
village

This is a bird that has enlarged its nest, judging by the evidence of
extension work that has gone on over the years to this big, well-run
Cotswold-stone pub. Outside it all looks trim and neat, the car park
with its orderly rosebeds dividing the sections 'a positive work of
art', according to a reporter. Inside, four heavily beamed rooms
comprise the area for bar eating, one of which contains a huge
inglenook fireplace, and there is also a separate restaurant. Diners
have both blackboards and printed menus to choose from. The
former might include dishes such as smoked salmon and mackerel
roulade on black olive salad, followed in the appropriate season by
roast red-leg partridge with herb rösti and wild mushroom gravy,
while the latter might offer pork tenderloin with black pudding
mousse and apple, sage and cider cream, or chicken breast stuffed
with pine nuts and sun-dried tomatoes. Light-bite baguettes and
sandwiches are also available. On tap are Old Speckled Hen,
Wadworth 6X, Fuller's London Pride, Flowers and Boddingtons,
and over 40 well-chosen wines are listed, with a dozen – including a
Monbazillac – sold by the glass. SAMPLE DISHES: melon and Parma
ham with apple, thyme and calvados jelly and fruit coulis £5.25;
fillet of plaice stuffed with salmon mousse on citrus and pink
peppercorn sauce £10; chocolate délice £3.50.

Licensee Chris Williams (Heavitree Inns)
Open *11 to 11, Sun 12 to 3, 7 to 10.30; bar food and restaurant 12 to 2, 7*
to 9.30, Sun 12 to 2, 7.15 to 9.15; closes 3pm 25 Dec
Details *Children welcome in bar eating area   Car park   Wheelchair access*
(also WC)   Garden and patio   No smoking in dining room   Background
music   Dogs welcome   Delta, Diners, MasterCard, Switch, Visa
Accommodation: 16 rooms, B&B £49.50 to £58

Halfway Bridge Inn 🍺

Halfway Bridge GU28 9BP   TEL: (01798) 861281
WEB SITE: www.thesussexpub.co.uk
*on A272, midway between Midhurst and Petworth, just S of
Lodsworth*

The first part of the name of this family-run pub probably relates to
its position between Midhurst and Petworth, but what the second
part refers to is anyone's guess. Whatever the explanation, the pub
itself is a charming sprawl of differently aged buildings, with an
attractive garden. In addition, eight letting rooms were planned to be
ready by spring 2001. Real fires throughout the several small rooms
provide plenty of warmth inside, and masses of dried hops adorn the
walls and low ceilings, with horsey pictures and various other bits of
bric-à-brac in between. Food is considered excellent value and well
above normal pub standards. A monthly-changing menu is supplemented by daily specials. At lunchtime, open sandwiches and lighter
meals are available, and main courses are things like Cumberland
sausage with grain mustard mash and onion gravy, or pheasant
breast wrapped in bacon with a wild mushroom and red wine sauce.
In the evening, snacks are dropped and the list of main courses is
longer, but otherwise the style is similar. Well-kept Gale's HSB,
Fuller's London Pride and Cheriton Pots Ale are the regular real ales;
weekly-changing seasonal guests come from local breweries such as
Harveys, Brewery on Sea and Hogs Back, and locally produced
méthode champenoise Gospel Green Cyder is also stocked. Seven
wines are sold by the glass. SAMPLE DISHES: crab and avocado salad
with lemon and dill dressing £5.50; roast half-shoulder of lamb with
roast potatoes £10.50; chocolate and orange baked cheesecake
£3.50.

Licensees Edric and Sheila Hawkins (freehouse)
Open *11 to 3, 6 to 11, Sun 12 to 3, 7 to 10.30; bar food and restaurant 12
to 2 (2.30 Sat and Sun), 7 to 10; closed Sun evening winter*
Details *No children   Car park   Garden and patio   No smoking in dining
room   Occasional live music   Dogs welcome in bar   Delta, MasterCard,
Switch, Visa*

---

*After the main section of the Guide is the special 'Out and about'
section listing additional pubs that are well worth a visit. Reports on
these entries are most welcome.*

HAMBLEDEN   Buckinghamshire   map 3

▲ *Stag & Huntsman Inn*

Hambleden RG9 6RP   TEL: (01491) 571227
off A4155 Henley to Marlow road, 1m from Mill End

The picturesque village of Hambleden, with its flint and brick
cottages and beautiful church, is a heavenly setting for an old-fashioned country pub. That is exactly what the Stag & Huntsman is,
with its cosy atmosphere and many nooks and crannies, though it is
from the smart end of the pub spectrum, rather than the rustic, with
an attractive red and green themed décor in the dining room. One
menu serves all three bar areas. The range covers starters/light meals,
such as aubergine, beef tomato and goats' -cheese tower, or Parma
ham salad, variations on the ploughman's theme, and a long list of
main-course options that take in salmon fishcakes, marinated chargrilled chicken, steaks with various sauces, and spinach and mushroom enchilada for vegetarians. A barbecue operates in the large beer
garden in summer. Regular beers are Brakspear Bitter and Wadworth
6X, and cider drinkers are offered Thatcher's and Stowford Press.
Just over a dozen wines are available, with a pair of house selections
at £9.25. SAMPLE DISHES: dressed crab with salad and lime mayonnaise £6.25; grilled lamb chops provençale £10; chocolate torte with
raspberry coulis £3.25.

Licensee Andrew Stokes (freehouse)
Open *11 to 2.30 (3 Sat), 6 to 11, Sun 12 to 3, 7 to 10.30; bar food (exc Sun
evening) 12 to 2, 7 to 9.30; closed 25 Dec*
Details *Children welcome in bar eating area   Car park   Garden   Background
music   No dogs   Delta, MasterCard, Switch, Visa   Accommodation: 3 rooms,
B&B £58 to £68*

HAMBLETON   Rutland   map 6

▲ *Finch's Arms*

Oakham Road, Upper Hambleton LE15 8TL   TEL: (01572) 756575
off A606, E of Oakham

This pub stands on a peninsula plunging into Rutland Water, but its
menu dives into the Mediterranean for inspiration. Warm
provençale tart with pesto-scented mayonnaise on watercress salad
makes a light snack or starter, perhaps followed by bouillabaisse, or
wild mushroom risotto with Parmesan in a Savoy cabbage crêpe with
plum tomato and basil sauce. Far Eastern notions take in pan-fried
spiced belly pork on sauté spinach, bean sprouts, and shiitake mushrooms with an oriental sauce vierge. For eclecticism in a single dish

it's hard to beat confit shoulder of lamb on haggis mashed potato in a cherry tomato and olive jus topped with Parma ham. Simpler tastes might choose the trio of home-made savoury sorbets – gin and tonic, black Russian vodka and Red Bull. Dessert confections include coffee and praline roulade on mocha sauce with hazelnut crunch and mascarpone, or warm banana and toffee tartlet with lime ice cream. Can't decide? Choose Finch's plate for two, a taste of all six desserts. Although a serious dining pub, it stocks Greene King Abbott Ale, Marston's Pedigree, Timothy Taylor Landlord and Black Sheep Best Bitter, while five wines are sold by the glass. SAMPLE DISHES: roast pigeon breast with bubble and squeak £4.50; cassoulet of mussels £8.50; Pimm's jelly with mascarpone and sauté fruit £4.

Licensees Colin and Celia Crawford (freehouse)
Open *11 to 11, Sun 12 to 10.30; bar food and restaurant 12 to 2.30, 7 to 9.30, Sun 12 to 3, 7 to 9*
Details *Children welcome   Car park   Garden   No smoking in dining room Occasional live or background music   No dogs   Delta, MasterCard, Switch, Visa   Accommodation: 6 rooms, B&B £55 to £70*

HAMSTEAD MARSHALL   Berkshire   map 2

▲ *White Hart*

Kintbury Road, Hamstead Marshall RG20 0HW
TEL: (01488) 658201
off A4, 4½m W of Newbury

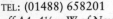

This sixteenth-century coaching inn is a corner of an English village that will be for ever Italy, for Nicola Aromando, who runs the pub with his wife Dorothy, has brought the cooking of his homeland to this otherwise quintessentially English part of the world. Though spaghetti bolognese and lasagne are available on the printed menu, blackboard specials take in many more interesting options: coniglio al forno (herb-stuffed rabbit braised in wine with lemon and black olives), fritelle (organic meatballs stuffed with mozzarella in a red wine sauce), or spaghetti frutti di mare (with seafood in a tomato and chilli sauce). This is all served in the relaxed setting of the bar, where logs burn in the central brick fireplace on cold days, and restaurant. The beautiful garden provides many of the herbs used in the kitchen, and the organic beef comes from a farm just across the road. House wines, at £11.50, are, as may be expected, Italian, while beers are Wadworth 6X and Hardy Country Bitter. Spirits drinkers might like to try the Juniper Green organic gin and Nutkins organic vodka. SAMPLE DISHES: insalata of mozzarella, tomato and basil £4.50; stincotto (braised lamb shank with rosemary gravy) £12.50; blackcurrant crème brûlée £4.50.

Licensee Nicola Aromando (freehouse)
Open *12 to 2.30, 6 to 11; bar food and restaurant 12 to 2, 6 to 9.30; closed*
2 weeks summer
Details *Children welcome in eating areas   Car park   Wheelchair access (not*
WC)   Garden   No smoking in dining room   Background music   No dogs
MasterCard, Visa   Accommodation: 6 rooms, B&B £60 to £90

HAROME   North Yorkshire

map 9

Star Inn ✿✿ ❦

Harome YO62 5JE   TEL: (01439) 770397
WEB SITE: www.yorkshireholidays.com/thestarinn.htm
off A170, 3m SE of Helmsley

The Star is an endearingly lopsided, part-thatched, whitewashed
building of some character set in a charming, diminutive village way
off the beaten track. Good cheer prevails within, as does some seriously accomplished cooking, which can be enjoyed in the restaurant,
with its bare wooden tables and spindle-backed chairs, or in the main
bar. (Note that bookings are not taken in the bar, but are advisable
for the restaurant.) Coming in for praise have been dishes such as
grilled goats' cheese on a croûton with beetroot pesto, pan-fried
venison with raisin sauce, and date and suet pudding with Yorkshire
curd ice cream and miniature raspberries. Dressed crab is the real
thing, and interesting ways with fish have included turbot on truffled
mash with wild mushrooms and a wine-based sauce. Market fish and
other specialities are chalked up on a board, and the handwritten
menus include such luxuries as medallions of beef fillet with foie gras
butter, chunky chips and a Yorkshire Blue salad. For those who still
have room there's chocolate indulgence, highly commended lemon
tart, or maybe steamed sticky ale cake with Theakston ice cream and
muscovado sauce. Real beers include Black Sheep Special, Theakston
Best, John Smith's Cask Bitter plus a local brew from Captain Cook,
as well as a few fine bottled ciders and Somerset cider brandy. It is
on wine, however, that most attention has been lavished, with a list
that wouldn't look out of place at an up-market restaurant. France is
well served, but the New World selections are imaginative, too, and
no fewer than ten bottles are available by the glass. SAMPLE DISHES:
grilled black pudding with pan-fried foie gras, apple and vanilla
chutney £9; braised lamb shank with root vegetables, parsnip purée,
rosemary and pearl barley £12; baked ginger parkin with rhubarb
ripple ice cream and hot spiced syrup £4.50.

Licensee Jacquie Pern (freehouse)
Open *Tue to Sat 11.30 to 3, 6 (6.30 winter) to 11, Sun 12 to 10.30; bar food*
and restaurant Tue to Sat 11.30 to 2, 6.15 to 9.30 (10 summer and Sat if
required), Sun 12 to 6; closed 1 week Nov, 25 Dec, 3 weeks Jan, bank hols

Details *Children welcome   Car park   Garden   No smoking in dining room*
Occasional live or background music   No dogs   Delta, MasterCard, Switch,
Visa

HASELBURY PLUCKNETT   Somerset   map 2

Haselbury Inn 🍇

North Street, Haselbury Plucknett TA18 7RJ   TEL: (01460) 72488
off A30, 2m NE of Crewkerne

This extended village inn was in an earlier incarnation a factory
where sail and rope makers used locally grown flax in their wares.
Now, in the words of owner Pat Howard, it is a 'food-orientated
freehouse', but it remains none the less a local. The atmosphere is
warm and welcoming, with a good dining ambience, and the old-
fashioned comforts extend to the beamed and carpeted bar. The
restaurant menu, also available in the bar (but not vice versa), is
characterised by traditional dishes with a modern twist, such as
melon filled with plum sorbet, or a filo tartlet of leeks in a creamy
sauce studded with chunks of freshly poached salmon. To follow
might be baked chicken rolled in coconut on a pool of mango and
white wine sauce, or wholly traditional mixed grill and steaks,
including that old favourite, steak Diane. Vegetarian dishes appear
on the daily specials blackboard, while bar snacks are of the
omelette, ploughman's and baguettes variety. Draught ales are
Marston's Pedigree, Wells Bombardier Premium Bitter, Ringwood
True Glory, and Otter Ale, with König Pils also on draught. Of the
60 or so wines available, 12 full and fruity ones are offered by the
small or large glass (by the bottle they're all under £12), while the
main range makes more than a passing nod at classic France. The list
is carefully laid out by style, and there are good tasting notes to help
guide choice. SAMPLE DISHES: smoked chicken baguette £5; sauté
lambs' liver with bacon, onions and mushrooms on mash £8; apple
and cinnamon slice £3.50.

Licensee Pat Howard (freehouse)
Open *Tue to Sat 11.30 to 2, 6.30 to 11, Sun 12 to 2, 6.30 to 10.30; bar food
and restaurant 11.45 (12 Sun) to 2, 6.30 to 9.30*
Details *Children welcome   Car park   Wheelchair access (also WC)   Garden
and patio   No smoking in dining room   Background music   No dogs   Amex,
Delta, Diners, MasterCard, Switch, Visa*

---

*Report forms are at the back of the book; write a letter if you prefer,
or email your pub report to whichcountrypubs@which.net.*

HASSOP   Derbyshire   map 9

Eyre Arms

Hassop DE45 1NS   TEL: (01629) 640390
on B6001, 2m N of Bakewell

According to a reader, 'there's a kind of glow' at this neat little
stone-built pub covered in Virginia creeper. Its back windows overlook an attractive garden with tables, and the location makes it a
good place from which to explore the southern Peak District. There
is no restaurant, but the long bar menu takes in main dishes such as
chicken Hartington – breast stuffed with leeks and Stilton – while an
Indian influence appears in medium-spiced lamb cooked with
coconut and black pepper. Fish, home-made pies, steaks and pasta
are other headings on the menu, and there are six interesting options
for vegetarians, including mushroom stroganoff, a mixture of button,
chestnut and oyster varieties cooked in cream sauce. Blackboard
specials point up more interest: coming in for praise have been
parsnip and pear soup followed by braised pheasant with Madeira
sauce. Even popular dishes such as scampi and chips are properly
cooked and attractively presented. Sandwiches, ploughman's and
jacket potatoes are also available at lunchtime, and puddings include
Derbyshire pie – apple, mincemeat and cranberries. On handpump
are Black Sheep Special Ale, Marston's Pedigree, and John Smith
Cask Bitter, and four wines are sold by the glass. SAMPLE DISHES:
sliced duck breast with mango £4; grilled Barnsley lamb chops with
redcurrant jelly £8; Bakewell pudding £2.75.

Licensee Lynne Smith (freehouse)
Open *11 to 3, 6.30 (7 winter) to 11; bar food 12 to 2, 6.30 (7 winter) to 9*
Details *Children welcome in bar eating area   Car park   Wheelchair access
(also WC)   Garden   No-smoking area in bar   Occasional background music
No dogs   Delta, MasterCard, Switch, Visa*

HAWKLEY   Hampshire   map 2

Hawkley Inn 🍺

Pococks Lane, Hawkley GU33 6NE   TEL: (01730) 827205
off A3, 2½m N of Petersfield

There's no restaurant here, just the simply furnished bar, and a pleasant garden with some tables. In a still-unspoilt corner of rural
Hampshire, the Hawkley is a friendly village local where very good
beers and unpretentious freshly prepared food are a draw. Beers
change frequently, and might be supplied by Ballard's, RCH, Itchen

Valley, Kitchen, Otter, Tisbury and Triple fff – and for cider drinkers there's the landlord's own Swamp Donkey. The very short wine list is entirely drawn from the New World, with four by the glass. Home-made vegetable soup, lasagne, and spinach, bacon and leek flan have been among dishes praised by reporters, or you might choose Stilton and mushroom soup, peppered chicken, or spinach and ricotta tart, plus for dessert treacle tart or lemon syllabub. SAMPLE DISHES: sausage ploughman's £6; ham and leek pancakes £8; mulled peaches £3.50.

Licensee Mrs E. Collins (freehouse)
Open *12 to 2.30, 6 to 11, Sun 12 to 3, 7 to 10.30; bar food 12 to 2, 7 to 9.30, Sun 12 to 2*
Details *Children welcome lunchtime and before 8pm   Wheelchair access (not WC)   Garden and patio   No-smoking area in bar   Live or background music   Dogs welcome   MasterCard, Visa*

HAWKSHEAD   Cumbria   map 8

▲ *Queen's Head Hotel*

Main Street, Hawkshead LA22 0NS   TEL: (015394) 36271
WEB SITE: www.queensheadhotel.co.uk
on B5285, 4m S of Ambleside

Rough black beams cross the low ceilings, walls and bar counters are handsomely panelled, pictures and decorative brass and china are well chosen to make the bar and separate restaurant attractive and worthy of the solid black and white exterior. Menus are interchangeable between restaurant and bar, so you can order main courses as traditional as Westmorland pie or as exotic as Thai chicken curry. Note the Herdwick lamb specials, from grilled leg steak studded with garlic and herbs, through roast shank on leek and tarragon cream, to shoulder baked with rosemary. Lunchtime bar snacks range from baguettes, salads or filled baked potatoes, and a full menu is also available: perhaps crab and salmon fritters, or pressed duck and apple terrine, followed by sauté mussels, or lambs' liver and onions. Intriguing vegetarian options include asparagus and root vegetables in filo, or a tortilla basket of tomato and basil filled with roasted vegetables dressed with red pepper sauce. A Robinson's pub, the Queen's Head stocks the brewery's Frederics and Hartleys XB, plus a guest. Four wines are sold by the glass, eight by the quarter-bottle, and there are thirty whiskies too. SAMPLE DISHES: fell-bred lamb toastie £4.50; Cumberland sausage with creamed potatoes and onion gravy £5.75; double chocolate charlotte russe £3.75.

Licensee Anthony Merrick (Robinson's)
Open *11 to 11, Sun 12 to 10.30; bar food and restaurant 12 to 2.30 (5 Sun), 6.15 to 9.30*

Details *Children welcome in family and dining rooms   Wheelchair access (also WC)   Patio   No smoking in family and dining rooms   Background music   No dogs   Delta, MasterCard, Switch, Visa   Accommodation: 13 rooms, B&B £42 to £84*

HAYDON BRIDGE   Northumberland   map 10

General Havelock Inn ❀

9 Ratcliffe Road, Haydon Bridge NE47 6ER   TEL: (01434) 684376
WEB SITE: www.haydonbridge.org
on A69, 8m W of Hexham, 100yds from junction with B6319

This roadside inn has had a change of owners since the last edition, and is now under the stewardship of Gary Thompson, 'clearly a high-class professional chef' according to one satisfied diner. He is helped with the running of the place by his wife Joanna and his mother. As might be expected, the emphasis is on the restaurant part of the operation, which has bare stone walls and a décor of pink and floral fabrics. Here the fixed-price menu might offer crab cakes with ginger dressing, pork wrapped in bacon with black pudding and caramelised apple, plus a daily fish special. But if you are after something less formal, the bar menu goes in for homely dishes such as beef and Guinness stew with wild mushrooms, Cumberland sausage with champ and onion gravy, or pasta with tomato sauce, pesto and Parmesan. Apple and cinnamon pie, or fresh fruit jelly terrine might be among desserts. Two real ales are served at all times, perhaps Timothy Taylor Landlord and Adnams Broadside, while nine each of red and white wines are offered, four of which are available by the glass. SAMPLE DISHES: large bowl of Cullen skink £3.50; chicken, leek and Cheddar pie £5.75; prune and almond tart £4.50.

Licensee Gary Thompson (freehouse)
Open *Tue to Sat 12 to 2.30, 7 to 11, Sun 12 to 2.30; bar food and restaurant Tue to Sun 12 to 2, Tue to Sat 7 to 9*
Details *Children welcome in bar eating area   Wheelchair access (also WC) Garden   No smoking in dining room   Occasional live music   Dogs welcome Delta, Switch, Visa*

HAYFIELD　　Derbyshire　　　　　　　map 8

▲ *Sportsman*

Kinder Road, Hayfield SK22 2LE　　TEL: (01663) 741565
on A624 Glossop to Chapel-en-le-Frith road

Kinder Scout and the moors can offer a cool reception to walkers, who will none the less find a warm welcome at this stone-built pub. Beer drinkers will be attracted by three handpumped ales from Thwaites: Best Bitter and Daniel's Hammer, plus a third that changes from time to time. A log fire adds to the comfort of wooden chairs and settles, and a small wall-mounted armoury deters wild game from entering. Its atmosphere is as relaxed as the service, which is efficient too, and although this is definitely an eating pub, there is no separate restaurant. Bar food is the thing, ranging from assorted baguettes and club sandwiches, to ploughman's, warm asparagus tart, steaks, and grills, including a grilled bulgur wheat rissole with courgette fritters and a fried egg. Daily special starters are as reassuringly familiar as black pudding with mustard sauce, or chicken and brandy pâté. More inventive main dishes might be lamb and pumpkin casserole, Seville chicken, and aubergine agrodolce. Bakewell tart, or boozy coconut ice cream might be among puddings. Two wines are available by the glass. SAMPLE DISHES: peppered mackerel with horseradish cream £3.25; beef chasseur £8.75; hot chocolate fudge cake £3.25.

Licensee John Dunbar (Daniel Thwaites)
Open *all week (exc Mon lunchtime) 12 to 3, 7 to 11 (10.30 Sun); bar food (exc Sun evening) 12 to 2, 7 to 9; closed 1 week Apr, 1 week Oct, 25 Dec*
Details *Children welcome　Wheelchair access (not WC)　Garden　No music Dogs welcome　Amex, Delta, MasterCard, Switch, Visa　Accommodation: 7 rooms, B&B £30 to £50*

HAYTOR VALE　　Devon　　　　　　map 1

▲ *Rock Inn*

Haytor Vale TQ13 9XP　　TEL: (01364) 661305
WEB SITE: www.rock-inn.co.uk
turn off A38 at Bovey Tracey on to A382; after 2m join B3387 to Haytor, then left at phone box

No connection with the Blackpool variety, still less with popular music, this rock is named after the granite outcrops in this distinctive area on the edge of Dartmoor. Traces of the pub's past as a coaching inn are few, but open fireplaces have survived modernisations. Printed menus are supplemented by blackboard specials, which might include crispy duck salad with mango dressing, or ostrich fillet with fig and red wine sauce. Starters on the printed menu could be pan-fried scallops with tomato, lemon and parsley vinaigrette, or duck and orange pâté with Cumberland sauce, while the list of main dishes is long and ambitious. Chargrilled steaks, steak and kidney suet pudding, and braised wild boar represent one aspect of the chef's style. The other side is evidenced in beef or chicken curries, and vegetarian roasted red pepper and spinach lasagne with mustard cheese sauce. The same breadth of styles shows in desserts, ranging from steamed lemon syrup sponge with custard, or blueberry Bakewell tart, to the 'famous cappuccino cup and saucer' of biscuit, chocolate mousse, almond cream and vanilla sauce. Dartmoor Best is the real ale stocked, and while the list of usefully described wines is conventional and not especially cheap there are ten by the glass. SAMPLE DISHES: goats' cheese in filo pastry £6; Dartmoor rabbit in mustard sauce £8; treacle and walnut tart with clotted cream £3.75.

Licensee Christopher Graves (freehouse)
Open *11 to 11 (10.30 winter); bar food and restaurant 11 to 2.30, 6.30 to 9.30; closed 25 Dec*
Details *Children welcome in family room   Wheelchair access (not WC) Garden   No smoking in dining room   No music   No dogs   Amex, Delta, Diners, MasterCard, Switch, Visa   Accommodation: 9 rooms, B&B £50.50 to £95*

HECKINGTON   Lincolnshire   map 6

▲ *Nags Head*

34 High Street, Heckington NG34 9QZ   TEL: (01529) 460218
off A17, 5m E of Sleaford

This charming, unpretentious country pub, with outdoor tables, is just beside the village green. Inside, the pub is cosy and welcoming, with two rooms knocked through and connected by an archway. Printed leather-bound menus are supplemented by blackboard specials with the occasional drop-dead bargain, such as a Sunday roast lunch for £3.50, worth looking out for. Traditional pub food is the name of the game, so expect garlic mushrooms, or pears and Stilton on toast, followed by steak and Guinness pie, or plaice stuffed with mushrooms in a white wine sauce, and finishing with sticky toffee pudding, or lemon meringue pie. Everything, including the puddings, is made on the premises. Tetley and Bass draught beers are available, as are a trio of wines by the glass. SAMPLE DISHES: mussels in white wine sauce £4; knuckle of lamb in port sauce £6; apple pie £3.

Licensees John and Teresa Clark (Pubmasters)
Open *11 to 11 (10.30 Sun); bar food and restaurant 12 to 2, 7 to 9*
Details *Children welcome   Car park   Garden and patio   No smoking in
dining room   Live or background music; jukebox   No dogs   Delta,
MasterCard, Switch, Visa   Accommodation: 3 rooms, B&B £20 to £45*

HEDLEY ON THE HILL   Northumberland   map 10

Feathers Inn

Hedley on the Hill NE43 7SW   TEL: (01661) 843607
*from New Ridley, signposted from B6309 N of Consett, follow sign
for Hedley on the Hill*

On the hill the village certainly is, with magnificent views extending
to the sea – and this solid, stone built pub with its inviting red door
is right in the middle of the village. In the small bars (there is no
restaurant) log fires burn brightly in winter, creating a welcoming
and comfortable atmosphere. The blackboard menu, which changes
twice a week, always includes vegetarian dishes including one for
vegans. Among tempting starters might be spiced root vegetable
soup, and smoked duck salad with cranberry sauce, which a reader
found 'simple and tasty'. The same feeling applied to honey-glazed
home-baked ham, venison sausage with red onion and port sauce,
and keema lamb tortilla. Desserts that have drawn praise have
included sticky toffee pudding with home-made vanilla ice cream,
and chocolate brandy praline brûlée, and those preferring to end
things on a savoury note could opt for 'excellent' Stilton, port and
walnut pâté with home-made oatcakes and chutney. Regular ales are
Boddingtons Bitter and, from the local Mordue Brewery, Workie
Ticket, which are joined by frequently changing guests from other
local breweries – perhaps Big Lamp Bitter, Northumberland Castles
Bitter, or beers from the Kitchen or Harviestown Breweries. Two
wines by the glass are available from a short wine list. SAMPLE DISHES:
crab and ginger pot £4; Mexican bean cakes with salsa £5.75; fig,
honey and almond tart £3.

Licensee Marina Atkinson (freehouse)
Open *Mon to Fri 6 to 11, Sat 12 to 3, 6 to 11, Sun 12 to 3, 7 to 10.30; bar
food (exc Mon evening) 12 to 2.30, 7 to 9; open bank hol lunchtime; closed
25 Dec*
Details *Children welcome in family and games rooms   Car park   Wheelchair
access (not WC)   No music   Dogs welcome   No cards*

---

*Food mentioned in the entries is available in the bar, although it may
be possible to eat in a dining room.*

HESKET NEWMARKET   Cumbria   map 10

Old Crown 🍺 NEW ENTRY   CURRIES

Hesket Newmarket CA7 8JG   TEL: (016974) 78288
from M6 junction 41 take B5305 toward Wigton; Hesket Newmarket
signposted

This converted row of stone cottages offers self-catering accommodation billed as 'the cottage with *en suite* pub', which just about sums
up its quirky sense of humour and independent spirit. The Old
Crown is a haven for walkers and cyclists, who come to these parts
for the fells. Indeed, the fells provide most of the names of the fine
real ales brewed in the Hesket Newmarket Brewery, which is housed
in a converted barn at the rear of the pub and is owned and run by a
local co-operative. The full range, including seasonal brews, can be
sampled in the tiny bar, along with what a reader called 'great-value
food'. At lunchtime a list of sandwiches is offered along with
chicken, pheasant and apricot pie; venison pâté; and Cumberland
sausages with egg and chips. In the evening the menu focuses on
curries: beef vindaloo, lamb dhansak and chicken muglai are typical.
'Other dishes' is the menu's heading for more traditional casseroles
and stews. Home-made puddings, such as blackcurrant and apple
crumble, are also on sale at the Fellside Stores in the village. Note
that the dining capacity is very small, so booking is essential. Wines
are a varied international bunch, the majority under £10. SAMPLE
DISHES: tomato and tarragon soup £2; Cumbrian lamb casserole
£5.75; gooseberry and macaroon tart £2.

Licensees Kim and Lyn Matthews (freehouse)
Open *Mon 5.30 to 11, Tue to Sat 12 to 3, 5.30 to 11, Sun 12 to 3, 7 to*
10.30; bar food and restaurant Tue to Sun (exc Sun evening) 12 to 2, 6.30 to
8.30; also open bank hol Mon 12 to 3
Details *Children welcome   Wheelchair access (not WC)   Patio   No smoking*
in dining room   Occasional live music; jukebox   Dogs welcome   No cards

HETTON   North Yorkshire   map 8

Angel Inn 🏵 🏵 🍇

Hetton BD23 6LT   TEL: (01756) 730263
WEB SITE: www.angelhetton.co.uk
off B6265, 5m N of Skipton

The Angel has been at the top of the A-list of country pubs for many
years now, though whether or not it is strictly a pub is a matter for
debate. It does fulfil the age-old function of the local hostelry as the
relaxed and informal focal point of village life, with good real ales

from the local Timothy Taylor and Black Sheep breweries served from the bar. Even so, it is the food that draws crowds from miles around and is responsible for queues forming at the door before opening time – proof for one visitor that if good food is being served, even if it is in the middle of nowhere, people will travel to eat it. On the one hand is the restaurant where a thoroughly modern menu offers the likes of tomato and basil risotto with Parmesan, followed perhaps by a duo of red and silver mullet with pappardelle pasta, steamed mussels and a tomato and saffron cream sauce. On the other hand, but in no way inferior, is a bar/brasserie menu for customers in the 'compact and bijou' bar. Typical offerings here include home-made black pudding with green lentils and veal jus among the 'smaller dishes', while 'more substantial dishes' might take in confit of Goosnargh duck leg on a salad of chorizo and lardons. A blackboard offers further temptations such as chargrilled free-range pork chop with grilled Tuscan vegetables, pesto and Parmesan. Over 300 wines – including 35 by the half-bottle and 20 by the glass – have been chosen for their 'quality and outstanding value', and a good deal of knowledge and passion for the list's content shows through. Nine house wines start at £10.90, and those in pursuit of finer wine will not be disappointed, with some excellent examples from Burgundy and Bordeaux, plus some top New World names (Henschke, Frog's Leap) to explore. SAMPLE DISHES: smoked salmon terrine £6.50; slow-cooked confit of Yorkshire lamb with thyme mash and rosemary sauce £9.75; strawberry brûlée crunch £4.50.

Licensees Denis Watkins and John Topham (freehouse)
Open *12 to 3 (2.30 winter), 6 to 10.30 (10 winter); closed 25 Dec; bar food and restaurant 12 to 2.15 (1.45 restaurant Sun), 6 to 9*
Details *Children welcome   Car park   Wheelchair access (also WC)   Patio No smoking in snug and lounge bar and part of dining room   No music   No dogs   Amex, MasterCard, Switch, Visa*

HEXHAM   Northumberland   map 10

Dipton Mill 🍺

BREW PUB

Dipton Mill Road, Hexham NE46 1YA
TEL: (01434) 606577
S of Hexham towards Blanchland and Hexham racecourse

This charming cottagey old pub can be found, as its name suggests, right by a river. It is set in wooded countryside, which is ideal for a pleasant stroll, starting or ending at the bar. Back in 1992, the owners converted a redundant farm building into the Hexhamshire Brewery, which now supplies beers for the pub with names like Devil's Elbow and Whapweasel, all much admired by real ale enthusiasts. Another strong suit here is cheese: the ploughman's comes in no fewer than ten versions, featuring top-notch farmhouse cheeses such as Berwick Edge, Coquetdale and Cotherstone. Other food options listed on the blackboard typically include lamb steak in wine and mustard sauce, ratatouille with couscous, and pork fillet with apple, orange and ginger. The selection of wines is limited, but four are available by the glass. Local attractions include Hadrian's Wall. SAMPLE DISHES: fresh dressed crab with salad £6; haddock baked with tomato and basil £5.25; apple and bramble crumble £1.75.

Licensee Geoff Brooker (freehouse)
Open *12 to 2.30, 6 to 11, Sun 12 to 4.30, 7 to 10.30; bar food 12 to 2.30, 6.30 (7.30 Sun) to 8.30; closed 25 Dec*
Details *Children welcome   Wheelchair access (also WC)   Garden and patio No music   Dogs welcome   No cards*

HEYTESBURY   Wiltshire   map 2

▲ *Angel* ✿ ❦   NEW ENTRY

High Street, Heytesbury BA12 0ED   TEL: (01985) 840330
WEB SITE: www.angelcoachinginn.co.uk
just off A36, 2m E of Warminster

This characterful seventeenth-century coaching inn creates a good impression with its neat, creeper-clad, cream and green façade, and it is equally attractive inside. The main bar, with its panelled and pinky-terracotta walls, old scrubbed tables, fine prints and open fire, has a convivial and relaxed atmosphere, and service is efficient and friendly. Baguettes are available at lunchtime, and the restaurant's seasonal menu, plus blackboard specials, operates throughout. Starters doubling as light bites include deep-fried Brixham scallops wrapped in bacon with salad, and 'deliciously pink' pan-fried pigeon breast on 'fresh, crisp leaves' drizzled with intense walnut oil. Among main dishes are Toulouse or pork and leek sausages with what the menu describes as 'killer mash', grilled sea bass fillet on a salad of new potatoes and rocket, and chargrilled calf's liver with crisp bacon and onion marmalade. West Country cheeses supplement desserts along the lines of sticky toffee pudding, or glazed lemon tart. Real ales are Ringwood Best Bitter, Timothy Taylor Landlord and Marston's Pedigree. Relatively high prices on the usefully annotated list of some 50-odd wines are justified by the quality, and around half a dozen come by the glass. There's a link here with Australia's prestigious Vasse Felix estate, which is owned by the Holmes à Court family, direct descendants of the first Baron Heytesbury. Vasse Felix's premium Chardonnay and Cabernet are on the list. SAMPLE DISHES: blue cheese and avocado tartlet with red pepper coulis £5.25;

sage-roasted chicken breast on sun-dried tomato risotto with grilled leeks £9.75; soup of black cherries marinated in cherry brandy £3.50.

Licensee Jeremy Giddings (freehouse)
Open *11 to 3, 6.30 to 11, Sun 12 to 3, 7 to 10; bar food and restaurant 12 to 2, 7 to 9 (9.30 Fri and Sat)*
Details *Children welcome in bar eating area   Car park   Wheelchair access (not WC)   Garden and patio   Occasional background music   Dogs by arrangement   Delta, MasterCard, Switch, Visa   Accommodation: 8 rooms, B&B £30 to £80*

HIGHCLERE   Hampshire   map 2

▲ *Yew Tree*

Hollington Cross, Andover Road, Highclere RG20 9SE
TEL: (01635) 253360
on A343, ½m S of Highclere

Built in the mid-seventeenth century, the brick and tiled Yew Tree stands beside the Newbury to Andover road, just south of the village of Highclere and not far from the castle of the same name. A front terrace and a garden are used for outdoor eating and drinking in benevolent weather, or else the deep sofas, scrubbed pine tables and inglenook with a log fire will beckon you inside in winter. Eating is a principal focus, and there is one more formal room as well as the bar for doing so, although the same menu – supplemented by blackboard specials such as pasta dishes – is served throughout. The Hampshire Brewery's King Alfred's ale is on handpump, as are Ringwood True Glory and Courage Directors, and five wines are served by the glass, including the Italian house wines, a Chardonnay and a Merlot. The cooking, meanwhile, tries to steer a slightly different course from the country pub norm, offering chargrilled tuna with yellow pepper coulis and pesto croûtons to start, followed perhaps by pork tenderloin on bacon rösti with a Marsala and sage sauce, or baked chicken breast with a smoked paprika sauce and roasted shallots. A reporter who hasn't been able to keep away from the place during the last four years describes the staff as 'unvaryingly warm and courteous'. SAMPLE DISHES: tiger prawns with sweet chilli dressing and leek julienne £7; half-shoulder of lamb slowly roasted with redcurrants, red wine and rosemary £14; blackcurrant crème brûlée £4.50.

Licensees Adrian Grainger and David Potter (Old Monk Company)
Open *12 to 3, 6 to 11, Sun 12 to 2.30, 7 to 10; bar food and restaurant 12 to 2.30, 6 to 9.30*
Details *Children welcome   Car park   Wheelchair access (also WC)   No smoking in dining room   Background music   No dogs   Amex, Delta, Diners, MasterCard, Switch, Visa   Accommodation: 6 rooms, B&B £55 to £75*

HIGHER BURWARDSLEY   Cheshire   map 7

▲ *Pheasant Inn*

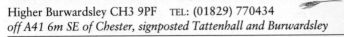

Higher Burwardsley CH3 9PF   TEL: (01829) 770434
off A41 6m SE of Chester, signposted Tattenhall and Burwardsley

The sandstone half-timbered pub with leaded windows and views over
the Cheshire plain stands on a hillside in remote walking country. It is
built around a courtyard, with one outbuilding housing the candle
workshop to which you are directed by signposts in the maze of minor
roads. The clientele, of all ages, includes visitors and walkers –
although no boots are allowed. As the Guide went to press, a major
refurbishment was about to start, with the intention of making the
restaurant more in keeping with the rest of the pub. The printed menu
and blackboard specials are available throughout. A reporter chose a
special starter for Sunday lunch – five accurately timed scallops coated
with sesame seeds and almonds arranged around a mound of cucumber julienne – and another who chose a main course of crab cakes
found a single 'football-sized' one surmounted by the same cucumber,
plus chervil, and complemented by 'a good buttery sauce' of lime and
coriander. The three changing draught ales might be Weetwood Best
Bitter, Bass or Timothy Taylor Landlord, and there are six wines by
the glass from a list of 30. SAMPLE DISHES: chicken liver pâté £4.50;
beef and horseradish sausages with mash £6.50; raspberry mousse £3.

Licensee Bridget McKone (freehouse)
Open *11.30 to 11, Sun 12 to 10.30; bar food and restaurant Mon to Sat 12
to 3, 6.30 to 9.30, Sun 12 to 9*
Details *Children welcome in family room   Car park   Wheelchair access (also
WC)   Garden and patio   No smoking in dining room   Occasional live music
No dogs   Amex, Delta, Diners, MasterCard, Switch, Visa   Accommodation:
10 rooms, B&B £55 to £80*

HILL TOP   Leicestershire   map 5

Nags Head Inn

Hill Top DE74 2PR   TEL: (01332) 850652
4m from M1, junction 24; on B6540, at S end of Castle Donington

The décor is pleasant, in traditional style, at this whitewashed pub
with a garden to the rear, although what draws in locals as well as
staff from East Midlands Airport and Castle Donington's motor-
racing circuit is the inventive food, served by friendly staff in a good
atmosphere. Even sandwiches are not quite ordinary, as they include
a baguette of Cajun chicken with tsatsiki on salad, or ciabatta filled
with smoked salmon with garlic dressing. Other lunchtime snacks
might be pasta with bacon and Brie in a cream sauce, prawn pancake

with mushroom and leek sauce, or, for unreconstructed traditionalists, Lincolnshire sausages with mash and onion gravy. A more substantial lunch or dinner might start with crab salad with mustard mayonnaise and go on to roast rack of lamb with creamy leek polenta, blackened swordfish with crème fraîche and lime, or chargrilled vegetables with curry oil and rice. Desserts, all home-made, include chocolate whisky trifle, and apple and blueberry crumble as well as the inevitable sticky toffee and bread-and-butter puddings. On draught are Marston's Bitter and Pedigree and Banks's Mild, and, from a list of around 30 wines, six are served by the glass. Note that no food is served on Sunday. SAMPLE DISHES: bacon and poached egg salad with garlic croûtons £4.75; roast venison with red onion marmalade £13; treacle oat tart £3.50.

Licensee Ian Davison (Wolverhampton and Dudley)
Open *12 to 2.30, 5.30 to 11, Sun 12 to 3, 7 to 10.30; bar food and restaurant Mon to Sat 12 to 2, 5.30 to 7 (9.30 restaurant)*
Details *No children   Car park   Wheelchair access (also WC)   Garden and patio   No smoking in dining room   No music   Dogs welcome in bar   Amex, Delta, MasterCard, Switch, Visa*

HINDON   Wiltshire   map 2

▲ *Grosvenor Arms* ✿

High Street, Hindon SP3 6DJ   TEL: (01747) 820696
1m from A350 between Warminster and Shaftesbury

Plumb in the middle of a picturesque village, the Grosvenor manages to be a restaurant and hotel without forgetting that it is first and foremost a pub. Stone walls and a flagged floor help to make the point as you enter the bar, but further back there is also a full-dress dining room overlooking a pretty garden area leading to the car park. As well as the blackboard bar menu advertising sausages and mash and a range of open sandwiches, there are fixed-price menus at lunch and dinner, with the option of going à la carte in the evening too (all menus apply throughout the pub). That last is where chef Chris Lee really shows his paces, producing the likes of red mullet fillet with roasted tomatoes and a basil and red onion dressing, or seared scallops with truffle and herb risotto among starters alone. Two perennial favourites come together in a main-course pairing of cod with Toulouse sausages, while high rollers might be tempted by Rossini-style fillet of beef topped with foie gras. Chocolate tart with clotted cream, and steamed orange and ginger sponge are the kinds of hearty puddings favoured, but the cheese selection – which offers a range of England's finest – should not be overlooked. Bass beers are supplemented by a changing guest ale and cider from Stowford Press, and an imaginative wine list begins with five by the glass –

prices starting at £2.85 – and also offers a good selection by the half-bottle. It is strongest on French wines, but there are also some good choices from Australia andSpain. SAMPLE DISHES: chicken liver terrine with apple purée and toasted brioche £4.75; roasted sea bass on aubergine and garlic compote with basil jus £16; raspberry mille-feuille with griottine cream £5.25.

Licensee Martin Tarr (freehouse)
Open *11 to 11; bar food and restaurant 12 to 2.30, 7 to 10*
Details *Children welcome   Car park   Wheelchair access (not WC)   Patio No smoking in dining room   No music   Dogs welcome   Amex, Delta, MasterCard, Switch, Visa   Accommodation: 7 rooms, B&B £45 to £95*

▲ *Lamb at Hindon* 🍺 🍇

High Street, Hindon SP3 6DP   TEL: (01747) 820573
WEB SITE: www.the-lamb.demon.co.uk
in village centre

Hindon is not short of a good pub or two, and this one is just across the road from Grosvenor Arms (see above). A weathered, wisteria-clad stone building, it was once notorious as a smugglers' haunt (the infamous Wiltshire Moonrakers had their headquarters here) and then as a coaching inn. A traditionally furnished long bar with three open fires, the central one a splendid stone inglenook, is the focal point, and slate floors and cushioned settles bolster the sense of period charm. It all makes for a homely atmosphere in which to enjoy the unpretentious, hearty bar food listed on blackboards, and there is a separate restaurant menu too. The bar menu deals in old favourites such as garlic tiger prawns, grilled lemon sole, smoked haddock fishcakes on watercress sauce, and steak and kidney pudding, while the dinner menu in the restaurant might take you from pigeon breast with redcurrant coulis, or smoked seafood with raspberry vinaigrette, through poached sea bass with fennel sauce, or fillet of beef with wild mushrooms, to crème brûlée. A pedigree showing of real ales on draught embraces Stonehenge Pigswill, Otter Ale, Hampshire Ironside and Fuller's London Pride, as well as Wadworth 6X, and the approach to wine is just as conscientious. A wide-ranging and soundly chosen list offers around 20 by the glass, and has helpful style groupings to guide choice. The classic whites and classic reds sections offer some expensive wines that will entice the keen connoisseur, though elsewhere there is fair choice under £15, and a dozen half-bottles. SAMPLE DISHES: mushroom soup £4; pork loin stuffed with apricots £8.50; bread-and-butter pudding £4.

Licensee Cora Scott (freehouse)
Open *11 to 11, Sun 12 to 10.30; bar food and restaurant 12 to 2, 7 to 10*
Details *Children welcome   Car park   Wheelchair access (also WC)   Garden and patio   No smoking in dining room   No music   Dogs welcome exc in dining room   Amex, Delta, MasterCard, Switch, Visa   Accommodation: 14 rooms, B&B £35 to £75*

HOGNASTON   Derbyshire   map 5

▲ *Red Lion* ❦

Main Street, Hognaston DE6 1PR   TEL: (01335) 370396
off A5035 between Ashbourne and Wirksworth

A particularly tranquil village is home to the Red Lion, which is a
friendly beast seemingly much loved by local people. The simple
white exterior conceals a surprisingly well-heeled atmosphere within,
though there is nothing pretentious about the approach; just a
commitment on the part of Philip Price to run a good hostelry that
pays due attention to detail. Marston's Pedigree and Old Speckled
Hen head up the draught ales, and there are guest beers to ring the
changes. The wine list is short and to the point, encompassing a trio
of South African house wines available by the glass, with another five
each of reds and whites and a brace of champagnes. Look to the
blackboard to see a rather inventive bill of fare: starters such as
terrine of smoked trout and fennel with sun-dried tomatoes and
sauce gribiche, or baby squid with citrus salad and chilli salsa, and
then main-course offerings of braised lamb shank with Marsala and
rosemary jus, or (wait for it) 'cushion of mirror carp resting on
ribbons of vegetable with a rose infused yellow pepper coulis'.
SAMPLE DISHES: peppered sweetbreads with a Parmesan tuile £4.50;
guinea fowl stuffed with leeks and foie gras served with salsa verde
£14; deep-fried rice pudding wrapped in filo, served with raspberry
ripple anglaise £4.75.

Licensee Philip Price (freehouse)
Open *all week (exc Mon lunchtime) 12 to 3, 6 (7 Sun) to 11.30; bar food Tue
to Sun 12 to 2 (2.30 Sat and Sun), Mon to Sat 6.45 to 9; closed lunchtime 25
Dec, evening 1 Jan*
Details *Children welcome in dining area   Car park   Wheelchair access (not
WC)   Garden   Background music   Dogs welcome at lunchtime   Delta,
MasterCard, Switch, Visa   Accommodation: 3 rooms, B&B £45 to £75*

HOLT   Wiltshire   map 2

Tollgate Inn ❦ 🍺 NEW ENTRY

Ham Green, Holt BA14 6PX   TEL: (01225) 782326
on B3107 between Melksham and Bradford-on-Avon

The Tollgate is a large, sprawling, grey-stone inn in a tiny village.
The first-floor restaurant has an eclectic décor that incorporates old
books and bottles, while the downstairs bar has comfortable sofas
and a log fire. Chef Alexander Venables comes with previous experience at the Savoy, but his food is not what you would find at a grand

hotel, nor is it ordinary pub stuff. Local oxtail braised in beer with carrots and onions, pan-fried sea bass with couscous and saffron sauce, and roasted pheasant breast with port and thyme sauce and onion confit are typical. There are some familiar dishes, such as Cornish mussels in white wine, herbs and cream, but invention is a feature of others: a salad of braised lambs' hearts with smoked bacon and balsamic vinaigrette, for example. Desserts range from familiar sticky toffee pudding to something along the lines of mango and chilli parfait with coconut ice cream. Weekly-changing real ales are a varied, quality bunch that might include Abbey Bellringer, Bath Gem, Tisbury Best and Fuller's London Pride. The pub may also have Weston's Old Rosie cider and scrumpy from a local farm. The carefully chosen and smartly presented wine list is succinct (25 wines), well-priced and has some nice surprises. Quinta de la Rosa's table wine from Port country is one; Boeger's California Zinfandel is another, this time from Gold Country, El Dorado. Four wines are served by the large or small glass. SAMPLE DISHES: white onion soup with Stowford Press cider £3.50; pan-fried medallions of local pork on ratatouille with a sage and apple cream sauce £10; pineapple and rum crème brûlée £5.

Licensees Alison Ward-Baptiste and Alexander Venables (freehouse)
Open *Tue to Sun 11.30 (12 Sun) to 3, Tue to Sat 6.30 to 11.30; bar food and restaurant 12 to 2, 7 to 9.30*
Details *Children welcome Sun lunchtime only   Car park   Wheelchair access (also WC)   Garden and patio   No smoking in dining room   Occasional background music   No dogs   Delta, MasterCard, Switch, Visa*

HOPE   Derbyshire   map 8

▲ *Cheshire Cheese Inn*

Edale Road, Hope S33 6ZF   TEL: (01433) 620381
on A625 between Chapel-en-le-Frith and Hathersage

'A sixteenth-century freehouse serving hand-pulled real ales' is the Cheshire Cheese's own accurate description of this sturdy stone-built pub in the Peak District National Park. Castleton and its caverns, the Ladybower and Derwent Reservoirs, and wild open moorland are within easy reach. The pub's three cosy rooms, on different levels, offer a warm welcome to tourists and walkers, particularly at lunchtime when snacks include giant Yorkshire puddings filled with sausage and onions, curried mushrooms or sliced beef or pork. There is even a 'hiker's special' of hot roast meat in gravy served on a bun with chips. Otherwise, the short menu takes in chicken jalfrezi and another curry of the day, grilled cod with lime and ginger butter, and smoked salmon with scrambled eggs, garlic, spinach and new potatoes. More conservative tastes might prefer Cumberland sausage, scampi and chips, or the 'mammoth mixed grill'. Vegetarian choices are listed on a board, as are daily specials. Oakwell Barnsley Bitter, Wentworth Venture, Bass and Black Sheep may be the draught ales, with Strongbow cider on tap, and six wines from the short, reasonably priced wine list are served by the glass. SAMPLE DISHES: giant Yorkshire pudding filled with liver and onions £5; gammon with pineapple, fried egg and chips £9; ginger pudding in lemon sauce £3.50.

Licensee David Helliwell (freehouse)
Open *Mon to Fri 12 to 3, 6.30 to 11, Sat 12 to 11, Sun 12 to 4, 6.30 to 10.30; bar food 12 to 2 (2.30 Sat and Sun), 6.30 to 9*
Details *Children welcome in eating areas   Car park   Garden   No smoking in dining room   Background music   Dogs welcome in bar   Amex, MasterCard, Switch, Visa   Accommodation: 1 room (double), B&B £60*

HOPTON WAFERS   Shropshire   map 5

▲ *Crown Inn* 🍇

Hopton Wafers DY14 0NB   TEL: (01299) 270372
WEB SITE: www.crownathopton.co.uk
on A4117, 2m W of Cleobury Mortimer

A mass of greenery grows up to the first floor of this imposing former coaching inn, which has been sympathetically modernised. Its decorative style is traditional, with exposed timbers in bar, restaurant and bedrooms. The Rent Room bar is so called because this was where stewards once collected rents from tenant farmers, while the restaurant takes the name of Poacher's. All menus are available throughout, and a notable feature is the size of the portions. Chargrilled trout weighs in at more than two pounds, and Rent Room specials include a 16-ounce T-bone steak, while rack of lamb on the restaurant's dinner menu is 'five-bone'. Blackboards list fish specials, such as spiced and seared salmon topped with scallion crème fraîche on a bed of couscous, while one 'extra' special might be a version of tournedos Rossini. Rent Room standards are indeed mostly standard pub fare, from sandwiches to scampi, beef casserole, and liver and bacon. Adnams Best Bitter, Banks's Bitter, Marston's Pedigree, and Taylor Landlord are real ales stocked alongside Stowford Press Cider and Scrumpy. There's enough to offer on the 100-strong wine list from New World and Old to enable serious food-matching. Bottle prices are mostly between £10 and £20, and eight regularly changing wines are served by the glass. SAMPLE DISHES: grilled parcel of feta and prosciutto £4.75; chicken en croûte stuffed with mushrooms, leeks and Brie £10; Bakewell tart with vanilla ice cream £4.

Licensees Alan and Elizabeth Matthews (freehouse)
Open *12 to 3, 6 to 11 (10.30 Sun); closed 25 Dec; bar food 12 to 2.30, 6 to
9.30 (9 Sun); restaurant Tue to Sat D 7 to 9.30 (9 Sun), open L if pre-booked*
Details *Children welcome in bar eating area   Car park   Garden and patio
No smoking in eating areas   Occasional background music   Guide dogs only
Amex, Delta, MasterCard, Switch, Visa   Accommodation: 7 rooms, B&B £44
to £78*

HORNDON ON THE HILL   Essex   map 3

▲ *Bell Inn* 🏵 🍺 🍇

High Road, Horndon on the Hill SS17 8LD   TEL: (01375) 642463
WEB SITE: www.bell-inn.co.uk
*off M25 junctions 30 and 31, signposted Thurrock, Lakeside; take
A13, then B1007 to Horndon*

Behind its cream-coloured frontage, this 500-year-old inn's flagstone
floors, standing timbers and collection of foundry memorabilia
produce a sympathetic ambience – and so does the service from polite,
knowledgeable and enthusiastic staff. Those who come in for just a
drink use the front bar, while the back bar next to the restaurant is
where those wishing to eat may settle (note that bar tables are not
bookable). The quite extensive menu, chalked on a blackboard, is
modern, imaginative and simply described. It may present starters
such as queenie scallops and crayfish sautéed with courgettes and
watercress, or veal bresaola with tomatoes and olives, before main
courses of roast fillet of beef with chorizo, pancetta and rösti, or roast
saddle of lamb with merguez and sweetbreads. Simpler items might
include beer-battered cod with mushy peas, a dish rated 'superb' by
one visitor. Additional touches such as stylish presentation of dishes,
and excellent breads generously offered, add to the feeling that this is
a well-run operation that knows what it's doing. A hundred wines are
listed, some very choice indeed, with a number under £15 and house
wines starting at £8.95. Sixteen are served by the glass. Real ale buffs
can choose Greene King IPA, Bass or one of the frequently changing
four guests such as Old Speckled Hen or Wolf Brewery's Granny
Wouldn't Like It. SAMPLE DISHES: turnip and mustard soup with crisp
tongue £4; roast partridge with braised leg and damson jus £14;
caramel-roasted apple with a brandy-snap and vanilla ice cream £4.

Licensees John and Christine Vereker (freehouse)
Open *Mon to Fri 11 to 2.30, 5.30 to 11, Sat 11 to 3, 6 to 11, Sun 12 to 4, 7
to 10.30; bar food and restaurant (exc bank hol Mon, 25 and 26 Dec) 12 to
1.45 (2.30 Sun), 6.45 to 9.45*
Details *Children welcome in eating areas   Car park   Wheelchair access (also
WC)   Patio   No smoking in dining room   No music   No dogs   Amex, Delta,
MasterCard, Switch, Visa   Accommodation: 15 rooms, room only £50 to £85*

▲ *Hoops Inn* 🍺

Horn's Cross EX39 5DL TEL: (01237) 451222
WEB SITE: www.hoopsinn.co.uk
on A39 just W of Horn's Cross, 5m SW of Bideford

Set in 16 acres of rolling countryside near the coast, this thirteenth-century inn was at one time a notorious smugglers' rendezvous. The long, white, thatched building displays its historical charm both outside and in. Water and fire are elements found inside, with a well in the bar and log fires roaring in winter. Much of the menu is traditional: for example, steak and kidney suet pudding, slow-roasted half-shoulder of lamb with onion sauce, or pork knuckle cooked in herbs and wine then flash-grilled for all-over crisp crackling. More modern vegetarian and other dishes include Stilton-stuffed baked pear wrapped in Parma ham, or chargrilled chicken breast with prawns and asparagus, and the day's fish blackboard might add grilled mullet fillet with apple beurre blanc and sweet potato mash; crab salad; or chargrilled sea bass with basil mash. Mainbrace Bitter from the Jollyboat Brewery at Bideford, Norman's Conquest from Cottage Brewing Co, and Indiana's Bones from Summerskills are among regular and guest ales. Thatcher's cider, malt whiskies and vodkas are other specialities, while 15 of 30-odd wines (mostly under £20) are sold by the glass. SAMPLE DISHES: smoked salmon and scrambled egg £6; Clovelly mackerel and chips £7; spotted dick £3.25.

Licensee Gay Marriott (freehouse)
Open *8am to 11pm, Sun 8.15am to 10.30pm; bar food and restaurant 12 to 3, 6 to 9.30, Sun 12 to 9.30 (food served all week 12 to 9.30 July to mid-Sept); closed 25 Dec*
Details *Children welcome in eating areas Car park Wheelchair access (also WC) Garden and patio No-smoking area in bar, no smoking in dining room Occasional live music Dogs welcome in bar Amex, Delta, Diners, MasterCard, Switch, Visa Accommodation: 12 rooms, B&B £50 to £130*

Beehive

The Street, Horringer IP29 5SN TEL: (01284) 735260
WEB SITE: www.the-bee-hive.co.uk
on A143, 3m SW of Bury St Edmunds

This attractive nineteenth-century flint cottage is on the main road between the old market town of Bury St Edmunds and the National

Trust-owned Ickworth House. It is easy to spot, thanks to the eponymous beehive on the small lawn in front of the pub. Enter via the car park at the rear into a warren of dimly lit, beamed and tile-floored areas furnished with smart scrubbed pine furniture. The menu is displayed on a rack of slates opposite the bar counter and veers towards a simple, homely style of cooking, though this is not to say it lacks imagination or interest. Typical are sauté scallops and monkfish cheeks with a squeeze of lime, slow-braised shank of lamb with root vegetables and chive mash, and sauté wild mushrooms and kidneys on brioche. Being so close to Bury St Edmunds, it is only natural that this should be a Greene King pub serving the brewery's range of beers. Wine drinkers are offered a short list with up to half a dozen by the glass. SAMPLE DISHES: chicken terrine with tomato chutney £4.50; roasted baby brill with chive butter £11; baked prune and raisin cheesecake £3.75.

Licensees Gary and Dianne Kingshott (Greene King)
Open *11.30 to 2, 7 to 11; bar food (exc Sun evening) 12 to 2, 7 to 9.30; closed 25 and 26 Dec*
Details *Children welcome   Car park   Wheelchair access (not WC)   Garden and patio   No music   No dogs   Delta, MasterCard, Switch, Visa*

HORSEBRIDGE   Hampshire   map 2

John of Gaunt 🍺

Horsebridge SO20 6PU   TEL: (01794) 388394
1m off A3057, 8m W of Winchester

This simple, rural, nineteenth-century brick-built pub in the Test Valley was a railway inn in the days when Horsebridge had a station. Its name harks back 500 years earlier than the pub itself, when the eponymous son of Edward III had a deer park hereabouts. With a terrace to one side and bench seating out front, it is a popular stop for cyclists and walkers (the Test Way long-distance path passes by a mere 100 yards away), who doubtless appreciate the unfussy country interior of dark wooden furniture and open fires. Well-kept real ales are a strong point: on draft might be Palmers IPA, Ringwood Best Bitter and Fortyniner, and Itchen Valley Fagin's. In addition, there's Thatcher's cider and around two dozen malt whiskies, plus a short wine list that offers three by the glass. The cooking is as devoid of unnecessary frills as the surroundings, with sandwiches, steak and kidney pie, vegetable Kiev, deep-fried fish, ploughman's, and burgers and chips all listed on the menu. The blackboard specials offer a few more unusual dishes, along the lines of home-made soups (e.g. pea and ham), fish (tuna steak with lime and chilli butter), rabbit casserole or local game in season. Puddings may run to coffee meringue, or marmalade cake. Portions are generous. SAMPLE DISHES: deep-fried whitebait £3.50; liver, bacon and onions £5.50; blackberry and apple crumble £2.50.

Licensees Graham and Lynda Atkins (freehouse)
Open *11 to 2.30 (3 Sat), 6 to 11, Sun 12 to 3, 7 to 10.30; bar food 12 to 2, 7 to 9.30 (9 Sun)*
Details *Children welcome in bar eating area   Car park   Garden   Background music   Dogs welcome   No cards*

HOUGHTON CONQUEST   **Bedfordshire**   map 6

▲ *Knife & Cleaver* ❦

The Grove, Houghton Conquest MK45 3LA   TEL: (01234) 740387
WEB SITE: www.knifeandcleaver.com
between A6 and B530, 5m S of Bedford

This attractive, well-maintained inn stands close to the village church, and has a pleasant courtyard and garden at the rear for summer use. Inside, the décor is 'immaculately maintained', according to a reader, with carpets, comfortable leather sofas, upholstered chairs and stylish table lamps – a style described as 'country house meets country pub'. It may seem more restaurant than pub, but real ale fans will find Batemans XB on handpump, and there is Stowford Press for cider drinkers. The bar menu features filled baguettes and ciabattas, ploughman's, and items such as marinated herrings, braised daube of beef with black olives, and Thai seafood with noodles. Dishes of the day on blackboards might include minted lamb lasagne, or salmon and shrimp pie. Fish is the main concern of the restaurant menu, with a page devoted to the daily catch from the market: grilled sea bass fillets with tarragon beurre blanc, or chargrilled tuna with creamed dill and mustard vinaigrette, for example. An excellent wine list that wings round the world offers an impressive 25 or so by the glass (two sizes) and by carafe, and includes a 'good-value' selection at the start of the main list to ease you into the vinous frame of mind. The focus begins with fruity, approachable grape flavours but the classics all make an appearance too. SAMPLE DISHES: large bowl of mussels £5.75; merguez with bubble and squeak £6; chocolate mousse £3.25.

Licensees David and Pauline Loom (freehouse)
Open *all week (exc Sun evening) 12 to 2.30, 6.30 to 10.30; bar food 12 to 2.30 (2 Sat), 7 to 9.30 (limited menu Sat evening and Sun lunchtime); restaurant (exc Sat lunchtime) 12 to 2.30, 7 to 9.30; closed 26 to 30 Dec*
Details *Children welcome in eating areas   Car park   Wheelchair access (not WC)   Garden and patio   No smoking in dining room   Background music No dogs   Amex, Delta, Diners, MasterCard, Switch, Visa   Accommodation: 9 rooms, B&B £45 to £74*

HUBBERHOLME   North Yorkshire   map 8

▲ *George Inn*

Kirk Gill, Hubberholme BD23 5JE   TEL: (01756) 760223
off B6160 at Buckden, 20m N of Skipton

The George shares this patch of North Yorkshire with the Red Lion,
which is at the other end of the fine bridge over the River Wharfe
(see entry, Burnsall). Within this long, whitewashed building in a
small village with a charming look of yesteryear about it is a pair of
flagstoned, low-beamed bars. An antique brass weighing-scale, a
stuffed trout in a glass case, a display of burnished toasting-forks and
a shelf of domino trophies are among the curios to look at, while
another sort of attraction is exerted by Black Sheep Special Ale and
Tetley Bitter on draught, plus guest beers such as Thwaites Best
Bitter and Jennings Cocker Hoop. Good home-made soups –
perhaps butternut squash – might start off a midday meal in hearty
style, and be followed by Yorkshire puddings supported by beef,
sausages, or onion gravy. In the evenings the menu goes a little
grander, bringing on Brie wedges with a fruity dip, smoked salmon
salad, lamb casseroled in some of that Black Sheep beer, or sliced
duck breast with a raspberry and red wine sauce. 'Boozy' bread-and-
butter pudding, and generously sized blueberry sponge pudding are
desserts that have been enjoyed by reporters. The wine list leads with
France and adds a couple of bottles each from a handful of other
regions, but only house red and white are available by the glass.
SAMPLE DISHES: trout pâté £3.75; steak Rossini £12; fruit pancakes in
brandy £3.25.

Licensees Terry and Jennifer Browne (freehouse)
Open *summer Mon to Fri 11 to 3, 6 to 11, Sat and Sun 11 to 11; winter all
week 11.30 to 3, 6.30 to 11; bar food 12 to 2, 6.30 to 8.45; closed 3 weeks
early Jan*
Details *Children welcome in bar eating area   Car park   Wheelchair access
(not WC)   Patio   No music   Dogs welcome   Delta, MasterCard, Switch, Visa
Accommodation: 7 rooms, B&B £28 to £60*

HUNTINGDON   Cambridgeshire   map 6

▲ *Old Bridge Hotel* ✿ ❀   NEW ENTRY

1 High Street, Huntingdon PE29 3TQ   TEL: (01480) 424300
off Huntingdon ring road, by river

This handsome ivy-clad eighteenth-century pub by the River Ouse is
a member of the Huntsbridge Group and follows the same formula
successfully applied at its sister establishments (see Three

Horseshoes, Madingley; Pheasant Inn, Keyston; and the Falcon, Fotheringhay). This means an approach to eating and drinking that combines the virtues of pubby informality with some seriously good cooking. Two menus operate, one a full-blown restaurant menu ostensibly serving the dining room, the other a list that includes lighter dishes offered in the lounge and garden-themed terrace room. In fact, you can mix and match from either menu wherever you choose to eat, and can order as much or as little as you like. The cooking style is distinctly modern, displaying lots of bright Mediterranean and Italian influences alongside more traditional ideas. This can result in such fusion dishes as Moroccan-spiced lamb shank with Parmesan polenta and root vegetables appearing on the lounge menu next to wild boar sausages with mash and Dijon mustard and onion sauce, or country pâté with piccalilli. The restaurant menu offers slightly more involved dishes: for example, roast partridge with walnut mash, Savoy cabbage and a quince and game sauce, or red mullet with aubergine purée, potato galette and hot pepper sauce. Adnams Best Bitter is the regular real ale; this is accompanied by two guests, one of which will be from a local brewery such as City of Cambridge, Potton or Elgood's. Every palate, pocket and potential wine lover will appreciate the well-selected wines available. There are 16 by the glass, starting at £2.60. Or, begin your meal with a sherry aperitif (£1.90 a glass) while you peruse the rest of the 100-strong list. Wines are grouped into 'top class' and 'under £20' sections for both red and white. All the classics are there, with some inspiring choices from the rest of the world thrown in too. SAMPLE DISHES: spiced crab with Thai dressing £6; seared Scottish salmon with pasta, mange-tout, lemon grass, fennel seed and coriander £13; banana soufflé with banana and almond strudel £7.

Licensees John Hoskins and Martin Lee (freehouse)
Open *11 to 11, Sun 12 to 3, 7 to 10.30; bar food and restaurant 12 to 3, 6 to 10.30*
Details *Children welcome   Car park   Wheelchair access (not WC)   Patio No smoking in dining room   No music   Dogs welcome exc in dining room Amex, Diners, MasterCard, Switch, Visa   Accommodation: 24 rooms, B&B £79.50 to £150*

ICKLINGHAM   Suffolk   map 6

Red Lion

The Street, Icklingham IP28 6PS   TEL: (01638) 717802
on A1101, 7m NW of Bury St Edmunds

On the edge of the King's Forest, the Red Lion has an attractive exterior, with gardens at the front and rear. Inside, it is relaxed, old and characterful. The main bar's winged armchairs are beside the open fireplace, which generates a pleasing aroma of wood smoke, and rugs are scattered over bare floorboards. On the walls are fishing rods and stuffed animals in glass cases. Blackboards list the daily menus and promote the house speciality of English country wines, with around 15 both by the glass and bottle. An inspector tried the rose (the flower, not the wine colour) and found it 'a lovely, light drink, delicately sweet and tasting vaguely of rosehip syrup'. Beer drinkers are offered Greene King IPA and Abbot Ale. Menus, interchangeable between bar and restaurant, are mainly English, if you allow that a dish of pasta with tomato, ham, white sauce and cheese is as English as Norfolk chicken breast with rice and a mild curry and mango sauce. More typical, and more traditional, are Barnsley chops, or lambs' liver and kidneys in mustard and bacon sauce. Fresh fish and shellfish might include mussels in white wine, cream and garlic sauce, and goujons of Lowestoft plaice with lemon and caper mayonnaise, a dish that pleased one reader. SAMPLE DISHES: asparagus soup £3.75; pork chops with apple and cider sauce £9.75; lime and papaya posset £4.

Licensees J. Gates and I.C. Hubbert (Greene King)
Open *12 to 3, 6 to 11, Sun 12 to 2.30, 6 to 10.30; bar food and restaurant 12 to 2.30, 6 to 10, Sun 12 to 2.30, 7.15 to 9.30*
Details *Children welcome   Car park   Wheelchair access (also WC)   Garden Background music   No dogs   Delta, MasterCard, Switch, Visa*

IDDESLEIGH   Devon   map 1

▲ *Duke of York* 🍺

Iddesleigh EX19 8BG   TEL: (01837) 810253
on B3217, 3m NE of Hatherleigh

If it's weathered venerability you're after in a country pub, look no further. This low-ceilinged, two-storeyed, thatched and whitewashed pub in an isolated north Devon village has been here since the twelfth century. Old oak tables, cushioned banquettes and (in winter) a blazing log fire greet visitors today. Bar food encompasses standards such as rollmop herrings, chicken liver and brandy pâté, battered cod and chips, or beef and Guinness casserole, as well as a handful of vegetarian options such as vegetable curry. A more ambitious fixed-price menu is offered in the separate restaurant area. There, you might opt for grilled scallops wrapped in smoked bacon, followed by pork escalopes with apple and calvados gravy, with chocolate trifle to finish. Real ales are a particular strength: Exe Valley Dob's Best Bitter, Cotleigh Tawny Bitter, Wye Valley Butty Bach, Palmers IPA and Adnams Broadside may be among those you'll find on tap. The wine list gives a fair crack to the New World and offers around ten by the glass. SAMPLE DISHES: smoked trout fillet with dill £4.50; lamb and mint pie £7; brown sugar meringues with raspberries in whipped cream £3.50.

Licensees Pippa Hutchinson and Jamie Stuart (freehouse)
Open *11 to 11; bar food 11 to 10; restaurant 6.30 to 10; open 25 Dec from 12 to 3 (no food)*
Details *Children welcome   Garden   Occasional live music   Dogs welcome Delta, MasterCard, Switch, Visa   Accommodation: 7 rooms, B&B £25 to £50*

IDRIDGEHAY   Derbyshire   map 5

Black Swan   NEW ENTRY

Wirksworth Road, Idridgehay DE56 2SG   TEL: (01773) 550249
village on B5023 between Duffield and Wirksworth

The Black Swan is not quite as it seems. From the outside it looks like any other Dales stone pub, surrounded as it is by farmland on the edge of a quiet village. Inside, however, the conversion is quite dramatic, with the original rooms knocked through to make one large, yellow-painted dining area divided by shelving and plants. Pass through this and you will wander into a huge conservatory with massive windows, plenty of foliage and a view on to a well-kept garden. Both bar and restaurant menus may be taken throughout, and the accent seems to be on standards that are given one or two contemporary twists. Thus, chicken liver pâté also contains Chardonnay, smoked trout comes with horseradish cream, and toasted goats' cheese is crusted with nuts and accompanied by a sauce made of blueberries. France, Italy, Thailand and more provide culinary inspiration. A reader was impressed by poached salmon salad with lime mayonnaise, and ham and lentil soup has been praised too. Other favourites that may crop up include fillet of beef in Stilton and port sauce, or tagliatelle with wild mushrooms. Finish with apple and apricot lattice, or rhubarb and orange crumble. Real ales on draught are Bass and Marston's Pedigree, and there are 30 wines to choose from, with five by the glass. SAMPLE DISHES: seafood chowder £5; venison in red wine sauce £14; chocolate torte £3.50.

Licensee Mike Buckland (freehouse)
Open *11 to 11, Sun 12 to 4; bar food and restaurant Mon to Sat 12 to 2, 7 to 9.30, Sun 12 to 4; closed evening 25 Dec*
Details *Children welcome   Car park   Wheelchair access (also WC)   Garden and patio   No-smoking area in dining room   Live or background music   No dogs   Delta, MasterCard, Switch, Visa*

IGHTHAM   Kent   **map 3**

Harrow Inn ✿

Common Road, Ightham TN15 9EB   TEL: (01732) 885912
just off A25 Sevenoaks to Borough Green road

Stylish bars with cushioned furniture, books as decoration, open fires
and, in one, an oriental carpet are enticements at this Kentish
ragstone pub near the National Trust's Ightham Mote. But first
things are not forgotten. On draught are Greene King IPA and
Abbott Ale along with guests. The restaurant menu, also available in
the bar, is varied but commendably short, like its descriptions of
dishes. Bread comes as a spectacular whole brown loaf with a thin
crust and a warm, moist interior. Grilled goats' cheese salad is lightly
dressed, its 'beautiful garnish', according to a reporter, including
pitted black grapes. Coarse country pâté wrapped in streaky bacon is
accompanied by cranberry compote and black olives, and citrus
sauce with crisp salmon and chive fishcakes has been described as
'stunningly buttery and not too sharp'. Also praised have been rack
of lamb with red wine and shallot jus, as well as salads and vegetables. A conventional wine list is mainly French at the upper and
lower ends, starting at £9.95. Around five wines are sold by the
glass. SAMPLE DISHES: grilled sardines with rock salt and chilli oil £6;
beef stew with herb dumplings £9; rhubarb crumble £4.

Licensee John Elton (freehouse)
Open *12 to 3, 6 to 11; bar food (exc Sun evening) 12 to 2.30, 6 to 9.30;
restaurant (exc Mon evening) 12 to 2.30, 6 to 9.30; closed 1 Jan, no food Mon
winter*
Details *Children welcome in dining room   Car park   Wheelchair access (not
WC)   Patio   No smoking in dining room   Background music   No dogs
MasterCard, Switch, Visa*

ILMINGTON   Warwickshire   **map 5**

▲ *Howard Arms* ✿

Lower Green, Ilmington CV36 4LT   TEL: (01608) 682226
WEB SITE: www.howardarms.com
off A3400, 4m NW of Shipston on Stour

In the shadow of a chestnut tree overlooking the village green, this
rambling pub, built of golden Cotswold stone, has a striking façade.
It started out as a pair of farm workers' cottages in the seventeenth
century, and the adjacent barn and stables, added in 1780, now form
the pub's dining area. Period charm abounds in the beautifully maintained bar, in the form of polished flagstone floors, heavy ceiling

beams, exposed-stone walls and two open fireplaces (one a huge inglenook). The neatly furnished dining area is decorated tastefully with prints and has a convivial atmosphere. One menu, displayed on blackboards, serves throughout, and the style blends modern and traditional ideas. Starters might take in tomato and rosemary soup, or smoked haddock and chive risotto cakes with hollandaise, while main courses run from beef, ale and mustard pie to John Dory with fennel and lemon butter sauce. Finish with raspberry crème brûlée, or sticky pear and ginger pudding with warm fudge sauce. Praise has come in for 'full' flavours and well-balanced portions, as well as the friendly welcome and attentive service. Real ales are well represented by Genesis from the local North Cotswold Brewery, as well as Everards Tiger Best and a regular guest, which might be Black Sheep Bitter or Timothy Taylor Landlord. Five white and five red wines are served in two glass sizes, and there's a handy selection of around 20 more well-chosen bottles to dip into after you've tried all these. SAMPLE DISHES: baked sardines with lemon and garlic £4.75; pan-fried duck breast with glazed nectarine and redcurrant jus £11.25; ginger syllabub with brandy-snap biscuit £4.

Licensees Rob Greenstock and Martin Devereux (freehouse)
Open *11 to 2.30, 6 to 11, Sun 12 to 3, 7 to 10.30; bar food 12 to 2, 7 to 9 (9.30 Fri and Sat); no food Sun evening in winter*
Details *No children   Car park   Wheelchair access (not WC)   Garden   No smoking in 2 rooms   No music   No dogs   Delta, MasterCard, Switch, Visa Accommodation: 3 rooms, B&B £40 to £85*

INKPEN   Berkshire   map 2

▲ *Swan Inn*   [NEW ENTRY]

Lower Green, Inkpen RG17 9DX
TEL: (01488) 668326
WEB SITE: www.theswaninn-organics.co.uk
off A338, 4m SE of Hungerford

Renovated to emphasise its antiquity, this seventeenth-century village inn has log fires and an open-plan layout. The long, rambling bar area is traditionally pubby, with green banquettes, polished wooden tables and old photographs. Ceilings are wood-beamed, and massive standing timbers in the restaurant contrast with formal settings on the pink-clothed tables. The pub must be unique in that it is owned by organic beef farmers, and most of the other ingredients used in the kitchen are organic too. Restaurant dishes (not available in the bar) happily combine retro and modern: avocado and prawns with marie-rose sauce could precede chicken breast wrapped in Parma ham stuffed with Brie. Bar dishes are similar and, except for vegetarian items, even more traditional. The blackboard's 15 or so generously served main courses might include braised lambs' liver and bacon, cottage pie, and steaks. A reader found beef and ale pie to be 'of superior flavour and texture, and very tender', with 'delicious' accompanying vegetables, and the apples in a crumble with custard had 'real flavour'. Beers on draught are Butts Bitter and Blackguard, and Hook Norton Best Bitter and Best Mild. Also on offer are Lambourn Valley cider and around 25 organic wines, most over £20 a bottle. Three are offered by the glass. SAMPLE DISHES: sausage and chips £4; savoury meat loaf with vegetables £7; organic ice cream £3.50.

Licensees Mary and Bernard Harris (freehouse)
Open *11 to 3, 7 to 11, Sun 12 to 10.30; bar food 12 to 2.30, 7 to 9.30; restaurant Wed to Sun 12 to 2.30, 7 to 9.30; closed 25 and 26 Dec*
Details *Children welcome in eating areas   Car park   Wheelchair access (also WC)   Garden and patio   No-smoking area in bar, no smoking in dining room Occasional live or background music   No dogs   Delta, MasterCard, Switch, Visa   Accommodation: 10 rooms, B&B £40 to £90*

ITTERINGHAM   **Norfolk**   **map 6**

Walpole Arms

The Common, Itteringham NR11 7AR   TEL: (01263) 587258
off B1354, 4m NW of Aylsham

Cobbled together from a group of old farm buildings, the Walpole Arms is a pub with plenty of personality. What was once a carting shed is now the restaurant, and linking that to the bar, which is given something of a period feel by its red-brick walls and stained beams, is a kind of conservatory. The whole place seems to buzz most nights with a happy press of custom. Five real ales, which might be Adnams and Woodforde's ales, plus Old Speckled Hen, are on handpump, and to these is added a wine list of over four dozen bins, with seven available by the glass that always includes a wine of the week. The cooking is built around ever popular pub stalwarts, such as scampi with chips and salad, and sirloin steak with onion rings and mushrooms. Beyond that, more adventurous dishes might be grilled tuna with a caper and tomato butter sauce, or a starter of marinated sardines on basil oil crostini. Finish with treacle and walnut tart or bread-and-butter pudding with whisky. Friendly service contributes to the enjoyment. SAMPLE DISHES: chorizo with red onion and fried potatoes £4; chicken braised in white wine with leeks and celery served with wild rice £8; chocolate and orange tart £3.

Licensee Paul Simmons (freehouse)
Open *12 to 3, 6 (7 Sun) to 11; bar food and restaurant 12 to 2, 7 to 9; closed evening 25 Dec*
Details *Children welcome   Car park   Wheelchair access (also WC)   Garden No smoking in dining room   Occasional background music   Dogs welcome exc in dining room   Delta, MasterCard, Switch, Visa*

KEIGHLEY   West Yorkshire   map 8

Quarry House Inn

Bingley Road, Lees Moor, Keighley BD21 5QE
TEL: (01535) 642239
off A629, 2m E of Haworth

A converted nineteenth-century farmhouse perched on Lees Moor, high above the town of Keighley, the inn commands superb views of the Worth Valley with its celebrated steam railway, and is only a couple of miles from Haworth, home of the even more celebrated Brontës. The main bar would answer most people's vision of what a country pub ought to look like, with its plush bench seating, while the presence of table linen indicates that you have entered the restaurant. The Barn, a function room to the rear, is used for wedding parties and other such occasions. Much traditional pub food is offered, served in both bar and restaurant, so those in search of creamy garlic mushrooms, battered scampi with lemon, big steaks with onion rings and salad, or home-made meat and potato pie will not be disappointed, and nor will the kids, if fish fingers or chicken nuggets appeal. Daily specials are chalked on a board in the bar and might run to more ambitious braised marinated wild boar with red wine sauce, or duckling breast in plum sauce, while fresh fish might be gratinated cheesy halibut with courgette ribbons. Real beer aficionados will be glad to see Timothy Taylor Golden Best and Landlord on draught, together with cask-conditioned Tetley Bitter, while the wine list explores the New World as well as Western Europe, with a range of house wines sold by the glass. SAMPLE DISHES: prawn cocktail £4.50; fillet steak with port and Stilton sauce £13.50; apple and blackberry crumble £2.50.

Licensees J.M. and C.M. Smith (freehouse)
Open *12 to 3, 7 to 11.30; bar food and restaurant 12 to 2, 7.30 to 10.30; closed 25 and 26 Dec, 1 Jan*
Details *Children welcome   Car park   Wheelchair access (also WC in 1 function room)   Garden   Background music   Dogs welcome in bar only Delta, MasterCard, Switch, Visa*

KEMPSEY   Worcestershire   map 5

▲ *Walter de Cantelupe Inn* ✿

Main Road, Kempsey WR5 3NA   TEL: (01905) 820572
on A38, 4m S of Worcester

A pub with a name like this needs its history told. This one is named after a thirteenth-century Bishop of Worcester who backed the doomed Simon de Montfort's cause against the future Edward I. It is a pint-sized place, with a little garden surrounded by shrubs and creeper-covered trellises to the rear. Inside is rather lavishly decorated in ruby-red and gold, with fleur-de-lis motifs and a large fireplace with a welcoming log fire in the winter. Timothy Taylor Landlord leads a distinguished repertoire of draught ales, with changing guest beers always worth a look. In addition, there are the equally traditional perry from Norbury's and even a local wine, Tiltridge's Elgar dry white. The other wines originate a little further from home but are an enticing and kindly priced bunch, with half a dozen by the glass. The cooking is a draw here, too, with classic bar food at lunchtimes and in the evenings, barbecues on Sunday evening in summer, and a blackboard menu of more enterprising items at dinner. Soft fish roe served hot in white wine and shallot cream sauce with toast, baked fillet of sea bass with mozzarella, tomato and basil, or a vegetarian stroganoff combining wild mushrooms, red onion and fennel on basmati rice are the kinds of things to expect. To ensure that local pride doesn't flag, there's Tewkesbury mustard in the sauce that comes with locally reared organic pork, and even a cheese made in the village itself. Or finish with hot banana and toffee pancake with crème fraîche. SAMPLE DISHES: smoked Scottish salmon with lemon, capers and parsley £4.50; roast breast of Barbary duck with wild mushrooms and red wine sauce £10.75; walnut and maple syrup suet pudding and custard £3.25.

Licensee Martin Lloyd-Morris (freehouse)
Open *Tue to Sat 11.30 to 3 (2.30 winter), 6 to 11, Sun 12 to 10.30 (12 to 3, 6 to 10.30 winter); bar food Tue to Sat 12 to 2.30 (2 winter), 6.30 to 9 (10 Fri and Sat), Sun 12 to 8; restaurant summer Tue to Thur 12 to 2, 7 to 9, Fri and Sat 7 to 10, Sun 12 to 2.30, restaurant winter Thur to Sat 7 to 9, Sun 12 to 3, 6 to 8*
Details *Children welcome in eating areas   Car park   Patio   No smoking in dining room   Occasional background music   Dogs welcome exc in dining room   Amex, Delta, MasterCard, Switch, Visa   Accommodation: 2 rooms, B&B £22 to £50*

If a pub has a special point of interest, this is indicated by a 'flashed' word or phrase at the top right of the entry.

Chequers Inn   NEW ENTRY

Pertenhall Road, Brook End, Keysoe MK44 2HR
TEL: (01234) 708678
WEB SITE: www.bigfoot.com/~chequers
on B660, 8m N of Bedford

In an attractive rural triangle formed by the A1, A6 and A14 roads, in a border area where Bedfordshire meets Northamptonshire and Cambridgeshire, the village of Keysoe nestles in the environs of the River Nene. At the village's northern edge, this whitewashed country pub has been in the same conscientious ownership for over 20 years. A number of rooms with head-banging beams all over the place cluster around a central bar, with a family room at the back. Hook Norton Best Bitter is on handpump alongside a regularly changing guest ale, and just three wines are served by the glass from a fairly run-of-the-mill list. Traditional pub food is the order of the day, but it is all appreciably well prepared and raw materials are good. Salmon fishcakes with lemon butter sauce are chunky and substantial, Thai chicken bristling with lemon grass is competently done, and there are the usual steaks, plus lamb cutlets, or perhaps trout in a sauce of Noilly Prat, almonds and cream. These might be preceded by chicken liver pâté, or fried Brie with cranberries, and rounded off by one of the flashy desserts: bananas flamed in Kahlùa, or lime and raspberry pavlova. Plain and toasted sandwiches and a separate children's choice are also available. SAMPLE DISHES: prawn cocktail £3.75; chicken breast stuffed with Stilton in chive sauce £8; caramel and walnut meringue £2.75.

Licensee Jeffrey Kearns (freehouse)
Open *Mon and Wed to Sat 11.30 to 2.30, 6.30 to 11, Sun 11.30 to 2.30, 7 to 10.30; bar food and restaurant 12 to 2, 7 to 9.45*
Details *Children welcome in family room and eating area   Car park Wheelchair access (also WC)   Garden and patio   No smoking in 1 room Occasional background music   No dogs   MasterCard, Visa*

Pheasant Inn 🏵🏵 🍇

Loop Road, Keyston PE18 0RE   TEL: (01832) 710241
on B663, just S of junction with A14

The Pheasant, a long, thatched pub, shares the same informal approach to eating and drinking as its sister establishments in the Huntsbridge Group, the Three Horseshoes, Madingley, the Old

Bridge, Huntingdon and the Falcon, Fotheringhay (see entries). This means one menu serves throughout, both in the more formal dining room and the relaxed lounge, and you can eat as much or as little as you like, from a full three-course meal to a light dish of tagliatelle with wild mushrooms, Jerusalem artichokes and truffle oil. As that dish might suggest, modern themes prevail in the cooking, and no small degree of invention is at work. Crispy mackerel on cauliflower macaroni with Parmesan is a typically unusual dish, as is a duo of foie gras: hot with mushy peas, and cold with Muscat jelly. On slightly more familiar territory are roast silverside of Cornish lamb with potato purée, flageolet beans and garlic, and Gloucester Old Spot sausage with mash and grain mustard sauce. The place confirms its pub credentials with its selection of fine real ales, which includes Adnams Best Bitter alongside the unusually named Village Bike from the local Potton Brewery. The wine list makes a jolly good read for any passing wine lover – it's worth a detour even, but make sure you leave plenty of time for choosing between the hundred or so wines available. From France, everything's there from Alsace Pinot Gris to Viognier, from Condrieu via some Burgundy and Bordeaux classics. And from the rest of the world, the range is just as impeccable. Sixteen house wines are available by the glass. SAMPLE DISHES: macaroni of scallops £8; blade of Aberdeenshire beef with creamed cabbage and foie gras sauce £13; crème brûlée infused with lemon grass and lime leaves £5.

Licensees Clive Dixon and John Hoskins (freehouse)
Open *12 to 3, 6 to 11, Sun 12 to 3, 7 to 10.30; bar food and restaurant 12 to 2, 6 to 10 (7 to 9.30 Sun); closed evenings 25 and 26 Dec and 1 Jan*
Details *Children welcome   Car park   Patio   No smoking in 2 rooms   No music   No dogs   Amex, Delta, Diners, MasterCard, Switch, Visa*

KINGSDON   Somerset   map 2

Kingsdon Inn   NEW ENTRY

Kingsdon TA11 7LG   TEL: (01935) 840543
village signposted off B3151 just N of A372

Picnic benches overlook the village playing field from the front lawn of this pretty thatched cottage, which a reader recommends as 'the perfect retreat for weary travellers heading to or from the West Country'. In the rambling rooms, with low ceilings and stone fireplaces, are rustic furnishings: cushioned wall seats and farmhouse chairs at scrubbed pine or old stripped deal tables. Two menus operate, one at lunchtime and the other – longer and more 'restaurant' in style – in the evening. Warm leek, Stilton and walnut tart, and lightly grilled goat's cheese are both accompanied by fresh salad. More substantial lunch dishes might include poached haddock with parsley sauce, chicken breast in creamy cider sauce, or casserole of pheasant legs. Smoked sausage and potato salad, or crab and prawn Mornay, then roast duck in scrumpy sauce, or wild rabbit in Dijon mustard sauce, might appear on the dinner menu. On draught are Cottage Brewery's Golden Arrow, Otter Bitter and Fuller's London Pride as well as Burrow Hill farmhouse and Stowford Press ciders. A fair selection of malt whiskies is available, while around half a dozen wines by the glass and about the same number of halves are among the 40-odd bins on the decently priced wine list. SAMPLE DISHES: Greek salad £3.75; oxtail in Guinness £6; toffee meringue temptation £3.25.

Licensees Leslie and Anna Marie Hood (freehouse)
Open *12 to 3, 6 to 11, Sun 12 to 3, 7 to 10.30; bar food 12 to 2, 6.45 to 9.30 (7 to 9 Sun)*
Details *Children welcome in bar eating area; no children under 12 after 8pm Car park   Wheelchair access (not WC)   Garden   No-smoking area in dining room   Background music   No dogs   MasterCard, Switch, Visa*

KINGSTEIGNTON   Devon   map 1

Old Rydon Inn 🍇

Rydon Road, Kingsteignton TQ12 3QG
TEL: (01626) 354626
from A380 take Kingsteignton turn-off, then first turning left into Brook Way, which becomes Rydon Road

---

The origins of this Grade II listed former farmhouse go back to the sixteenth century, and the bar (in what used to be the stables) features an original cider loft. An informal tone is set by cask seats, an open log fire and whitewashed stone walls. This area is popular with drinkers, who will find Bass, London Pride and guests such as Adnams, Breakspear Bitter or Abbot Ale on tap. Those here for food tend to head for the large conservatory, with its leafy vines, bougainvillea and other exotic plants. The printed menu includes toasted muffins with various fillings, warm salads and things like Hungarian goulash soup alongside staples such as steak sandwich, jacket potatoes and ploughman's; additional offerings on a blackboard are as diverse as nasi goreng, and Exmoor venison stew with juniper berry sauce. The separate restaurant, in the oldest part of the building, has its own menu, which shows a blend of the classical and the modern: for example, chargrilled tiger prawns with mango, red onion, chilli and coriander salsa, followed by Barbary duck breast with a raspberry and red wine sauce, or roast saddle of lamb stuffed with sun-dried tomatoes, mushrooms, garlic and rosemary. Around

50 wines on an enterprising list keep mostly below £15, and includes some old favourites with one or two modern touches thrown in – Peter Lehmann Barossa Shiraz from Australia and Aotea Sauvignon Blanc from New Zealand, for example. A section each for fine reds and fine whites affords some indulgence. Three house wines are available by the small or large glass as well as half-litre carafe. SAMPLE DISHES: crisp fried potato skins with creamy blue cheese dip £4; warm salad of chargrilled sweet-cured bacon £5; chocolate cheesecake £3.

Licensee Martin Webb (Heavitree)
Open *11 to 3, 6 to 11, Sun 12 to 3, 7 to 10.30; bar food 11.30 to 2, 6.30 to 9.30, Sun 12 to 2, 7 to 9.30; restaurant Mon to Sat 7 to 10; closed 25 Dec*
Details *Children welcome in bar eating area   Car park   Wheelchair access (not WC)   Garden and patio   No smoking in dining room   Occasional background music   Dogs welcome exc in dining room   Amex, Delta, Diners, MasterCard, Switch, Visa*

KINTBURY   Berkshire   map 2

▲ *Dundas Arms* ✿ 🍺

53 Station Road, Kintbury RG17 9UT
TEL: (01488) 658263
WEB SITE: www.dundasarms.co.uk
1m S of A4, between Newbury and Hungerford

Set between the Kennet and Avon Canal and the River Kennet, the Dundas Arms makes the most of its aquatic location with some outdoor tables for fine-weather eating. Inside, the décor is predominantly modern, with some bright splashes of colour and the public bar wood-panelled and hung with prints. The cooking has produced successes that are not in the mode of traditional pub catering: starters of duck liver terrine with sweet red pepper relish, and grilled red mullet on crushed potatoes with tapénade, for example. Main courses might take in baked cod with saffron sauce, or roast rump of lamb with spiced aubergine, and coming in for praise have been grilled scallops with peppers and tarragon, followed by pigeon breasts with mushrooms and pasta, and then mango and toffee ice creams. Well-kept handpumped ales include Ringwood Best Bitter, Greene King IPA, Barbus Barbus from local brewery Butts, plus guests such as Adnams Regatta and Ringwood's Boon Doggle. An enterprising wine list with classic French bins at its core starts at £13.50 but soon spills over the £20 mark; in fact, those really wanting to splash out can opt for a bottle of Château Latour 1966 at only £300. There are plenty of half-bottles, and four wines are served by the glass. Note that the pub does not serve food on Sunday. SAMPLE

DISHES: smoked eel and bacon salad with horseradish cream £6; roast guinea fowl with lemon and garlic sauce £10; chocolate pavé with coffee-bean sauce £4.

Licensee D.A. Dalzell-Piper (freehouse)
Open *11 to 2.30, 6 to 11, Sun 12 to 2.30, 7 to 10.30; bar food Mon to Sat 12 to 2, Tue to Sat 7 to 9; restaurant Tue to Sat 7 to 9; closed Sun evening winter*
Details *Children welcome Car park Patio No smoking in dining room No music No dogs Amex, Delta, MasterCard, Switch, Visa Accommodation: 5 rooms, B&B £60 to £80*

KIRKBY LONSDALE   Cumbria   map 8

▲ *Snooty Fox Tavern* ♀

Main Street, Kirkby Lonsdale LA6 2AH   TEL: (015242) 71308
WEB SITE: www.mortal-man-inns.co.uk/snootyfox

The solid virtues of this seventeenth-century town tavern on the high street include its short, varied restaurant menu. Among starters might be game terrine, mozzarella gâteau with plum tomatoes and red onion, or pine kernels and raspberry vinegar with warm chicken livers. Vegetarians might choose main courses of fresh pasta, or roasted aubergine filled with a julienne of vegetables in tomato sauce, while the specials board includes the day's fresh fish and something like steak and kidney pudding, or the perfect simplicity of roast shoulder of lamb. The lunchtime bar menu offers various baked potatoes, baguettes, ciabatta melts, pasta and burgers, and also light bites, from soup with a cheese bap to beef stew. All menus are available in the restaurant and the bars. The inn's décor features hunting, with a stuffed fox to greet you on entry, and in the restaurant a huntsman's horn and a hunting jacket hang from the ceiling. On the solid wooden tables, some with settle seats, are hunting-red candles and napkins. Among three or four regularly changing ales might be Timothy Taylor Landlord, Theakston Best Bitter, Woodforde's Wherry Best Bitter, Ushers Best Bitter, or Oakham JHB. The modestly priced wine list is strong in the New World, with around a dozen by the glass. SAMPLE DISHES: chicken liver pâté with Cumberland sauce £4; ham shank on horseradish mash with Dijon mustard sauce £8.25; lemon posset £3.25.

Licensee Hugo Broadfoot (freehouse)
Open *11 to 11, Sun 12 to 10.30; bar food 12 to 2.30, Sun 12 to 9.30; restaurant all week 12 to 2.30, 6.30 to 9.30*
Details *Children welcome Car park Wheelchair access (not WC) Garden*

No-smoking area in dining room   Occasional background music   Dogs welcome   Amex, Delta, MasterCard, Switch, Visa   Accommodation: 9 rooms, B&B £30 to £60

KIRTLING   Cambridgeshire

map 6

Red Lion

214 The Street, Kirtling CB8 9PD   TEL: (01638) 731976
off B1063, 5m SE of Newmarket

This long, low building, built in a typical Suffolk style (even though Kirtling is just over the border in Cambridgeshire), is at one end of the main road through this sprawling village close to Newmarket. It is Kirtling's only pub, following the demise of the Queen's Head, which, like many country pubs, has become a private residence. Still, if you have only one pub in your village, you probably would be happy to have this old-fashioned local, where you can find well-kept beers and straightforward food. The cooking style is mostly traditional, with a few modern ideas, and the lengthy menu has sections devoted to fish, poultry, 'from the grill', specials, and vegetarian dishes. Three blackboards – devoted to fish, meat, and snacks – add further choice, and there is a three-course Sunday lunch menu. One visitor praised a generous portion of tasty fish curry, packed with fish and vegetables and served with rice and a mixed salad. Other specialities might include home-cooked ham with egg and chips, tournedos Rossini, or poached cod with prawn sauce. The décor in the bar is a mixture of old and new, with modern prints and signs alongside an original bread oven set in one wall, and a blackened iron range in the fireplace. There is also a chintzy dining room served by the same menus. Beers from Adnams are supplemented by guest ales, and the list of 25 wines is also supplied by Adnams. SAMPLE DISHES: crispy filo prawns with chilli sauce £5.50; breast of chicken in creamy mushroom sauce £11.50; coconut jam tart with custard £3.75.

Licensees Michael and Annette Rolfe (freehouse)
Open *Tue to Sun 11 to 2.30, 6.30 to 11; bar food and restaurant 12 to 2, 7 to 9.30; closed 26 Dec*
Details *Children welcome in dining room   Car park   Wheelchair access (also WC)   Patio   No smoking in dining room   Background music   No dogs Delta, Diners, MasterCard, Switch, Visa*

♣ ♣ *indicates a pub serving food on a par with 'seriously good' restaurants, where the cooking achieves consistent quality.*

KNIGHTWICK   Worcestershire

map 5

▲ *Talbot* 🍺

LOCAL PRODUCE

Knightwick WR6 5PH   TEL: (01886) 821235
*from Worcester turn right off A44 just before crossing River Teme on
to B4127, signposted Martley; pub at bottom of hill*

At the rear of this fourteenth-century village inn you will find the
Teme Valley Brewery, which produces beers called This, That and
T'Other for the pub. Both are owned and run by the Clift family,
who are keen supporters of local produce (including the hops for the
beer). Indeed, the Talbot is a veritable cottage industry, with many
ingredients coming from the pub's own chemical-free gardens or
gathered from the surrounding fields and hedgerows, and used to
produce preserves, breads, black pudding, and raised pies. Bar food is
hearty stuff. For starters, wild mushrooms might be fried with onion
and garlic, garnished with nasturtium leaves and served on crisp toast.
To follow there may be belly pork with lentils and shallots, or sausage
and chicken hotpot. The main bar area is an open-plan room with
tables and chairs grouped around a wood-burning fire; there is also a
taproom and a restaurant. Here the menu goes in for more sophisticated fare, such as smoked duck breast salad, scallop beignets, roast
cod with pesto, or roast loin of lamb from the family farm. Around
40 wines are offered on a list where prices are good and familiar
grape varieties plentiful; a creditable 22 are served by the glass. Those
who take advantage of the inn's accommodation will be treated to a
'superb' breakfast. SAMPLE DISHES: pea and mint soup £3.50; lamb
koftas with fresh tomato sauce £7; treacle holly gog £3.50.

Licensee A.C. Clift (freehouse)
Open *11 to 11, Sun 12 to 10.30; bar food and restaurant 12 to 2, 6.30 to
9.15; closed evening 25 Dec*
Details *Children welcome in eating areas   Car park   Wheelchair access (also
WC)   Garden and patio   No smoking in dining room   Jukebox in back bar
Dogs by arrangement   Amex, Delta, MasterCard, Switch, Visa
Accommodation: 10 rooms, B&B £30 to £67.50*

KNOWL HILL   Berkshire

map 3

▲ *Bird in Hand* 🍇

Bath Road, Knowl Hill RG10 9UP   TEL: (01628) 826622
on A34, 3m NE of Twyford

This small hotel has been in the same family's hands for three gener-
ations and, although some parts date from the fourteenth century, it
has been much modernised, with extensions including conference

rooms. In the relaxed main bar are leather armchairs and cosy alcoves. The restaurant menu is available in the bar but not the other way round, but an extensive bar menu offers tortilla wraps, quiche, whitebait, and omelettes, as well as a buffet of cold meats, fish and salads. Daily specials might be fried red sea bream fillets marinated in Chinese spices on buttered noodles, or turkey, leek and mushroom pie. Restaurant dishes take in wild mushroom ravioli, mixed Loch Fyne shellfish, wiener schnitzel, and lamb cutlets stuffed with walnuts, thyme and apricots and wrapped in filo. The long (nearly 100 bins), reasonably priced wine list is divided into sections defined by the wines' character – 'subtle' and 'cool, green and crisp' whites, for example. The 'quirky' section includes a Languedoc Viognier at £11.75, and the 'spicy' group takes in D'Arenberg's Footbolt Shiraz. About a dozen are offered by the glass. Real ale buffs can enjoy Brakspear Bitter, Timothy Taylor Landlord, Wadworth 6X, and Fuller's London Pride. SAMPLE DISHES: crispy duck pancake with sweet-and-sour plum sauce £6; guinea-fowl hotpot £9.75; home-made ice cream £4.

Licensee Caroline Shone (freehouse)
Open *11 to 3, 6 to 11, Sun 12 to 4, 7 to 10.30; bar food 12 to 2.30, 6 to 10, Sun 12 to 2.30, 7 to 9.30; restaurant 12 to 2, 7 to 9.45; closed evenings 25 and 26 Dec*
Details *Children welcome in eating areas   Car park   Wheelchair access (also WC)   Garden and patio   Occasional background music   Dogs welcome Amex, Delta, Diners, MasterCard, Switch, Visa   Accommodation: 15 rooms, B&B £55 to £110*

KNOWSTONE   Devon   map 1

Masons Arms Inn

Knowstone EX36 4RY   TEL: (01398) 341231
WEB SITE: www.masonsarmsinn.com
1½m N of A361, midway between South Molton and Tiverton

This Grade II listed Devon longhouse opposite the church is in a peaceful hamlet in the foothills of Exmoor, making it a popular lunch venue for walkers. Enthusiastic and friendly owners have recognised the potential of the thatched, thirteenth-century building while remaining sympathetic to its history, and have invested heavily in all areas to make sure this is a real destination pub for both food and atmosphere. The main bar is in classic style, with heavy black beams, large, rustic pine tables, old settles and a huge inglenook with a roaring log fire. Both the modern dining room extension and a terrace enjoy fine views over Exmoor. The printed and blackboard menus offer a wide choice, with starters ranging from prawn and pepper pâté to tomato stuffed with garlic and herb cream cheese, and main courses encompassing chicken, leek and bacon crumble, roast duck with Grand Marnier sauce, seafood pancake, and provençal scallops with new potatoes. Cotleigh Tawny Bitter is drawn straight from the barrel, and two wines are served by the 175ml glass. SAMPLE DISHES: curried parsnip soup £3; chargrilled Cajun chicken with sauté potatoes and salad £6.50; Bailey's cheese-cake £3.50.

Licensees Paul and Jo Stretton-Downes (freehouse)
Open *12 to 3, 6 to 11, Sun 12 to 3, 7 to 10.30; bar food 12 to 2, 7 to 9; closed 25 Dec*
Details *Children welcome in dining room   Car park   Patio   Background music   Dogs welcome in bar*   Delta, MasterCard, Switch, Visa

LANGTON GREEN   Kent   map 3

Hare 🍺

Langton Green TN3 0JA   TEL: (01892) 862419
on A264, 2½m W of Tunbridge Wells

The Hare sits on a corner on the edge of suburban Langton Green; it is a green and white building that backs on to the village green, where cricket matches are played in summer. Between the pub and the car park is a herb patch, and two visitors were pleased to see one of the kitchen staff busily snipping rosemary as they arrived. Oriental rugs on a pine floor immediately tell you that this is not typical country-pub style. That said, the place is festooned with antique memorabilia, from chamber pots to brass kettles. Large blackboard menus on the stairs as you go in are duplicated in printed form, and the cooking is as modish as the surroundings would indicate. Starters might be peppered strawberry, walnut and melon salad, or deep-fried goats' cheese with red pepper chutney, while main courses explore such byways as mackerel stuffed with prawns, lime and chilli with gooseberry sauce, roast monkfish tail with mango salsa, or an inventive vegetarian option, such as Gruyère-topped sweet potato and honeyed pepper tart with country garden pickle. More tradi-tional things are done well too: roast sirloin comes with crisp little Yorkshire puddings and heartily rich gravy. Portions are substantial, but if you've room you might finish with pumpkin pie with crème fraîche, or a slice of tray-baked dates and cinnamon with custard. Four real ales are on tap and may include Greene King Abbot Ale and IPA, Old Speckled Hen, Wells Bombardier Premium Bitter, and Wychwood Hobgoblin. On top of those, around a dozen wines are sold by the glass from a list that gives roughly equal weight to Europe and the New World. SAMPLE DISHES: chicken liver, mushroom and peppercorn pâté with orange and redcurrant sauce £5; whole plaice stuffed with tomato, avocado and onion £12; mango and passion-fruit pavlova £4.50.

Licensees B. K. Whiting and O. Slade (Brunning and Price Ltd)
Open *11 to 11, Sun 12 to 10.30; bar food 12 to 9.30 (9 Sun)*
Details *Children welcome in dining room Car park Wheelchair access (also WC) Garden and patio Background music Dogs welcome in bar Amex, Delta, MasterCard, Switch, Visa*

LAPWORTH   **Warwickshire**   **map 5**

Boot

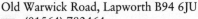

Old Warwick Road, Lapworth B94 6JU
TEL: (01564) 782464
take A3400 from Hockley Heath SW for 2½m; Lapworth signposted on left

---

Bargees with a taste for modern British cuisine can tie up outside the back of this stylish pub, have a drink on the terrace at the side, then go into the lively bars for a relaxed meal. The stylish design of the interior extends to the colourful printed menu offered in both bars and restaurant. It is modern food with considerable Mediterranean and oriental input, as in starters such as field mushrooms and Roquefort on bruschetta, or mussels in Thai broth, caramelised ginger and pickled cucumber. Roast cod in a Parmesan crust with vine tomatoes on mash is among main courses on the menu, and more fresh fish is listed on blackboards. Otherwise there might be Toulouse sausage with spiced onions on champ, lamb shank pot-roast with tomatoes and herbs in red wine, or roast duck with blackberry and apple compote and watercress on mashed roots. Old Speckled Hen and Wadworth 6X are on draught, along with John Smith's, and an eclectic wine list includes 35 bottles, while six wines are offered by the glass. SAMPLE DISHES: duck and griottines terrine £6; linguine di mare £9.50; Eton mess £4.75.

Licensees James Elliot and Paul Salisbury (Whitbread)
Open *11 to 11; bar food and restaurant 12 to 2.30, 7 to 10 (9.30 Sun); closed 25 Dec*
Details *Children welcome Car park Wheelchair access (also WC) Garden and patio Background music Dogs welcome exc in dining room Amex, Delta, MasterCard, Switch, Visa*

All details are as accurate as possible at the time of going to press, but pubs often change hands, and it is wise to check beforehand by telephone anything that is particularly important to you.

LAVENHAM   Suffolk   map 6

▲ *Angel* 🍺 🍇

Market Place, Lavenham CO10 9QZ   TEL: (01787) 247388
WEB SITE: www.lavenham.co.uk/angel
on A1141, 6m NE of Sudbury

Lavenham is a well-preserved medieval market town, and the Angel,
a grand white-painted building decked with flower boxes, stands on
the picturesque ancient square – one visitor reckoned that if it
weren't for all the parked cars it would look like the set for a historical film. Inside, there are two bar areas, one in the characterful old
part of the inn, the other in a more recent extension, designed and
decorated in keeping with the building's antiquity (it was first
licensed in 1420). This is not really a place for casual drinkers, but
the fact that all tables are set for eating simply reflects the demands
of the clientele, who come for homely, traditional cooking using fine
local produce: home-made pork pie with pickles, steak and ale pie,
skate wing with prawns, lemon and capers, or pot-roast local
partridge. A few more modern international dishes may also feature,
such as tomato, mozzarella and basil salad. To finish, perhaps try
apricot and passion-fruit syllabub, or pear and almond tart. Adnams
Best Bitter, Nethergate Suffolk County Best Bitter, and Greene King
IPA and Abbot Ale are the regular real ales served, accompanied by
changing guest beers from local breweries. The 50-strong wine list,
focused mainly on France, is not particularly adventurous but it is
excellent value for money, and all eight house wines are available by
the glass or on the part-bottle basis (you are charged for what you
drink). A couple of classics from Bordeaux and Burgundy are there
for deeper pockets, and don't miss the local wine, Shawsgate
Vineyard Müller-Thurgau. SAMPLE DISHES: warm salad of smoked
duck and bacon £5.25; grilled monkfish with saffron and chives
£9.50; raspberry crème brûlée £3.50.

Licensees Roy Whitworth and John Barry (freehouse)
Open *11 to 11, Sun 12 to 10.30; bar food and restaurant 12 to 2.15, 6.45 to
9.15; closed 25 and 26 Dec*
Details *Children welcome   Car park   Wheelchair access (not WC)   Garden
No-smoking area in bar, no smoking in dining room   Occasional live music
Dogs welcome in bar   Amex, Delta, MasterCard, Switch, Visa
Accommodation: 8 rooms, B&B £45 to £70*

LEVINGTON   **Suffolk**   map 6

Ship

Levington IP10 0LQ   TEL: (01473) 659573
off A45 to Felixstowe, 6m SE of Ipswich

Immaculately whitewashed and with a pristine thatched roof and
hanging baskets overflowing with colourful flowers, the Ship is more
deserving than most buildings of the epithet 'idyllic'. It is an oasis of
rural charm in a much built-up village, and inside is just as appealing,
the low-ceilinged interconnecting rooms furnished with cushioned
settles and decorated with a motley collection of old jugs and numerous prints and pictures, many with a nautical theme. The fairly short
menu, chalked up on a board, offers unpretentious traditional food,
along the lines of steak and kidney pudding, beef casserole, kippers,
pork in plum sauce, and variations on the ploughman's theme; equally
homely desserts might include lemon and ginger flan, or syrup
pudding. Beers are from local breweries Adnams and Greene King,
while wines (also supplied by Adnams) are mainly French, with a few
from Spain and the New World; three are available by the glass.
Outdoor seating is provided for fine days. SAMPLE DISHES: ham ploughman's £4.50; broccoli, cheese and potato bake £6.50; apple pie £3.25.

Licensees William and Shirley Waite (Pubmaster)
Open *11.30 to 3, 6 to 11, Sun 12 to 3, 7 to 10.30; bar food and restaurant
12 to 2, 7 to 9; closed evenings 25 and 26 Dec*
Details *No children exc in garden/patio   Car park   Wheelchair access (also
WC)   Garden and patio   No smoking in dining room   No music   No dogs
Delta, MasterCard, Switch, Visa*

LEYBURN   **North Yorkshire**   map 9

▲ *Sandpiper Inn* ✿   NEW ENTRY

Market Place, Leyburn DL8 5AT
TEL: (01969) 622206

If you can find your way to the marketplace in Leyburn, you can find
the Sandpiper. Look for the Methodist church just off the square,
and the inn is right next to it. Two well-maintained and restored
stone buildings with gardens front and back have been linked
together to make up the pub, and the place is welcomingly floodlit in
the evenings. Corner seats, alcoves and a crackling fire make the
place homely, and the cheeriness of the staff adds to the air of
conviviality. A separate dining area where hops hang from the beams
has around a dozen tables. Lighter options, including sandwiches and
such dishes as omelette Arnold Bennett, and ham and eggs with fried

potatoes, may be had at lunchtimes. The dinner menu, served in the bar as well as the restaurant, deals in the sort of food you might find at smart city restaurants, spanning a main-course range from lamb chump with blueberries and mint to pork fillet wrapped in Parma ham with roasted peppers, sun-dried tomatoes and Parmesan macaroni. Starters are slightly more traditional: smoked salmon with lemon and black pepper, fishcakes with parsley and chive sauce, or warm goats' cheese on a red onion and tomato salad, for example. Bread-and-butter pudding has been praised, or there might be raspberry croustillant with Chantilly cream. Black Sheep ales, Theakston Best Bitter, and Dent Aviator Ale are real ales on offer, and the wine list of 30-plus bottles is good in France and the New World alike, with eight sold by the glass. Lovers of malt whiskies have no fewer than a hundred to choose from. SAMPLE DISHES: roasted tomato and lobster soup £3; crispy duck leg with fried potatoes, salad and oriental dressing £10; iced lemon meringue terrine £3.50.

Licensees Jonathan and Michael Harrison (freehouse)
Open *Tue to Sat and bank hol Mon 11.30 to 3, 6.30 to 11, Sun 12 to 3, 7 to 10.30; bar food 12 to 2; restaurant Tue to Sat 6.30 to 9, Sun 12 to 2, 6.30 to 9; closed Tue after bank hol*
Details *Children welcome in eating area and before 8 in dining room   Car park   Garden and patio   No smoking in dining room   Background music   Dogs welcome in snug area of bar   Delta, MasterCard, Switch, Visa   Accommodation: 2 rooms, B&B £35 to £55*

LICKFOLD   West Sussex   **map 3**

Lickfold Inn ✿ ▮

Lickfold GU28 9EY   TEL: (01798) 861285
off A272 Midhurst to Petworth road, signposted Lodsworth, 4m NE of Midhurst

---

This up-market dining pub none the less still caters well for beer aficionados, offering Ballard's Best and Lickfold Best, plus guests such as Ringwood Fortyniner, Fuller's ESB, Badger Tanglefoot and Wadworth 6X. Six wines come by the glass from a list that was under review as the Guide went to press. The timber-framed building, with herringbone brickwork, dates from 1460 and has a flowery terrace and garden. Such splendour attracts racegoers from Goodwood, spectators from the nearby polo ground at Midhurst, and walkers on the South Downs. On weekday lunchtimes, open sandwiches are served with chips, and the dining room offers an imaginative menu. Black-bean, baby sweetcorn and noodle soup, or wood-roasted sardines with tomato and herb sauce might be starters or snacks. A reporter commended the presentation, quality of ingredients and accuracy of cooking of freshly made pancakes generously filled with succulent strips of crispy duck with cucumber and home-made chutney, and chunky rabbit and chorizo terrine with decently dressed mixed leaves. Main dishes might include venison steak with mustard mash and red onion marmalade, or gilt-head bream with coconut, coriander and chilli. The formal restaurant on the first floor is open only for Friday and Saturday dinner and Sunday lunch. SAMPLE DISHES: Parma ham and mozzarella salad £6.25; organic sirloin steak with béarnaise £13.50; baked medlar parcel with praline mascarpone £4.75.

Licensees Mr and Mrs Portman (freehouse)
Open *11 to 3, 6 to 11, Sun 12 to 3, 7 to 10.30; bar food 12 to 2.30, 7 to 9.30; restaurant Fri and Sat 7 to 9.30, Sun 12 to 2.30*
Details *Children welcome in bar eating area Car park Wheelchair access (also WC) Garden and patio Background and occasional live music; jukebox Dogs welcome Amex, Delta, Diners, MasterCard, Switch, Visa*

LIDGATE   **Suffolk**   map 6

Star Inn

Lidgate CB8 9PP   TEL: (01638) 500275
on B1063, 6m SE of Newmarket

Formed from a pair of cottages with origins in the fifteenth century and set in an attractive, well-maintained village, this pink-washed building is the epitome of the traditional English pub, both outside and in its three connecting rooms (one a non-smoking dining room), where logs burn in huge fireplaces on chilly days. It may then come as some surprise to find Spanish posters on the walls (as well as a dartboard) and several Spanish dishes on the lengthy blackboard menus. Salmon à la Gallega and hake à la Vasca might appear along-side venison in port, or roast chicken aux herbes, with sorbets from Minorca next to sticky toffee pudding on the desserts list. The expla-nation comes in the shape of friendly landlady Maria Teresa Axon, who hails from Catalonia, and her efforts to combine two strong traditions is successful and evidently popular. This means that on some days there may be no room for casual drinkers, although the atmosphere is down-to-earth and pubby. Beers are from the Greene King brewery in nearby Bury St Edmunds, while five house wines are offered at £11 a bottle, or £2.25 a glass, from a lengthy list. SAMPLE DISHES: smoked duck breast salad £6; paella valenciana £11.50; lambs' kidneys in sherry £10.50.

Licensees M.T. and A. Axon (Greene King)
Open *11 to 3, 5 to 11, Sun 11 to 3; bar food and restaurant 12 to 2 (2.30 Sun), 7 to 9.30*
Details *Children welcome Car park Garden No smoking in dining room Occasional live or background music Dogs welcome exc in dining room Amex, Delta, MasterCard, Switch, Visa*

LIFTON   Devon   map 1

▲ *Arundell Arms* 🌹 🍇

Lifton PL16 0AA   TEL: (01566) 784666
just off A30, 4m E of Launceston

Twenty miles of salmon and trout fishing rights on the River Tamar
and its tributaries are one of the many reasons why this sixteenth-
century coaching inn, covered in a blanket of creepers, attracts
legions of sporting types. The beautiful countryside – the village is
close to Dartmoor – also offers plentiful opportunities for shooting,
riding, bird-watching and walking. After all that activity, the warmth
and comfort of the traditionally furnished bar is very welcome, not
to mention the excellent food. The frequently changing bar menu
opens with a page of starters and light meals, ranging from smoked
salmon with cucumber pickle, and terrine of partridge and duck with
toasted honey bread and apricot chutney, to sandwiches such as
croque-monsieur, or rib of Devon beef with horseradish. Hot main
dishes might include roasted Cornish cod with creamed lentils,
garlic, herbs and griddled potatoes, or slow-cooked confit duck leg
with parsnip and celeriac purée, bacon and Madeira. There are also
various salads, perhaps of home-cured gammon with Cumberland
sauce and potato salad, with, to finish, excellent local cheeses, or
things like blackcurrant mousse with red wine syrup and crème
fraîche. The elegant restaurant has its own fixed-price menu in similar style. No real ales are offered, but the wine list is impressive, with
around a dozen wines available by the glass (including two wines of
the month) and a good selection of half-bottles. Those willing to
splash out a little will feel quite at home with the Bordeaux and
Burgundy selections, but those with more modest aspirations are
well catered for too: plenty of varietal, fruity wines, many at under
£15 a bottle, are there to select from. SAMPLE DISHES: salad of sweet
peppers with pickled anchovies, Parmesan and basil relish £5.75;
fillet of salmon in beer batter with chips and tartare sauce £11; warm
date and ginger sponge pudding with clotted cream £4.50.

Licensee Anne Voss-Bark (freehouse)
Open *11 (12 Sun) to 11; bar food 12 to 2.30, 6 to 9.30; restaurant 12.30 to
2, 7.30 to 9.30; closed evenings 24, 25 and 26 Dec*
Details *Children welcome   Car park   Wheelchair access (not WC)   Garden
and patio   No smoking in dining room   Background music   Dogs welcome
exc in dining room   Amex, Delta, Diners, MasterCard, Switch, Visa
Accommodation: 28 rooms, B&B £46.50 to £117*

LITTLE HAMPDEN   **Buckinghamshire**   map 3

▲ *Rising Sun*   NEW ENTRY
Little Hampden HP16 9PS   TEL: (01494) 488393
WEB SITE: www.rising-sun.demon.co.uk
from Great Missenden take road signposted Rignall and Butler's
Cross; after 2m take turn marked 'Little Hampden only'

Deep in the heart of walking and mountain-biking country, at the
end of a single-track lane with passing places, the Sun also rises. It
may look quite ordinary from the outside, with a few picnic benches
on the front terrace, but it could lay claim to being the Prime
Minister's local, since his country residence, Chequers, is little more
than a mile up the road. Plenty of beams, a wood-burning stove, a
brick-built bar and a chain of three interconnecting rooms are to be
found within, as are some nattily attired staff in the house navy-blue
polo-shirt and striped aprons. Adnams Best, Brakspear Bitter and
Marston's Pedigree are the real ales dispensed, and 12 wines are
available by the glass or bottle. Food, ordered at the bar, is listed on
blackboards. Some innovative and enterprising cooking is going on
here, as witness a starter menu that extends from an oriental king
prawn platter with chilli mayonnaise and garlic bread, through
sweet-cured herrings with dill dressing, to calf's liver with crispy
bacon and raspberry vinaigrette. These may be followed by a version
of chicken korma in a sauce containing pineapple and peppers, or a
huge piece of lamb shoulder with a rib-sticking sauce of honey and
rosemary. Seafood shows up strongly, too, the range taking in
dressed Norfolk crab with Gruyère and grain mustard, and an
unusual treatment of rainbow trout, in which the baked fish is filled
with mushrooms, raisins and hazelnuts and sauced with red wine and
blackcurrants. Finish with 'seriously good' caramelised fruit tart with
whipped cream and ice cream, or perhaps creamy bread-and-butter
pudding with apricot and orange sauce. SAMPLE DISHES: grilled king
scallops wrapped in bacon with basil and walnut vinaigrette £6;
home-smoked pork joint with red wine and plum sauce £9; Jamaican
toffee banana pancake with cream £3.25.

Licensee Rory Dawson (freehouse)
Open *Tue to Sat 11.30 to 3, 6.30 to 11, Sun 12 to 3; bar food 11.30 (12*
Sun) to 3, 6.30 to 11
Details *Children welcome   Car park   Garden and patio   No-smoking area in*
bar   Background music   No dogs   Delta, MasterCard, Switch, Visa
Accommodation: 3 rooms, B&B £30 to £58

LITTLE LANGDALE   **Cumbria**   map 8

▲ *Three Shires Inn*   NEW ENTRY

SETTING

Little Langdale LA22 9NZ   TEL: (015394) 37215
WEB SITE: www.threeshiresinn.co.uk
on unnumbered road to Wrynose Pass from A593 just W of
Skelwith Bridge

Here is a pub in a jewel of a location, a Lakeland valley of stunning
beauty with roads so convoluted and steep that great care is required
if driving conditions are bad, and where even local delivery vans
forbear to venture. If remote is your style, go for the Three Shires
(named because it stands near what were once the triple county
boundaries of Cumberland, Westmorland and Lancashire). It dates
from the latter half of Victoria's reign and makes the most of its
setting with outdoor tables on a patio overlooking a stream.
However cut off the situation may seem to be, you won't lack for
company in the form of fell walkers and families, who pour in for
simple lunches of baguettes, baked potatoes, or dishes such as
Cumberland sausage with onion rings, and Whitby scampi with chips
and a generous salad. Soups are a feature, too, usually based on one
vegetable such as leek or spinach. In the evenings, a fuller menu may
take you from pan-fried scallops with herb risotto to salmon fillet in
red wine sauce, while blackboard specials might include terrine of
ham hock with parsley potato salad and a mustard dressing, followed
by fillet of brill with leek fondue. Lakeland ice creams are proudly
served, or you might fancy white chocolate brûlée with dark chocolate sauce. Dinner in the restaurant is a set-price deal of four courses.
Jennings Best Bitter and Cumberland Ale and the Coniston
Brewery's Old Man Ale are the beers on offer, and there is a large
selection of whiskies, as well as mulled wine. Five wines from a list
of over 40 are served by the glass. SAMPLE DISHES: home-cured marinated salmon with a dill and whisky sauce £5; medallions of fillet
steak with a pineapple and black pepper butter £12.50; baked egg
custard with dairy ice cream laced with nutmeg £3.75.

Licensee I.K. Stephenson (freehouse)
Open *11 to 11, Sun 12 to 10.30 (12 to 3, 8 to 10.30 winter); bar food 12 to*
2, 6 to 8.45; closed Jan; no evening food Dec and Jan exc New Year week
Details *Children welcome   Car park   Wheelchair access (also WC)   Garden*
No-smoking area in bar, no smoking in dining room   No music   Dogs
welcome in bar   Delta, MasterCard, Switch, Visa   Accommodation: 10
rooms, B&B £29.50 to £82

Recommendations for good country pubs will be very welcome.

LLANFAIR WATERDINE　　Shropshire　　map 5

▲ *Waterdine* 🏵️🏵️ 🍺 🍇　NEW ENTRY

Llanfair Waterdine LD7 1TU　TEL: (01547) 528214
4m NW of Knighton, off B4355 Knighton to Newton road, over Teme bridge at Lloyney

Anyone arriving in Llanfair Waterdine looking for the Red Lion will find that the sixteenth-century longhouse opposite the church and close to Offa's Dyke Path has been renamed the Waterdine. A change of ownership has brought various other alterations (refurbishment was in progress as the Guide went to press), but the wild and isolated Teme Valley setting, with views over the river towards the mountains, remains a draw. So, too, does the selection of beers: various real ales from local microbreweries might include Jack Snipe and Red Kite from Woodhampton in nearby Leominster. More of an emphasis is placed on food than before, and there is 'not a boring dish in sight' on the short bar menu. The style is not what might be called pub grub, though a commendable ploughman's is offered, but nor is it in the wildly eclectic modern vein. The real strength of the cooking lies in the fact that everything is freshly made using fine regional ingredients. Thus the blackboard over the fireplace may list cream of watercress soup, or black pudding with vegetable confit among starters, with honey-roasted chicken breast with fennel, watercress and orange salad, or confit of duck with plum and star anise sauce on steamed potatoes to follow. The separate restaurant has a more formal atmosphere, though its menu is also available in the bar, and might feature dishes such as cappuccino of chestnuts with truffle oil, followed by roast local partridge on beetroot risotto with parsnip mousse and Madeira sauce. Wines on the extensive list are divided simply into reds and whites, with two pages of special recommendations. Most major wine-producing countries are represented, and there is good choice under the £15 mark, though there's room for higher spenders to splash out, particularly in Burgundy and Bordeaux. Three white wines and one red are served by the glass. SAMPLE DISHES: curried lambs' kidneys with salad £5.50; lightly cured loin of Gloucester Old Spot pork with root vegetables £13.50; rhubarb crème brûlée £4.50.

Licensee Ken Adams (freehouse)
Open *Tue to Sat 12 to 3 (2.30 winter), 6.30 (7 winter) to 11, Sun 12 to 2.30, 7 to 10.30; bar food (exc Sun evening) 12.15 to 2, 7 to 9.30; restaurant 12.15 to 1.30, 7 to 9; closed Sun evening winter, 1 week Nov to Dec, 1 week Jan to Feb*
Details *Children welcome in bar eating area　Car park　Garden　No smoking in lounge or dining room　No music　No dogs　MasterCard, Switch, Visa Accommodation: 3 rooms, B&B £35 to £70*

▲ *Loders Arms*

Loders DT6 3SA   TEL: (01308) 422431
off A3066, 2m NE of Bridport

Fans of traditional pub games should check out the skittle alley at this charming local watering hole in a small, typically Dorset-style village of thatched stone cottages. Bar food, listed on blackboards, ranges from various filled baguettes and familiar pub staples along the lines of lasagne, chilli and soups. The separate restaurant menu, also available in the bar, offers a few more up-market options: perhaps a salad of pigeon breasts, or fresh anchovies for starters, followed by venison steak, smoked haddock fishcakes, or whole sea bass, with vanilla terrine, or chocolate truffle torte to finish. The Loders is a Palmers pub, serving Bridport Bitter, IPA and 200 – the brewery itself is in nearby Bridport and holds the distinction of being Britain's only thatched brewery. Eight wines by the glass are also listed on a blackboard. SAMPLE DISHES: crab and coriander parcel £4.25; beef stroganoff £9.25; crème brûlée £3.25.

Licensees Helen and Roger Flint (J.C. and R.H. Palmer)
Open *11.30 to 3, 6 to 11, Sun 12 to 10.30; bar food and restaurant 12.30 to 2, 7.15 to 9*
Details *Children welcome in eating areas   Car park   Wheelchair access (also WC)   Garden and patio   No smoking in dining room   Occasional background music   Dogs welcome exc in dining room   MasterCard, Visa Accommodation: 2 rooms, B&B £25 to £45*

Red Lion

Longdon Green WS15 4QF   TEL: (01543) 490250
just off A51 Lichfield to Rugeley road, about 2m N of Lichfield

Chef/landlord Andrew Purcell and landlady Davina have been commended for the food, and its service, at this unassuming Victorian red-brick pub in a quiet village. It is a pleasant and comfortable place, with a few old paintings, mirrors and displays of dried flowers, and fresh ones on the polished, dark wooden tables. At lunchtime, among the fillings for baguettes and ciabatta bread might be bacon and Brie, marinated peppers topped with toasted cheese, or tuna mayonnaise with diced peppers, red onion and melted cheese. Main courses at lunchtime follow a conventional route, from steaks or chops to cod in batter. The evening menu is longer and more ambitious, with starters of perhaps baked Camembert in filo with Cumberland sauce, tandoori chicken, or Greek salad, with main courses of roast Gressingham duck with Cointreau gravy, or pork chop with apple and red onion marmalade, and various grills. Daily specials might include smoked haddock fishcakes, tournedos topped with haggis and whisky sauce, or chargrilled tuna. Marston's Pedigree and Worthington are on draught, and four wines are served by the glass. SAMPLE DISHES: vegetable soup £3; breast of chicken stuffed with bacon and Brie £11; caramelised oranges with brandy sauce £3.50.

Licensee Andrew Purcell (Enterprise Inns)
Open *12 to 2.30, 6.30 to 11; bar food (exc Sun evening and Mon) 12.30 to 2.30, 6.30 to 9; closed Mon to Fri lunchtime winter*
Details *Children welcome   Car park   Wheelchair access (also WC)   Garden and patio   Background music   Dogs by arrangement   Delta, MasterCard, Switch, Visa*

LONGSTOCK   Hampshire   map 2

▲ *Peat Spade* 🍺
Longstock SO20 6DR   TEL: (01264) 810612
off A3057, 1m N of Stockbridge

Although a dining pub, the Peat Spade remains a warm and comforting country inn. Open log fires, collections of toby jugs and pipes, prints and other pictures vie for attention with plants. And above all the pub stocks local ales – Hampshire King Alfred's and Ringwood Fortyniner – as well as a guest beer and Thatcher's cider. The wine list is short but carefully selected and fairly priced, with around a half-dozen sold by the glass. The blackboard menu offers a handful of starters, with meat represented perhaps by rabbit terrine with apricot chutney, and fish by fresh anchovy fillets on tomato and basil. Main dishes are broader in scope, ranging from roast roe deer loin fillet with grillotines sauce, Gressingham duck breast with hoisin dressing, Aberdeen Angus ribeye steak, and lambs' liver, bacon and onions with mash. But it is fish and vegetables that seem to excite the kitchen's interest and imagination, so you might find baked Dorset scallops and chorizo with sesame, fresh basil tagliatelle with local smoked trout, or monkfish with crab and mussel sauce. SAMPLE DISHES: tian of avocado with sweet pepper salsa £4.50; local free-range pork bangers and mash £6.75; poached fresh figs in Muscat sauce with crème fraîche £4.25.

Licensees Sarah Hinman and Bernard Startup (freehouse)
Open *Tue to Sat 11.30 to 3, 6 to 11, Sun 11.30 to 3; bar food 12 to 2, 7 to 9 (9.30 Fri and Sat)*
Details *Children welcome   Car park   Wheelchair access (also WC)   Garden and patio   No-smoking area in bar   Dogs welcome   No cards Accommodation: 2 rooms, B&B from £58.75 (double room)*

LONGWORTH   Oxfordshire   map 2

Blue Boar Inn

Tucks Lane, Longworth OX13 5ET   TEL: (01865) 820494
off A420 at Kingston Bagpuize, 7m W of Abingdon

This small, friendly, old village pub is more an eating than a drinking place. Its busy main bar, painted in terracotta, has a beamed ceiling decorated with dried hops, and at its eight or so old tables you can sit on chairs or benches. There is no separate restaurant, and the short menu includes such pub favourites as Thai fishcakes with yoghurt sauce, deep-fried Brie with port and cranberry sauce, home-made burger with Brie or Stilton, cod in Morrells Ale batter, and gammon, egg and chips. Four or five specials might include half a shoulder of lamb with port and rosemary gravy, salmon filo parcel on spinach, or Mediterranean beef skewers. Finish with sticky toffee pudding with butterscotch sauce, or death by chocolate. Oxford Bitter and Grumpy Cow may sound like dons from a local seat of learning but are actually the Morrells ales on draught. Four of the 30 or so wines are sold by the glass. SAMPLE DISHES: pan-fried calamari with Thai sauce £4.25; bacon-wrapped beef fillet with brandy and mushroom sauce £14; French lemon tart £4.25.

Licensee Craig Foster (Morrells)
Open *12 to 3, 6 to 11; bar food 12 to 2, 7 to 10*
Details *Children welcome   Car park   Wheelchair access (also WC)   Garden Occasional live or background music   No dogs   Delta, MasterCard, Switch, Visa*

LOSTWITHIEL   Cornwall   map 1

▲ Royal Oak 🍺

Duke Street, Lostwithiel PL22 0AG   TEL: (01208) 872552
off A390, 5m SE of Bodmin

In the thirteenth century Lostwithiel was the second busiest port on the south coast. Times have changed a little since then, and this inn, which dates all the way back to that lost heyday, enjoys a more tran-quil setting today. Inside, it retains a pleasing period feel, with low-slung beams, and a stone-flagged floor in the main bar. The extensive carpeted lounge makes a comfortable place in which to eat. Fuller's London Pride, Greene King Abbot Ale, Marston's Pedigree, Sharp's Own, Eldridge Pope Royal Oak and Spingo ales might be the real ales on tap, and are supplemented by a cosmopolitan range of bottled beers. The wine list is enterprising in extent, making a particularly good fist of the classic French regions, with seven available by the glass. Eileen Hine's cooking has the ring of home-made authenticity about it, according to a pair of reporters who enjoyed roast pork with apple sauce and the house speciality, cow pie (steak and kidney marinated in ale). Otherwise, there are grilled Dover sole with melted butter and a squeeze of lemon, poached salmon in cream sauce, and beef bourguignon. If you're not from round these parts, don't miss the clotted cream, perhaps served with home-made fruit pie or treacle tart. Even at busy times, service is quick and eager. SAMPLE DISHES: French onion soup £2.50; sauté chicken in red wine £7.50; apple pie £2.

Licensees M.G. and E.P. Hine (freehouse)
Open *11 to 11, Sun 12 to 10.30; bar food and restaurant 12 to 2.30 (2 winter), 6.30 to 9.30 (9 winter)*
Details *Children welcome in family room   Car park   Wheelchair access (not WC)   Garden and patio   Jukebox   Dogs welcome in public bar   Amex, Delta, Diners, MasterCard, Switch, Visa   Accommodation: 6 rooms, B&B £36 to £63*

LOWER CHICKSGROVE   Wiltshire   map 2

▲ *Compasses Inn*

Lower Chicksgrove SP3 6NB   TEL: (01722) 714318
1m NW of A30 between Swallowcliffe and Fovant

This remote pub is well signposted, which is just as well, since you will find it along a web of narrow lanes deep in rolling countryside. The sixteenth-century, thatched inn attracts people to the tiny hamlet, which has given its name to one of the beers served here – Chicksgrove Churl is brewed by Wadworth, whose 6X is also kept, as well as Bass and Tisbury Stonehenge. Of 20 wines only one is over £20, and four are sold by the glass. Service is said to be polite and efficient even when staff are under pressure at busy periods. The menu is on blackboards, with additional daily specials written on the canopy of a wood-burning stove in the inglenook of the low-beamed, unspoilt bar. The food, well presented on large white plates, has been described as 'modern and imaginative with a varied choice'. You might begin with goats' cheese and pesto on a toasted garlic croûte, or baked avocado with walnuts and Blue Vinny cheese. Follow with perhaps slowly cooked half-shoulder of lamb with honey, molasses and soy sauce; salmon fillet with ginger, lime and spring onions; or pan-fried pigeon breast with wild mushrooms. Home-made desserts range from the lightness of poached pears to the richness of apple and banana toffee crumble. SAMPLE DISHES:

baked red pepper with tomato and anchovies £5; lamb stew with dumplings £9; raspberry and pear syllabub £3.75.

Licensee Jonathan Bold (freehouse)
Open *Tue to Sat 12 to 3, 6 to 11, Sun and bank hol Mon 12 to 3, 7 to 10.30; bar food (exc Sun evening) 12 to 2, 7 to 9*
Details *Children welcome Car park Garden and patio No music Dogs welcome Delta, MasterCard, Switch, Visa Accommodation: 4 rooms, B&B £40 to £55*

LOWER ODDINGTON   Gloucestershire   map 5

▲ *Fox Inn* ✿

Lower Oddington GL56 0UR   TEL: (01451) 870555
off A436, E of Stow-on-the-Wold

Kirk and Sally Ritchie, who took over the Fox in spring 2000 and who previously managed the Lygon Arms in Broadway, have been praised for not making too many changes at this upmarket-style pub with its creeper-covered, honey-coloured walls, and what they have done are improvements. The interior, with bare or stripped wooden furniture and coir or flagstone floors, is spacious and civilised, with a large stone fireplace surmounted by three foxes' heads. Menus change roughly every four weeks, and Moroccan vegetable curry with couscous is the furthest excursion from the modern European style. Daily specials might be seared scallops with mizuna, ginger and shallot dressing, or cod fillet baked with fennel and leeks, and, from the main menu, dishes to comfort traditionalists include salmon fish-cakes with parsley sauce, and steak and kidney pie. Toffee apple crumble with clotted cream, or pear and ginger steamed pudding might round things off alongside Cashel Blue with biscuits. Staff deal efficiently with a consistently busy place. Regulars on tap are Hook Norton Best Bitter and Badger Tanglefoot, but guest beers such as Old Speckled Hen, Jennings Cumberland Ale and beers from Brakspear also make an appearance. The wine list of around 40 bins, with 11 by the glass, is well balanced and modestly priced. SAMPLE DISHES: goats' cheese, tomato and pesto tart £5; chicken breast with Dijon mustard sauce £8.75; black cherry and chocolate trifle £3.75.

Licensee Kirk Ritchie (freehouse)
Open *12 to 3, 6.30 to 11, Sun 7 to 10.30; bar food 12 to 2, 7 to 10 (9.30 Sun); closed 25 Dec, 26 Dec evening, 31 Dec, 1 Jan*
Details *Children welcome Car park Garden and patio Occasional background music No dogs Delta, MasterCard, Switch, Visa Accommodation: 3 rooms, B&B £48 to £85*

Wellington Inn 🏵 🍇

19 The Green, Lund YO25 9TE   TEL: (01377) 217294
on B1248 between Beverley and Malton

Lund is set in the Yorkshire Wolds, in a lesser-known tract of the
East Riding. The Wellington, still very much a local pub, sits on one
side of the village green facing the war memorial, and benefits from
interior touches such as open log fires in winter and real beams. The
blackboard bar lunch menus deal in the sorts of dishes you might
expect to find in such an ambience, with smoked haddock fishcakes,
and country pork terrine among starters, and main courses such as
beef casserole served with broccoli and mash. The menus change
daily, and evenings could see Caesar salad followed by chicken breast
filled with mozzarella wrapped in Parma ham on pesto with tagliatelle, or calf's liver with mash and onion gravy. Those not in the
market for a full-scale midday meal might opt for a granary sandwich containing anything from hot steak to crab. The sweet-toothed
can enjoy syrup and ginger sponge with custard, or banana and
toffee cheesecake. The separate dinner menu in the restaurant might
overlap with what's on offer in the bar, offering perhaps salad of
sauté duck liver, fresh apricots and ginger, then pan-fried fillet of
beef with anchovy and mixed pepper butter. On handpump are
Timothy Taylor Landlord and Dark Mild, Black Sheep Best Bitter
and John Smith's Cask Bitter, but wines are good, too, running to
nearly five dozen well-chosen bins and encompassing virtually all the
major producing countries. Toasted Head Chardonnay from
California and Lebanon's Château Musar give some idea of the
breadth. Six are served by the glass. SAMPLE DISHES: red onion and
shallot tarte Tatin with toasted goats' cheese £4.75; pan-fried veal
cutlet with lemon and rosemary on roasted garlic mash £14; syrup
and ginger sponge £4.

Licensees Russell and Sarah Jeffery (freehouse)
Open *Tue to Sun 12 to 3, all week 6.30 to 11 (10.30 Sun); bar food Tue to
Sun 12 to 2, Tue to Sat 7 to 9; restaurant Tue to Sat 6.30 to 9*
Details *Children welcome lunchtime only in bar eating area   Car park
Wheelchair access (also WC)   Patio   No-smoking area in bar   Background
music   No dogs   Delta, MasterCard, Switch, Visa*

LUSTLEIGH   Devon   map 1

Cleave

Lustleigh TQ13 9TJ   TEL: (01647) 277223
off A382, 4m SE of Moretonhampstead

The charming village of Lustleigh is in a peaceful wooded valley on
the edge of Dartmoor. Its thatched cottages and thirteenth-century
church draw many visitors, some of whom join the locals in this
friendly and welcoming fifteenth-century thatched inn tucked away
at the heart of the village. There are inglenooks, low, beamed ceilings, antique settles and stone walls, and the family room and
colourful garden are popular in summer. Both the lunchtime and
evening menus are supplemented by blackboard specials that usually
include pasta. Lunch dishes are mainly traditional, but the odd
surprise includes an intriguing range of ploughman's, including rare
roast beef, home-cooked ham, cold roast pork, and home-made pâté.
Evening main dishes might include grilled local trout, vegetarian
pancakes with ratatouille, chicken curry, and roast silverside with
Yorkshire pudding. Wadworth 6X is usually stocked, with two guest
ales, which may be Old Speckled Hen, Fuller's London Pride or
Brakspear Special, and there is Addlestone's cider. All 15 wines are
priced by both the bottle and glass. SAMPLE DISHES: deep-fried Brie
with sweet-and-sour sauce £4.75; Chagford pork sausage with chips
£6; toffee apple pie £3.50.

Licensee A. Perring (Heavitree)
Open *11 to 11, Sun 12 to 3, 6.30 to 11; bar food 12 to 9 (12 to 2.30, 6.30
to 9 winter); closed Mon winter*
Details *Children welcome in family room   Car park   Wheelchair access (not
WC)   Garden   No-smoking area in bar, no smoking in dining room   No
music   Dogs welcome   Delta, MasterCard, Switch, Visa*

LUXBOROUGH   Somerset   map 1

▲ Royal Oak of Luxborough 🍺

Luxborough TA23 0SH   TEL: (01984) 640319
off A396, 4m S of Dunster

This unspoilt fourteenth-century inn sits beside a stream at the
bottom of a steep-sided valley in the Exmoor National Park. Within
are a rambling series of rooms with flagged or cobbled floors, low
beams and, in the main bar, a large open fireplace, plus a pair of
civilised dining rooms with deep-green walls hung with hunting
prints, and a convivial atmosphere. Bar snacks include sandwiches,
ploughman's, chilli beef tacos and chicken satay, while more substan-

tial dishes can be found on printed menus supplemented by a blackboard showing a catch of the day and other specials. You might begin with Caesar salad, or a plate of smoked salmon with capers and shallots, and go on to whole roast sea bass with spring onions and ginger finished with hoisin sauce, grilled red mullet on pesto mash with a tomato and lemon sauce, or roast rack of lamb on buttered spinach with garlic and rosemary. Home-made puddings might include cherry frangipane tart or raspberry cheesecake, or try some of the good Somerset cheeses on offer, or Cropwell Bishop Stilton from further afield. An interesting and commendable selection of draught beers includes Exmoor Gold, Cotleigh Tawny Bitter, Palmers Dorset Gold and a guest ale (perhaps Hop Back Crop Circle or Palmers 200), as well as local farm ciders and a good choice of whiskies. Three wines are served by the glass. SAMPLE DISHES: goujons of sole with lime mayonnaise £6.50; seared loin of pork on Bramley mash with calvados cream sauce £10.25; Bakewell tart and custard £3.25.

Licensee Cecil Barrow (freehouse)
Open *12 to 2.30, 6 to 11 (10.30 Sun Oct to May); bar food and restaurant 12 to 2, 7 to 9.30*
Details *Children welcome in bar eating area and family room   Car park Wheelchair access (not WC)   Garden   No smoking in dining room   No music Dogs welcome   MasterCard, Switch, Visa   Accommodation: 12 rooms, B&B £40 to £75*

LYDDINGTON   Rutland   map 5

▲ *Old White Hart*

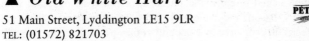

51 Main Street, Lyddington LE15 9LR
TEL: (01572) 821703
off A6003, 2m S of Uppingham

This is one of few English pubs where 'piste' means a patch of ground where pétanque is played – they have ten lanes in the pretty walled garden. Tradition rules inside the mellow-stone, sixteenth-century building. Dominoes is played in a room with a wood-burning stove, while a log fire warms the snug main bar area. A reporter has described the food as unpretentious and cooked to perfection. It runs from toad-in-the-hole with 'the tastiest of sausages' (they are home-made) to wild duck in season. Other game dishes might include a terrine with herb vinaigrette, or partridge pudding, and vegetarians might be offered roast pepper stuffed with goats' cheese and hazelnuts with pesto dressing. Puddings take in 'heaven-sent' chocolate truffle cake with praline ice cream, or mango and passionfruit marshmallow pavlova. Greene King Abbot Ale and Black Sheep are on draught, and the list of about 30 wines, with seven or eight by the glass, is strong in French classics. SAMPLE DISHES: home-cured gravad lax £6.25; deep-fried Grimsby haddock £9; cherry and almond tart with cinnamon ice cream £3.75.

Licensees Stuart and Holly East (freehouse)
Open *12 to 3, 6.30 to 11, Sun 12 to 3, 7 to 10.30; bar food and restaurant (exc Sun evening) 12 to 2 (2.30 Sun), 6.30 to 9; closed 25 Dec*
Details *Children welcome   Car park   Garden and patio   No smoking in dining room   Occasional live or background music   No dogs   Delta, MasterCard, Switch, Visa*

LYDFORD   Devon   map 1

▲ *Castle Inn*

Lydford EX20 4BH   TEL: (01822) 820242
WEB SITE: www.smoothhound.co.uk/hotel/castle.html
off A386, 7m N of Tavistock

To find the Castle Inn, first find the edifice after which it is named – the pub is just next door. It has stood the test of time better than its namesake, which is now no more than a ghostly ruin, and is a popular and busy local with a cosy public bar whose focal point is a large inglenook. There is also a no-smoking snug and a dining room plus a lounge, all with a warm, old-fashioned appeal; the fireplace in the dining room is believed to date from Saxon times, when it would have been part of the castle. The wide-ranging menu, available throughout, features a 'game-keeper's corner' of dishes like Somerset wild rabbit baked in cider and mustard, or pot-roast pheasant with mushrooms, bacon, red wine and herbs. Main courses range from Thai green chicken curry to steak and kidney pie, and a page of grills might offer gigot of lamb marinated in basil and garlic with crispy polenta and red wine jus. A decent range of real ales includes Flowers IPA and Fuller's London Pride. Ten wines by the glass and a full list of around 40 more cover the classics, from simple white Burgundy to Australian Shiraz-Cabernet Sauvignon without breaking the £20 mark. SAMPLE DISHES: parsnip and apple soup £4; braised wild boar steaks with mushrooms, button onions and lardons £12.25; Glenfiddich bread-and-butter pudding with custard £4.

Licensees Mike and Lyn Hazelton (Heavitree)
Open *Mon to Thur 11.30 to 3, 6 to 11, Fri to Sun 11.30 to 11; bar food and restaurant 12 to 2.30, 6.30 to 9.30; no food 25 Dec*
Details *Children welcome in eating areas   Car park   Wheelchair access (also WC)   Garden and patio   No-smoking areas in bar, no smoking in dining room   No music   Dogs welcome exc in dining areas   Delta, MasterCard, Switch, Visa   Accommodation: 9 rooms, B&B £25 to £79*

Dartmoor Inn ✿

Lydford EX20 4AY   TEL: (01822) 820221
on A386 Tavistock to Okehampton Road

'Someone in the kitchen certainly knows what they are doing,' reckoned a visitor, who felt that the journey to reach this desolate spot was well worth the effort, even in the depths of winter. The interior décor is reminiscent of New England, with tongue-and-groove panelling, muted greens and creams, and dried flowers in painted pots and buckets – 'all very tasteful without being formal' – and the atmosphere is of a smart, up-market dining pub rather than somewhere for drinking. That said, a couple of real ales and a real cider are offered, including some decent guest beers such as Dartmoor Best Bitter. Menu options include a weekday set-price deal and light suppers. Soups are a strong point: roasted tomato with nutmeg cream, and turnip have both been recommended. The varied menu also includes some inventive twists on traditional themes, such as grilled sardines with anchovy and rosemary butter, and crisp-fried Gressingham duck with a hot vinaigrette of leeks and a peppercorn sauce, as well as straightforward grills and dishes from the modern repertoire like chargrilled tuna with sweet peppers and oriental dressing. With around six bottles also listed by the glass, the wine list is chosen with an eye to price, so while you can indulge in St Hallett's wonderful Blackwell Shiraz for £25 a bottle, most of the other wines come in at significantly lower sums. Menetou-Salon from Henri Pellé at £16 is a real bargain. SAMPLE DISHES: game soup £3.50; fritters of sea fishes in saffron batter with salad, chips and green mayonnaise £10.75; gingerbread pudding with caramel sauce and clotted cream £4.50.

Licensees Philip Burgess, Ian Brown and Anne Voss-Bark (freehouse)
Open *Tue to Sat 11.30 to 2.30, 6 (6.30 winter) to 11, Sun 11.30 to 2.30; bar food and restaurant 12 to 2, 6.30 to 9.45*
Details *Children welcome in dining room; no children under 5 on Fri and Sat evenings   Car park   Patio   No smoking in dining room   Background music   Dogs welcome in bar   Delta, MasterCard, Switch, Visa*

LYDGATE   **Greater Manchester**   **map 8**

▲ *White Hart* ✿✿ 🍇

51 Stockport Road, Lydgate OL4 4JJ
TEL: (01457) 872566
on A6050, 3m E of Oldham

The White Hart is very much a modern interpretation of the traditional coaching inn, verging on being a fully fledged hotel. It is a comfortable, tastefully decorated place with a brasserie downstairs and a restaurant in an extension that also houses accommodation. There is still a bar area where those who wish to come for just a drink can enjoy a pint of Pendle Witches Brew, from the local Moorhouses Brewery, or JW Lees Bitter, but food and wine are the main preoccupations of the place. The brasserie menu features the products of the Saddleworth Sausage Company, based on the premises, which come in inventive varieties, such as maize-fed chicken and smoked bacon, lamb and mint, or spicy pork, and are served with various flavoured mashes. Otherwise, the style is typically modern and cosmopolitan, ranging from starters of spiced chicken terrine with sweetcorn fritter to main courses along the lines of roast rump of lamb with beans, chives and olives in pasta, roasted venison loin with buttered Savoy cabbage, crushed potatoes and juniper jus, and tempura of cod with minted peas and fried potatoes. To finish, the cheeseboard is one for enthusiasts, featuring Mrs Kirkham's smoked Lancashire, Sharpham Brie, and Cropwell Bishop Stilton; those with a sweet tooth might prefer raspberry cheesecake, or apple tart with vanilla ice cream. The restaurant menu is in similar vein and only slightly more formal. The well-laid-out wine list has an impressive 28 bottles by the glass and over 100 choices in total. Grape varieties are shown wherever possible to keep you in the picture, and wine lovers will be impressed by some interesting old vintages – 1985 Ch. Palmer, Spanish treasures from the early 1990s and from 1970. Prices are pitched at every level (glasses from £2.20 to £6.50, for a California pudding wine), so there's something for everyone. SAMPLE DISHES: warm salad of smoked salmon and scallops with tapénade £7; roast Barbary duck breast with sauté sweetbreads and thyme potato purée £14.50; chocolate fondant tart with pear and ginger ice cream £4.50.

Licensee Charles Brierley (freehouse)
Open *12 to 11 (10.30 Sun); bar food Mon to Sat 12 to 2.30, 6 to 9.30, Sun 1 to 8; restaurant Sun 1 to 3, Tue to Sat 6.15 to 9.30*
Details *Children welcome in bar eating area and dining room   Car park Wheelchair access (also WC)   Garden   No smoking in dining room Background music   Dogs welcome exc in dining areas   Amex, Delta, MasterCard, Switch, Visa   Accommodation: 12 rooms, B&B £62.50 to £90*

MADINGLEY   Cambridgeshire   map 6

Three Horseshoes 🏵 🏵 🍇

High Street, Madingley CB3 8AB   TEL: (01954) 210221
off A1303, 2m W of Cambridge, close to M11 junction 13

Teetering on the brink of being a fully fledged restaurant rather than a pub, the Three Horseshoes nevertheless has a pleasantly unstuffy and informal atmosphere. In this respect it is much like its sister establishments in the Huntsbridge Group (see the Pheasant, Keyston, the Old Bridge Hotel, Huntingdon, and the Falcon, Fotheringhay). The picturesque white-painted thatched building certainly looks like a pub from the outside, and you enter a smart, clean bar area; beyond is a slightly more formal conservatory dining room, but one menu serves throughout. The cooking is highly individual and lively, using plenty of bold, modern flavours in inventive – not to mention colourful – combinations. Start with a salad of buffalo mozzarella with figs, rocket, basil and pomegranate, or perhaps sugar-cured venison with soba noodles, red cabbage, pink grapefruit and horseradish cream. Main courses are just as likely to make an impact: try turbot with capers, marjoram and lemon with olive oil-braised leeks, zampone, bay and crushed purple potatoes. To cater for the beer drinker, the bar stocks Adnams Best plus a guest ale, usually from the local City of Cambridge Brewery. The wine list is all you could ever hope for. But then with John Hoskins MW behind it, that's hardly a surprise. Sixteen house wines are served by the glass (starting at £2.60), or for a crisper, tangier aperitif, fino, amontillado and manzanilla sherry are available by the glass for just £1.90. The main wine list is divided into 'top class' and 'under £20' selections for red and white, with all the wines imaginatively chosen and presenting some tough decisions for wine lovers. SAMPLE DISHES: crab salad with lemon, celery, dandelion, chilli and treviso £5.50; chargrilled marinated rump of lamb with chargrilled green and yellow courgettes, fried artichokes and radicchio £13.75; malted milk chocolate semi-freddo with zabaglione ice cream and espresso caramel £5.

Licensees John Hoskins and Richard Stokes (freehouse)
Open *12 to 2.30, 6 (7 Sun) to 10.30; bar food and restaurant 12 to 2, 6.30 to 9.30 (7 to 9 Sun)*
Details *Children welcome Car park Garden No smoking in dining room No music No dogs Amex, Diners, MasterCard, Switch, Visa*

MAIDENSGROVE Oxfordshire map 2

Five Horseshoes

Maidensgrove RG9 6EX TEL: (01491) 641282
off B480 and B481, 5m NW of Henley-on-Thames

Tucked along a single-track lane and with fine views of the Chiltern Hills, this vine-covered brick-built pub dates from the seventeenth century. Banknotes from around the world, old photographs, a collection of old tools, low ceilings and a wood-burning stove give it a very pubby atmosphere. Nevertheless this is very much a dining pub, and tables in the conservatory dining room at the back may need pre-booking at busy times, and barbecues in the garden on summer Sundays draw a crowd. A single-page written menu, supplemented by daily-changing blackboard specials, features some up-to-the-minute offerings such as warm tartlette of goat's cheese on a fondue of cherry tomatoes and basil set on warm red pepper coulis, or baked aubergine stuffed with a fricassé of asparagus and mushrooms. These might be followed by an equally trendy warm salad of scampi and crab claws tossed in Thai spices, or stincotto (braised knuckle of Parma ham). For those who prefer something more traditional there is crab and prawn Mornay, grilled steaks and roast rack of lamb. This is a Brakspear pub, with its Special and Bitter on offer, and the 60-strong wine list, mostly modestly priced under the £20 mark, pays good attention to fruity New World favourites and familiar French names alike. Some of the vintages listed may be out of date so it's worth asking which is on offer. Seven are available by the glass. SAMPLE DISHES: chargrilled Mediterranean vegetables £5.50; grilled breast of duck £14.50; ice-creams in a brandy-snap basket £4.

Licensee Graham Cromack (Brakspear)
Open *11.30 to 2.30, 6 to 11, Sun 12 to 10.30 (7 winter); bar food and restaurant 12 to 2, 7 to 10, Sun 12 to 9 (5 winter)*
Details *Children welcome in bar eating area   Car park   Garden and patio No-smoking area in restaurant   No music   Dogs welcome on leads MasterCard, Switch, Visa*

MARKBEECH   Kent   map 3

Kentish Horse 🏵 🍺   NEW ENTRY

Markbeech TN8 5NT   TEL: (01342) 850493
Markbeech signposted off B2026 S of Edenbridge

Tucked away down country lanes on the Surrey–Kent border, Markbeech is a tiny hamlet comprising no more than a few houses and this part-weatherboarded, white-painted pub. Inside, a small log fire burns at one end of the long main room, where dark-green-painted walls are adorned with country themed prints, and wreaths of hops garland the beams. The wholesomely unpretentious atmosphere is translated on to the blackboard menus that hang over the fireplace: start with 'some kind of soup', which might turn out to be thick and tasty roasted vegetable served with a fresh-from-the-oven crisp baguette. As well as various pub staples, such as ploughman's, local sausages with mash, or home-cooked ham with egg and chips, are some less commonly sighted offerings like corned beef hash with parsnip crisps, Indonesian curry, and balsamic chicken with caramelised lime. However, what really sets the cooking apart from the run of the mill is the fact that the simple things are done with a high level of care and attention: one reporter's steak and kidney pudding, for example, featured an exemplary thin, light suet crust and a generous filling of good-quality meat. Similar consideration is given to real ales: Fuller's London Pride, Harveys Sussex Best and local Larkins Best are served in prime condition. Wine drinkers are offered a list of fourteen, of which three come by the glass; there is also a selection of flavoured vodkas, including one with chocolate. The smart dining room at the rear of the pub is more formally set but operates from the same menu. SAMPLE DISHES: sauté mushrooms on toast £4.25; black pudding with smoked bacon, mash and grain mustard sauce £7.25; French apple tart £3.50.

Licensee John Evanson (freehouse)
Open *12 to 11, Sun 12 to 10.30 (5 winter); bar food and restaurant (exc Sun and Mon evenings) 12 to 3 (2.30 Sun), 7 to 9; closed 26 Dec*
Details *Children welcome   Car park   Garden and patio   Occasional live or background music   Dogs welcome in bar   Delta, MasterCard, Switch, Visa*

MARKET OVERTON   Rutland   map 6

▲ *Black Bull*

Market Overton LE15 7PW   TEL: (01572) 767677
off B668 Oakham to Stretton road, 2m N of Cottesmore

The village may be deserted in the evenings, but a convivial atmosphere is usually guaranteed at the Black Bull, where people pile in to enjoy country hospitality at its cosiest and best. A series of thick-walled and small-windowed rooms makes up the interior, with plenty of lamps to light the typical ambience of beams and dark wood. Food, listed on a vast blackboard, is ordered at the bar and brought to table. Good, hearty country cooking it is, too, offering the likes of French onion soup, scallops and bacon as a warm salad, sirloin steaks, game pie, lemon chicken, fresh fish and a pasta dish of the day. Puddings are of the apple pie and treacle sponge school. Five real beers are offered: Hook Norton, Marston's Pedigree, Wells Bombardier Premium Bitter, John Smith's Cask Bitter and – appropriately enough – Theakston Black Bull Bitter. For £12.95 you can opt for a 'pick-your-own' wine selection, and two wines are served by the glass. SAMPLE DISHES: pasta of the day £8; chicken stuffed with cheese with a wild mushroom sauce £10; lemon soufflé £3.25.

Licensees John and Val Owen (freehouse)
Open *12 to 2.30, 6 to 11; bar food and restaurant 12 to 1.45, 6.30 to 9.45*
Details *Children welcome   Patio   No smoking in dining room   No music   Dogs welcome on leads   Delta, MasterCard, Switch, Visa   Accommodation: 2 rooms, B&B £30 to £45*

MARSH BENHAM   Berkshire   map 2

Red House   NEW ENTRY

Marsh Benham RG20 8LY   TEL: (01635) 582017
off A4 between Newbury and Hungerford

Formerly listed in the Guide as the Water Rat, this thatched red-brick cottage on the main road through the village has been transformed in other ways than just its name. It is now an up-market dining pub, with the emphasis on the dining rather than the pub, though real ale drinkers can still enjoy Fuller's London Pride, and there is a lunchtime bar menu, chalked on a blackboard, of soup and two main-course choices. The large main room has a pleasant ambience and smart décor with a red theme, while the adjoining dining room has more of a light and airy feel, with prints of flowers and birds on the walls. The menu, available both in bar and restaurant, is cosmopolitan in its scope, ranging from roasted skate wing with creamed potatoes and grenobloise sauce to mixed fish in a Thai-style broth scented with lime leaves and coriander. It also encompasses braised shank of lamb on mash, crab spring roll with stir-fried vegetables and sweet-and-sour sauce, and rib of Scotch beef with spicy herb butter. The short wine list opens with four house selections at £11.95, or £2.95 a glass. SAMPLE DISHES: risotto of wild mushrooms with Parmesan basket £6.50; slow-cooked shin of veal with tomatoes, garlic and white wine £13.50; warm prune and armagnac tart £4.50.

Licensee Xavier Le-Bellego (freehouse)
Open *Tue to Sun (exc Sun evening) 12 to 11.30; bar food and restaurant 12 to 2, 7 to 10*
Details *Children over 6 welcome in eating areas   Car park   Wheelchair access (also WC)   Garden and patio   No-smoking area in bar, no smoking in dining room   Background music   No dogs   Amex, Delta, MasterCard, Switch, Visa*

MARSH GIBBON   Buckinghamshire   map 5

Greyhound Inn

West Edge, Marsh Gibbon OX62 7HA
TEL: (01869) 277365
off A41 Bicester to Aylesbury road, 4m E of Bicester

THAI

Heading eastwards out of Bicester in the direction of nearby Waddesdon Manor (a gem of a National Trust property), turn off the A41 into the centre of this venerable stone village. The rather austere-looking inn is entered via a back door, and presents something of the feel of a castle within, with its bare walls and stone floor, lent warmth by a blazing log fire. A single U-shaped bar is adjoined by a public room and a carpeted dining area with heavy-topped tables and dark padded chairs. In this apparently quintessential English setting, it might seem a little incongruous to be offered an exclusively Thai menu (with a takeaway option for those in a hurry), but that is where the owners hail from. The cooking proves to be impressive, replete with fresh herbs and spices and everything seemingly cooked to order. You might begin, familiarly enough, with chicken satay, or crisp vegetable spring rolls full of bean sprouts, before proceeding to yum sam rod goong (prawns with apple and cashew nuts in a spicy dressing). Main courses are built around good raw materials, such as succulent beef and tasty duck, and come with accurately cooked rice. Choose from a variety of ice creams to finish. As well as being a fine Thai restaurant, the Greyhound is also a good local pub, with Greene King Abbot Ale and IPA and Fuller's London Pride on handpump, and specialities such as Polish vodka and (of course) bottled Singha Thai beer. The house wines are the only ones served by the glass. SAMPLE DISHES: spare ribs £5; Weeping Tiger (8oz sirloin steak marinated and grilled, served with hot sauce) £10; coconut ice cream £2.75.

Licensee Richard Kaim (freehouse)
Open *Tue to Sun 12 to 3, 6 (7 Sun) to 11; bar food and restaurant 12 to 3, 6 (7 Sun) to 10*
Details *Children over 8 welcome   Car park   Wheelchair access (not WC) Garden   No smoking in dining room   Occasional background music   No dogs   MasterCard, Switch, Visa*

MARSHSIDE   Kent   map 3

Gate Inn 🍺

Marshside CT3 4EB   TEL: (01227) 860498
between A28 and A299, 3m SE of Herne Bay

This is one for 'real pub fans', according to a reader, with all the virtues of a proper old-fashioned village watering hole. It is evidently the focal point of this small rural community – witness notices about local events, photographs of the annual Christmas mummers, and the fact that most of the clientele and staff appear to know each other. Visitors will also feel welcome, thanks to the friendly atmosphere plus the warmth of a log fire in winter and an attractive garden complete with stream in summer. Tiled floors, dark beams hung with hops, and old photographs of the village enhance the traditional feel. Like the décor, food veers away from sophistication: this is basic pub grub prepared with care and using quality ingredients; portions are hearty and prices very fair. Highlights from the long menu are listed on a board: the Gate mega grill, steak and mushroom torpedo (baguette), nachos with cheese and bacon, pasta and pesto, and the politically correct ploughperson's. Well-kept beers from Shepherd Neame, including seasonal ales and three regulars (Mild, MasterBrew and Spitfire), are chalked on a board behind the bar, but there are no handpumps on the counter; pints are drawn direct from the casks in a back room. A decent selection of wines completes the picture, including wines of the month and 15 by the glass. SAMPLE DISHES: cheesy salad gateburger £3.25; spicy bean and vegetable hotpot with black pudding £5.25; Indian ice cream £2.25.

Licensee Christopher Smith (Shepherd Neame)
Open *11 to 2.30 (3 Sat), 6 to 11, Sun 12 to 4, 7 to 10.30; bar food 12 to 2, 6 to 9, Sun 12 to 2.15, 7 to 9*
Details *Children welcome in family room   Car park   Wheelchair access (also WC)   Garden   No-smoking area in bar (lunchtime only)   No music   Dogs welcome   No cards*

MARSHWOOD Dorset   map 2

Bottle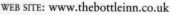

Marshwood DT6 5QJ   TEL: (01297) 678254
WEB SITE: www.thebottleinn.co.uk
on B2165 between Crewkerne and Lyme Regis, 4m SW of Broadwindsor

ORGANIC

This pub's thatched roof covers a long, varied history, for the place may have been an alehouse since the sixteenth century. Its name comes from the late eighteenth, when it was the first local inn to sell bottled beers; it has also housed the village shop and, during the Second World War, the village school. Although a genuine local, it has some metropolitan features, notably its approach to healthy eating, with the menu declaring that 'we have a zero tolerance policy to genetically modified foods'. Vegetarian and a few vegan dishes appear on the menu, and about 70 per cent of the food is organic. Regular pub food is not excluded: for instance, fried seafood platter with chunky chips and peas, or cheeseburger. Blackboard specials might include organic garlic mushrooms with organic bread to mop up, and such exotic main dishes as Spanish chicken with pomegranate, almonds and rice. The vegetarian and vegan board might offer organic kumara pie of sweet potatoes baked with lemon grass and spices in yoghurt and cream, or Mexican tortillas stuffed with 'veggie chilli'. Beers kept include local Otter Bitter, Wadworth 6X, Old

Speckled Hen and organic Caledonian Golden Promise, and there are organic ciders, beers and lagers, and organic wines (two of which are served by the glass). SAMPLE DISHES: hummus with warm organic wholemeal pitta £4.25; Thai tiger prawn curry £13; American chocolate fudge cake £4.

Licensees Shane Pym and Chloë Fox-Lambert (freehouse)
Open *all week 12 to 3.30, Tue to Sun 6.30 to 11 (10.30 Sun); bar food 12 to 2, 6.30 to 9 (9.30 Sat)*
Details *Children welcome Car park Wheelchair access (not WC) Garden No-smoking area in bar Occasional background music No dogs Delta, MasterCard, Switch, Visa*

MELLOR Lancashire map 8

▲ *Millstone Hotel*

Church Lane, Mellor BB2 7JR TEL: (01254) 813333
off A677, 3m NW of Blackburn

The Millstone, once a coaching inn, is now more of a country-house hotel, and is set in a village overlooking the Ribble Valley. Inside are wooden panelling, beams, hunting prints, and china dogs, and the atmosphere is homely and welcoming. The restaurant menu is short and well thought out, with imaginative ideas such as warm duck liver salad with spicy chorizo and rocket, or a main course of chicken breast on beetroot risotto. The bar menu includes an oriental combination of spare ribs and spring rolls, as well as tandoori chicken. But there are also scallops baked in the shell with garlic and Gruyère, and prawn cocktail, with, among main courses, bacon chop with a Cumberland sausage on colcannon, plaice goujons with pea purée, and chargrilled ribeye with béarnaise. A reader who stuck to the daily specials enjoyed 'beautiful, fresh' deep-fried cod in 'light, crisp' batter with home-made tartare sauce, followed by rum-flavoured banana sponge with butterscotch sauce. Thwaites beers are well kept, and six wines are offered by the glass, with the full restaurant list of around 40 bottles also available in the bar. SAMPLE DISHES: crispy duck and watercress salad with soy and sesame dressing £4.75; braised lamb shank on white bean mash with red wine jus £8; treacle tart with crème anglaise £3.75.

Licensees N.W. Sim-Lamb and R.J. Wade (Shire Inns Ltd)
Open *11.30 to 11 (10.30 Sun); bar food and restaurant 12 to 2, 6.30 to 9.30*
Details *Children welcome Car park Wheelchair access (also WC) No smoking in dining room Background music Dogs welcome Amex, Delta, Diners, MasterCard, Switch, Visa Accommodation: 24 rooms, B&B £45 to £108*

MELLS   Somerset   map 2

▲ *Talbot Inn*

Selwood Street, Mells BA11 3PN   TEL: (01373) 812254
3m W of Frome

You enter this fifteenth-century coaching inn by double doors
under an archway leading to a cobbled courtyard which adjoins a
quiet garden with its lawn, wooden tables and benches. The pub
stands next to the church whose old tithe barn, with ancient beams
and lime-washed stone walls, has become the inn's public bar.
Menus are interchangeable between bar and restaurant, but some
bar snacks are offered only at lunchtime. They include home-made
soup; baked aubergine with tomato, mozzarella, and tagliatelle;
and various omelettes, salads and a ploughman's with local ham or
Cheddar. Restaurant main dishes might include steaks from the
charcoal grill; wild rabbit casserole with mustard and marjoram; or
ragout of brill, scallops and flaked crab in Noilly Prat and tarragon
sauce. The day's fish specials, fresh from Brixham, are shown on
the blackboard. A two- or three-course Sunday lunch might offer a
choice between fish and a traditional roast as main course. Service,
and indeed the whole ambience, is warm and friendly. Butcombe
Bitter is served straight from the barrel, and four house wines are
£9.50, or £2.30 per glass. SAMPLE DISHES: hot ratatouille and cheese
flan £6.25; griddled bratwurst and mash £7; hot Somerset apple
cake with custard £4.25.

Licensee Roger Elliott (freehouse)
Open *12 to 2.30, 6.30 to 11, Sun 12 to 3, 7 to 10.30; bar food and
restaurant 12 to 2, 7 to 9.30; restaurant closed 25 Dec*
Details *Children welcome   Car park   Garden and patio   Occasional live
music   No dogs   Delta, Diners, MasterCard, Switch, Visa   Accommodation:
8 rooms, B&B £40 to £75*

MELMERBY   Cumbria   map 10

Shepherds Inn 🍺

Melmerby CA10 1HF   TEL: (01768) 881217
WEB SITE: www.shepherdsinn.net
on A686 Penrith to Alston road, 8m NE of Penrith

This eighteenth-century sandstone inn on the village green has officially become a part of the Lakeland tourist trail – a brown tourist
board road sign indicates the route to its door from as far away as
Penrith. This means that at times the place can be packed, but it

remains a reliable bet for a sustaining meal. The menu is divided into sections under whimsical headings such as 'The Ultimate Ploughman's' and 'Old Favourites'. 'Great Beginnings' are things like confit duck leg, or a bowl of chilli, and 'Gap Fillers' take in hunter's lunch (home-cooked ham with bread, salad and pickles), and Cumberland pasty with chips, or you might go for baked Ullswater trout under the 'If you like Fish' category. A further page of 'Cook's Creations of the Week' might feature venison and Roquefort crumble, chicken korma, and Cumberland sausage hotpot. Beers are a quality selection, including local brews Jennings Cumberland Ale and Hesket Newmarket Pigs Might Fly, plus guests such as Greene King Abbot Ale. There is also a good selection of Continental bottled beers, English fruit wines and more than 50 malt whiskies. A succinct wine list of around 30 wines has all the classics at some very fair prices, and a more off-beat selection of bin ends to stretch the imagination. Eight wines are listed by the glass. SAMPLE DISHES: carrot and orange soup £3; steak and kidney pie £7; tutti-frutti sponge £3.50.

Licensee Martin Baucutt (freehouse)
Open *11 to 3, 6 to 11, Sun 12 to 3, 7 to 10.30; bar food 11 to 2.30, 6 to 9.45, Sun 12 to 2.30, 7 to 9.45; closed 25 Dec*
Details *Children welcome Car park Wheelchair access (not WC) Patio No smoking in 1 bar Occasional live music; jukebox Dogs welcome in 1 bar Amex, Delta, Diners, MasterCard, Switch, Visa*

MICKLEHAM **Surrey**   **map 3**

King William IV

Byttom Hill, Mickleham RH5 6EL   TEL: (01372) 372590
off A24, between Leatherhead and Dorking, 2m S of Leatherhead

Reached via steep steps from the road, the King William IV is on a hillside with garden views across a road over Norbury Park and the Mole Valley. This small pub was built in the late eighteenth century and was extended in Victorian times before it became an alehouse for Lord Beaverbrook's estate staff. Blackboards list the usual sandwiches, ploughman's and jacket potatoes before going on to starters such as chicken liver pâté, or avocado filled with assorted seafood with melted mozzarella. Main dishes range from steak, kidney and mushroom pie, or a pie of cod, cockles, mussels and salmon to calf's liver and bacon, while the 'star' dish of an inspection was sea bass delicately flavoured with coriander and lemon grass. Desserts might take in gingerbread and apple pudding, or blackberry and apple crumble. On draught are Adnams Best Bitter, Badger Dorset Best, Hogs Back TEA, a monthly-changing guest ale, and a cider such as Scrumpy Jack. A handful of wines from the short list are sold by the glass. SAMPLE DISHES: goats' cheese and apple in filo £3.75; rump steak with green peppercorn sauce £9.75; hot chocolate fudge cake £3.50.

Licensees Mr and Mrs C.D. Grist (freehouse)
Open *11 to 3, 6 to 11, Sun 12 to 3, 7 to 10.30; bar food 12 to 2, 7 to 9.30; closed 25 and 31 Dec*
Details *Children welcome Garden and patio Occasional live music No dogs MasterCard, Switch, Visa*

MIDFORD   Bath & N.E. Somerset   map 2

Hope & Anchor Inn

Midford BA2 7DD   TEL: (01225) 832296
on B3110, 3m S of Bath

Look out for a bridge and a tricky bend in the road to avoid missing this simple, stone-built pub. It's just as unassuming inside, with an open fire, walls either panelled or painted deep red, and wooden furniture. A reader has described the reasonably priced food, especially on the bar menu, as 'proper home cooking'. Provençale fish soup, and thickly sliced home-cooked ham with fried eggs and sauté potatoes have both been praised. Enlivening the menu are Spanish dishes, such as chicken and prawn paella with mussels, and a selection of tapas comprising chorizo, jamón, spicy mushrooms, tuna salad and olives. The restaurant is slightly more sophisticated, with a carpeted floor and white-clothed tables, and its menu is also a tad more ambitious. Home-smoked salmon with celeriac, or smoked chicken with prawns and avocado might precede fillet of venison, or fried skate with artichoke and chilli salsa. 'Exceptionally good' desserts might include moist sticky toffee pudding 'flooded with fantastically rich sauce cut by a squeeze of lemon'. Butcombe Bitter, Caledonian Deuchars IPA, Fuller's London Pride and Bass are on draught, and Estrella, a Spanish bottled beer, could accompany the Spanish dishes. Seven wines from a short list come by the glass. SAMPLE DISHES: tortilla, tuna salad and garlic bread £5; salmon fishcakes with tarragon mayonnaise £6; lemon and lime cheesecake £3.25.

Licensee Richard Smolarek (freehouse)
Open *11.30 to 2.30, 6.30 to 11, Sun 12 to 3, 7 to 10.30; bar food and restaurant 12 to 2, 6.30 to 9.30; closed 25 Dec, evening 26 Dec*
Details *Children welcome Car park Garden and patio No smoking in dining room Background music No dogs MasterCard, Switch, Visa*

▶ *indicates a pub serving exceptional draught beers.*

MILLBANK West Yorkshire map 8

Millbank 🏵 ❘NEW ENTRY❘

Millbank HX6 3DY   TEL: (01422) 825588
signposted on A58 between Sowerby Bridge and Ripponden

The pub of the same name as the village is on the side of a steep hill above Sowerby Bridge. It is an old stone house entered through a low doorway, and a much modernised interior shows stripped-down walls and floors, plus a few nice individual touches, such as church chairs with their prayer-book boxes still attached, some abstract paintings, and a fireplace filled with stone heads and candles. Eating goes on to either side of the small main bar area, and hearty portions are the norm. Visitors have enjoyed, among other things, a bowl of frothy pea and ham soup, Barnsley chop with a cassoulet of beans and cabbage, and black pudding ('the best I have ever eaten') with bacon and sage mash and mustard gravy. Vegetarians might like to try butternut squash with bean and pepper ragoût, and on the fishy side of things there might be something like fillet of red snapper with potato and red onion confit salad. Finish with chocolate chip pudding with chocolate sauce, or poached pears with honey and brandy ice cream and raspberry sauce. A good range of bottled Belgian beer and English cider supplements the handpumped Timothy Taylor Landlord and Black Sheep ales, along with Stowford Press cider. The wine list is usefully divided up by wine style, and there are nine by the glass. SAMPLE DISHES: avocado with salmon and an apple and horseradish dressing £5.25; saddle of venison with haggis potato cake and whisky sauce £13.50; mascarpone cheesecake with dried fruit compote in red wine £4.

Licensees Christine and Paul Halsey (freehouse)
Open *Tue to Fri 12 to 3, 5 to 11, Sat and Sun 12 to 11; bar food and restaurant Tue to Sat 12 to 2, 6.30 to 9.30, Sun 12.30 to 3.30*
Details *Children welcome   Wheelchair access (not WC)   Garden   No smoking in dining room   Live or background music   Dogs welcome   Amex, MasterCard, Switch, Visa*

MILTON STREET East Sussex map 3

Sussex Ox

Milton Street BN26 5RL   TEL: (01323) 870840
off A27, 1m NE of Alfriston

The nearby Long Man of Wilmington keeps a watch over this isolated pub, which has a serious approach to food as well as a smart bar with a genuine pubby feel. The owners 'have made a good job of refurbishment' writes an inspector, and the garden, with great views across to the South Downs, has a well-equipped adventure playground for children. The very young will appreciate the family room, called the Sty Restaurant, where they can enjoy a 'really good, meaty, herby' sausage with fat, crispy chips from the kids' menu. The same main menu is served in here as in the Harness Restaurant and the bar. One blackboard displays fish specials, such as pan-fried red mullet, or scallops with bacon, and another announces simpler things like ploughman's. Generous main courses of moules marinière, Sussex pie – puff pastry filled with sausage meat, ham, mushrooms, and green peppers – or grilled tuna steak with hollandaise might be preceded by shell-on prawns with mayonnaise, or goats' cheese with roasted vegetables. Harveys Sussex Best Bitter, with Old Ale in winter, is supplemented by guest ales, and the interesting and fairly priced wine list includes Cuckmere as house white. SAMPLE DISHES: mackerel and chive pâté £4; chicken breast with asparagus and cheese sauce £6.25; apple and nut strudel £3.25.

Licensees Doug and Jeanne Baker, and Harry Findlay (freehouse)
Open *11 to 3, 6 to 11, Sun 12 to 3, 6 to 10.30; bar food and restaurant 11 to 2, 6 to 9*
Details *Children welcome in family room and dining room   Car park Wheelchair access (not WC)   Garden   No smoking in family room   Live or background music   Dogs welcome   MasterCard, Switch, Visa*

MITHIAN   Cornwall   map 1

Miners Arms

Mithian TR5 0QF   TEL: (01872) 552375
on B3285, 2m E of St Agnes

There are no tin-miners now in Mithian, one of Cornwall's oldest villages in beautiful countryside near St Agnes. In the pub's long history, it has been a mine owner's office, a courthouse and a chapel. The entrance is through a cobbled courtyard bounded on three sides by the oldest parts of the building. Each of the four cosy ground-floor rooms has a distinct character, and behind the fireplace in one is a tunnel that once led to the manor house. The printed menu is augmented by a blackboard of daily specials: lentil and tomato soup with crusty bread, say, or king prawns cooked in garlic butter with tomato salsa. To follow might be glazed salmon tartlet with hollandaise, or venison casseroled in Burgundy, a robust, satisfying winter warmer. Cornish crab, wild boar sausages, lamb cutlets with mint and apple chutney, and local cheeses feature on the printed menu, along with an unusual vegetarian dish of spicy bean and chickpea goulash. On tap might be Sharp's Doom Bar Bitter, Flowers IPA,

Wadworth 6X and Ringwood Fortyniner. A board lists up to eight house wines mostly available by the glass. SAMPLE DISHES: Cornish Brie salad £4; monkfish and prawns in vermouth sauce £8.75; fruit crêpes with clotted cream £2.75.

Licensee Andrew Bown (Inn Partnership)
Open *12 to 3 (2.30 winter), 6 (6.30 winter) to 11; bar food and restaurant 12 to 2.30 (2 winter), 6.30 (7 winter) to 9.30*
Details *Children welcome in dining room   Car park   Wheelchair access (also WC)   Patio   No smoking in dining room and 1 bar   Occasional background music   Dogs welcome in bar   Delta, MasterCard, Switch, Visa*

MONKSILVER   Somerset   map 2

Notley Arms

Monksilver TA4 4JB   TEL: (01984) 656217
on B3188, 5m S of Watchet

The pub is easy enough to find, standing slap in the middle of the village, with parking in a small square to one side. The interior is centred on an L-shaped bar with a family room at one end and a dining area at the other. Furnishings are as simple and homely as one hopes for in a country pub, with a multifarious collection of knick-knacks and pictures, scrubbed pine tables and bookshelves, and menus are written up on blackboards. One pair of visitors started with a portion of garlic bread and a bowl of cucumber soup with French bread, and then went on to roast salmon with seasonal vegetables and braised lamb with rosemary and redcurrant sauce. Finish with something like lemon or treacle tart. Smiles Best, Exmoor Ale and Wadworth 6X are on handpump, and Thatcher's dry cider is on tap as well. Eight wines, including some fruit wines, are sold by the glass, with around a dozen by the bottle. Smiling, helpful staff give the impression that nothing is too much trouble. SAMPLE DISHES: roasted vegetable and goats' cheese feuilleté £5; salmon fishcakes £6; brown-bread ice cream £2.50.

Licensees Sarah and Alistair Cade (Nomura)
Open *11.30 to 2.30, 6.30 to 11, Sun 12 to 2.30, 7 to 11 (10.30 winter); bar food Mon to Sat 12 to 2, 7 to 9.30, Sun 12.30 to 1.45, 7 to 9*
Details *Children welcome in family room   Car park   Wheelchair access (not WC)   Garden   No-smoking area in bar   Occasional live music   Dogs welcome   Delta, MasterCard, Switch, Visa*

Report forms are at the back of the book; write a letter if you prefer, or email your pub report to whichcountrypubs@which.net.

MORDEN   Dorset   map 2

Cock & Bottle   NEW ENTRY

Morden BH20 7DL   TEL: (01929) 459238
on B3075 between A35 and A31

Some parts of this brick-built inn in a quiet village are 400 years old.
It stands close to the road in front, but picnic benches in the rear
garden enjoy lovely views across open fields. The interior is comfortably rustic, with tiled and wooden flooring and an open fireplace in
the main bar, while the dining area has farmhouse chairs, cushioned
wall settles, attractive prints and an open log fire; partitions form
cosy alcoves. The enthusiasm of the landlord of this Hall &
Woodhouse pub shows in the appealing blend of pub favourites and
more imaginative dishes and is also reflected by chatty, friendly bar
staff, and polite, speedy food service. On the light lunch menu are
sandwiches, beefburger with Stilton and smoked bacon, and smoked
salmon accompanied by avocado. Blackboard starters might include
crab and ginger tartlet with 'melt-in-the-mouth pastry', and main
courses of perhaps tuna with tapénade of olives, capers and sun-
dried tomatoes, or roast boned quails on bubble and squeak with
wild mushroom jus. Badger Best and Tanglefoot and King & Barnes'
Sussex may be on tap, with German beers by the bottle. Six of the
fairly priced wines on the list of 30-plus are offered by the glass.
SAMPLE DISHES: spicy crab cakes with sweet chilli dipping sauce
£5.75; braised rump of lamb in rosemary and red wine sauce £9;
Drambuie cream with raspberry and orange compote £3.75.

Licensee Peter Meadley (Hall & Woodhouse)
Open *11 to 3, 6 to 11, Sun 12 to 3, 7 to 10.30; bar food and restaurant 12
to 2, 6 (7 Sun) to 9; closed 25 and 26 Dec*
Details *Children welcome in dining room   Car park   Wheelchair access (also
WC)   Garden and patio   No smoking in dining room   No music   Dogs
welcome   Delta, MasterCard, Switch, Visa*

MOULTON   North Yorkshire   map 9

Black Bull Inn ✿

Moulton DL10 6QJ   TEL: (01325) 377289
1m SE of Scotch Corner

Set in a pretty village, this well-kept dining pub has a long, low
cottagey front and, inside, a Victorian air, with dark wood panelling,
velour-covered bar stools and benches, and on the walls old prints,
caricatures of Victorian politicians and a huge stuffed fish. Here the
Pagendam family have offered grand Yorkshire hospitality since the

1960s. Beers are few, wines many, and while the New World is not neglected the emphasis is on French classics, particularly Burgundies, which would be hard to match even at shop prices. House wines start at £9.50, with many other bottles under £20, but just three wines are served by the glass. In the restaurant, housed in the conservatory and in the ex-Brighton Belle Pullman carriage in the garden, seafood takes pride of place, though bar food too is a few strokes above the norm and wide ranging, though served only at lunchtime. Fish and shellfish figure prominently here too, from prawn salad, or 'enormous' oysters to start, to main courses of curried fish Mornay, or roast salmon fillet topped with pesto, pine nuts and Parmesan. Meat eaters could opt for something like carpaccio, then barbecued spare ribs in a 'gloopy, tangy' sauce, or bangers and mash, and among puddings might be meringue with fruit compote, or crème brûlée. SAMPLE DISHES: fresh or smoked salmon sandwich £3.25: queenie scallops in garlic with Wensleydale and thyme crumb £5.75; hot orange liqueur pancakes £3.50.

Licensees G.H., A.M.C. and S.C. Pagendam (freehouse)
Open *Mon to Sat 12 to 2.30, 6 to 10.30; bar food Mon to Sat 12 to 2; restaurant Mon to Sat 12 to 2, 6.45 to 10.15; closed 24 to 27 Dec*
Details *No children Car park Garden No music No dogs Amex, Delta, Diners, MasterCard, Switch, Visa*

MUCH WENLOCK   Shropshire   map 5

George & Dragon 🍺 NEW ENTRY

2 High Street, Much Wenlock TF13 6AA   TEL: (01952) 727312
on A458, between Shrewsbury and Bridgnorth, 8m NW of Bridgnorth

---

This sixteenth-century inn, on the high street of the historical town of Much Wenlock, is every inch the traditional unspoilt local, and a place real ale enthusiasts should seek out. Over 300 different beers feature throughout the course of a year: at any one time you may find four on offer, perhaps including such esoteric examples as Beowulf Mercian Shine and Hobsons Town Crier alongside more familiar names like Hook Norton Old Hooky. Another attraction is the cosy atmosphere in the small bar, where low beams are adorned with hundred of jugs, and brewing memorabilia decorate the walls. It also offers simple, reliable food, ranging from lunchtime snacks, such as versions of Welsh rarebit, jacket potatoes and sandwiches, to more substantial traditional fare: for example, Stilton and walnut pâté to start, followed by home-baked ham with parsley sauce, or breast of chicken in Shropshire mead and cream sauce with raisins and apple. All three house wines are sold by two sizes of glass as well as by the bottle, and there are around another 20 to choose from. SAMPLE

DISHES: savoury crispy parcels with spicy dip £4; breast of duck with honey and ginger sauce £10.50; crème brûlée with pineapple and ginger compote £2.75.

Licensee Barry Blakeman (freehouse)
Open *12 to 2.30, 6 to 11; bar food and restaurant (exc Wed and Sun evenings) 12 to 2 (2.30 bank hols), 6 to 8.30; closed Wed lunchtimes exc during school hols*
Details *Children welcome   Wheelchair access (not WC)   No smoking in dining room   No music   No dogs   No cards*

MUNDFORD   Norfolk   map 6

▲ *Crown Hotel*   NEW ENTRY

Crown Road, Mundford IP26 5HQ   TEL: (01842) 878233
pub signposted from A1065 in village

Mundford is an archetypal English village, so this large, white-painted traditional inn, dating from the mid-seventeenth century, stands on the green opposite the post office-cum-village store. It offers two bar areas, each with a very different atmosphere: the beamed Village Bar is the more basic, with a large brick hearth housing an iron grate and an anvil, as well as a pool table and dartboard. The Squires Bar is in a more genteel style, with fresh flowers on small round tables; a spiral iron staircase in here leads up to the first-floor dining room (as the pub is built into a hill, it is possible to enter directly into the dining room from the rear). The same range of menus are offered through-out, comprising a long list of mostly pub staples such as a platter of prawns and smoked salmon, various sandwiches, steaks and burgers, and chicken jalfrezi, with more ambitious dishes on the restaurant menu. There is also a list of daily specials, which might include the rustic concoction of roughly chopped new potatoes and chorizo on a bed of onion, pepper and salad enjoyed by one reporter. Also praised has been 'tender' roast lamb with 'proper' gravy. Beers might include Woodforde's Wherry Best Bitter and something from the local Iceni Brewery. Around 20 well-priced wines are listed, including six by the glass and some classic choices: Italian Pinot Grigio, New Zealand Sauvignon, Beaujolais, Bordeaux and Burgundy. SAMPLE DISHES: bang-bang chicken £4.25; griddled halibut steak with green-lip mussels and beurre blanc £8; chocolate fudge cake £3.

Licensee Barry Walker (freehouse)
Open *11 to 11, Sun 12 to 10.30; bar food and restaurant 12 to 3, 7 to 10*
Details *Children welcome   Wheelchair access (also WC)   Garden and patio   No smoking in dining room   Jukebox   Dogs welcome in bar   Amex, Delta, Diners, MasterCard, Switch, Visa   Accommodation: 20 rooms, B&B £35 to £55*

MUNGRISDALE Cumbria map 10

▲ *Mill Inn* NEW ENTRY

Mungrisdale CA11 0XR TEL: (017687) 79632
on unclassified road from A66 to Caldbeck

The Mill Inn enjoys a typically fine Lakeland setting in a tiny hamlet.
As you drive up from the A66, you will see it looming above you on
the left, and you must drive past, take the next left turn and double
back. It is a long, whitewashed building in the centre of fell-walking
country, with tables set outside the better to drink in the sumptuous
views. Low ceilings and roughcast white walls set the tone within. A
number of open-plan rooms lead to a bar at the far end, above which
is a collection of brass plates inscribed with jokey mottoes of the
'free beer tomorrow' variety. Cockermouth brewery Jennings
supplies Bitter and Cumberland Ale, and malt whiskies are something of a speciality. The short but imaginative wine list displays a
penchant for New World wines, and up to six bottles are served by
the glass. Some enterprising cooking is going on: you might start
with curried egg on a bed of rice and go on to duck breast sauced
with honey, port and coriander. Grilled black pudding on a bed of
herby mash with a bacon and mustard sauce makes a substantial and
popular starter, and the house speciality – also highly recommended
– is lamb Henry: a 12-ounce hunk roasted on the bone after being
marinated in honey, garlic and mint, and served with a minty gravy.
Side orders of things like garlic bread and deep-fried mushrooms
may be taken, and a separate menu is offered to children. SAMPLE
DISHES: broccoli and Stilton soup £2; venison casserole £7; sticky
toffee pudding £2.25.

Licensees Jim and Margaret Hodge (freehouse)
Open *11 (12 winter) to 11, Sun 12 to 10.30; bar food and restaurant 12 to
2.30, 6 to 8.30 (longer in summer); closed 25 and 26 Dec*
Details *Children welcome Car park Wheelchair access (not WC) Garden
and patio No smoking in dining room Background music Dogs welcome
Delta, MasterCard, Switch, Visa Accommodation: 9 rooms, B&B £25 to £60*

MUNSLOW Shropshire map 5

▲ *Munslow Inn*

Munslow SY7 9ET TEL: (01584) 841205
WEB SITE: www.thecrown.clara.net

Having acquired the Dog Inn in Worfield (see entry), Victor Pocock
now spends most of his time there, leaving son Mike and his wife
Zoë in charge of this ancient inn – until recently called the Crown –

in picturesque Corve Dale, an Area of Outstanding Natural Beauty. Neither the menu nor the food on the plate have changed much in the transfer of responsibility, and the short, interesting menu still features plenty of local produce cooked in an exotically tinted style that covers anything from potted chicken and steak au poivre to Thai beef salad and Barbary duck breast with orange and lime marmalade. A blackboard lists routine pubby stuff like ploughman's, baguettes and soup of the day, plus daily specials, which might be steak and kidney pie, or smoked haddock. Real ale is definitely a strong suit here, and Butcher's Best and Mild, the house beers, do not have far to travel from place of production to point of sale: the brewery is visible from the bar. The succinct wine list covers all the familiar flavours and grapes, with a handful of wines staying close to the £10 mark (house wines are £8.95). For an alternative, you could always splash out on the Château Bellegrave Pomerol – a treat at £29.95. The pub itself, a Tudor building with a Georgian façade, is a warren of linked rooms with uneven flagstone floors, walls of grey stone and old red brick, and ceilings heavy with timeworn beams, with a Bakelite radio and an old sewing machine adding decorative touches. SAMPLE DISHES: chicken livers bonne femme £3.75; baked sea bass with black olive mash and warm vinaigrette £11; double chocolate pudding £3.

Licensees Victor, Michael and Zoë Pocock (freehouse)
Open *12 to 2.30, 7 to 11, Sun 12 to 3, 7 to 10.30; bar food and restaurant 12 to 2, 7 to 9.30*
Details *Children welcome   Car park   Wheelchair access (not WC)   Garden and patio   No smoking in dining room   No music   Dogs welcome   Amex, Delta, MasterCard, Switch, Visa   Accommodation: 4 rooms, £30 to £45*

MYLOR BRIDGE   Cornwall   map 1

Pandora Inn 🍇

Restronguet Creek, Mylor Bridge TR11 5ST
TEL: (01326) 372678
off A39 from Truro, take B3292 signposted Penryn, then Mylor Bridge road, and follow steep road down to Restronguet

A superb location is the prime draw for this old thatched pub, parts of which date from the thirteenth century. It stands hard by the water's edge, with an outdoor sitting area overlooking the estuary – at high tide the sea almost comes into the car park – and its name is appropriately of naval origin (the *Pandora* was the ship sent to retrieve the *Bounty*'s mutineers). Some tables are on a pontoon that extends over the water. The menu is a straightforward list of pub staples, such as mussels in white wine, garlic and herbs, local sausages with apple chutney, and deep-fried crab cakes with parsley and coriander. A small blackboard by the bar displays daily specials, such as tomato and lentil soup, chicken, ham and leek pie, or deep-fried plaice with chips and peas. The separate restaurant menu is equally traditional but follows a more formal route. The pub is owned by the St Austell Brewery and offers beers from its range, including Tinners Ale and Daylight Robbery. The nicely presented, accessible wine list has something from everywhere. New World fruity grape choices and French classics all make an appearance. A highly respectable 14 wines are listed by the glass (starting at £2.50), and very little comes in over £20. SAMPLE DISHES: crab thermidor £8.50; garlic chicken with chips and garlic mayonnaise £7; super Pandora surprise sundae £4.25.

Licensee R.J. Milan (St Austell)
Open *11 to 11 (11.30 to 3, 7 to 11 winter), Sun 12 to 10.30; bar food and restaurant 12 to 2.30, 6.30 (7 winter) to 9.30*
Details *Children welcome   Car park   Wheelchair access (also WC)   Patio No-smoking area in bar, no smoking in dining room   No music   Dogs welcome exc in dining room   Delta, MasterCard, Switch, Visa*

NEWTON   Norfolk   map 6

George & Dragon   NEW ENTRY
Newton PE32 2BX   TEL: (01760) 755046
on A1065, 4m N of Swaffham

The village of Newton consists of not much more than this rambling brick and flint inn, dating from 1750, and the neighbouring eleventh-century church, with its Saxon tower. The pub is easy to spot, standing in a prominent position on the main road. Inside, the bar and dining areas are spread across a series of adjoining spaces. Copper pans and horse brasses on the wall over the fireplace, china plates and prints, red patterned carpets and chintz curtains provide a homely feel, helped by light background pop music. Food, also in a homely style, is listed on a lengthy menu, with specials on a board behind the bar. One visitor was well satisfied with a hearty portion of crisply deep-fried whitebait with a decent accompanying salad; other options might be noisette of lamb with shallots and walnuts in a Madeira jus, mixed grill, or trout with mushrooms and anchovies. There is also a list of bar snacks and lighter meals. To drink, there are Greene King IPA plus a guest ale (maybe Black Sheep Bitter) and a wine list from Stowells with four by the glass. SAMPLE DISHES: spiced prawn timbale £3.50; pork loin with apricots and brandy £8.75; profiteroles £3.

Licensees Ann Ward and Derek Edwards (freehouse)

Open *11.30 to 2.30, 6.30 to 11, Sun 12 to 2.30, 7 to 10.30; bar food and restaurant 12 to 1.45, 6.45 to 9.15 (9.30 Fri and Sat)*
Details *Children welcome in dining room   Car park   Garden   No smoking in dining room   Background music   No dogs   MasterCard, Switch, Visa*

NEWTON LONGVILLE   Buckinghamshire   map 3

Crooked Billet ✿ 🍺 ❦   NEW ENTRY

2 Westbrook End, Newton Longville MK17 0DF
TEL: (01908) 373936
WEB SITE: www.the-crooked-billet-pub.co.uk
take left turn off B4146 from Leighton Buzzard towards Milton Keynes

John Gilchrist and Emma Sexton are a pair of London refugees who, like many another, have forsaken the big city for rural pastures. Emma used to cook at fashionable Nicole's in the West End, and John has experience as a sommelier. They have pitched camp in a thatched, timber-framed inn with a grandly proportioned lawn full of shrubs and flowers, outdoor tables and a brick-built barbecue. The place is still very much a traditional village pub, although to the left as you enter you will notice two rooms set aside for eating, one tiled and one carpeted. This restaurant area is open only in the evenings, when a full-dress menu (not available in the bar) of elaborately inventive cooking comes into play, offering perhaps crispy marinated squid with black beans, chilli, lemon and parsley, or crispy duck with a cucumber and onion salad and hoisin dressing. The bar menu, which changes weekly and is available only at lunchtime, produces ploughman's (with a choice of good cheeses plus homemade piccalilli); 'hedgehog' rolls filled with perhaps minute steak or chicken, spiced honey and mustard mayonnaise; starters such as crostini with goats' cheese, red peppers and tapénade, or spiced cherry tomato soup; and main courses of cod fishcakes with chips and peas, or sausages and mash. For dessert there might be chocolate pot, or try cheeses from Neal's Yard. The Crooked Billet is also running one of the best wine lists featured in this Guide. Not only is it wide-ranging and impeccable in its selections, but everything on it is available by the glass: that's about 250 to choose from. The most expensive glasses are the £32.50 measures of Latour, Lafite or Mouton-Rothschild (no surprises there), but the majority can be had for around £3 to £5. French classics feature highly but there are New World bargains too. Beer drinkers are not neglected: Bateman XXXB, Old Speckled Hen, as well as IPA, Triumph and Abbot Ale from Greene King, and more, are on handpump. SAMPLE DISHES: chicken liver paté with onion chutney £4; roasted vegetable tagliatelle with mozzarella and pesto £7.50; apple and raisin crumble with custard £3.75.

Licensees John Gilchrist and Emma Sexton (Greene King)
Open *12 to 2.30, 5.30 to 11, Sun 12 to 4, 7 to 10.30; bar food Tue to Sun 12 to 2; restaurant Tue to Sat 7 to 10; closed first 2 weeks Jan*
Details *Children welcome in eating areas   Car park   Wheelchair access (also WC)   Garden and patio   No smoking in dining room   Occasional live or background music   Dogs welcome exc in dining room   MasterCard, Switch, Visa*

NEWTON-ON-THE-MOOR   Northumberland map 10

▲ *Cook and Barker Inn* 🅩 🍇

Newton-on-the-Moor NE65 9JY   TEL: (01665) 575234
¼m W of A1, in middle of village

From its elevated position, this attractive stone-built family-run inn, set in a picturesque village, enjoys views of the Northumbrian coast. Enter the beamed main bar area, which has an old-fashioned decorative style; leading off it are the snug bar, the informal dining area and the restaurant, which operates from the same menu. If you are eating in the smart, spacious restaurant, the form is to give your order at the bar before being shown to your table; otherwise, order in the bar and choose where to sit. The standard menu is printed on a card, with an extensive selection of daily specials on a blackboard. The cooking style ranges from the adventurous to the firmly traditional. Start perhaps with a warm chicken breast with king prawns and caper sauce, and follow it with pan-fried scallops and bacon with ratatouille, breast and leg of mallard with garlic sauce, or lambs' liver and black pudding. Both cooking and presentation have been highly praised, and the place is considered well above average for an inn-cum-restaurant. The relaxed atmosphere and friendly and efficient service are also appreciated. A decent selection of real ales includes Timothy Taylor Landlord, Fuller's London Pride, and Black Sheep Bitter. Around 90 wines, 10 by the half-bottle and 12 by the glass, make up a comprehensive wine list that keeps its prices low and its grape varieties to the fore, so you know exactly what you are getting. Among the classics listed (Bordeaux, Barolo) are some nice old vintages. SAMPLE DISHES: Chinese crispy duck £6; roast sea bass with pesto and sweet potato mash £11; warm blueberry crème brûlée with home-made ice cream £3.75.

Licensee P.J. Farmer (freehouse)
Open *11 to 3, 6 to 11; bar food and restaurant 12 to 2, 6 to 9; closed evening 25 Dec*
Details *Children welcome   Car park   Wheelchair access (also WC)   Garden No-smoking area in bar   Occasional live music   No dogs   Amex, Delta, MasterCard, Switch, Visa   Accommodation: 5 rooms, B&B £37.50 to £80*

NORTH CERNEY Gloucestershire map 2

▲ *Bathurst Arms*

North Cerney GL7 7BZ TEL: (01285) 831281
on A435, 4m N of Cirencester

The pub may be on the A435, but it's as countrified a stretch of A-road as you'll find anywhere. A partly creeper-covered, very long old building with an extensive garden containing a huge old copper beech, the Bathurst Arms also boasts a fine riverside setting. Inside, all areas are set out for eating, and food here aims for the kind of comfort that the setting suggests: start perhaps with a slice of farmhouse terrine with side salad and toast, or freshly made soup with granary bread, before going on to salmon fishcakes with ginger and spring onion served with hollandaise, beef stroganoff on saffron rice, or a trio of local Gloucester Old Spot sausages with onion mash. Filled baguettes are served at lunchtime, and the sweet of tooth should get set for banoffi pie or blackberry and apple crumble. British and Irish cheeses are served with home-made walnut bread, celery and an apple. Draught Bass, Wadworth 6X as well as Archers and Hook Norton ales are on handpump, and there is also Weston's cider. Care and effort have gone into the compilation of the wine list, which makes a discernible attempt to offer a variety of flavours at sensible prices. Ten come by the glass. SAMPLE DISHES: Scottish smoked salmon with salad £5.50; lamb leg steak with mint jus £9; bread-and-butter pudding £3.50.

Licensee Michael Costley-White (freehouse)
Open *11 to 2.30, 6 to 11; bar food and restaurant 12 to 2, 7 to 9; closed evening 25 Dec*
Details *Children welcome Car park Wheelchair access (not WC) Garden No smoking in 1 dining room Background music No dogs MasterCard, Visa Accommodation: 5 rooms, B&B £35 to £60*

NORTON Shropshire map 5

▲ *Hundred House Hotel* ✿ 🍺

Bridgnorth Road, Norton TF11 9EE TEL: (01952) 730353
WEB SITE: www.hundredhouse.co.uk
on A442, 6m S of Telford

With its twin chimney stacks towering above a pitched roof, this red-brick inn looks every inch an elegant Georgian hotel, and indeed the main building is of that period, though the thatched barn, which once served as the local courtroom, dates from the thirteenth century. A mature garden and orchard, including a herb patch that supplies the kitchen, is only part of the allure. This is a fine, all-round operation, from the enveloping sense of hospitality that the Phillips family has made its own to the fine quality of food and drink. Notwithstanding the fact that there are ten guest rooms, the place has retained its identity as a true village local too. Phillips Heritage Ale, which is brewed in-house, must be the star of the show, but there are also Highgate Saddlers Celebrated Best Bitter and a number of regularly changing guest ales. Beck's farmhouse cider is on tap as well. Wines are a pedigree globetrotting collection, led by house wines in four styles from a southern French cooperative available by the glass. Stuart Phillips cooks both a brasserie-style and full restaurant menu, enhanced by daily blackboard specials, and he has some good ideas. Lighter dishes might be garlic-rubbed bruschetta topped with tomatoes, tapénade and basil, the house lasagne, or a vegetarian option such as aubergine fritters with goats' cheese and tomato in a red wine sauce. The more formal menu brings on griddled scallops with stir-fried rice cakes and a sauce of carrot, ginger and tamarind, local lamb chump with rosemary jus and macaroni gratin, or loin of Ludlow venison with braised red cabbage, blue cheese polenta and sauce poivrade. Crowd-pleasing desserts are of the crème brûlée, tiramisù and two-toned chocolate mousse variety. SAMPLE DISHES: shellfish bisque with brandy and croûtons £4.50; Alderson's Bridgnorth pork sausages with mash and onion gravy £6; red fruit mille-feuille with vanilla ice cream and lemon anglaise £4.50.

Licensee Henry Phillips (freehouse)
Open *11 to 11, Sun 11 to 3, 7 to 10.30; bar food 12 to 2.15, 6 to 9.30 (8.45 Sun); restaurant (exc Sun evening) 12 to 2.15, 6 to 9.30; closed evening 25 Dec*
Details *Children welcome in bar eating area   Car park   Wheelchair access (also WC)   Garden   No smoking in dining room   Occasional background music   No dogs   Amex, Delta, MasterCard, Switch, Visa   Accommodation: 10 rooms, B&B £69 to £110*

NORTON ST PHILIP   Somerset   map 2

▲ *George*

High Street, Norton St Philip BA3 6LH
TEL: (01373) 834224
on A366 at junction with B3110, 6m S of Bath

This magnificent Grade I listed building claims to have been a pub for over 700 years, making it one of the longest-running licensed premises in Britain. Restored by the brewery owners in 1998, it certainly looks the part, with ancient stone, half-timbered walls and leaded windows. It is built around a cobbled central courtyard over-looked by a gallery with guest rooms leading off it. Inside, there are two equally atmospheric bar areas. The Monmouth (also known as the Dungeon) has flagstone floors and an arched stone ceiling, and is where locals gather; the Charterhouse is a grand high-ceilinged room warmed by an open fire. Wadworth beers and light refreshments are served in both. Diners also have the choice of two rooms, and menus take a traditional line, in keeping with the ambience: game terrine with chutney, lamb steak with redcurrant and mint sauce, local trout with lemon butter, and gammon steak with egg are typical. The wine list extends to more than 30 bottles, of which a handful are served by the glass. SAMPLE DISHES: whitebait with brown bread £5.50; steak and 6X pie £8; profiteroles £4.

Licensee D.J. Satchell (Wadworth)
Open *11 to 2.30, 5.30 to 11, Sun 12 to 2.30, 6.30 to 10.30; bar food 12 to 2.30, 7 to 9.30; open 11 to 11 Sat and Sun summer*
Details *Children welcome in dining room   Car park   Wheelchair access (also WC)   Garden   No smoking in dining room   Background music   Dogs welcome in bar   Amex, Delta, MasterCard, Switch, Visa   Accommodation: 8 rooms, B&B £60 to £90*

NUNNINGTON   North Yorkshire   map 9

Royal Oak

Church Street, Nunnington YO62 5US   TEL: (01439) 748271
on B1257, 2m N of Hovingham

On the border of the North York Moors National Park and set between a triple-arched river bridge and the parish church, the Royal Oak is a foursquare edifice of local stone, located in tranquil coun-tryside. Nunnington Hall, a seventeenth-century manor run by the National Trust, draws the tourist trade in season, and the Oak is handily positioned to cater for them. A plethora of rural artefacts, including agricultural implements and stone jugs, adorns the interior, which benefits from open fires on chilly days and the equally warm welcome extended by landlord Tony Simpson. On handpump are Tetley Bitter as well as Theakston Best and Old Peculier, and a trio of wines are sold by the glass. The cooking is built around a mainstay of classic pub dishes, such as breaded scampi, ploughman's lunch (including pineapple), and steak and kidney casserole with a herb dumpling. Vegetarians are not neglected, however, and might opt for crisply battered sweet-and-sour vegetables with rice. Italian-inspired dishes include ham and mushroom tagliatelle with garlic bread, or a lasagne of aubergine, mushrooms and peppers. SAMPLE DISHES: toasted goats' cheese £4.75; roast duckling with orange sauce £10.50; hazelnut meringue sundae £3.75.

Licensee A.K. Simpson (freehouse)
Open *Tue to Sat 12 to 2.30, 6.30 to 11, Sun 12 to 2.30, 7 to 10.30; bar food and restaurant 12 to 2, 6.30 to 9*
Details *Children welcome in dining room   Car park   Wheelchair access (also WC)   Garden   No smoking in dining room   Occasional background music   No dogs   Delta, MasterCard, Switch, Visa*

NUTHURST   **West Sussex**   **map 3**

Black Horse 🍺

Nuthurst RH13 6LH   TEL: (01403) 891272
off A281, 3m S of Horsham

This particular horse's paddock is a well-cultivated woodland garden with a tinkling stream crossed by a wooden bridge. Outside seating here, and also facing the road in front of the pub, encourage appreciation of the pretty surroundings. In both the restaurant and the bars are blackboards displaying the daily specials – focusing on fish – supplementing the short printed menu. An exploratory mind is shown by the varieties of garlic breads, open sandwiches and filled potato skins, some with quite inventive ingredients. Main dishes, too, have an eclectic touch, as in teriyaki-glazed salmon, mussels mouclade (a lightly spiced curried sauce), fajitas, and chilli con carne with tortillas. But Sussex herby sausages are offered as well, with fruit crumbles, or banoffi pie for pudding. Fuller's London Pride, Harveys Sussex Pale Ale, Wadworth 6X, and Weltons Dorking Pride are stocked, along with Stowford Press cider, and four wines are sold by the glass. SAMPLE DISHES: garlic bread with roasted tomato, olives and mozzarella £3.50; fillet of cod with caraway and lemon crust £8; apple pie £3.25.

Licensees Karen Jones and Mark Watts (freehouse)
Open *11 to 3, 6 to 11, Sun 12 to 3, 7 to 11; bar food and restaurant 12 to 2.45, 6 to 9, Sun 12 to 3, 7 to 9.30; closed evening 25 Dec*
Details *Children welcome   Car park   Garden and patio   No-smoking area in bar, no smoking in dining room   Occasional live or background music   Dogs welcome exc in dining room   MasterCard, Switch, Visa*

OAKWOODHILL   Surrey   map 3

Punch Bowl Inn

Oakwoodhill RH5 5PU   TEL: (01306) 627249
off A29 Dorking to Horsham road, 5m NW of Horsham

Parts of this charming old pub, peacefully located on the edge of the
hamlet, date from the fourteenth century. It's a substantial, double-
fronted, tile-hung building in the Wealden style. In summer you can
sit at tables in the front garden and on the patio while watching
cricket on the green. The spacious main bar has lots of character,
with its polished slate-flagged floor, huge inglenook with a log fire,
scrubbed tables, long benches and old photographs of the pub on the
walls. The adjoining dining area is low-ceilinged and carpeted, and
the whole place is well maintained. The blackboard menu is quite
short, and some dishes show imaginative variations on traditional
themes. Hot gazpacho soup, or smoked salmon steak with green
salsa may be among starters, for instance, with game casseroled in ale
with apples, or king prawns provençale among main courses.
Otherwise you might find generously filled mushroom and Stilton
tart with 'melt-in-the-mouth' pastry, or chicken liver and quail pâté,
followed by sizzling Cajun sirloin steak, salmon fillet on Singapore
stir-fried noodles, or tuna steak with a Thai broth. Badger Dorset
Best and Tanglefoot and King & Barnes Sussex Bitter and Old Ale
are on draught, and five wines are available by the glass. SAMPLE
DISHES: nachos £4; home-baked ham, egg and chips £7; chocolate
gâteau £4.

Licensees Phillip and Wendy Nisbett (Badger Inns)
Open *11 to 11, Sun 12 to 10.30; bar food and restaurant 12 to 2.15, 6.30 to
9.30*
Details *Children welcome in dining room   Car park   Wheelchair access (not
WC)   Garden and patio   No smoking in dining room   Background music;
jukebox   Dogs welcome   MasterCard, Switch, Visa*

OARE   Kent   map 3

Shipwrights Arms 🍺

WATERSIDE

Hollowshore, Oare ME13 7TU   TEL: (01795) 590088
*from A2 just W of Faversham take exit to Oare, then right towards
Davington, left into Ham Road; follow signs across the marshes*

'Well worth knowing about if you are travelling along the north
Kent coast by boat,' thought a visitor to this remote family-run inn.
Indeed, it is easier to reach by water, being next to a boatyard on a
creek, protected from the water by a dyke. The alternative is a

bumpy, narrow road across marshland that seems to go on for ever. Whatever your transport, the location merits the journey, and the small, cottagey seventeenth-century building is itself full of charm. Its warren-like interior, with low ceilings, beams and standing timbers, is partitioned into cosy areas around a central brick fireplace. A row of casks stands behind the tiny bar counter, dispensing fine beers from the local Goacher's Brewery – which also provides the house beer, Shipwrecked Ale – joined by a variety of guests. Two wines are served by the glass from a list of just eight. Food is reasonably priced, straightforward and hearty, with sandwiches, jacket potatoes, and light bites such as chips topped with melted cheese. Main courses might be home-cooked ham, egg and chips, or chicken tikka masala, and specials have included a giant Yorkshire pudding containing a large Cumberland sausage and onion gravy. Children will appreciate the large garden at the rear in summer. SAMPLE DISHES: crispy-coated Camembert with cranberry sauce £3.25; deep-fried cod in batter with chips and peas £5.50; spotted dick £2.75.

Licensees Derek and Ruth Cole (freehouse)
Open *summer 11 to 11; winter Sun to Fri 12 to 3, 7 to 11 (10.30 Sun), Sat 11 to 11; bar food (exc Sun evening) 12 to 2.30, 7 to 9*
Details *Children welcome in family room   Car park   Wheelchair access (not WC)   Garden   No-smoking area in bar   Occasional live or background music Dogs welcome   No cards*

OCKLEY   Surrey   map 3

Old School House 🍇

Stane Street, Ockley RH5 5TH   TEL: (01306) 627430
on A29 Bognor Regis road, 8m S of Dorking

This old, dark-beamed pub with its unassuming but comfortable interior draws in fish-lovers both in the bar and in its separate, more formal Bryce's restaurant. Bar menus might offer starters of Cullen skink, or home-cured gravlax, and main courses of seafood lasagne, deep-fried scampi in tempura, or pan-fried fillet of salmon on potato and celeriac rösti. Carnivores need not feel excluded, however, as dishes such as lasagne bolognese, and calf's liver on garlic and shallot mash, are also likely to feature, while vegetarians can enjoy aubergine charlotte on spicy Puy lentils, or spinach and feta ravioli. Open sandwiches are also served. Some of the bar dishes are available in the restaurant, where choice might also extend to Loch Fyne oysters, mille-feuille of seared swordfish loin with crab couscous, and Catalonian fish stew. Real ales on offer take in Gale's Butser Bitter, GB and HSB. Fourteen well-priced house wines are available by the glass (or £10.95 per bottle), while much of the rest of the list sits enticingly under the £20 mark. French and Australian wines feature highly; 'Bryce's Special Cellar' is worth delving into for some of the big classics. SAMPLE DISHES: Brie fritters on spring onion salsa £4.75; linguine with prawns, calamari, salmon and chives in a cream sauce £6.50; lemon and mascarpone tart with mago sorbet £3.75.

Licensee Bill Bryce (freehouse)
Open *all week 11 to 3, 6 to 11; bar food and restaurant all week 12 to 2.30, 6.30 to 9.30 (9 Sun); closed Sun evening Oct to Feb, 25 and 26 Dec, 1 and 2 Jan*
Details *Children welcome　Car park　Wheelchair access (also WC)　Patio No smoking in dining room　Occasional background music　Dogs welcome exc in restaurant　Delta, MasterCard, Switch, Visa*

ODELL　Bedfordshire　map 6

Bell

Horsefair Lane, Odell MK43 7AU　TEL: (01234) 720254
off A6, 8m NW of Bedford

On a minor road connecting the pretty villages of Harrold and Sharnbrook and right by the River Ouse stands the Bell. Riverside gardens complete with an aviary offer access to the local country park, which is itself worth a visit. The compact, thatched pub contains a series of interconnecting rooms rambling around a large bar, with a big family room at the back. Log fires and low ceilings make the place feel like a real rural retreat in colder months. The Bell is a Greene King house, and the brewery's IPA and Abbot Ale, as well as its seasonal beers, are on handpump. Half a dozen wines are served by the glass. Daily specials are chalked on a blackboard above the bar, and at busy sessions, such as Sunday lunch, there may well be quite a jostle to choose before the popular items are wiped off. These might include duck à l'orange, lamb shank 'cassoulet' with borlotti beans and leeks, or salmon steak poached in white wine. Otherwise, the printed menu lists standards such as lasagne, shepherd's pie, sausages with onion gravy, salads, and generously filled omelettes, described as 'excellent'. A wide choice of desserts ranges from apple pie to 'boozy mousse'. SAMPLE DISHES: asparagus and mushroom cream pasta £6; breaded pink trout fillet coated with almonds £6; steamed syrup sponge pudding with vanilla ice cream £2.50.

Licensees Derek and Doreen Scott (Greene King)
Open *11 to 2.30, 6 to 11, Sun 12 to 2.30, 7 to 10.30; bar food (exc Sun evening) 12 to 2, 7 to 9.30*
Details *Children welcome in bar eating area　Car park　Wheelchair access (not WC)　Garden and patio　Background music　No dogs　Delta, MasterCard, Switch, Visa*

OFFHAM   East Sussex   map 3

Blacksmith's Arms

London Road, Offham BN7 3QD   TEL: (01273) 472971
off A275, 2m N of Lewes

This village local right next to a busy main road is easy to pass by,
but is worth the stop for some distinctly above-the-norm pub food,
and smooth and courteous service to boot. Dark wooden tables and
chairs, and a roaring log fire in winter, set the tone inside. The same
menu is on offer in both bar and restaurant, but snacks – ploughman's, or ham, egg and chips, say – are not available on Friday and
Saturday evenings. Main dishes range from simple deep-fried plaice
and chips, or steak and kidney pie, to grilled chump chops on
parsnip and coriander purée, or baked cod on a smoked salmon
pancake with lemon and dill sauce. Among starters are surprises like
Thai-style marinated prawns on red onion, mango and coriander
salsa with a tortilla, or Chinese-spiced crabmeat tartlet with a salad
dressed with ginger, lime and sesame. Among desserts are pecan and
toffee bread-and-butter pudding with whisky sauce and ice cream, as
well as rice pudding with almonds, apricots and nutmeg. Real ales
are from Harveys of Lewes, and three or four wines are sold by the
glass from the short, reasonably priced list. SAMPLE DISHES: scallops
with garlic and bacon £5.75; game casserole with herb dumplings
£9; caramelised apple tart with cinnamon custard £3.75.

Licensee Jean Large (freehouse)
Open *all week (exc Sun evening) 11 to 3, 6.30 to 11; bar food and restaurant
12 to 2, 7 to 9; closed 25 and 26 Dec*
Details *No children   Car park   Wheelchair access (also WC)   Patio   No
music   Dogs welcome   Delta, MasterCard, Switch, Visa*

OLDBURY-ON-SEVERN   S. Gloucestershire   map 2

Anchor Inn

Church Road, Oldbury-on-Severn BS35 1QA
TEL: (01454) 413331
off B4061, 2m NW of Thornbury

Looking across meadows to the Severn, this truly rural pub
welcomes locals, business people and holiday makers. You can sit in
the attractive main bar with its stone fireplace, easy chairs, settles
and window seats, or in the split-level lounge bar with its beamed
ceilings. One menu operates throughout, offering a wide choice of
food that is nevertheless 'up-to-the-minute fresh'. Light meals

include such things as smoked salmon with salad and bread, soups, pâté, and a range of interesting salads. Generously portioned main dishes might run to boozy beef pie, faggots in onion gravy, or fillet of smoked haddock on pasta with mushrooms, potatoes and vegetables or salad – or even beans bourguignon for vegetarians. Robust appetites can then go on to chocolate lumpy bumpy bumpy cheesecake with chocolate sauce and cream, or Oldbury mud pie. Bass, Black Sheep Best Bitter, Theakston Best and Old Peculier, Butcombe Bitter, and Stowford Press Cider are stocked. Twelve of the wines on the short list are available by the glass and no fewer than 75 whiskies are offered too. SAMPLE DISHES: sliced smoked chicken breast and fresh orange £4.25; lasagne £5; caramel apple granny £3.

Licensees Michael J. Dowdeswell and Alex de la Torre (freehouse)
Open *Mon to Fri 11.30 to 2.30, 6.30 to 11, Sat 11.30 to 11, Sun 12 to 10.30; bar food and restaurant 11.30 to 2, 6.30 to 9.30, Sun 12 to 3.30, 7 to 9.30; closed 25 Dec and evening 26 Dec*
Details *Children welcome in dining room   Car park   Wheelchair access (also WC)   Garden   No smoking in dining room   Music very occasionally   Dogs welcome exc in dining room   MasterCard, Visa*

OLD HEATHFIELD   East Sussex   map 3

Star Inn

Old Heathfield TN21 9AH   TEL: (01435) 863570
off B2203 or B2096, just S of Heathfield

Tucked away from the main road through the village, the Star's location is nothing if not tranquil, and the comfortable atmosphere within – deriving not least from an inglenook fireplace with a real fire in the winter – is warm and welcoming. Although there are distinct bar and restaurant areas, one menu operates throughout, with the day's specials chalked on a board. Virtually everything you will eat is made in-house, and the repertoire might take you from a pâté, such as smoked salmon or chicken liver, through a ten-ounce ribeye steak sauced with mustard, cream and mushrooms, or maybe a vegetarian version of moussaka, to something from the frequently changing dessert range. The last might be chocolate fudge cake, strawberry meringue, or sticky toffee pudding. As well as the two permanent cask-conditioned ales, Harveys Sussex Best Bitter and Shepherd Neame, there is always one guest ale (how about Marlow Brewery's Hangover from Hell?), and five wines are served by the glass. SAMPLE DISHES: flat-cap mushroom stuffed with mozzarella and peppers £5; Cajun-spiced goose breast with sauté potatoes £11.50; banoffi pie £4.50.

Licensee Fiona Airey (freehouse)
Open *11.30 to 3, 5.30 to 11, Sun 12 to 3, 7 to 10.30; bar food and restaurant 12 to 2.15 (2.30 Sat and Sun), 7 to 9.30 (9 Sun); closed evening 25 Dec*
Details *Children welcome   Car park   Garden   Live or background music Dogs welcome in bar   Delta, MasterCard, Switch, Visa*

OMBERSLEY   Worcestershire   map 5

▲ *Crown & Sandys Arms* NEW ENTRY
Ombersley WR9 0EW
TEL: (01905) 620252
off A449 Worcester to Kidderminster road, 4m W of Droitwich

SEAFOOD

This gabled seventeenth-century hostelry in a pretty village of ancient timber-framed cottages is obviously old inside despite clever modernisation. Two old bars have been converted into a single, airy, long one, although flagstone flooring and a good mixture of sturdy furnishings remain, from old settles and pews to traditional tables and chairs. The dining areas are like modern bistros in style. Most of the well-assorted clientele come to eat, but drinkers can enjoy a pint of up to six draught ales, perhaps including Greene King Abbot Ale, Adnams Best Bitter, Tetley Bitter or Marston's Pedigree. More than half of the 50-odd bottles on the list of largely French wines are under £20; four are served by the glass. The lunchtime bar menu lists sandwiches and baguettes with imaginative fillings, while main dishes include a warm salad of chicken, bacon and avocado, or something like seafood linguine. The emphasis of the lengthy main menu is on fish and seafood, from plump and juicy pan-fried scallops and bacon drizzled with teriyaki, or half a dozen oysters, to fillet of monkfish wrapped in Parma ham, or a Thai curry of mixed fish. Meat dishes are not overlooked, taking in 'delicious' steak and kidney pudding, Chinese-spiced Gressingham duck breast, and bangers and mash. SAMPLE DISHES: mushroom mille-feuille £4.50; half a lobster grilled with garlic butter and dressed with mussels and prawns £19; chocolate and rum tart £4.25.

Licensee Richard Everton (freehouse)
Open *Mon to Fri 11.30 to 3, 5 to 11, Sat and Sun 11.30 to 11; bar food and restaurant Mon to Sat 12 to 2.30, 6 to 10, Sun 12 to 10*
Details *Children welcome   Car park   Wheelchair access (also WC)   Patio No smoking in dining room   Occasional live or background music   No dogs Amex, Delta, MasterCard, Switch, Visa   Accommodation: 3 rooms, B&B £50*

Use the maps at the back of the book to plan your trip.

Kings Arms

Ombersley WR9 0EW　TEL: (01905) 620142

This charmingly crooked-looking, black and white timbered inn is named after a reputed stopover made here by Charles II in 1651 when he was fleeing from his defeat at the Battle of Worcester. Even then, the place was over 200 years old, and it still exudes the kind of charm that guarantees it popularity in the tourist season. The inside boasts no fewer than three open fires and several intimate nooks and crannies within its series of interconnecting rooms, and in the evenings it is appealingly dimly lit. Frequently changing large printed menus are supplemented by blackboard specials, and the culinary range shows imagination. For lunch, there might be field mushrooms on toast with garlic, thyme and chilli, or a selection of farmhouse cheeses with pickled shallots, and in the evenings a choice of Parma ham and asparagus tart on mixed leaves, or salade niçoise with seared tuna to start. Main courses take in ribeye steak, grilled pork chop with apples, apricots and shallots on creamy mash, or fish specials, such as gutsily flavoured hake in a pesto and walnut crust, or monkfish and bacon kebabs with hollandaise. Brandy-spiked chocolate pots, or summer pudding with clotted cream might be ways to finish. An ale from the local Cannon Royall brewery is offered alongside Marston's Pedigree and Banks's Bitter. Half a dozen wines are available by the glass, and in all there are about 30 to choose from – with just about every wine-producing country covered. SAMPLE DISHES: pan-fried sweetbreads with Dijon sauce and rocket salad £4.25; roasted sea bass on sun-dried tomatoes and basil £14; gooseberry fool with almond biscuits £3.75.

Licensee J. Willmott (freehouse)
Open *11 to 2.30, 5.30 to 11, Sun 12 to 10.30; bar food 12 to 2.15, 5.30 to 10, Sun 12 to 10; closed 25 Dec*
Details *Children welcome   Car park   Wheelchair access (also WC)   Patio No music   No dogs   Delta, MasterCard, Switch, Visa*

OVER PEOVER　　Cheshire　　　　　　　　　　　map 8

▲ *Dog Inn* 🍺

Well Bank Lane, Over Peover WA16 8UP　TEL: (01625) 861421
off A50 between Knutsford and Holmes Chapel; turn at Whipping Stocks pub and continue for 1½m

---

The Dog is a pub of two distinct halves. In the bar you will find mostly locals drinking beer; those who want to drink wine or eat need to head through to one of the two dining rooms and place orders at the desk. The décor remains true to the building's 1930s roots, and tables are set with fresh flowers; even if there is no fire burning in either of the two fireplaces, central heating in cold weather provides plenty of warmth. The kitchen grows its own herbs and makes good use of local produce, which turns up on the menu in a wide range of mostly traditional dishes, such as turkey and mushroom pie, roast leg of lamb with mint sauce, poached salmon in a cucumber jus, and steak casseroled in red wine. The range of beers is both varied and excellent, featuring highly regarded real ales such as Hydes Traditional Bitter, Moorhouses Black Cat and Weetwood Best Bitter and Old Dog (local brews). Wines, too, are a decent bunch and reasonably priced, with six by the glass. Mulled wine may be on draught all year long, and a wide selection of malt whiskies is stocked. SAMPLE DISHES: smoked chicken with melon and orange salad £4.50; ham shank with parsley sauce £10; sticky toffee pudding with custard £3.50.

Licensee Stephen Wrigley (freehouse)
Open *11.30 to 3, 5.30 to 11 (10.30 Sun); bar food 12 to 2.30, 7 to 9.30*
Details *Children welcome Car park Wheelchair access (also WC) Garden and patio No smoking in dining room Occasional live or background music No dogs MasterCard, Switch, Visa Accommodation: 6 rooms, B&B £55 to £100*

OVER STRATTON Somerset map 2

Royal Oak

Over Stratton TA13 5LQ TEL: (01460) 240906
off A303, take Ilminster town centre turn away from South Petherton, turn left after 300 yards

In a picturesque village set amid stunning Somerset scenery, the Royal Oak is a thatched amalgam of cottages. It is a child-friendly pub, complete with play area next to the patio and barbecue, making it a good summer family destination. Old beams, open fires and a lack of pretentiousness are the backdrop for ploughman's lunches, together with turkey dinosaurs for the kids, and a fairly extensive spread of modern dishes too. Handwritten menus are supplemented by blackboard specials such as seasonal game, fresh fish and home-made soup of the day. These might include Thai-style mussels with crusty bread; lobster, crab and asparagus risotto with Parmesan; and main courses of glazed duck breast with okra, bok choy and Chinese mushrooms sauced with honey, soy and sesame. Traditional English sponge puddings are a mainstay, or there may be banana pancakes with lime butterscotch sauce and clotted cream ice cream. For real-beer drinkers there's Badger Best and Tanglefoot, and French house wines in four styles are served by the glass. SAMPLE DISHES: grilled

smoked goats' cheese with marinated aubergine, roast cherry tomatoes and chive and basil dressing £4.50; calf's liver sautéed in sage
and lime with pancetta, deep-fried wild mushrooms and creamed
potatoes £12.75; crème brûlée with fresh fruit £4.

Licensee Mark Warrener (Woodhouse Inns)
Open *11 to 3, 6 to 11, Sun 12 to 3, 7 to 10.30; bar food and restaurant 12
to 2.30, 6.30 to 10*
Details *Children welcome   Car park   Wheelchair access (also WC)   Garden
and patio   No smoking in dining room   Occasional background music   Dogs
welcome exc in dining room   Delta, MasterCard, Switch, Visa*

PAXFORD   Gloucestershire   map 5

▲ *Churchill Arms* ♥♥

Paxford GL55 6XH   TEL: (01386) 594000
WEB SITE: www.thechurchillarms.com
2m E of Chipping Campden

This food pub has no restaurant, although it does have a games room
which can get happily exuberant at times. Anywhere else in the
open-plan bar, or outside at trestle tables, you can enjoy some
sophisticated cooking overseen by Sonya Brooke-Little, the dishes
written on daily-changing blackboards. The nearest the style gets to
traditional pub fare are honey-roast ham with egg and chips, or
cottage pie, and even this is lifted by red wine and rosemary in the
meat and horseradish in the mash. Typical of starters are duck,
fennel and grapefruit salad, or ox-tongue with crisp sweetbreads,
diced beetroot and Cumberland sauce. Mains could be John Dory
with red wine risotto, capers and spring onions in olive oil and tapénade, or braised lamb shank with a casserole of haricot beans, thyme
and chorizo. Desserts, except sticky toffee pudding, lean to the light
fantastic: for example, pannacotta with orange and nutmeg parfait.
Arkell's 3B and Hook Norton are on draught, while the wine list
offers thirty bottles, with nine by the glass. The Brooke-Littles also
run the Hare & Hounds at Foss Cross (see entry). SAMPLE DISHES:
pan-fried scallops with spring onion mash and crisp pancetta £8;
lemon sole in a herb crust with sweet red pepper sauce £10; passion-
fruit mousse with mango parfait and white chocolate sauce £4.

Licensees Richard Barnes and Leo Brooke-Little (freehouse)
Open *11.30 to 3, 6 to 11, Sun 12 to 3, 7 to 10.30; bar food 12 to 2, 7 to 9*
Details *Children welcome   Wheelchair access (not WC)   Garden and patio
No music   No dogs   Delta, MasterCard, Switch, Visa   Accommodation: 4
rooms, B&B £40 to £60*

🍺 *indicates a pub serving exceptional draught beers.*

PEMBRIDGE   Herefordshire   map 5

▲ *New Inn*

Market Square, Pembridge HR6 9DZ
TEL: **(01544) 388427**
on A44, between Kington and Leominster, 6m E of Kington

Don't be fooled by the name: the origins of this ancient black and white half-timbered inn lie in the early fourteenth century, making it one of the oldest pubs in England. Any building of this age is bound to have hosted some historically significant events, and so it is that the New Inn claims to be where the treaty was signed that made Edward IV king of England in 1461. As might be expected, the atmospheric bar has heavy beams, flagstone floors and a huge open fireplace, and a mainly local clientele gives the place a friendly atmosphere. There is nothing particularly new about the menu either, with old favourites such as deep-fried Brie with redcurrant jelly, beef and mushroom pie, or fish and chips. Lunches include not only ploughman's (Cheddar), but a version for woodcutters (home-cooked ham) and one for gentlemen farmers (Stilton). There are also various crusty sandwiches, soups and salads. Beers include Black Sheep Bitter and Fuller's London Pride; Weston's organic cider and 32 whiskies are also available. A local English wine appears on the international list, along with various fruit wines; six wines are served by the glass. SAMPLE DISHES: half-pint of prawns with salad and crusty bread £6; sausage and red onion hotpot £6; salmon steak baked in lemon and parsley butter £9.50.

Licensee Jane Melvin (freehouse)
Open *11 to 3 (2.30 winter), 6 (6.30 winter) to 11, Sun 12 to 3, 7 to 10.30; bar food and restaurant 12 to 2, 7 to 9.30 (9 Sun); no food served first week Feb*
Details *Children welcome in eating areas   Car park   Wheelchair access (not WC)   No smoking in dining room   Occasional live music   No dogs   Amex, Delta, MasterCard, Switch, Visa   Accommodation: 6 rooms, B&B £18.50 to £37*

PETER TAVY   Devon   map 1

Peter Tavy Inn �._ 🍺

Peter Tavy PL19 9NN   TEL: **(01822) 810348**
off A386, 3m NE of Tavistock

'What a find this place is,' noted a couple of this white-washed Dartmoor village inn reportedly dating from the fifteenth century. The stone-flagged, low-beamed interior, with candlelight in the evenings, creates a cosy atmosphere, bolstered in no small measure by the friendly attentions of the staff. Don't miss the fascinating collection of postcards originally sent to troops in the trenches of the Great War. Dark wooden tables and a motley assortment of chairs furnish the dining area, where you will eat well-prepared comfort food. Wild boar pâté might be on the menu, plus avocado and bacon salad, prawns in lemon and ginger, or a hearty soup such as tomato and basil. The cooking casts its net way beyond the usual pub standards to take in pot-roast pheasant, blackened Cajun-spiced tuna, and vegetable tikka masala. Finish with authentic black treacle tart, chocolate truffle torte, or strawberry and rhubarb crumble. The selection of real ales provides interesting choice, from Princetown Jail Ale and Summerskills Tamar to weekly-rotating guest beers such as Scattor Rock Devonian. Luscombe's organic ciders are available too. The wine list spins the globe in a brisk and concise fashion, opening with French house wines at £7.95 a bottle. Eight wines are served by the glass. SAMPLE DISHES: bacon and Camembert parcels £4; braised lamb shank with garlic mash £11; banana toffee pudding £3.50.

Licensees Graeme and Karen Sim (freehouse)
Open *all week 12 to 2.30 (3 Fri and Sat), 6 (6.30 winter) to 11 (10.30 Sun); bar food 12 to 2, 7 (6.30 Fri and Sat and all week summer) to 9; closed 25 Dec*
Details *Children welcome in family room   Car park   Garden and patio   No smoking in dining room   Background music   Dogs welcome   Delta, MasterCard, Switch, Visa*

PHILLEIGH   Cornwall   map 1

Roseland Inn   NEW ENTRY

Philleigh TR2 5NB   TEL: (01872) 580254
take Philleigh turning off A3078 St Mawes road

A friendly and atmospheric pub in a tiny village reached down a narrow lane, the Roseland is a slate-roofed, white pebble-dash inn that prides itself on catering to an enthusiastic clientele. Though off the beaten path, it can get very busy. Two rooms are served by the same small bar, and there is a separate carpeted dining room. Very low ceilings contribute to the pint-pot feeling, and plenty of wall adornment provides visual interest, including a gigantic, locally caught lobster. Bar snacks such as ploughman's, sandwiches and what the house describes as 'a proper Cornish pasty', as well as a short choice for children, supplement the main menu, which deals modishly in the likes of a tart of Mediterranean vegetables, rocket, melon and Parmesan salad; Singapore spicy pork with peanut sauce and wild rice; and grilled salmon steak glazed with honey and mustard. Daily specials, perhaps a serving of guinea fowl stuffed with bacon, chestnuts and sage, are chalked on a blackboard. Desserts might include pecan pie, or lemon tart, and chocolate ice cream is well reported. Sharp's Doom Bar Bitter, Bass and Marston's Pedigree are on handpump, and there may well be guest ales from Smiles, Ringwood and the like as well. A reasonable choice of around twenty wines includes eight by the glass. SAMPLE DISHES: garlic mushrooms topped with Stilton £6; crab cakes with tomato and basil dressing £10; espresso crème brûlée £4.

Licensees Colin and Jacque Phillips (freehouse)
Open *11 to 3, 5.30 (6 winter) to 11, Sun 12 to 3, 6 to 10.30; bar food and restaurant 12 to 2.30, 6 to 9*
Details *Children welcome   Car park   Wheelchair access (also WC)   Garden   No smoking in dining room   No music   Dogs welcome   MasterCard, Switch, Visa*

PICKERING   North Yorkshire   map 9

▲ *White Swan* 🍇

Market Place, Pickering YO18 7AA   TEL: (01751) 472288
WEB SITE: www.white-swan.co.uk
turn off roundabout at junction of A169 and A170

As it is close to many of Yorkshire's tourist attractions, it is hardly surprising that the bustling market town of Pickering is a popular place. Many visitors seem to end up in the White Swan, a sixteenth-century coaching inn with a relaxed and informal bar, warmed by a log fire in winter, and a smart restaurant. At lunch, the extensive list of bar food offers great variety, ranging from simple potted shrimps or dressed Whitby crab, to Thai chicken curry or confit duck leg with mash, black pudding and apple chutney. The dinner menu, more up-market and more expensive, has something of an Italian flavour provided by dishes like carpaccio of beef fillet with Parmesan and lemon, or breast of chicken wrapped in Parma ham with sun-dried tomatoes and sage stuffing. All beers come from Yorkshire breweries; alongside regular Black Sheep Best and Special from Masham might be guest ales from Black Dog of Whitby and Hambleton of Thirsk, for example. An impressive 200-strong wine list has eight by the glass which have been rigorously selected for their drinkability. A specialist section of Saint-Emilions, with an impressive range of old vintages (not cheap, though), will appeal to wine connoisseurs. The main wine selection strays just about every-where else in the world but not too far over the £20 mark. SAMPLE DISHES: grilled Swaledale goats' cheese with tomato chutney, rocket and basil oil £5; roast rack of lamb with bubble and squeak, glazed baby vegetables £13.50; lemon and lime tart with Earl Grey syrup and lemon and mascarpone cream £4.50.

Licensee V.J. Buchanan (freehouse)
Open *Mon 10.30 to 11, Tue to Fri 11 to 3, 6 to 11, Sat 11 to 11, Sun 12 to 3, 7 to 10.30; bar food 12 to 2, 7 to 9*
Details *Children welcome in eating areas Car park Wheelchair access (not WC) Garden and patio No smoking in bar eating area and dining room Occasional live music Dogs welcome exc in dining room Amex, Delta, MasterCard, Switch, Visa Accommodation: 12 rooms, B&B £60 to £140*

PICKHILL North Yorkshire map 8

▲ *Nag's Head* ❦

Pickhill YO7 4JG TEL: (01845) 567391
WEB SITE: www.nagsheadpickhill.co.uk
off A1, 5m SE of Leeming

While this country inn can boast a lineage of some 200 years, the tiny village that it stands in the centre of is mentioned in the Domesday Book. It is an area steeped in history, with plenty to look at and to visit, and – as the name might indicate – racecourses aplenty in the vicinity. Bucolic gentility might best sum up the ambience of the Nag's Head. Summer meals may be taken under a handsome portico addition at the front, while, inside, diners may head for the smartly appointed dining room or the comfortable main dark-panelled bar with its green velour bench seating. Drinkers of real ales will find Hambleton's Bitter, John Smith's and Black Sheep Best Bitter on tap, while the range of speciality spirits encompasses a fine collection of malts, cognacs and armagnacs. Some highly inventive cooking is going on here, too. Try casuela soup (a Chilean recipe combining chicken wings, carrots, potatoes, chilli and coriander) to start with, or perhaps sauté lambs' kidneys sauced with sherry and mustard, before going on to salmon steak with capers and garlic butter, or stir-fried chicken with egg noodles and Szechuan-style sauce. More traditional tastes are catered for with moules marinière, roast rack of lamb with minted gravy, and generously sized sirloin steak with Stilton sauce, as well as more mainstream bar meals. Lemon tart, or a chocolate version of crème brûlée, may be among puddings. The wine list makes a very thorough tour of France but does not neglect the rest of the world's vineyards, making some interesting and representative choices. Most bottle prices are well within the £20 mark, so won't break the bank, and a choice of six wines by the glass and seven by the half-bottle are equally complementary to the food on offer. SAMPLE DISHES: smoked haddock florentine £4.50; wild pigeon breast on a bed of leeks with cheese and cabbage mash £11; champagne syllabub £3.50.

Licensees Edward and Raymond Boynton (freehouse)
Open *11 to 11, Sun 12 to 10.30; bar food and restaurant 12 to 2, 6 to 9.30; closed 25 Dec*
Details *Children welcome   Car park   Wheelchair access (also WC)   Garden and patio   No smoking in dining room   No music   Dogs welcome   Delta, MasterCard, Switch, Visa   Accommodation: 17 rooms, B&B £40 to £60*

PILLEY   Hampshire   map 2

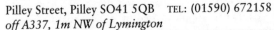

Fleur de Lys

Pilley Street, Pilley SO41 5QB   TEL: (01590) 672158
off A337, 1m NW of Lymington

On the edge of the New Forest, this ancient thatched pub was at one time a pair of foresters' cottages. In the stone-flagged entrance passage, the tree roots and the fireplace opening (an old New Forest rights tradition) can still be seen. Three interconnecting rooms have heavy beamed ceilings, bric-à-brac, a comfortable mix of traditional pub chairs and tables and a huge inglenook with a log fire over which a cauldron is sometimes used to make soup. The regular ales, Ringwood Best and Flowers Original, are accompanied by a guest that changes frequently; draught ciders, such as Strongbow, Scrumpy Jack or Thatcher's, change from time to time. Fourteen wines are served by the glass, and there is a range of Gale's country wines. The menus offer 'doorsteps' as well as ordinary sandwiches, and enterprising main dishes might include trout fishcakes, stuffed peppers on couscous with coriander and yoghurt salsa, roast monkfish tails with watercress mash, and local faggots with mash. SAMPLE DISHES: 'traditional ploughperson's' £6; hock of pork £9; steamed raspberry sponge £3.75.

Licensee Neil Collins Rogers (Whitbread)
Open *11 to 2.30/3.00, 6 to 11, Sun 12 to 3, 7 to 10.30; bar food 12 to 2, 6.30 to 9.30; closed evenings 25 and 26 Dec*
Details *Children welcome in family room   Car park   Wheelchair access (not WC)   Garden and patio   No-smoking area in bar   Occasional live or background music   Dogs welcome   Delta, MasterCard, Switch, Visa*

PLAYLEY GREEN   Gloucestershire   map 5

Rose & Crown

Playley Green GL19 3NB   TEL: (01531) 650234
on A417, just east of Redmarley D'Abitot and 1m S of M50 junction 2

This fine example of the 'country pub experience' comes in the form of a large, cream-washed building adorned with flowers in tubs and hanging baskets, set in rolling countryside on the not-too-busy main road between Hereford and Gloucester. Inside are a warm welcome and two bar areas, one with pool table and darts, the other with polished tables, wood panelling and exposed stone. There is also a large dining room, though this and the bar are served by the same printed menu of filled rolls, ploughman's and things like ham, eggs and chips or steaks. This is supplemented by a blackboard of daily and seasonal specials, such as pork tenderloin with creamy apple sauce, or lamb and apricot curry, and a fresh fish dish of the day, perhaps tuna steak with tomato and balsamic dressing. Flowers Original is joined by a regularly changing guest ale (e.g. Adnams Broadside, Young's Special) and local Weston's cider. Four wines from the short list are available by the glass at £1.55; bottle prices are all (except champagne) under £13. SAMPLE DISHES: smoked salmon and prawn roulade £4.75; beef and Guinness casserole £7; lemon and ginger tart £3.

Licensee Robin Bunnett (Pubmaster)
Open *11 to 2.30, 6 to 11, Sun 12 to 3, 7 to 10.30; closed 25 Dec; bar food and restaurant all week 12 to 2, Mon to Sat 6.30 to 9 (9.50 Fri and Sat); restaurant may close for non-busy sessions*
Details *Children welcome in eating areas and games room   Car park Wheelchair access (also WC)   Garden and patio   No smoking in dining room Occasional background music   Dogs welcome exc in restaurant   Delta, MasterCard, Switch, Visa*

PLUCKLEY   Kent   map 3

▲ *Dering Arms* 🍇

Station Road, Pluckley TN27 0RR
TEL: (01233) 840371
off B2077, close to Pluckley railway station

FISH

Once a hunting-lodge belonging to the Derings of Kent, this rather imposing old stone building with its arched windows and elaborate gables makes an enjoyably atmospheric country pub. The décor within is certainly rustic enough, with farming implements and garlands of hops hung about, and there are open fireplaces to cheer the spirit on winter nights. Real ales from Goacher's of Maidstone are brewed especially for the Dering Arms. In addition to that, there is an enormous wine list that encompasses some fine New World offerings as well as a plethora of mature clarets back to the early 1980s. Eight wines are served by the glass. Check the blackboard for house recommendations. Check it also for the day's fish specials, which supplement an ambitious and wide-ranging menu. Lunchtime bar snacks run from Sussex smokies – 'smoked mackerel flaked into a creamy cheese sauce and flashed under the grill' – and prawns by the half-pint, to ploughman's lunches and home-made pies. In the evening, grilled skate with capers and beurre noisette, grilled fillet of salmon with Pernod and lemon butter sauce, or ribeye steak with cracked black pepper and a cream and brandy sauce are the norm, while the specials might feature guinea fowl casseroled in sherry and tarragon. A choice of two desserts is usually on offer: perhaps white chocolate mousse on orange and Cointreau coulis, and local strawberries with cream. SAMPLE DISHES: Irish oysters with shallot and red wine vinegar £6; confit of duck with bubble and squeak and wild mushroom sauce £13; tiramisù parfait with coffee sauce £4.

Licensee James Buss (freehouse)
Open *11 to 3, 6 to 11, Sun 12 to 3, 7 to 10.30; bar food and restaurant Tue to Sat 12 to 2, 7 to 10, Sun 12 to 2; closed 26 to 28 Dec*
Details *Children welcome   Car park   Garden   Occasional live music   Dogs welcome   Amex, Delta, Diners, MasterCard, Switch, Visa   Accommodation: 3 rooms, B&B £30 to £40*

PLUSH   Dorset   map 2

▲ *Brace of Pheasants*

Plush DT2 7RQ   TEL: (01300) 348357
off B3143, 2m N of Piddletrenthide

With its neat thatch, brilliant white-painted walls and wreaths of greenery, this sixteenth-century inn looks every inch the archetypal English country cottage. Inside, the bar has lots of black beams, horse brasses and old fireplaces, and you may meet the two friendly resident dogs. The ambitious menu is listed on blackboards and offers quite a large choice. Food changes with the seasons, which in winter means crusty pies (perhaps venison), warming soups, and game: roast partridge with Madeira and mushrooms, for example. In summer it is possible to eat in the garden, and appropriately the menu takes on a lighter feel, with dishes like scallops and prawns on basil tagliatelle. Note that Tuesday is pasta night, curries are the speciality on Thursday, and Friday is surf and turf night. The pub also holds regular themed 'wine and dine' evenings. Beers, dispensed direct from casks behind the bar, might come from Fuller's, Ringwood and Tisbury; there is also Stowford Press cider. A blackboard by the bar lists several wines by the glass in two sizes, and the short list of bottles – about a dozen – focuses on a different region each month. SAMPLE DISHES: honey-cured salmon with lemon and dill dressing £5.25; chicken breast stuffed with prawns with a curry and mango cream sauce £11; Cassis and raspberry mousse £3.75.

Licensees Jane and Geoffrey Knights (freehouse)
Open 12 to 2.30, 7 to 11, Sun 12 to 3, 7 to 10.30; bar food 12 to 1.45, 7 to 9.30; restaurant 12 to 1.30, 7 to 9.30
Details Children welcome in family room Car park Garden and patio No smoking in dining room No music Dogs welcome exc in dining room Delta, MasterCard, Switch, Visa Accommodation: 4 rooms, B&B £32.50 to £65

PORTHLEVEN Cornwall map 1

Ship Inn

Porthleven TR13 9JS TEL: (01326) 564204
off B3304, 2m SW of Helston, on W side of harbour

Dramatically sited on granite rocks overlooking the harbour wall, this pub serves locals all through the year as well as visitors in season. The main bar fills the width of the building, and the family room is in what was the old smithy – a fine granite building with its own entrance. Service is friendly and efficient. There are daily specials, with another blackboard of tempting fish dishes, from which a reporter chose creamy crab soup: 'light saffron in colour, full of white crabmeat, enriched with brown.' A trio of fish with chilli and lime dip turns out to be generous portions of steamed sole, haddock and monkfish 'cooked to perfection'. Other fish dishes might include Cornish fish pie, crab claws, and a shellfish platter. Devoted meat eaters can choose steaks, chicken tikka masala, and 'tender and nicely flavoured' lamb shank in red wine. Snacks take in a wide range of toasties, crusties, jacket potatoes, ploughman's and salads, and sponge puddings feature among desserts. 'Kiddies Meals' at £2.95 include turkey dinosaurs served with waffles, bread and butter and beans or peas. On draught are Courage Best Bitter and Directors, Greene King Abbott Ale, Sharp's Doom Bar Bitter, and local organic Lizard Point. Six red and six white wines feature on the list, from £6.75, with three wines by the glass. SAMPLE DISHES: platter of locally smoked fish £5; crab and prawn Mornay £10; home-made apple torte £3.

Licensee Colin Oakden (freehouse)
Open *11.30 to 3 (3.30 Sat), 6.30 to 11, Sun 12 to 3.30, 6.30 to 10.30; bar food 12 to 2, 7 to 9; open 11.30 to 11 July to Sept, Easter and spring bank hol*
Details *Children welcome in family room   Garden   Background music   Dogs welcome   MasterCard, Switch, Visa*

POWERSTOCK   **Dorset**   map 2

▲ *Three Horseshoes*

Powerstock DT6 3TF   TEL: (01308) 485328
off A3066 at Gore Cross, 4m NE of Bridport

It would be hard to come across a more idyllic location: reach the Three Horseshoes along winding country lanes enveloped in places by overhanging trees. Just along the road from the village church, it is a stone-built inn with red-brick facings, a red-tiled roof and shrubs planted in half-barrels outside. Inside are two rooms, the main bar to the right and the dining room to the left as you enter. In the absence of a thatched roof, the canopy over the bar itself has been thatched. Palmers Bridport Bitter and 200, together with Dorset Gold, head up the real ale range, and eight wines by the glass are available from an extensive chalked list. Look to the blackboards also for details of what to eat. One shows lunchtime items such as sandwiches and ploughman's, while the other offers more interesting cooked dishes, perhaps pan-fried scallops with bacon in a vermouth cream sauce. Warm goats'-cheese salad might make an appetising starter, and main courses deal in the likes of cider-braised pheasant with celeriac fritters, whole Lyme Bay plaice, or lasagne. You might finish with home-made apple strudel, or mango sorbet spiked with Grand Marnier. SAMPLE DISHES: fish soup £4; pheasant in red wine £11; treacle tart £3.50.

Licensee Miss A. Halliwell (Palmers)
Open *summer 11 to 11; winter 11 to 3, 6 to 11, Sun all year 12 to 3, 7 to 10.30; bar food and restaurant (exc Mon evening) 12 to 1.50, 7 to 8.50*
Details *Children welcome   Car park   Wheelchair access (also WC)   Garden and patio   No smoking in dining room   No music   Dogs welcome MasterCard, Switch, Visa   Accommodation: 3 rooms, B&B £35 to £55*

If you visit any pubs that you think should appear in the Guide, write to tell us -- The Which? Guide to Country Pubs, FREEPOST, 2 Marylebone Road, London NW1 4DF.

PRESTON BISSETT　　Buckinghamshire　　map 5

White Hart　NEW ENTRY

Pound Lane, Preston Bissett MK18 4LX　TEL: (01280) 847969
off A421, 4m SW of Buckingham

Having arrived in this little sprawly village, look for a turning marked 'The Square', which leads directly into Pound Lane. The thatched, black and white seventeenth-century pub with a smattering of ivy on the front has a small garden with picnic tables on both lawn and patio. Inside are a couple of small bars at the front, and a pint-sized dining room towards the back, all with common access to the central bar; glass-fronted cabinets contain drink-related memorabilia, such as antique brass cask taps. Given that space is at a premium, diners are advised to book ahead. The range of food on offer is chalked on boards, although the repertoire seems pretty constant. Three big flat mushrooms sautéed in garlic and topped with melted goats' cheese make a rich and satisfying starter, as do prawn moneybags with two dipping sauces and a bottle of home-made yoghurt-based dressing. Main courses offer pancetta-wrapped chicken breast stuffed with mozzarella and pesto, roast salmon with fine beans, cherry tomatoes and olives, and lamb, apricot and rosemary pie. Popular puddings such as sticky toffee, on the other hand, come with a choice of custard, ice cream or cream. Real ales take in Marston's Pedigree, Adnams Bitter and Brains SA. There is also Addlestone's cider, a dozen single-malt whiskies and around two dozen wines, including 12 by the small glass and a wine of the month. SAMPLE DISHES: bresaola with Parmesan £5; cod and chips served in the *Financial Times* £8; hot waffle with maple syrup and ice cream £3.50.

Licensees Duncan and Lisa Rowney (County Estates Management)
Open *Wed to Sat 12 to 2.30, Mon to Sat 6.30 to 11, Sun 12 to 3, 7 to 10.30; bar food and restaurant 12 to 1.45, 7 to 9; closed evening 25 Dec*
Details *No children　Car park　Garden and patio　No smoking in dining room　Background music　Dogs welcome exc in dining room　MasterCard, Visa*

PRESTWOOD　　Buckinghamshire　　map 3

Polecat Inn

170 Wycombe Road, Prestwood HP16 0HJ　TEL: (01494) 862253
on A4128 Great Missenden to High Wycombe road, 2m W of Great Missenden

Along a busy road lined with tidy, rather nice houses amidst lots of greenery stands the Polecat, a yellow-painted inn with an extensive garden behind. Pass through the entrance, which has its own little pitched roof, and the first impression is that this is very much a pub devoted to eating. There are tables all over the place, with a choice of printed and blackboard menus to look at. The specials on the latter might be monkfish in saffron cream with crayfish risotto, a pastry lattice of asparagus, leek and Brie in champagne sauce, or duck breast with a sauce of rhubarb and ginger. Beef ragoût with porcini and other mushrooms, as well as a daube of wild boar with red cabbage and honey-glazed chestnuts, show that richly sustaining winter dishes are done well. Raspberry shortcake with a matching coulis, or bitter chocolate tart with white chocolate ice cream could well turn up among puddings. Lunchtime snacks, such as sandwiches and jacket potatoes, are always available. Lovers of real ales will be pleased to find Marston's Pedigree, Old Speckled Hen, Ruddles County, Wadworth 6X and Theakston Best Bitter on draught, and there is a broad-minded choice of around a dozen wines by the glass. SAMPLE DISHES: sardine and pimento crostini with anchovy dressing £4.25; pan-fried sea bass fillets on a coulis of morello cherries £10; pear and hazelnut praline £3.50.

Licensee John Gamble (freehouse)
Open *11.30 to 3, 6 to 11, Sun 12 to 3; bar food 12 to 2, 6.30 to 9; closed 25 and 26 Dec, evening 31 Dec, 1 Jan*
Details *Children welcome in bar eating area   Car park   Wheelchair access (also WC)   Garden   No-smoking area in bar   Background music   Dogs welcome   No cards*

RAMSBURY   Wiltshire   map 2

Bell 😕 🍇   NEW ENTRY

The Square, Ramsbury SN8 2PE   TEL: (01672) 520230
off A4192, 6m E of Marlborough

The Bell is on the main street of this red-brick and flint village, by the rotted stump of a huge old oak that once stood here, now usurped by a mere stripling of no more than about 20 feet tall. Behind the whitewashed exterior is a modern, comfortable pub with rag-rolled cream walls hung with monochrome prints of local scenes, some old beams and jute flooring. Although there is a separate, opulently furnished restaurant area, food can also be ordered at the bar, the tone being pleasingly casual throughout. Stylish cutlery, crisp white napery and voluminous wine glasses suggest that gastronomy is taken seriously, and so it proves. The main dinner menu might offer an appetiser such as very fine pan-fried duck livers on salad leaves with a balsamic reduction, or a lightly spiced crab cake with tomato chutney. Indeed, you may feel there is a certain air of metropolitan sophistication to the cooking until you see the country-sized portions of main courses: perhaps red mullet fillets with Parma ham-wrapped scallops on black pudding and pea risotto, or more classic fillet of beef with fondant potato, wild mushrooms and a red wine sauce. If a cheese selection to finish doesn't appeal, the dessert menu might entice you with pink grapefruit and orange gratin on lemon sabayon, cranberry cheesecake, or tarte Tatin. Simpler bar food staples such as calf's liver and bacon, or deep-fried cod in beer batter, are available earlier in the day. A trio of real ales changes weekly, and might well include Wadworth 6X, Greene King IPA or the Wood Brewery's Shropshire Lad, and the wine list is a dream. Divided into Classic, Innovative and Fine and Rare sections, it is a thoroughly up-to-date compilation of some of the more exciting flavours around. Eleven table wines are sold by the glass. SAMPLE DISHES: creamy butter bean soup with asparagus and ham £5; duck leg confit on parsnip purée with horseradish and marjoram sauce £15; chocolate roulade £5.

Licensee Stephen Bedford (freehouse)
Open *12 to 3, 6 to 11, Sun 12 to 3, 7 to 10.30; bar food and restaurant (exc Mon evening and Sun) 12 to 2.15, 7 to 9.30*
Details *Children welcome   Car park   Wheelchair access (also WC)   Garden No-smoking area in dining room   Dogs welcome in bar only   Live or background music   Amex, Delta, MasterCard, Switch, Visa*

RAMSDEN   Oxfordshire   **map 5**

▲ *Royal Oak* 🍺 │ NEW ENTRY │

Ramsden OX7 3AU   TEL: (01993) 868213
take B4022 from Witney, turn right just before Hailey and follow road to village

---

The Royal Oak is a listed seventeenth-century coaching inn built of Cotswold stone, sitting on the main road in the centre of the village opposite the church and war memorial. It is a smallish place that has the requisite stone walls, exposed beams and open fires within, plus one or two idiosyncratic touches such as a two-foot-high carved bear and animal-motif place mats. Hook Norton, Arkell's and Archers lead a great range of real ales from small independent breweries, conferring on the place a richly deserved reputation for good beer. There's also Dunkerton's cider, and a wine list that makes some canny selections in Western Europe and the southern hemisphere and offers six to eight by the glass. A traditional approach to pub catering is taken: bar food such as excellent steak and kidney pie, spare ribs, and chicken tikka is supplemented by a more ambitious menu plus blackboard specials. Monkfish brochette with lemon butter sauce, pheasant pot-roasted in claret with mushrooms and shallots accompanied by garlic potatoes, chicken tagine, or char-grilled Aberdeen Angus fillet with the full works (brandy, Madeira, cream and green peppercorns) indicate the lavishness of the approach. Even something as simple as a winter vegetable pie that turned out to be layers of thinly cut parsnip and carrot sandwiched with mushroom pâté and served with sweet onion chutney was deemed 'scrumptious'. Finish in like manner with tiramisù, perhaps, or treacle sponge with custard. Sympathetic and welcoming staff work to a 'really brilliant' standard. SAMPLE DISHES: avocado, bacon and walnut salad £4; Mediterranean-style lamb casseroled in red wine and coriander served with couscous £9.50; trifle £3.50.

Licensee Jonathan Oldham (freehouse)
Open *11.30 to 2.30, 6.30 to 11, Sun 12 to 3, 7 to 10.30; bar food and restaurant 12 to 2, 7 to 9.45; closed 25 and 26 Dec, 1 Jan*
Details *Children welcome in eating areas   Car park   Wheelchair access (also WC)   Patio   No smoking in dining room   Occasional live music   Dogs welcome exc in dining room   MasterCard, Switch, Visa   Accommodation: 4 rooms, B&B £35 to £55*

RAMSGILL   North Yorkshire   map 8

▲ *Yorke Arms* 🍷🍷 🍇

Ramsgill HG3 5RL   TEL: (01423) 755243
WEB SITE: www.yorke-arms.co.uk
take Low Wath road from Pateley Bridge, then 4m to Ramsgill

High on the wild and windy moors, in a remote and picturesque setting, stands this majestic creeper-clad eighteenth-century shooting lodge. Though it looks rather grand from the outside, the atmosphere is not at all snobby – you can even buy jars of home-made jam and chutney from the bar – and the unspoilt interior is a warren of charming rooms with polished flagstone floors and plenty of low oak beams. The restaurant at the Yorke Arms is not only good by the standards of country inns but has become one of the best restaurants in England since it was taken over by Gerald and Frances Atkins in 1996. Frances Atkins's cooking is straightforward and unpretentious but also inventive and highly accomplished: wild mushroom, parsley and champagne risotto, for example, might be followed by grilled turbot with spinach and chicken ravioli, and dessert options have included roast fig with coconut mascarpone and redcurrants. The restaurant menu only is served in the evening, but it is also available in the bar. Otherwise, bar lunches feature an appealing selection of snacks, such as steak and mustard sandwich, or British cheeses with home-made relish and bread, and light main dishes, including ricotta, mushroom and spinach frittata, or Swiss potato cake with smoked bacon and Parmesan. Black Sheep Special travels the short distance from the brewery in Masham to keep beer drinkers happy, while wine-lovers can choose from ten by the glass, or take a little longer to wade through 300 bottles on the main list. Either way, the options are exceptionally good for the connoisseur and beginner alike; for Burgundy-lovers there's everything from Bonneau du Martray's Corton-Charlemagne to Bonnes Mares from Drouhin-Laroze, but Henschke Riesling from Australia, Spice Route South African Chenin Blanc, some fine Bordeaux châteaux, and six Alsace wines show both vinous versatility and attentiveness to the food-lover too. There's plenty under £20 a bottle, and almost as much over £50, with house wines coming in between £12 and £15. SAMPLE DISHES: artichoke & tomato tartare with tuna £5.50; brill, scallop and crab risotto £13; passion-fruit sablé £5.50.

Licensees Gerald and Frances Atkins (freehouse)
Open *11 to 11, Sun 12 to 3, 7 to 10.30; bar food 12 to 1.45; restaurant Mon to Sat (and residents Sun) 7 to 9; closed 2 weeks Feb, 1 week June, 1 week Nov*
Details *No children   Car park   Wheelchair access (not WC)   Garden and patio   No smoking in dining room   Background music   Dogs welcome in bar   Amex, Delta, Diners, MasterCard, Switch, Visa   Accommodation: 13 rooms, B&B and dinner £90 to £175*

RATTLESDEN   Suffolk   map 6

Brewers Arms

Lower Road, Rattlesden IP30 0RJ   TEL: (01449) 736377
off A14, 5m W of Stowmarket

If you can find Rattlesden, a small village a few miles from Bury St Edmunds, you will find the Brewers Arms. It is an attractive old pub, well maintained on the outside, with cream walls and green window frames and doors, though it looks slightly incongruous next to the neighbouring thatched cottages. In the bar, beams and exposed brickwork reveal that the pub is older than it appears, though it has been smartly done up, with polished horse brasses and rows of ency-clopedias on shelves; there is an adjacent restaurant too. Menus offer wide choice and plenty of variety. Starters of crab and avocado salad with seafood mayonnaise, chicken and bacon pâté, or Stilton and port rarebit, are followed with mostly traditional main courses, such as slow-roasted ham hock with cider and whole-grain mustard gravy, steak and Guinness casserole, or salmon fishcakes with creamy watercress sauce. Regular real ales are from the local Greene King Brewery, which owns the pub, and wines are mostly priced between

£10 and £20, with three by the glass. SAMPLE DISHES: herrings marinated in Madeira £4.50; marinated shank of lamb with port and
mint gravy £11; blackberry and elderflower granita in a filo basket
£4.

Licensees Jeff and Nina Chamberlain (Greene King)
Open *Tue to Sat 12 to 2.30, 6.30 to 11, Sun 12 to 2.30, 8 to 10.30; bar food
and restaurant (exc Sun evening) 12 to 2, 7 to 9.30; closed bank hol Mon exc
Easter*
Details *Children welcome in eating area of bar   Car park   Wheelchair access
(also WC)   Garden   No smoking in dining room   Background music or
occasional live music   Dogs welcome in bar   MasterCard, Switch, Visa*

REDE   **Suffolk**   **map 6**

Plough

Rede IP29 4BE   TEL: (01284) 789208
off A143 Bury St Edmunds to Haverhill road

This beautifully maintained sixteenth-century village inn is at the end
of a lane surrounded by trees. You will recognise it by its pale pink
walls, its tall chimneys and the eponymous plough on the lawn to the
front. But its most distinctive feature is the roof, which is partly
thatched and partly tiled. Inside, the separate bar and restaurant
areas are characterised by black beams, red carpets and a log fire;
both are set up for eating rather than drinking, though Greene King
ales are on draught. For wine drinkers, bottles are chalked on a
board in the restaurant. The same menus are available wherever you
choose to eat. Typical starters might be smoked venison topped with
Parmesan, or sauté chicken livers in garlic and herb butter. Follow
this perhaps with monkfish créole, chicken breast in a Stilton, walnut
and celery sauce, or braised lamb shank with sage, mash and Madeira
gravy. To finish, try the intriguingly named lemon meringue melt-
down. SAMPLE DISHES: goats'-cheese melts £5; hock of venison
braised in red wine with bacon £9; mulled wine pudding £3.50.

Licensees Brian and Joyce Desborough (Greene King)
Open *11 to 3, 6.30 to 11, Sun 12.30 to 3, 7 to 10.30; bar food and
restaurant 12 to 2, 6.30 to 9.15*
Details *Children welcome   Car park   Wheelchair access (not WC)   Garden
Background music   No dogs   Amex, Delta, Diners, MasterCard, Switch, Visa*

---

*Many pubs have separate restaurants with very different menus. These
have not been inspected. A recommendation for the pub/bar food does
not necessarily imply that the restaurant is also recommended.*

REDMILE   Leicestershire   map 5

▲ *Peacock Inn*

Church Corner, Main Street, Redmile NG13 0GA
TEL: (01949) 842554
off A52, 7m W of Grantham

At the centre of the village, next to the canal, this converted stone cottage is considered a 'superb' building. Inside, the décor is modish and contemporary, though the atmosphere remains relaxing and welcoming, and flagstone floors, beamed ceilings and real fires add a traditional note. Bar snacks are listed on a specials board, and the à la carte restaurant's menu is available throughout the pub: the relaxed format means you can eat as much or as little as you like. The style blends modern and traditional ideas to produce a range of dishes that might include pumpkin soup, lamb shank with ratatouille, fish pie, or hot beef baguette with Yorkshire pudding, and bread-and-butter pudding to finish. Flowers IPA, Timothy Taylor Landlord and Marston's Pedigree are the regular offerings for real ale drinkers, and the wine list runs to over 50 bins, with six by the glass. SAMPLE DISHES: pan-fried pigeon breast on haggis with rich game sauce £5; suprême of guinea fowl on a tomato risotto £15.50; Toblerone and Amaretto parfait £5.

Licensee Stephen Hughes (freehouse)
Open *11 to 11, Sun 12 to 10.30; bar food and restaurant 12 to 2.30 (3 Sun), 7 to 9.30*
Details *Children welcome   Car park   Wheelchair access (also WC)   Patio No-smoking area in bar, no smoking in dining room   Live or background music   Amex, Delta, Diners, MasterCard, Switch, Visa   Accommodation: 9 rooms, B&B £55 to £80*

RIPPONDEN   West Yorkshire   map 8

Old Bridge Inn 🍺 ❧

Priest Lane, Ripponden HX6 4DF
TEL: (01422) 822595
off A58, 6m S of Halifax

Look for the tall spire of Ripponden parish church and you'll find this whitewashed inn just next to it. Nearby is the packhorse bridge after which it is named. A plaque outside the inn claims it's 'possibly Yorkshire's oldest hostelry, dating from 1380'. Inside, coal fires blaze in winter, and oak beams and panelling in three split-level rooms, together with ornaments such as an old copper warming pan, make all the right impressions. From blackboards you might choose a hearty, rustic soup and a crusty roll to start with, and then spicy pork and lentil cannelloni with garlic bread, or meat and potato pie under a suet pastry lid served with mushy peas. Finish with plum and orange crumble, or banana and toffee pancakes. The separate Over the Bridge restaurant, reached in precisely the direction its name indicates, is a little more highfalutin, offering perhaps asparagus soufflé in Gruyère sauce, and prosciutto-wrapped salmon fillet in tarragon mustard sauce. Handpumped ales include a range from Timothy Taylor, Moorhouses Premier Bitter and Black Sheep Special Ale, while those with a taste for bottled Belgian fruit beer need not feel neglected. A succinct, 16-wine list in the bar (of which 12 are available by the glass) covers all options from Saint-Véran to Australian Shiraz. Prices begin at a very attractive £8.75 for house red and white and never climb above £16.50. For those wanting even more choice, the full restaurant list of over 100 bins is also available in the bar. SAMPLE DISHES: deep-fried cauliflower florets with chutney dip £3.25; Italian chicken sausages with garlic and herb mash £5.25; blueberry crème brûlée £2.75.

Licensee Ian Beaumont (freehouse)
Open *Mon to Fri 12 to 3, 5.30 to 11, Sat 12 to 11, Sun 12 to 10.30; bar food all week 12 to 2, Mon to Fri 6 to 9.30; restaurant Tue to Sat 7 to 9.30*
Details *Children welcome   Car park   Wheelchair access (not WC)   Patio No music   No dogs   MasterCard, Switch, Visa*

ROCKBEARE   Devon   map 1

Jack in the Green ✿ 🍺 ❧
London Road, Rockbeare EX5 2EE   TEL: (01404) 822240
WEB SITE: www.jackinthegreen.uk.com
on A30, 3m NE of Exeter

The professionalism of this pub's management shows in its colourful newsletter and in the warmth of the welcome coupled with the efficiency of the service. It's a dining pub where restaurant customers order from two- or three-course set-price menus, while in the neat bar with its comfortable chairs and log fire you can choose from those or from bar snacks. In this part of the world a 'snack' might run to half a roast chicken with red peppers, olives, salad and new potatoes, or a 10-ounce rump steak, and Devon ploughmen don't just lunch on fine English and Irish farmhouse cheeses, but also on home-cooked ham or chicken liver pâté. On the restaurant menus you might find gazpacho with crab, rabbit Wellington with confit of its thigh, or poached and grilled wood pigeon breast with foie gras sauce and tagliatelle – and those are just starters. Main courses include best end of lamb with honey and cloves, salmon pithiviers with tarragon and beurre blanc, or pork loin with stir-fried vegetables, noodles and black-bean sauce. Real ales include Cotleigh Tawny Bitter and Otter Ale plus guests such as Dob's Best Bitter from Exe Valley Brewery, and Branscombe Vale Branoc. Twelve wines are sold by the glass from a long list notable for its good French and outstanding New World bottles at reasonable prices. SAMPLE DISHES: steak and kidney pie with chips and vegetables £7; shiitake and cep risotto with Parmesan and sugar snaps £7.25; sticky toffee pudding with butterscotch sauce £3.50.

Licensees Paul Parnell and Joanne Richards (freehouse)
Open *11 to 3, 6 to 11, Sun 12 to 10.30; bar food and restaurant 11 to 2, 6 to 9.30, Sun 12 to 9.30; closed 25 Dec to 2 Jan*
Details *Children welcome in bar eating area   Car park   Wheelchair access (also WC)   Garden   No smoking in dining room   Background music   No dogs   Delta, MasterCard, Switch, Visa*

ROCKBOURNE   Hampshire   map 2

Rose & Thistle

Rockbourne SP6 3NL   TEL: (01725) 518236
WEB SITE: www.roseandthistle.co.uk
off B3078, 3m NW of Fordingbridge

The next time some Hollywood film-maker scours England for a country pub, the Rose & Thistle would seem to be a sure-fire bet: a pair of sixteenth-century thatched cottages joined together to make an inn shortly after 1800. It sits a little back from the village lane, behind a garden furnished with benches and sunshades and, with its dovecote and tiny windows, evokes an era in which even the Great War is yet to happen. Inside, the feeling is echoed in standing timbers and beams, cushioned settles, barrel chairs and evening candlelight that give the place its charm. The cooking is a little more up to date than all that, but not by too much. Prawns by the pint and half-pint, Welsh rarebit, and local sausages with mash and onion gravy are served at lunchtime, with today's choice of pie or casserole chalked on a board. Pork fillet stuffed with apricots and pistachios on Marsala sauce is a touch more daring, or there's chicken breast in a creamy white wine sauce with grapes. Fish specials, such as sea bass fillet pan-fried in lemon butter, are chalked up too, and old-school puddings might be sticky toffee and date, or steamed syrup sponge. Young's Bitter and Fuller's London Pride are the beers on offer, as well as Hop Back Brewery's Summer Lightning. A fine French-led wine list offers no fewer than ten by the glass. SAMPLE DISHES:

avocado and crab topped with grilled cheese £5; steak and kidney pudding £9; Rockbourne Knoll (home-made vanilla and chocolate ice cream in a meringue nest with hot chocolate sauce and flaked almonds) £4.25.

Licensee Tim Norfolk (freehouse)
Open *11 to 3, 6 to 11, Sun 12 to 3, 7 to 10.30; bar food and restaurant (exc Sun evening Nov to Easter) 12 to 2.30, 7 to 9.30*
Details *Children welcome in dining room   Car park   Wheelchair access (not WC)   Garden and patio   No-smoking area in bar, no smoking in dining room No music   Dogs welcome in bar   Delta, MasterCard, Switch, Visa*

ROMALDKIRK   Co Durham   map 10

▲ *Rose and Crown* ❦ ❦

Romaldkirk DL12 9EB   TEL: (01833) 650213
WEB SITE: www.rose-and-crown.co.uk
on B6277, 6m NW of Barnard Castle

This traditional village inn, built in 1733, is in a remote location in the heart of Teesdale, hidden away down winding country lanes. This means that those who come for dinner would be well advised to take advantage of the comfortable accommodation. In the bar, with its log fire, separate weekly-changing menus are offered for lunch and supper, the main difference being that the lunch version also includes baps and ploughman's. Both offer a long list of starters and main courses with plenty of fish options: smoked mackerel pâté, gratin of scallops, salmon and cod fishcakes, or baked whiting fillet with prawns, mushrooms and Noilly-Prat cream, for example. Among non-fish choices might be Mr Peat's pan-fried pork sausage with black pudding and confit of onions; steak, kidney and mushroom pie with Theakston ale gravy; or breast of wood pigeon with a fried potato cake and juniper berry sauce. Finish with orange liqueur cheesecake, or walnut and syrup tart. The oak-panelled dining room operates a fixed-price four-course dinner menu and is also open for Sunday lunch. Beers come from Black Sheep and Theakston, and the clearly laid-out wine list numbers over 100 well-chosen bins, with ten wines available by the large or small glass. House Chilean red and white are £9.95, and there's plenty to choose from around the £15 mark. New World, single-grape styles feature strongly, but pay a little more and there are interesting white and red Burgundies, not to mention Bordeaux and Alsace favourites. SAMPLE DISHES: chive and potato pancake with hot and cold smoked salmon £6; shank of lamb with butter bean cassoulet and mint pesto £11; crème caramel with stewed fruit £3.25.

Licensees Christopher and Alison Davy (freehouse)
Open *11.30 to 3, 5.30 to 11, Sun 12 to 3, 7 to 10.30; bar food 12 to 1.30,
6.30 to 9.30; restaurant Mon to Sat 7.30 to 9, Sun 12 to 1.30; closed 24 to
26 Dec*
Details *Children welcome   Car park   Wheelchair access (also WC)   Patio
No smoking in dining room   No music   Dogs welcome exc in dining room
and lounge   MasterCard, Switch, Visa   Accommodation: 12 rooms, B&B £62
to £100*

ROSEDALE ABBEY   North Yorkshire   map 9

▲ *White Horse Farm Hotel*

Rosedale Abbey YO18 8SE   TEL: (01751) 417239
WEB SITE: www.whitehorsefarmhotel.co.uk
*on A170 turn right signposted Wrelton and Rosedale, 3m NW of
Pickering*

If you like vast expanses of verdant rolling countryside, it would be
well worth visiting this eighteenth-century hotel, which is high on
the western side of Rosedale, overlooking the pretty ex-mining
village of Rosedale Abbey. Set in the heart of the North York Moors
National Park, it is an ideal base for walking or touring, and other
reasons for dropping in include the above-average bar food, which
makes good use of local produce and fish from Whitby. A giant
Yorkshire pudding with the chef's roast of the day is typical of the
straightforward style; there are also pies (fisherman's, chicken and
mushroom, or steak and ale), deep-fried scampi, and toad-in-the-
hole, and the grill turns out steaks with various sauces, and bangers
and mash, among other things. The restaurant has its own daily-
changing set-price menu, which goes in for slightly more up-market
fare. Regular hand-pulled real ales from the Black Sheep Brewery are
joined by weekly-changing guests, which have included beers from
Gale's and Wychwood, and an international list of 30 wines features
five house selections by the small, large or extra-large glass (£1.60,
£2.20 and £3.10 respectively), as well as by the half-litre (£6.40) and
bottle (£9). SAMPLE DISHES: deep-fried Brie with mango mayonnaise
£5; Barnsley chop with minted gravy £8.75; toffee, apple and pecan
pie £3.

Licensee Stuart Adamson (freehouse)
Open *11.30 to 2.30, 6 to 11 (10.30 Sun); bar food 11.30 to 2, 6.30 to 9.30;
restaurant Sun 12 to 2.30, Mon to Sat 7 to 8.45; closed Mon to Thur
lunchtime Nov, Jan and Feb*
Details *Children welcome   Car park   Garden   No smoking in dining room
Live or background music   Dogs welcome   Amex, Delta, Diners, MasterCard,
Switch, Visa   Accommodation: 15 rooms, B&B £33 to £95*

ROTHERFIELD PEPPARD   Oxfordshire   map 2

Greyhound ✿ NEW ENTRY

Gallowstree Road, Rotherfield Peppard RG9 5HT
TEL: (0118) 972 2227
off B481 N of Sonning Common

A rather splendidly named village is the setting for this picture-post-card brick and timber inn with a wonky tiled roof, a pretty garden at the front and a patio behind. The spacious main bar is furnished with leather easy chairs and small round tables, and a wealth of prints and paintings adorns the walls of the cosy dining area, which leads to the adjacent barn, where there are rugs strewn on wooden floors, hops strung from the rafters and an interesting collection of *objets d'art*. TV chef Antony Worrall Thompson consulted initially on the menus here, and the commitment to good food is further shown in the appointment of a chef who has cooked at some very ritzy addresses. That said, there is a refreshing simplicity about the menus, so that lunch might offer a choice ranging from eggs Benedict, or salmon fishcakes with a delicately flavoured pea sauce, to local sausages with an onion and Madeira gravy, or chicken jalfrezi with naan bread and lime pickle. In the evenings, it all goes a bit more swanky, so expect parsnip and truffle oil soup, scallops with a tomato dressing, crown of pheasant with roasted root vegetables and deep-fried thyme, or mussels with lemon grass and chilli. Entrecôte steak is always available. Puddings bring things back down to earth via the sticky toffee and chocolate mousse route. Brakspear Bitter and Fuller's London Pride are on handpump, and four house wines (from South Africa, France and Italy) are served by the glass from a list of around 20. SAMPLE DISHES: warm chicken livers with pancetta, mushrooms, sage and cream £5.50; confit of duck with red cabbage and anise sauce £11.50; pears poached in red wine and cinnamon £4.75.

Licensees Desiree Van Reeuwrjk and Ray Argyle (freehouse)
Open *Tue to Sat 12 to 3, 5.30 to 11, Sun 12 to 6; bar food 12.15 to 2.30 (3 Sat and Sun), 7 to 9.30 (10 Fri and Sat); closed 25 to 28 Dec*
Details *Children welcome in eating areas   Car park   Garden and patio Occasional live or background music   Dogs welcome exc in dining room Delta, MasterCard, Switch, Visa*

ROWDE   Wiltshire   map 2

George & Dragon 🏵️🏵️ 🍺 🍇

High Street, Rowde SN10 2PN
TEL: (01380) 723053

The exterior of this roadside pub hardly attracts casual travellers,
although the building is more pleasingly higgledy-piggledy from the
back, where there is a pleasant garden. Inside is a tiny bar, and a
more spacious black and white timbered dining room colourfully
decorated with pictures and with displays of home-made preserves
and chutneys. Fish is the speciality. It comes from Cornwall, and the
day's specials, listed on a blackboard, might take in simple grilled
lemon or Dover sole, turbot or lobster, something more complex
like red mullet fillet with orange and anchovy, or pan-fried scallops
in a bacon and shallot sauce. On the printed menu are starters plus a
few mains, including some for committed carnivores, such as tagliatelle with creamy ham and mushroom sauce, or lamb korma.
Nadder Valley Cider is on draught, and among four changing guest
ales might be Bass, Wadworth 6X and something from Goff's micro-
brewery. Twelve bottled beers include Belgian Leffe Blond and
Chimay Red, and also bottle-conditioned Thomas Hardy 1996,
which is among the world's strongest beers at 12 per cent abv. Up to
ten of the 50-plus wines on the largely French and European list
(which also has a good smattering from the New World) are available by the glass. Many of them are priced above – some well above
– £20, but quality is there, and bottle prices start at £9.50. SAMPLE
DISHES: mussel and oyster soup £5; salmon steak with rhubarb £10;
iced lime soufflé £4.50.

Licensee Tim Withers (freehouse)
Open *all week (exc Mon lunchtime) 12 to 3, 7 to 11 (10.30 Sun); bar food
and restaurant Tue to Sat 12 to 2, 7 to 10; closed 25 Dec, 1 Jan*
Details *Children welcome in eating areas   Car park   Garden   No smoking in
dining room   No music   Dogs welcome in bar   Delta, MasterCard, Switch,
Visa*

ROYDHOUSE   West Yorkshire   map 8

▲ *Three Acres Inn* 🏵️

Roydhouse HD8 8LR   TEL: (01484) 602606
off B6116 (from A629), 1m E of Kirkburton

One way to enter the bar and restaurant at this long, stone roadside
pub is via the delicatessen, which sells cured meats and cheeses, plus
packaged specialities from the kitchen to take home. Within, all the

tables are set for meals, and waitresses usually cope with the rush. There is some overlap between bar and restaurant menus. The shell-fish display includes huge crabs, lobsters and oysters, while fresh fish comes from Cornwall. Queenie scallops are flash-grilled with Gruyère, garlic and mustard, but a reporter who asked for the shell-fish to be served plain found them 'sweet, fresh-tasting and well timed'. Dressed crab is impressive, as is haddock, chips and mushy peas. Serious carnivores might choose chicken liver parfait with Sauternes-poached grapes, then braised oxtail with horseradish mash and buttered cabbage. Yorkshire pudding with onion gravy is a starter on the restaurant's set-price lunch menu, but not necessarily an accompaniment to the bar's lunchtime roast of the day. Portions are large, but those who can manage a pudding could go for roast banana and passion-fruit pavlova, or chocolate and Amaretto cheese-cake. Timothy Taylor Landlord, Marston's Pedigree, Mansfield Bitter, and Adnams Bitter are stocked, and around 60 whiskies. Over 70 wines are listed 'at a glance' (all on one page), with some interest-ing choices. Many bottles are pricey, but eight are served by the glass, around 12 by the half-bottle, and a smattering around the £10 to £12 mark mean digging deep isn't essential. SAMPLE DISHES: hot Cumberland sausage sandwich £3.25; sea bass tempura with chilli salad and cumin couscous £14; rice pudding with cinnamon-spiced plums £5.

Licensees Neil Truelove and Brian Orme (freehouse)
Open *12 to 3, 6 to 11; bar food and restaurant 12 to 2, 7 to 9.45; closed 25 and 31 Dec, 1 Jan*
Details *Children welcome   Car park   Wheelchair access (not WC)   Patio Background music   No dogs   Amex, Delta, MasterCard, Switch, Visa Accommodation: 20 rooms, B&B £45 to £75*

RUDGE   Somerset   map 2

▲ *Full Moon*

Rudge BA11 2QF   TEL: (01373) 830936
WEB SITE: www.thefullmoon.co.uk
off A36/A361, 3m W of Westbury

Rudge, once known as Ridge after the high escarpment nearby, is right on the Somerset–Wiltshire border, only about 12 miles from Bath. It is a straggle of stone, brick and flint cottages, and the Full Moon is the sole surviving hostelry serving the community (it once sat opposite another called – what else? – the Sun). Dating from the late seventeenth century, it has gardens front and back and, within, a series of small rooms, including a flagstone-floored taproom that now acts as a dining area. When the Giffords acquired the inn in

1990, it didn't offer so much as a packet of crisps by way of food. All that has happily changed, and a full menu, including a separate vegetarian slate of five choices, is on offer. You might begin with the house special, a creamy dish of Arbroath smokies with mushrooms and onions topped with breadcrumbs, or perhaps a trendy tart of goats' cheese and red onion marmalade, before going on to duck breast in a sauce of mixed peppercorns, or braised half-leg of lamb with redcurrants and mint. Fresh fish varies according to the market but has included more exotic items such as marlin, shark or tilapia, and all the bread is baked in-house. Puddings might be passion-fruit and kiwi parfait, or chocolate and pear terrine. Bass and Butcombe supply the handpumped ales, and there is also Thatcher's Cheddar Valley dry cider. Ten wines are served by the glass. SAMPLE DISHES: avocado and bacon salad with garlic croûtons £4.50; corn-fed chicken breast in korma sauce with mango and gooseberry preserve £9.25; apple charlotte with cinnamon ice cream £4.

Licensees Patrick and Christine Gifford (freehouse)
Open *12 to 11 (10.30 Sun); bar food and restaurant 12 to 2.30 (2 sittings Sun lunchtime carvery, 12 and 2), 6.30 to 9.30 (9 winter)*
Details *Children welcome in eating areas   Car park   Wheelchair access (also WC)   Garden and patio   No smoking in dining room   No music   Dogs welcome exc in dining areas   Amex, Delta, MasterCard, Switch, Visa Accommodation: 5 rooms, B&B £40 to £70*

RUSHLAKE GREEN   East Sussex   map 3

Horse and Groom

Rushlake Green TN21 9QE   TEL: (01435) 830320
off B2096, 4m SE of Heathfield

There's plenty of green to be seen at Rushlake (hence the name of the village), and this friendly, cosy pub stands right next to it. The Chappells are experienced and capable proprietors, previously running the Star at Old Heathfield (see entry) as well as this, and they benefit from much in the way of keen local support. A pair of little rooms is decorated in traditional style with horse brasses and photographs of the environs, and a log fire warms the place a treat in cooler weather. Blackboard menus offer some rewarding modern cookery of the likes of Thai-spiced steamed mussels, asparagus wrapped in smoked salmon, chump of lamb, or monkfish rolled in oats and dill served on home-made pasta in white wine sauce. There can't be many country pubs making their own pasta, and equal care is lavished on other fish specials, such as red snapper with prawns and Mediterranean vegetables in a Pernod sauce, as well as on local game, which might be pheasant braised in white wine. Finish with one of the texturally interesting desserts: lemon ginger crunch, perhaps, or squidgy meringue with chocolate mousse and nuts. Harveys Sussex Best Bitter and Shepherd Neame Master Brew Bitter are on handpumps, and five wines are available by the glass. SAMPLE DISHES: Shetland scallops £6.75; poached lemon sole with fennel and cheese sauce £10; plum and almond tart £4.50.

Licensees Mike and Sue Chappell (freehouse)
Open *11.30 to 3, 5.30 to 11; bar food and restaurant 12 to 2.30, 7 to 9.30*
Details *Children welcome   Car park   Wheelchair access (also WC)   Garden Occasional live or background music   Dogs welcome   Delta, MasterCard, Switch, Visa*

ST MAWES   Cornwall   map 1

▲ *Rising Sun* ❦   NEW ENTRY

The Square, St Mawes TR2 5DJ
TEL: (01326) 270233
off A3078, S of Trewithian; or reached by ferry from Falmouth

---

This attractive, well-appointed hotel is situated close to the harbour in the heart of the delightful small town of St Mawes – just a short ferry ride across the water from Falmouth. Inside, it has an upmarket and cared-for feel, being elegantly and tastefully decorated throughout. The cooking combines the virtues of chef Ann Long's 'indefatigable' search for the best ingredients with her flair, imagination and experience, although Ann's hands-on involvement (except for desserts) is in the restaurant side of the operation. There a set-price two- or three-course menu typically offers crab and mango with lobster and smoked salmon pâté and balsamic cream sauce to start, followed by baked duck breast with pistachio and lemon, wrapped in bacon and served with a red wine sauce. The blackboard menu in the bar is a lighter affair, listing snacky items such as an open sandwich of salt beef, or straightforward main courses such as roast cod fillet on vegetable casserole, cottage pie, or sirloin burger in a bun with anchovy and egg. Finish with raspberry oatmeal meringue or fruit crumble. This St Austell pub regularly serves HSD, Tinners and Cornish IPA, supplemented by seasonal beers. House wines start around the £10 mark (£2.65 a glass); the full list runs to about 50 bottles, of which 18 are available by the glass. Emphasis is on classics and New World grape varietals alike, with a few interesting wines from Portugal thrown in. SAMPLE DISHES: smoked mackerel ploughman's £5.25; chicken and lamb pie with poppy-seed pastry £9.25; Yorkshire parkin, fruit and cream £3.50.

Licensee John Milan (St Austell Brewery)

Open *11 to 11, Sun 12 to 10.30; bar food 12 to 2, 6.30 to 9; restaurant all week 7 to 9*
Details *Children welcome Car park Wheelchair access (also WC) Patio No smoking in dining room Live music Dogs welcome Amex, Delta, MasterCard, Switch, Visa Accommodation: 8 rooms, B&B £29.50 to £99*

SAWLEY **North Yorkshire** map 9

Sawley Arms

Sawley HG4 3EQ   TEL: (01765) 620642
off B6265 Pateley Bridge to Ripon road, 5m SW of Ripon

A short walk from Fountains Abbey, in a pleasant village, the Sawley Arms is a charming sprawl of stone buildings heavily decorated with colourful flowers in tubs, window boxes and hanging baskets. Inside are four comfortable interconnecting rooms furnished with wing armchairs and cushioned wall benches, with plates and prints on the walls. The emphasis is on food – though real ales from Theakston are on handpump – and it is a popular dining venue with both locals and visitors. Menus are in traditional vein: starters of Stilton, port and celery pâté, or salmon mousse, for example, with the occasional twist on old themes, as in prawn, celery and apple cocktail. Typical of main courses are battered scampi with tartare sauce and chips, plaice Mornay, and steak pie. An extensive wine list offers reasonable value, with three or four by the glass. SAMPLE DISHES: salmon and herb pancake glazed with cheese £5; curried chicken breast with rice £7.75; apple pie £3.25.

Licensee June Hawes (freehouse)
Open *11.30 to 3, 6.30 to 10.30; bar food and restaurant 12 to 2, 6.30 to 9; closed Sun evening, Mon evening exc bank hols, 25 Dec*
Details *No children Car park Wheelchair access (also WC) Garden No-smoking area in bar, no smoking in dining room Background music No dogs MasterCard, Switch, Visa*

SAXTON **North Yorkshire** map 9

Plough Inn 🌸 🍇

Headwell Lane, Saxton LS24 9PB   TEL: (01937) 557242
off A162, between Tadcaster and Sherburn in Elmet

The Plough cuts a rather grand figure with its steep pitched roofs, standing as it does on a corner of the main road through this tiny village near Tadcaster. Lunchtime baguettes are served in the small bar, along with such dishes as pork and leek sausages with mash and gravy, or breast of chicken with couscous and mushroom sauce. A blackboard gives details of more elaborate evening menus on offer in the L-shaped dining room, with its simple wooden tables, spindle-back chairs and dark pink walls. Reporters have commended a starter of smoked salmon with crab and prawn mousse, and there might also be a salad of smoked chicken with mozzarella, sun-dried tomatoes and pesto, or avocado with toasted goats' cheese. Main courses range from pan-fried calf's liver with bacon and red wine sauce, or fillet of pork on apple and apricot with Dijon mustard, to fillet of sea bass on Gruyère mash with lobster sauce. Desserts run from classic lemon tart to the indulgent end of the spectrum in the shape of sticky toffee pudding, or baked Alaska with butterscotch sauce. Black Sheep and Timothy Taylor Landlord are among the well-kept beers on tap, and the wine list is surprisingly ambitious. Starting with three house wines at £9.25 and rarely breaking the £20 barrier, it offers more than 50 imaginative selections, with half a dozen by the glass and a pair of wines of the month. SAMPLE DISHES: pumpkin soup £3.50; fillet of beef on parsnip mash with green peppercorn sauce £14; orange cheesecake £4.

Licensees *Simon and Nicky Treanor (freehouse)*
Open *Tue to Sat 12 to 3, 6 to 11, Sun 12 to 4, 6 to 10.30; bar food Tue to Sun 12 to 2 (3 Sun); restaurant Sun 12 to 2, Tue to Sun 6.30 to 10; closed 25 and 26 Dec, 2 weeks Jan*
Details *Children welcome   Car park   Patio   No smoking in dining room Background music   No dogs   Delta, MasterCard, Switch, Visa*

SCAWTON   **North Yorkshire**   **map 9**

Hare Inn   NEW ENTRY

Scawton YO7 2HG   TEL: (01845) 597289
off A170, 7m E of Thirsk

In a tiny hamlet near Rievaulx Abbey amid country enjoyed by walkers and drivers, this cream-painted stone pub with its dark green woodwork and wavy tiled roof has something of a dolls'-house look. Its eccentricity lies inside, in its various collections of old radios, puppets, crockery and neck ties dangling from ceiling beams; reports call it 'a granny's attic'. Service is 'cheerful and assiduous' and children are allowed in all parts, so it attracts an interestingly mixed clientèle. The menu, available throughout, is mainly traditional with some European ideas. Snacks include sandwiches, potted shrimps and fried Camembert and Cambazola, and starters take in 'tasty' potted rabbit and confit of duck, crisp outside, moist inside. Roast knuckle of pork, and fried fresh Whitby haddock come with highly acclaimed trimmings: apple sauce and cider gravy with the pork, and mushy peas and home-made chips with the fish. A light sticky toffee pudding, and cafetière coffee have been praised too. Theakston Best Bitter and Timothy Taylor Landlord are on draught, there is Scrumpy Jack Cider, and a well-balanced, 40-strong wine list offers nine by the glass. SAMPLE DISHES: venison pâté and plum chutney £4.50; roast local suckling pig £10.50; hazelnut vacherin with apricot cream £3.50.

Licensee Graham Raine (freehouse)
Open *Tue to Sat 12 to 2.30, Mon to Sat 6.30 to 11, Sun 6.30 to 10.30; bar food and restaurant 12 to 2.30, 6.30 to 9.30; closed 1 week March*
Details *Children welcome　Car park　Garden　No-smoking area in bar, no smoking in dining room　Background music　No dogs　Delta, MasterCard, Switch, Visa*

SEAHOUSES　Northumberland　　　　map 10

▲ *Olde Ship Hotel*

9 Main Street, Seahouses NE68 7RD
TEL: (01665) 720200
WEB SITE: www.seahouses.co.uk
on B1430, 3m SE of Bamburgh

The Olde Ship has more maritime connections than an online octopus, starting with its location overlooking the busy harbour, often full of fishing boats. The nearby pier is the gateway to the birds and seals on the Farne Islands, and there is a coastal walk to Bamburgh, which is the birth- and resting-place of Grace Darling and where there is also a great twelfth-century castle. Inside the stone and red-tiled pub, which has been under the same family's ownership for over 80 years, the sea is embodied in memorabilia that include compasses and sextants decorating the main bar, lit by stained glass windows. The sea also contributes generously to the menus, with smoked fish chowder, crab soup, stuffed whiting and bosun's fish stew of prawns squid and cod offered in the bar or restaurant. Carnivores may find beef olives, chicken or lamb curry, or braised steak. The bar lunch served in the cabin bar and locker room is great value, with soup from £1.95 followed by a wide choice of main dishes all priced at £5.50 and sweets at £2.20. At least four real ales, more in summer, might include Black Sheep, Marston's Pedigree, Old Speckled Hen, Bass and Theakston's. The wine list is short but 12 are available by the glass. SAMPLE DISHES: sweet pickled herring £3.40; creamy lemon pork £6.50; raspberry roly-poly £3.50

Licensees Alan and Jean Glen
Open *11 to 11, Sun 12 to 10.30; bar food and restaurant 12 to 2, 7 to 8.30*

Details *Children welcome in family room   Car park   Wheelchair access (also WC)   Garden   No smoking in dining room and 1 bar   Occasional background music   Guide dogs only   MasterCard, Switch, Visa Accommodation: 18 rooms, B&B £35 to £80*

S E A S A L T E R   Kent   map 3

Sportsman ❀ NEW ENTRY

Faversham Road, Seasalter, Whitstable CT5 4BP
TEL: (01227) 273370
take Whitstable exit from A299, go through Whitstable and follow signs for Seasalter; pub at far end of village

---

The Sportsman is seemingly in the middle of nowhere, looking across marshes to the small seaside town of Whitstable in the distance. It is an unprepossessing old pub that looks as though it might have seen better days, but confidence is quickly restored once you enter: the three spacious rooms are simply done out in a clean, spare, modern style, with chunky wooden furniture built locally from reclaimed timbers; and the 'short and sweet' blackboard menu, based predominantly on fish, quickly dispels any lingering doubts. Bright, bold flavour combinations characterise the style of the food. There may be 'zingy' marinated salmon cured in lemon and vodka, or oysters with hot chorizo to start, while main courses might be roast cod fillet with horseradish sauce, wild sea bass with thyme and roast garlic, or crisply roasted leg of duck with chilli salsa. There is also a selection of 'ultra-thin' pizzas that live up to their description and may be topped simply with fresh tomato sauce and mozzarella or artichokes. This is a Shepherd Neame pub (the brewery is only a few miles away) serving their usual range of real ales, including seasonals. A blackboard by the bar lists the 12 wines available; five of these are also served by the glass. SAMPLE DISHES: pear and Roquefort salad £5; seared salmon with cherry tomato sauce £12; banana and toffee parfait with chocolate sorbet £4.50.

Licensees Phil and Steve Harris (Shepherd Neame)
Open *12 to 3, 6 to 11, Sun 12 to 10.30; bar food and restaurant 12 to 2, 7 to 9, Sun 12 to 2.45; closed 25 Dec*
Details *Children welcome in bar eating area and children's room   Car park Garden and patio   No smoking in 1 room   Occasional live music   Dogs welcome if on leads   Delta, MasterCard, Switch, Visa*

Recommendations for good country pubs will be very welcome.

SEAVIEW　　Isle of Wight　　　　　map 2

▲ *Seaview Hotel*

High Street, Seaview PO34 5EX　TEL: (01983) 612711
WEB SITE: www.seaviewhotel.co.uk
on B3340, 2m E of Ryde

Undoubtedly, Seaview is time-warp England. A quiet Victorian
seaside resort a little way from Ryde, its neat streets, which descend
towards a rocky shoreline and bay, are hung about with flags and
bunting. The town's hotel houses two restaurants and a bar, as well
as a public bar festooned with more seafaring memorabilia than you
could shake an oar at. On handpump are Goddard's Special Bitter,
which is brewed on the island, and Greene King Abbot Ale. There is
a large range of malt whiskies, and the sort of classical wine list
(mature clarets and posh Burgundies leading the way) that you
would expect to find in a hotel of this calibre. Five wines are served
by the glass. The bar menu is what will most interest droppers-in. It
offers a wide range, from chicken liver and wild mushroom pâté
with red onion chutney, or grilled goats'-cheese salad, to pork and
leek sausages and mash, and ribeye steak with chips. Interspersed
with these are a few more challenging dishes: try Cajun salmon fillet
with lime yoghurt dressing, for example, or Thai-style marinated
chicken with rocket, chard and tomato. Round things off in style
with iced lemon brûlée, or hot chocolate sponge served with local
cream. SAMPLE DISHES: herring roes and capers on a toasted muffin
£4.50; swordfish steak with ginger mash and lemon-grass oil £12;
poached meringue with praline and crème anglaise £4.

Licensee N.W.T. Hayward (freehouse)
Open *10.30 to 3, 6 to 11, Sun 12 to 3, 7 to 10.30; bar food 12 to 2, 7 to
9.30; restaurant (exc Sun evening) 12 to 2, 7 to 9.30; closed Christmas*
Details *Children welcome in bar eating area　Car park　Wheelchair access
(not WC)　Patio　No smoking in 1 dining room　Background music　Dogs
welcome　Amex, Delta, Diners, MasterCard, Switch, Visa　Accommodation:
16 rooms, B&B £55 to £135*

SELLACK　　Herefordshire　　　　　map 5

Lough Pool Inn

Sellack HR9 6LX　TEL: (01989) 730236
off A49, 3m NW of Ross-on-Wye

Finding this seventeenth-century inn, which is well off the beaten
track and surrounded by beautiful countryside, is well worth the
effort, and doubly so now that Stephen Bull, a restaurateur of some

reputation, took over the pub in late 2000. As the Guide went to press, the planned changes to the menu had yet to occur, but you can expect quite a few, with local produce featuring strongly in both bar food and restaurant-style dishes. In the meantime, a printed menu continued to list a range of familiar pub staples plus a selection of specialities of the house, such as lamb with candied lemons, poached salmon steak with mustard and horseradish sauce, and beef braised with chestnuts in red wine. Additional daily offerings on a board might include salmon mousse, spicy chicken wings, duck in cherries, and grilled swordfish. Butty Bach from the Wye Valley Brewery in nearby Hereford is among the real ales served, and cider drinkers are offered Weston's Stowford Press and Scrumpy Supreme. Three wines are sold by the glass from a modestly priced list, though changes to the list are likely. SAMPLE DISHES: Stilton and Guinness pâté £3.75; grilled lemon sole £11; walnut and honey tart £3.

Licensee Stephen Bull (freehouse)
Open 11.30 to 2.30, 6.30 to 11, Sun 12 to 2.30, 7 to 10.30; bar food and restaurant 12 to 2, 7 to 9.30 (9 Sun)
Details Children welcome in dining room Car park Wheelchair access (also WC) Garden No smoking in dining room Background music No dogs Delta, Diners, MasterCard, Switch, Visa

SHAVE CROSS   Dorset   map 2

Shave Cross Inn ✿   NEW ENTRY

Shave Cross, Marshwood Vale DT6 6HW   TEL: (01308) 868358
off B3165, in Marshwood Vale, 5m NW of Bridport; leave B3164 at Marshwood, follow signs to Shave Cross

The Village of Shave Cross is little more than a scattering of houses and the eponymous pub, which sits at the junction of two narrow lanes in a pretty, hilly area called Marshwood Vale. It is a thatched, flint-faced building with a picturesque garden, and a rather clandestine feeling to the entrance corridor that takes you past the kitchens into the small main bar. While the flagstone floor and inglenook fireplace have been retained, there has been some sensitive refurbishment, with the walls done in a warm yellow, smart curtains hanging at the windows and a picture of a monk recalling the days when devotees on pilgrimage would stop here to have their tonsures touched up. A pair of ancillary rooms are reserved for dining. Food is listed on a couple of blackboards, with lunch options changing daily and the dinner menu weekly. The former deals in pub favourites such as prawns sautéed in garlic, salmon fishcakes, and stuffed mushrooms, but also takes in the likes of New York-style corned beef hash, and stefado (a Greek recipe for rabbit stew). In the evenings, the choice might extend to warm chorizo salad, smoked venison, fillet of beef on five-spice deep-fried parsnip, and stir-fried duck with plum sauce and egg noodles, a dish which an inspector found 'very good indeed'. Finish with a dessert such as crème brûlée or maybe a selection of cheeses. Otter Best Bitter is a mainstay of the handpumps, but constantly changing guest beers might well include Hook Norton or Robinson's powerful Old Tom. Thatcher's cider is also on draught, and every wine on the 31-strong wine list is available by the glass. SAMPLE DISHES: home-made seafood soup £4.25; medallions of pork with cashew-nut cream sauce £13; chocolate mousse £4.

Licensees Nic and Lisa Tipping (freehouse)
Open *Tue to Sat 11 to 3, 7 to 11, Sun 12 to 3, 7 to 10.30; bar food and restaurant 12 to 2, 7 to 9 (exc Sun evening winter); closed 25 Dec evening*
Details *Children welcome   Car park   Wheelchair access (also WC)   Garden and patio   No smoking in dining room   Background music   Dogs welcome on leads exc in dining areas   Delta, MasterCard, Switch, Visa*

SHEPTON MONTAGUE   Somerset   map 2

▲ *Montague Inn*   NEW ENTRY

Shepton Montague BA9 8JW   TEL: (01749) 813213
village signposted off A359 between Bruton and Castle Cary

This whitewashed stone inn is adorned with hanging baskets, with creepers on a side wall; an attractive terrace behind has peaceful rural views. The main bar is tastefully decorated with green and apricot paintwork and has cushioned wall benches, old dark pine furniture and an open log fire. An inglenook dominates one of the two adjacent dining areas. The bar menu encompasses ciabatta with various fillings, or perhaps pasta with asparagus and spinach. The restaurant menu, served throughout, might run to vegetarian choices such as steamed wild mushroom and smoked pimento in vine leaves with orange, mango and chive salsa, or mozzarella and tomato tart with a duet of pesto and olive jus. Blackboard specials could include brochettes of grilled monkfish wrapped in smoked bacon on saffron noodles, and influences from distant places result in Louisiana gumbo soup, Tuscan seafood broth, and haggis with neeps and tatties. From closer to home come medallions of venison with juniper jus, pan-fried breast of pheasant, and shepherd's pie. Greene King IPA and Butcombe Bitter are kept, along with Great Western Revival cider. Of 20-plus fairly priced wines, three come by the glass. SAMPLE DISHES: marinated seafood cocktail £4.75; pan-fried kidneys in a rich gravy on puff pastry nests £8; glazed chocolate parfait with plum sauce £3.50.

Licensee Patricia Elcock (freehouse)
Open *Tue to Sun 12 to 2.30, 6.30 to 11 (10.30 Sun); bar food and restaurant 12 to 1.45, 6.30 to 9*
Details *No children   Car park   Garden   No smoking in dining room   No music   Dogs welcome   Delta, MasterCard, Switch, Visa   Accommodation: 3 rooms, B&B £40 to £50*

SHIPSTON ON STOUR   **Warwickshire**   map 5

▲ *White Bear*

4 High Street, Shipston on Stour CV36 4AJ   TEL: (01608) 661558
just off A429 Ettington to Moreton-in-Marsh road

This popular local watering hole dates from the sixteenth century, but the fact is not obvious from its outward appearance: like many buildings, it was 'improved' by the Georgians and later architectural stylists. Inside, the true age is more apparent, thanks to low, beamed ceilings, though green gingham tablecloths and dark red walls determine the feel of the bistro-style restaurant. Both restaurant and bar are served by the same menu, which opens with a page of hot and cold filled baguettes and sandwiches. Otherwise, start perhaps with spicy grilled prawns and jalapeño peppers, and follow them with half a roast Warwickshire duckling with apricot and brandy gravy, Thai vegetable curry, or grilled plaice with lemon and parsley butter. A specials board enhances the already generous range. Bass, Marston's Pedigree and Brew XI are the beers; Weston's perry is also served, as well as a wide range of whiskies, cognacs and so on. The list of around two dozen wines includes three own-label French bottles at £9.95 and a small selection of classics from Bordeaux and Burgundy. SAMPLE DISHES: bacon and black pudding baguette £4.50; roast organic pork stuffed with apple and sage £7.50; orange and passion-fruit teardrops £3.25.

Licensees Baggy and Sheelagh Saunders (Punch Group)
Open *11 to 11, Sun 12 to 10.30; bar food and restaurant 12 to 2, 6.30 to 9.30 (10 Fri and Sat), Sun 12 to 2; closed 25 Dec*
Details *Children welcome   Car park   Wheelchair access (also WC)   Garden and patio   Occasional live music; jukebox in bar   Dogs welcome   Amex, Delta, MasterCard, Switch, Visa   Accommodation: 10 rooms, B&B £25 to £50*

NEW ENTRY *indicates that pub was not a main entry in the previous edition (though it may have featured in the 'Out and about' section.)*

SHOCKLACH   Cheshire   map 7

Bull Inn

Shocklach SY14 7BL   TEL: (01829) 250239
off A534 Wrexham to Nantwich road; turn right after crossing River Dee, then 3m to village

This basic, homely pub in a bucolic village has no restaurant but offers a surprisingly long, reasonably priced bar menu that changes daily and includes full descriptions of exotica. These might include spicy Tuscan mixed bean and vegetable soup, Acapulco chicken in hot tomato and garlic sauce, Moroccan lamb tagine with saffron and cinnamon sauce, or Shanghai chicken in ginger and lemon sauce. And there is always a home-made curry with rice. Basics are not forgotten either, with carrot and orange soup, and avocado with prawns among starters, while local trout grilled with almonds, lamb and rosemary hotpot with red cabbage, grilled sea bass, and roast duckling are just a few of the main dishes. The honesty of the menu extends to a note that the deep-fried scampi are re-formed. Desserts are generally such time-honoured favourites as apple pie with custard, or bread-and-butter pudding, but some might describe as exotic Toblerone mousse, or chocolate and toffee pudding with Mars bar sauce. Sunday lunch, three courses at £9.25, includes a choice of roasts and two fish dishes. Draught Bass and Burtonwood Bitter are the real ales, and six wines from the short list are offered by the glass. SAMPLE DISHES: deep-fried Camembert with redcurrant jelly £4.25; Normandy pork in paprika, cream and calvados sauce £8.50; fresh fruit and brandy meringue £3.25.

Licensees Alan and Jan Morley (freehouse)
Open *all week (exc Mon lunchtime) 12 to 3, 7 to 11; bar food 12 to 2, 7 to 10; open bank hol Mon lunchtime; closed 25 Dec*
Details *Children welcome   Car park   Wheelchair access (also WC)   Patio Background music   No dogs   Delta, MasterCard, Switch, Visa*

SHORTBRIDGE   East Sussex   map 3

Peacock

Shortbridge, Piltdown TN22 3XA   TEL: (01825) 762463
just off A272 SW of Uckfield

Located in a tiny village this black and white half-timbered pub is more authentic and some three hundred years older than its (in)famous neighbour, Piltdown Man. Ascend the steps to the front door, which is guarded by two ancient yews, and enter one of two totally traditional bars, with log fires, horse brasses, parquet floors with rugs, and small windows whose light is augmented by soft shaded lamps. Apart from home-made pâté, starters are mainly fish, with smoked salmon on blinis, whitebait or king prawns. A couple of chef's daily specials augment the regular menu. They might be rump steak on garlic mash, naturally smoked haddock with cheese and chive sauce, or game pie with mustard mash. Fish appears in the main courses as seafood pancake or fisherman's pie, both comprising salmon, cod and smoked haddock. Vegetarians might consider spinach, mushroom and peppers en croûte or spinach and ricotta cannelloni, while carnivores can opt for fillet steak plain pan-fried, or 'Marilyn Monroe' style with mushrooms, Tabasco, Worcester-shire sauce, brandy and cream, or an 'Old England' version stuffed with Stilton wrapped in bacon with mushrooms and baked in the oven. Harveys Best, Wadworth 6X Fuller's London Pride, and Old Speckled Hen might be among the real beers you'll find on tap. SAMPLE DISHES: smoked haddock pot £4; steak and kidney pudding £8; hot chocolate fudge brownie £3.75.

Licensee Matthew Arnold (freehouse)
Open *11 to 3, 6 to 11, Sun 12 to 3, 7 to 10.30; open all day Sat and Sun summer; bar food and restaurant 12 to 2.30, 6.30 to 10, Sun 12 to 2.30, 7 to 9; food all day Sat and Sun summer; closed 25, 26 and 31 Dec*
Details *Children welcome   Car park   Garden and patio   No smoking in restaurant after 9.30   Background music   Dogs welcome exc in eating areas Delta, MasterCard, Switch, Visa*

SHOULDHAM   **Norfolk**   **map 6**

Kings Arms   NEW ENTRY

The Green, Shouldham PE33 0BY   TEL: (01366) 347819
off A134/A1122; pub on main road through village

The Kings Arms is a distinctive dusky shade of pink and stands right on the edge of the village green, so no one should have any trouble finding it. The sign outside bills it as a 'country dining room and freehouse', and the two sides of the operation are quite distinct. The freehouse part comprises two smart and attractively decorated rooms, one a lounge with sofas, the other with a more traditionally pubby feel, thanks to dark wood tables and a small stone bar counter in the corner; both have log fires, tiled floors, plenty of beams and exposed brick walls adorned with sailing prints. Well-kept real ales are Greene King Abbot Ale and IPA plus a guest, which might be Slated from the local Payn brewery; and six house wines are always available by the glass or bottle alongside four wines of the month, and the full restaurant list of 24 bottles. Bar food, served lunchtimes only, is simple fare along the lines of omelettes (perhaps with smoked salmon, or vintage Cheddar), soup, pâtés and sandwiches – and a good-value Sunday roast. Evening meals in the tiny dining room are by booking only, and the weekly-changing four-course menus go in for a country-house style of cooking using excellent local produce, notably venison, free-range pork from the village and fen vegetables. SAMPLE DISHES: garlic mushrooms on toast £5; mixed jacket potato platter £6; pineapple fritters with butter toffee sauce and crème fraîche £4.

Licensee Andrew Burrell-Saward (freehouse)
Open *Wed to Sun 12 to 2 (2.30 Sat and Sun), Tue to Sat 7 to 11; bar food Wed to Sat 12 to 2; restaurant open evenings only and must be pre-booked; closed 2 weeks Sept*
Details *No children   Car park   Wheelchair access (not WC)   Garden and patio   No smoking in dining room   Background music   No dogs   Amex, Delta, Diners, MasterCard, Switch, Visa*

SIBFORD GOWER   Oxfordshire   map 5

Moody Cow at the   NEW ENTRY
Wykham Arms

Sibford Gower OX15 5RX   TEL: (01295) 788808
WEB SITE: www.moodycow.co.uk
village is signposted off B4035 between Banbury and Shipston-on-Stour

Opposite the magnificent manor house in the heart of a delightful village, this 'picture-postcard pretty' mellow Cotswold stone local has been given a new lease of life, as a modern style dining pub resembling its Herefordshire elder sibling at Upton Bishop (see entry). Minimal décor is smart and relaxing, with slate floors, exposed stone walls, tasteful prints and paintings, and open fires. The single menu for restaurant and bars offers nearly 20 each of starters and main dishes, plus daily fresh fish and other specials. The food manages to combine simplicity with interest and trendiness, with a focus on freshly prepared local produce. Prawn crackers are offered with the basket of olive ciabatta, French and wholemeal bread, and you might begin with parfait of chicken liver and foie gras, or whole baked sardines with dressed leaves. Four pastas include one for vegetarians, who also find tomato and chickpea curry among three 'spicy dishes'. Main courses might take in pork, apple and leek bangers with coriander mash; or salmon marinated in red wine and thyme with saffron sauce. Service is efficient and friendly. Ales on draught are Arkells 2B and Kingsdown, and Hook Norton Best Bitter. Seven wines from the short list are offered by the glass. SAMPLE DISHES: chef's home-made lasagne £5; pheasant, wild mushroom and Madeira pie £11; lavender crème brulée £4.50.

Licensee James Lloyd (freehouse)
Open *Tue to Sat 12 to 2.30, 6.30 to 11, Sun 12 to 3 (also open Sun evening and all day Mon on bank hol weekends); bar food and restaurant 12 to 2, 6.30 to 9.30*
Details *Children welcome in eating areas   Car park   Wheelchair access (also WC)   Garden and patio   No smoking in dining room   Live or background music   Dogs welcome in 1 bar only   Amex, Delta, MasterCard, Switch, Visa*

SINNINGTON   **North Yorkshire**   map 9

▲ *Fox and Hounds* ✿

Sinnington YO62 6SQ   TEL: (01751) 431577
off A170 between Helmsley and Pickering

'Genuinely superior' cooking is a major attraction of this old stone pub. One menu serves the two traditional bars as well as the candlelit dining room, offering cooking that is somewhat more cosmopolitan than may be expected in such a remote setting: salmon, crab and sweet potato cakes with a chilli and fennel salsa, grilled cod on char-grilled vegetables and couscous with a lime and balsamic dressing, and confit duck leg accompanied by a pepper and peach schnapps marmalade. There may even be ostrich fillet (served with damson and artichoke risotto) among the chef's specials, and for dessert try perhaps marshmallow crème brûlée. The pub also has ten guest rooms, and its position in an unspoilt village on the edge of the North York Moors, within easy driving distance of both York and the coast, makes it a good base for exploring the area. Black Sheep Special is provided for real ale drinkers, but wine enthusiasts fare better: a concise but varied and fairly priced list opens with five house selections, all available by the bottle (£11), or by the small or large glass (£2 and £2.75). SAMPLE DISHES: wild mushroom and saffron tartlet with tarragon and coriander pesto £4.50; pan-fried John Dory fillet with sweet potato cake and lemon butter sauce £15; blueberry, port and vanilla bavarois £3.75.

Licensees Andrew and Catherine Stephens (freehouse)
Open *12 to 2.30, 6 (6.30 winter) to 11, 6.30 to 10.30 Sun; closed second week in Jan; bar food and restaurant 12 to 2, 6.30 to 9 (8.30 Sun)*
Details *Children welcome   Car park   Wheelchair access (also WC)   Garden No smoking in dining room   Background music   Dogs welcome exc in dining room   Amex, MasterCard, Switch, Visa   Accommodation: 10 rooms, B&B £50 to £70*

SLAIDBURN   Lancashire   map 8

▲ *Hark to Bounty Inn*

Slaidburn BB7 3EP   TEL: (01200) 446246
on B6478, 7m N of Clitheroe

This traditional village pub with its intriguing name is in an
untouristy village beside a river surrounded by wild open country.
An unusual feature is the function room, which housed a local court
from the fourteenth century until the 1930s. The pub's own description of the food from a single bar and restaurant menu is 'imaginative country fare', and the kitchen makes its own bread to go with
such specials as home-potted salmon and prawns, or chicken and
mushroom soup. Favourites include Cumberland sausage with apple
sauce, or fishcakes on tomato and basil sauce, and a starter of prawn
cocktail is described as 'almost a meal in itself'. Children's portions
of many starters and mains are offered in addition to sausage,
burger, chicken, and fish fingers with chips. Vegetables, integral to
main dishes, have been described as 'particularly well prepared and
presented'. Courage Directors and Theakston Best Bitter, Mild and
Old Peculier are on draught, and three wines are sold by the glass.
SAMPLE DISHES: local black pudding with mustard sauce £3.50; steak
and kidney pie £6; hot chocolate fudge cake and cream £3.

Licensee Isobel Bristow (freehouse)
Open *11 to 11, Sun 12 to 10.30; bar food and restaurant 12 to 2 (2.30 Sat),
6 to 9 (9.30 Sat, 8 weekdays winter), Sun 12 to 8 (12 to 2.30, 5.30 to 8
winter)*
Details *Children welcome   Car park   Wheelchair access (not WC)   Garden
Occasional background music   Dogs welcome exc in eating areas   Delta,
MasterCard, Switch, Visa   Accommodation: 9 rooms, B&B £24.75 to £60*

SLAPTON   Buckinghamshire   map 3

Carpenters Arms

1 Horton Road, Slapton LU7 9DB
TEL: (01525) 220563
off A4146, 3m S of Leighton Buzzard

Across the courtyard from this brick-built pub with its 'marvellous
atmosphere' and 'unpretentious' décor is a barn encompassing an
impressively stocked (20,000 volumes) second-hand bookstore. If
you want to buy a book, just ask for it to be added to your pub bill.
The bar area is just for drinkers, but in the eating area the fare
includes baguettes, pies of the day (a reporter's steak and kidney was
'very appealing, with a high and light crust'), and a written list of

more ambitious dishes. Herrings in a dill marinade, or a pint of prawns could be followed by a warm salad of Cajun chicken ('hot!' warns the menu), or grilled tuna steak with garlic butter. Two real ales are offered at any one time, and they might be from the local Tring or Vale breweries. The wine list, approaching 40 bottles, is packed with excitements, both classic and New World, at reasonable prices. Six are offered by the glass. SAMPLE DISHES: smoked salmon with pickled samphire £6.50; mixed game pie £8.50; treacle tart £3.50.

Licensee Jim Vogler (freehouse)
Open *Mon to Fri 12 to 3.30, Mon to Sat 7 to 11, Sun 12 to 3, 7 to 10.30; bar food (exc Sat lunchtime and Sun) 12 to 2, 7.30 to 9.30*
Details *Children welcome   Car park   Patio   No music   No dogs MasterCard, Visa*

SLAPTON   Devon   map 1

▲ *Tower Inn* 🍺

Slapton TQ7 2PN   TEL: (01548) 580216
off A379, 5m SW of Dartmouth

When it was built in about 1347, the inn was part of the Collegiate Chantry of St Mary, established probably as the college's guesthouse to dispense alms and hospitality to the deserving. Much of the chantry tower is still standing, and in its shadow sits the inn, with bench seating at the front and back, and an extremely narrow doorway to squeeze through. Inside, it is all low ceilings, stone walls and open fires, coming into its own particularly in the evening, when candlelight creates even more atmosphere. Separate menus operate at lunch and dinner. The former may see you starting with a full-flavoured seafood pancake with good cheese sauce, and going on to a rich and traditional 'Black Velvet pie', deliciously tender beef cooked in dark Guinness gravy under a lid of properly made pastry. Evenings go a touch more elaborate, with smoked prawns in garlic mayonnaise, followed by Barbary duck breast in blackcurrant coulis, grilled swordfish with lime butter, or tenderloin of pork cooked with apricots and cider. Daily specials are chalked on a board, and the range of favourite puddings might include home-made apple pie, tangy lemon tart, or Salcombe ice creams and sorbets. If the four-teenth-century architecture doesn't draw you, the cask-conditioned ales should. The superb range extends from Dartmoor Best Bitter and Exmoor Ale to Badger Tanglefoot plus guests such as Exmoor Gold and Badger Champion Ale. Ciders from Weston's and Addlestone are available, as is a well-chosen wine list with seven by the glass. SAMPLE DISHES: salmon and tuna fishcakes with dill sauce

£4; grilled sirloin steak with mushrooms £10; sticky toffee pudding with Devon clotted cream £3.50.

Licensees Josh and Nicola Acfield (freehouse)
Open 12 to 3, 6 to 11, Sun 12 to 3, 7 to 10.30; bar food (exc Sun evening winter) 12 to 2.30 (3.30 Sun winter), 6 to 9.30 (7 Sun); closed 25 Dec
Details Children welcome in family room Car park Wheelchair access (not WC) Garden No smoking in 1 room Occasional live or background music Dogs welcome MasterCard, Switch, Visa Accommodation: 3 rooms, B&B £30 to £50

SMARDEN   Kent   map 3

Bell Inn 🍺

Bell Lane, Smarden TN27 8PW   TEL: (01233) 770283
off A274, 7m SW of Charing; pub is ½ mile outside village (sign-posted from village)

Situated on a country lane just outside the village, the Bell looks and feels every inch the archetypal country pub. Parts of the building date from the thirteenth century, though most of it is no more than a few hundred years old. Inside, it looks its age – the main bar is in traditional style with beams, tiled floor, and hops adorning the bar counter, but beware the low ceilings in the tiny rear 'cellar' bar and dining area. Food is very much in the old-fashioned English style, with a printed menu listing a fair selection of pub staples: good local sausages with chips, for example. More interesting is the daily blackboard, which includes several straightforward fish dishes, perhaps simply baked whole trout garnished with sprigs of rosemary and thyme, or other local specialities such as lamb and pearl barley stew. Five real ales are on handpump, and might include beers from Fuller's, Greene King, Shepherd Neame and Harveys, plus seasonal ales; local Biddenden cider is also offered. The continually updated wine list has five reds and four whites by the glass, and prices stay resolutely below the £20 mark. The 20 or so wines to choose from have been selected for easy-drinking and approachability – they'll be pretty good with food too. Behind the pub is an attractive garden with lots of shrubs and trees, including fruit trees, plus plenty of tables for fine days. SAMPLE DISHES: wild boar and juniper pâté £5; steak and kidney pie £7; lemon and lime brûlée £3.50.

Licensee Craig Smith (freehouse)
Open 11.30 to 3, 6 to 11, Sun 12 to 10.30; bar food 12 to 2.30, 6.30 to 10; closed 25 Dec
Details Children welcome Car park Wheelchair access (also WC) Garden No-smoking area in bar Jukebox Dogs welcome MasterCard, Switch, Visa

▲ *Chequers Inn* NEW ENTRY

The Street, Smarden TN27 8QA
TEL: (01233) 770217
village is off A274 Maidstone to Tenterden road, signposted just south of Headcorn

Right in the centre of the unspoilt old village is this attractive, weatherboarded inn, parts of which date from the fourteenth century. The well-maintained rustic interior, with low-beamed ceilings and flagstoned floors, must look much as it did when the place was new. Food is served in two dining areas, but there is plenty of room for drinkers, who are offered Harveys Sussex Best Bitter, Fuller's London Pride and guest ales, plus a 35-bottle wine list that starts in France and takes a brisk trot round the world. Around a dozen wines are served by the small or large glass. Frequently changing menus, listed on blackboards, offer a mostly familiar range – steak and ale pie, for example – but less-usual options might include aromatic duck pancakes with spring onion salad and hoisin sauce, sea bass with tomato and chilli dressing, or baked pheasant with orange and celeriac. Directly behind the pub is a paved terrace furnished with attractive wrought-iron tables and chairs, and surrounded by shrubs and flowers in tubs. Beyond this is a beautifully landscaped garden with a large pond and views of the village church, an idyllic setting for sitting outside on a sunny summer's day. SAMPLE DISHES: salmon and potato fishcake with lemon herb cream £5; medallions of fillet steak with whisky and onion sauce £12; bread-and-butter pudding £3.50.

Licensee Lisa Bullock (freehouse)
Open *Mon to Fri 11 to 3, 6 to 11, Sat and Sun 11 to 11; bar food and restaurant 12 to 2.15, 6.30 to 9.30*
Details *Children welcome in eating areas   Car park   Garden   No smoking in 1 dining room   Background music   Dogs welcome   Delta, MasterCard, Switch, Visa   Accommodation: 4 rooms, B&B £35 to £65*

SMART'S HILL   Kent   map 3

Bottle House Inn   HAUNTED

Smarts Hill, Penshurst TN11 8ET
TEL: (01892) 870306
WEB SITE: www.bottlehouseinn.freeserve.com
off B2188 1m S of Penshurst

Hidden away among narrow lanes near Penshurst, the little hamlet of Smart's Hill has good reason to be grateful for the existence of the Bottle House, which seems to be well-versed in the art of dispensing good cheer. There may or may not be a female ghost in attendance during your visit, but if there is, the likelihood is she has been drawn by the prospect of a glass of hand-pumped Larkins, the local bitter, or Harveys Sussex Best Bitter or a guest such as Courage Directors. The local wine – Penshurst Müller-Thurgau – appears on a list that also takes in the more renowned wine-making countries; half a dozen are sold by the glass. Printed menus offer a wealth of choice, some of it a little out of the ordinary, as in garlic swordfish suprême with scallops and prawns, but most keeping to a tried-and-true repertoire. That might mean game terrine with fruit chutney, proper gravad lax, ribeye steak with green peppercorn sauce and chips, or fisherman's pie with fresh vegetables. Vegetarians might opt for wild mushroom stroganoff with rice and salad, while the children's menu offers the likes of chicken dippers or sausages served with beans and chips. Finish with blueberry cheesecake or hot cherry Bakewell pudding with custard. SAMPLE DISHES: deep-fried sesame-coated Brie with plum and apple chutney £5; rack of lamb with redcurrant and rosemary sauce and dauphinoise potatoes £15; lemon and passion-fruit bavarois £3.50.

Licensees R.G. Meer and P. Hammond (freehouse)
Open *Mon to Fri 11 to 2.30, 6 to 11, Sat 11 to 11, Sun 12 to 10.30; bar food and restaurant Mon to Fri 12 to 1.45, 6 to 9, Sat 12 to 10, Sun 12 to 9*
Details *Children welcome   Car park   Garden   No smoking in dining room Background music   Dogs welcome exc in dining room   MasterCard, Switch, Visa*

SNAPE   **Suffolk**   map 6

▲ *Crown Inn*

Bridge Road, Snape IP17 1SL   TEL: (01728) 688324
off A1094, on way to Snape Maltings

The Crown is a cream-painted fifteenth-century pub on a crossroads in this picturesque village, not far from Snape Maltings and handy for the Aldeburgh Festival. Inside, brick floors, beams and simple wooden furniture set the tone, and the walls are adorned with still-life paintings that are mostly for sale. All tables are laid up for eating, and booking is advisable. Fish is straight off the nearby boats, and may turn up on the plate as a first course of crayfish tails with Thai mayonnaise, or main courses of seared scallops with roast plum tomatoes and lemon dressing, or fillet of sea bass with tiger prawns and garlic butter. For less fishy tastes, there is Serrano ham with roasted red peppers, or Woodbridge smoked duck with chutney, followed perhaps by roast rack of lamb with garlic mash. Lemon tart, or chocolate truffle with strawberries, might await the sweet of tooth at dessert stage, or there are home-made ice creams. The Crown is an Adnams pub, so on handpump are the brewery's Best Bitter, Regatta and Broadside. The wine list has much to offer, roaming the world to pick up a bottle here and a bottle there and offering most of them at well under £20. Eight wines, including champagne, are sold by the glass. SAMPLE DISHES: salmon, cod and dill fishcake £4.50; 8oz fillet steak with chips, mushrooms and salad £12; plum and cinnamon crumble £3.75.

Licensee Diane Maylott (Adnams)
Open *12 to 3, 6 to 11, Sun 7 to 10.30; bar food and restaurant 12 to 2, 7 to 9; closed 25 Dec, evening 26 Dec*
Details *No children   Car park   Wheelchair access (also WC)   Garden and patio   No smoking in dining room   No music   No dogs   Delta, MasterCard, Switch, Visa   Accommodation: 3 rooms, B&B £40 to £60*

SNETTISHAM   Norfolk   map 6

▲ *Rose & Crown*

Old Church Road, Snettisham PE31 7LX   TEL: (01485) 541382
just off A149, 4m S of Hunstanton

The A149 divides Snettisham from its beach, and this old pub – constructed of local stone and brick – is on the inland side, in a quiet back lane near the church. Much expansion over the years has produced a warren of varied rooms, the best of which perhaps is the family room that looks out, through French windows, on to the garden. A modish restaurant with linen tablecloths and, in the oldest part, a cosy snug and a locals' bar are there to be explored too. Several menus are offered. At lunchtime there are lighter items, such as sandwiches (including one of home-cooked ham and Meaux mustard) and salads (perhaps black pudding with bacon and garlic croûtons). Then there is a more extensive evening menu dealing in goats' cheese, olive and chorizo salad, stir-fried duck with Thai curry sauce and peppered noodles, or cod and mustard fishcakes with rocket salad, supplemented by blackboard specials: perhaps game pâté, moules marinière, or chargrilled swordfish seasoned with garlic and coriander. Children have their own menu to peruse, including lasagne, fish and chips, or sausages and mash. Finish with something like fruit crumble with a 'deliciously tangy fruit stew' of blackcurrants, redcurrants and blackberries, or pears poached in red wine. Adnams Broadside, Bass and Greene King ales are on draught, and the well-chosen wine list offers eight by the glass. SAMPLE DISHES: ham and butter-bean soup £3.25; pan-fried lambs' kidneys with sweet sauerkraut, new potatoes and Madeira gravy £8.50; treacle pudding £3.25.

Licensees Anthony Goodrich and Julie Jennings (freehouse)
Open *11 to 11, Sun 12 to 10.30; bar food and restaurant 12 to 2 (2.30 Sun),
6.30 to 9 (9.30 Fri and Sat)*
Details *Children welcome in bar eating areas   Car park   Wheelchair access
(also WC)   Garden   No-smoking area in bar, no smoking in dining room   No
music   Dogs welcome   MasterCard, Switch, Visa   Accommodation: 11
rooms, B&B £50 to £80*

SOUTH LEIGH   Oxfordshire   map 2

▲ *Mason Arms*

South Leigh OX8 6XN   TEL: (01993) 702485
off A40, 3m SE of Witney

Gerry Stonhill's Individual Mason Arms, to give this thatched
fifteenth-century inn its full title, states its manifesto in various signs
about the place (no dogs, no children, no mobile phones) and in a
note on the back of the menu exhorting the enjoyment of food,
drink and Cuban cigars. Its atmosphere has been likened to that of a
gentleman's club. The cooking could not be called sophisticated but
instead makes a virtue of simplicity, showing off fine raw materials
to their best. Among starters might be Mr Baxter's potted shrimps
('as supplied to the Queen Mother'), and main courses – plain or
with a choice of sauces – typically include thick-cut sirloin steak,
crisp-skinned roast duck, and various fresh fish (Mr Stonhill buys
only very large specimens); one reader praised a curry served with
pickles made by a local Indian lady. Prices are not cheap but 'you
will remember the food long after you have forgotten the cost'.
Burton Ale is drawn directly from the barrel in the cellar, and the
exclusively French wine list includes a house Beaujolais produced by
a friend of the owner. However, the speciality, drinks-wise, is the
selection of whiskies and vintage armagnacs dating back to 1917.
Those arriving by helicopter will be pleased to know that co-ordi-
nates of the inn's landing pad can be provided. SAMPLE DISHES: rough
liver pâté £6; grilled Dover sole (price varies); treacle tart £5.50.

Licensee Gerry Stonhill (freehouse)
Open *Tue to Sun 12 to 3.30, Tue to Sat 6.30 to 11; bar food and restaurant
Tue to Sat 12 to 2, 7.30 to 10.30, Sun 12 to 3; closed 24 to 30 Dec*
Details *No children   Car park   Wheelchair access (not WC)   Patio
Occasional background music   No dogs   Amex   Accommodation: 2 rooms,
B&B £35 to £50*

---

*Report forms are at the back of the book; write a letter if you prefer,
or email your pub report to whichcountrypubs@which.net.*

SOUTH POOL Devon map 1

Millbrook Inn

South Pool TQ7 2RW TEL: (01548) 531581
WEB SITE: www.millbrookinn.co.uk
1½m S of A379 at Frogmore, SE of Kingsbridge

This tiny seventeenth-century pub in the centre of a small, picturesque village has no parking of its own, but this need not be a problem as it is possible to arrive by boat; South Pool is on one of the inlets of Salcombe Bay. A narrow stream runs past the rear of the pub, too, and a narrow covered terrace on the bank allows for outdoor eating and drinking. Inside are three small, cosy rooms, one with a collection of china ducks in an alcove to complement the real ones that gather outside. Polished mahogany tables, horse brasses, clay pipes on the beams, a ship's wheel and a number of sporting trophies all add up to create a welcoming atmosphere. A blackboard menu supplements the printed list, and soups appear to be a speciality: there may be no fewer than four available at a time, including perhaps tomato and basil, or carrot and leek. Otherwise the menu offers good old-fashioned dishes like Scottish sirloin steak in cream, brandy and mushroom sauce, and various ploughman's, as well as more modern dishes such as pasta with pesto and Parmesan, or hummus with garlic bread. Bass is on draught, and on handpump are Fuller's London Pride and guests such as Jekyll's Gold Premium Ale from Hydes, and eight wines are sold by the glass. SAMPLE DISHES: kiln-roasted salmon with dill sauce £5; bouillabaisse £9; chocolate biscuit cake £3.

Licensee Elizabeth Stirland (freehouse)
Open *11.30 (12 winter) to 2.30, 5.30 (6 winter) to 11, Sun 12 to 3, 5.30 (6 winter) to 10.30; bar food 12 to 2, 6.30 to 9.30 (7 to 9 winter); closed evening 25 Dec*
Details *Children welcome in family room Wheelchair access (not WC) Patio Occasional background music No dogs No cards*

SPARSHOLT Hampshire map 2

Plough Inn

Sparsholt SO21 2NW TEL: (01962) 776353
off B3049 1½m W of Winchester

The Plough is a much-extended 200-year-old cottage on the edge of a peaceful village. Its shrub-filled garden, with its paddock and wooden chalet, attracts families, and children are also welcome in the family and dining rooms. The spacious bar area and the cosy and convivial front rooms in the original cottage are furnished with sturdy pine tables and chairs to create a rustic and comfortable atmosphere, and attractive prints and farm tools adorn the walls. Booking for dinner is advisable, for this is a very popular place. Blackboard menus offer lunchtime sandwiches and ploughman's and more elaborate restaurant-style dishes, such as generous, accurately cooked rack of lamb on rösti with shallots and garlic, or medallions of pork tenderloin in a garlicky tomato sauce. From further afield comes Szechuan monkfish and king prawns with pepper couscous and saffron sauce, while traditional dishes include honey-roast ham hock with carrot and swede mash, and chicken breast with wild mushroom cream. Service is commended as 'swift, polite and efficient'. Three or four Wadworth ales might include 6X, Henry's Original IPA, Summersault, Farmers Glory, or Malt & Hops. Ten wines and two champagnes from the short list are sold by the glass. SAMPLE DISHES: chicken and wild mushroom terrine £6; courgette, pepper and tomato lasagne with salad and garlic bread £7.25; poached pear with butterscotch and caramel ice cream £4.

Licensees Richard and Kathryn Crawford (Wadworth)
Open *11 to 3, 6 to 11, Sun 12 to 3, 6 to 10.30; bar food and restaurant 12 to 2, 6 to 9 (9.30 Fri and Sat, 8.30 Sun and Mon); closed 25 Dec*
Details *Children welcome in family and dining rooms   Car park   Wheelchair access (also WC)   Garden and patio   No-smoking area in bar   No music Dogs welcome   Delta, MasterCard, Switch, Visa*

STANDLAKE   Oxfordshire   map 2

Bell ✿

21 High Street, Standlake OX8 7RH   TEL: (01865) 300784
off A415, 5m SE of Witney

The Bell might look like a quintessentially English pub: a white-washed building with a little garden behind a picket fence in the middle of a peaceful Thames Valley village. The décor within, though, is understated in the best modern sense, with soft lighting and an attractive green and gold colour scheme, with a tiny bar the focus of it all. There are newspapers and board games for those with time on their hands, and the hosts – who may be summoned by a clang of the eponymous bell on the counter if they are not in evidence – are enthusiastically welcoming. This is very much an eating venue (in fact, it might realistically be classed as a gastro-pub), and the cooking is pretty daring in scope. You might begin with Shetland mussels in Thai green curry spices and coconut milk, or curly kale sautéed with bacon and red wine, topped with chargrilled lambs' kidneys and white bean purée. Main courses span the spectrum from skate wings with sauce vierge, to roast partridge in caul served with barley braised with leeks and thyme and a creamy lemon sauce. Some of these dishes turn up in modified portions on the lighter lunchtime menu, alongside items such as corned beef hash, or cured beef with sauerkraut and Gruyère. Dessert might be bread-and-butter pudding with apricots and brandy, or rice pudding spiced with saffron and cardamom and served with mango purée. Morland Bitter is on handpump, together with one or two changing guest beers, perhaps Old Speckled Hen or Bateman XXXB. Otherwise choose from the 20 single-malt whiskies or and ten wines by the glass from an enterprising list that allows a good shout to the New World. SAMPLE DISHES: cream of cauliflower and smoked cheese soup £3; chicken breast stuffed with farmhouse black pudding on tomato sauce £10; marmalade and whisky ice cream with a brandy-snap and caramel oranges £3.75.

Licensees Nicholas Heaney and Barbara Colaço (Greene King)
Open *Mon 6 to 11, Tue to Sun 12 to 3, 6 to 11 (10.30 Sun); bar food Tue to Sat and bank hol Mon 12 to 2.30; restaurant Sun 12 to 2, Tue to Sat 6.30 to 9.30 plus bank hol Sun and Mon 7 to 9; open 25 Dec 12 to 2, 1 Jan 6 to 11*
Details *Children welcome in dining room   Car park   Garden   No smoking in dining room   Background music   Dogs welcome exc in dining areas   Delta, MasterCard, Switch, Visa*

STANFORD DINGLEY   **Berkshire**   **map 2**

Old Boot Inn

Stanford Dingley RG7 6LT   TEL: (01189) 744292
from M4 junction 12 take A340 N towards Pangbourne, then follow signs to Bradfield, then to Stanford Dingley

This friendly and relaxed dining pub is also a local with chatty and welcoming regulars from the pretty, well-kept village. The attractive white-painted brick building proclaims its purpose, past and present, with a sign reading 'eighteenth-century free house'. Two bars, with old-fashioned paintings and prints, have wood-burning fires, and beside one is a giant boot holding the fire irons. The restaurant extends into a non-smoking conservatory, and the blackboard menus also apply in the bars. Two boards list lunch and dinner specials, others the fish of the day and puddings. As bar food you might choose 'lovely, large' local sausages and mash with 'properly cooked, al dente' vegetables. A more formal restaurant meal might start with poached pear and Parma ham, or grilled sardines with lime and ginger vinaigrette. Fish could be Cajun tuna steak on tagliatelle, and typical of meat dishes are pork fillet en croûte with herb and apple stuffing and calvados sauce, or 'generous' Moroccan lamb stew with citrus couscous. Service is 'friendly, quick, but not at all obtrusive'. Ales on draught are likely to be from Brakspear, West Berkshire Brewery, Bass or Archers Ales, and there is Stowford Press cider. Half a dozen wines by the glass, plus another two dozen by the bottle, are fairly priced and carefully chosen. SAMPLE DISHES: chicken and herb terrine £5; lambs' liver and bacon £9; steamed jam suet pudding £4.

Licensee John Haley (freehouse)
Open *11 to 3, 6 to 11; bar food and restaurant 12 to 2.15, 7 to 9.30*
Details *Children welcome   Car park   Wheelchair access (not WC)   Garden and patio   No smoking in conservatory   No music   Dogs welcome   Delta, MasterCard, Switch, Visa*

STANTON WICK   Bath & N.E. Somerset   map 2

▲ *Carpenters Arms*

Stanton Wick BS39 4BX   TEL: (01761) 490202
off A368, ½m W of junction with A37 Bristol to Shepton Mallet road

The eponymous aproned carpenter is seen hard at work with his plane on one side of the inn sign of this picturesque pub in a little village barely 20 minutes' drive from Bath. While the conversion of what was a row of miners' cottages has been slickly done, the place none the less retains the feel of a cosy, friendly local. A bright colour scheme throws into relief the country-pub backdrop of brick walls, low, beamed ceilings and dark wood panelling. Food is served throughout: in the main public bar, in Cooper's Parlour and in the dining room. Blackboard specials augment the printed menus. At its most elaborate, in the dining room, the cooking shows such fashionable flourishes as roast red pepper and goats'-cheese stack with smoked red chilli oil, filo-topped seafood 'symphony' with vanilla fondue, and slow-roast knuckle of lamb on parsnip purée and a spiced redcurrant sauce. More down-to-earth dishes served elsewhere include salmon fishcakes with a good, plain, home-made tomato sauce, or baked flat mushrooms layered with tomato, mozzarella and basil on a bed of chargrilled aubergine. Chips are properly crisp and brown. Sticky toffee pudding and crème brûlée are among the desserts on offer. Handpumped Butcombe, Bass and Wadworth 6X ales are supplemented by the West Country pedigree of Addlestone's naturally cloudy cider, and there is an extensive range of malt whiskies and brandies. Clarets are a speciality on a wine list that offers ten of its listings by the glass. SAMPLE DISHES: locally cured gravad lax with potato and caper salad £6; chargrilled Cumberland sausage on garlic and herb mash with red onion gravy £9; fruit crumble £3.50.

Licensees S.R. Pledge, A.M. Jones and T.S.C. Ruthven (freehouse)
Open *11 to 11, Sun 12 to 10.30; bar food 12 to 2, 7 to 10 (9 Sun);
restaurant Sun 12 to 2, Mon to Sat 7 to 10*
Details *Children welcome in dining room   Car park   Patio   No smoking in 1
dining room   Occasional live music   Dogs welcome in bar   Amex, Delta,
Diners, MasterCard, Switch, Visa   Accommodation: 12 rooms, B&B £60 to
£80*

STARBOTTON   North Yorkshire   map 8

Fox & Hounds

Starbotton BD23 5HY   TEL: (01756) 760269
on B6160, 16m N of Skipton

Despite being right on the road running through a tiny hamlet, this
friendly, rustic pub has spectacular views across the hills. It is deep in
the Yorkshire Dales, and locals are joined by walkers. Floors are flagstoned, some interior walls are natural stone, others painted white
and decorated with plates and copper pans and jugs. The tables are
polished dark wood on iron bases, and while one of the two small
bars is a non-smoking area the other has an open log fire. The short
blackboard menu changes seasonally and might include deep-fried
king prawns, or four-cheese soufflé, followed by rack of lamb, or
mixed-bean and vegetable curry. A reporter chose black pudding in
filo parcels – 'a generous amount' – and found plenty of tender steak
and mushrooms in a main-course pie. Typical of desserts are sticky
toffee pudding and home-made ice cream. On draught are Black
Sheep, Timothy Taylor Landlord, Theakston Old Peculier and
Blackthorn cider, and a handful of wines are served by the glass from
an enterprising list. SAMPLE DISHES: Stilton and apple salad £3.75;
Thai chicken green curry £7.25; chocolate and ginger pudding £3.

Licensees James and Hilary McFadyen (freehouse)
Open *Tue to Fri 11.30 to 2.30, 7 to 10.30, Sat 11.30 to 3, 7 to 11, Sun 12 to
3, 7 to 10.30; bar food 12 to 2, 7 to 9; closed Jan to mid-Feb*
Details *Children welcome in bar eating area   Car park   Wheelchair access
(not WC)   Patio   No-smoking area in bar   Background music   No dogs
Delta, MasterCard, Switch, Visa*

▲ Sea Trout Inn

Staverton TQ9 6PA   TEL: (01803) 762274
WEB SITE: www.seatroutinn.com
off A385, 2m N of Totnes

Named in honour of a splendid fish caught in the River Dart by a
former landlord, this attractive white-painted village inn, dating back
to the fifteenth century, is popular with fishermen and walkers. The
landscaped patio-style garden has a pond and fountain, and the
décor of the rambling lounge area continues the fishy theme with
specimens in showcases. Drinkers in this dining pub may retreat to
the separate poolroom. The conservatory restaurant, overlooking the
garden, offers a three-course set-price menu, not available in the bar.
But there you find a wide range of things, from lunchtime sandwiches to avocado with crispy bacon, burgers, chargrilled venison, or
pork with mustard-seed sauce. Special seasonal dishes might run to
salads, such as poached salmon with roasted red onions and tomatoes, or winter warmers like West Country beef stew with herb
dumplings, or gammon with parsley sauce. A platter of local cheeses
makes a good finish. Ales from the owners, Palmers of Bridport,
include IPA, Dorset Gold and 200. There is farmhouse cider too,
and ten wines by the large or small glass, carafe or bottle, with more
than 20 bottles on the list. SAMPLE DISHES: game terrine £4.25; baked
Brixham plaice £8; maple and walnut Salcombe dairy ice cream £3.

Licensees Nick and Nicky Brookland (Palmers)
Open *11 to 3, 6 to 11, Sun 12 to 3, 7 to 10.30; bar food 12 to 2, 6.30 (7
winter) to 9 (9.45 weekends); restaurant Tue to Sun (exc Tue winter) 12 to 2,
6.30 (7 winter) to 9 (9.45 weekends); no accommodation 24 and 25 Dec*
Details *Children welcome in bar eating area and poolroom   Car park
Wheelchair access (also WC)   Garden and patio   No smoking in dining room
Live music; jukebox   Dogs welcome   Amex, Delta, MasterCard, Switch, Visa
Accommodation: 10 rooms, B&B £39.50 to £76*

Hamilton Arms

School Lane, Stedham GU29 0NZ
TEL: (01730) 812555
WEB SITE: www.thehamiltonarms.co.uk
off A272, 2m W of Midhurst

THAI

Thai dishes are now on many pub menus, but the Hamilton Arms
was one of the first to introduce them, and remains one of very few

pubs which are also authentic Thai eating places. This doesn't deter locals and others from enjoying the bar's pubby atmosphere, real ales and traditional bar meals, such as cottage pie, hamburgers and scampi. The exterior, with a small, flowery terrace for alfresco dining, gives no hint of the ornate interior, where the décor incorporates carved furniture, low tables and stools, displays of Thai handicrafts, and a stall selling oriental foodstuffs. The Thai bar menu illustrates 20 dishes, many with a choice of ingredients. They range from a platter of assorted starters including spring rolls, and pastry-wrapped prawns, to rice- or noodle-based dishes with, for example, beef, oyster sauce, mushrooms and spring onions; and red or green curry. Five vegetarian options include noodles with broccoli, or sweet-sour vegetables on rice. On draught are Ballards Best, Fuller's London Pride and seasonal guests, while bottled beers include Thai Chaing. Devoted seekers of authenticity should try Bangyikhan Distillery's Mekhong Thai rum. The serious, eclectic list of 26 wines includes only one over £20. SAMPLE DISHES: sausage, egg and chips £3.75; honey roast pork with cucumber and two sauces on rice £6.25; fried thick noodles with soya sauce and vegetables £5.50.

Licensee Suhail Hussein (freehouse)
Open *Tue to Sun 11 to 3, 6 to 11, and bank hol Mon lunchtime; bar food and restaurant 12 to 2.30, 6 to 10.30 (9.30 Sun)*
Details *Children welcome in eating areas Car park Wheelchair access (also WC) Garden and patio No smoking in dining room Background music Dogs welcome on leads in bar area only Delta, Diners, MasterCard, Switch, Visa*

STIFFKEY Norfolk map 6

Red Lion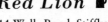

44 Wells Road, Stiffkey NR23 1AJ
TEL: (01328) 830552
on A149, 4m E of Wells-next-the-Sea

'Worn but comfortable' was how one visitor summed up the ambience of this solid, white-painted brick and flint pub on the north Norfolk coast road. It is simply decorated and furnished, with tiled floors, a log-burning inglenook in one of the series of bars, and has the feel of a real old-fashioned pub, even down to an upright piano in one area. It is a popular place with walkers and bird-watchers, who are attracted by the local salt marshes. They come for a menu of hearty rustic cooking that makes the most of local supplies of game and seafood served in generous portions: whole plaice or lemon sole, deep-fried Blakeney whitebait, Norfolk game casserole, roast stuffed breast of pheasant, and mussels, which are provided by a local fisherman. Desserts are mostly traditional pies and crumbles. They also come for the fine beers, all supplied by local breweries – Woodforde's, Adnams and others. Wine drinkers have a choice of eight by the glass. SAMPLE DISHES: mussels in white wine and cider sauce £6; fisherman's pie £7; treacle tart £3.50.

Licensee Matthew Rees (freehouse)
Open *11 to 3, 6 to 11; bar food 12 to 2.15, 6.30 to 9.15*
Details *Children welcome   Car park   Wheelchair access (also WC)   Garden and patio   No smoking in dining room   Occasional live music   Dogs welcome   Delta, MasterCard, Switch, Visa*

STILTON   Cambridgeshire   map 6

▲ *Bell Inn*

Great North Road, Stilton PE7 3RA   TEL: (01733) 241066
WEB SITE: www.thebellstilton.co.uk
off A1, 6m SW of Peterborough

This stone-built coaching inn's place in history was assured back in the early part of the eighteenth century, when a certain type of cheese made its first public appearance here. Nowadays, the Bell is a smart hotel with a rather formal restaurant and uniformed staff, but the Village Bar still manages to generate a pubby feel, thanks to a flagstone floor, exposed stone walls, beams and an open fire. The clientele is a mixture of locals drinking at the bar and people out for a light meal from the modern bar menu. They might be eating marinated artichoke and plum tomato salad, or salmon fishcakes with lemon butter sauce, followed by confit of duck on black pudding and chorizo salad with orange salsa, or moules marinière with crusty bread. Naturally, the famous cheese features in several dishes – in dumplings to accompany beef braised in ale, for example. Over the course of a year, as many as 70 different guest ales will join the regular line-up of JHB (from the local Oakham Brewery), Marston's Pedigree and Greene King Abbot Ale. A constantly changing selection of six decent wines by the glass is also offered. SAMPLE DISHES: chicken satay £5; rack of English lamb with watercress, Stilton, and red onion salad £10.50; sticky toffee pudding £4.

Licensee Liam McGivern (freehouse)
Open *12 to 2.30, 6 to 11, Sun 12 to 3, 7 to 10.30; bar food and restaurant 12 to 2, 6.30 to 9.30, Sun 12 to 2, 7 to 9; open 11 to 1 on 25 Dec*
Details *Children welcome in bar eating area   Car park   Wheelchair access (not WC)   Garden and patio   No-smoking area in bar, no smoking in dining room   Occasional background music   No dogs   Amex, Delta, Diners, MasterCard, Switch, Visa   Accommodation: 19 rooms, B&B £55 to £105*

STOCKLAND   Devon   map 2

▲ *Kings Arms Inn* ❦

Stockland EX14 9BS   TEL: (01404) 881361
WEB SITE: www.kingsarms.net
*signposted from A30 Chard to Honiton road, or from A35 take Shute
garage exit W of Axminster*

A whitewashed, thatched inn in a small village in the east of Devon,
not far from Honiton, the Kings Arms is a homely and comfortable
kind of place. On a stone-built chimney breast in the main bar,
blackboard listings tell what dishes are on offer, but there is also a
full-dress, red-carpeted dining-room with quality napery and handsome high-backed chairs. A wide-ranging menu is offered, on which
many of the expected pub standards crop up, but take their chances
among some rather more unusual items. Smoked ostrich fillet, king
prawn thermidor, lamb rogan josh, pigeon Rossini and monkfish
provençale give some idea of the catholicity of the range, but more
mainstream tastes are catered for with the likes of steak au poivre,
calf's liver and Denhay bacon, and halves of roast duck. Crowd-
pleasing puddings include chocolate truffle torte, banana pavlova
and tiramisù. Look to the handpumps for premium beers such as
Exmoor Ale and Gold and Otter Ale, and a dozen wines by the glass
lead off an exemplary list, on which much care and attention has
been lavished. Classic French wines, particularly mature claret, are a
notably strong suit. A good selection of whiskies is kept too. SAMPLE
DISHES: Pacific prawns in garlic £5; suprême of guinea-fowl £9.50;
blueberry cheesecake £3.50.

Licensees Heinz Kiefer and Paul Diviani
Open *12 to 3, 6.30 to 11.30; bar food and restaurant 12 to 1.45, 6.30 to 9;
closed 25 Dec*
Details *Children welcome in bar eating area   Car park   Wheelchair access
(not WC)   Garden and patio   No smoking in dining room   Live music in bar
weekends; background music in dining room   Dogs welcome exc in eating
areas   MasterCard, Switch, Visa   Accommodation: 3 rooms, B&B £30 to £50*

STOKE-BY-NAYLAND   Suffolk   map 6

▲ *Angel Inn*

Stoke-by-Nayland CO6 4SA   TEL: (01206) 263245
on B1068 5m SW of Hadleigh

This open-plan version of a country pub with only standing timbers
where once there were walls also has massive beams, country prints
and, in the Well Room, exposed brick walls. It is called the Well

Room not because the others are unhealthy, but because of its 52-foot-deep well. The Angel's long-serving former owner Peter Smith sold the Angel in late 2000, and his manager, Michael Everett, is now the licensee. With the chef and other staff remaining the same, it is expected that things should carry on as before, with a daily-changing blackboard menu operating throughout. You might start with fresh dressed crab with homemade mayonnaise, soup of the day or steamed mussels in white wine. Follow perhaps with grilled haddock, plaice or skate, steak and kidney pudding with onion gravy, or more adventurous chicken and king prawn brochette, or roast duckling ballottine with cassis sauce. Steamed apple pudding with vanilla sauce, dark chocolate ganache gâteau, and raspberry Bavarois may be among desserts. The wine list with over 50 bins is interesting and eclectic, and five are sold by the glass. Real beers offered are Greene King Abbot Ale and IPA, plus Adnams Best Bitter. SAMPLE DISHES: homemade fishcakes with remoulade sauce £4; honey glazed roast rack of new season's lamb £11.50; German-style bread pudding £3.50.

Licensee Michael Everett (Horizon Inns)
Open 11 to 2.30, 6 to 11, Sun 12 to 3, 6 to 10.30; closed 25 and 26 Dec, 1 Jan; bar food and restaurant 12 to 2, 6.30 to 9
Details No children   Car park   Patio   No smoking in eating areas   No music No dogs   Amex, Delta, Diners, MasterCard, Switch, Visa   Accommodation: 6 rooms, B&B £48 to £63

STOKE DOYLE   Northamptonshire   map 6

▲ *Shuckburgh Arms*

Stoke Doyle PE8 5TG   TEL: (01832) 272339
WEB SITE: www.shuckburgharms.co.uk
2m SW of Oundle

On a quiet road in a tiny village, this fine seventeenth-century stone-built building with its attractive covering of ivy is a child-friendly place, complete with children's menus (or cut-down portions from the main menu) and, in an outdoor play area, slides, swings and things to climb on. Big people, too, can enjoy the garden, where there are barbecues in summer and plenty of tables for outdoor eating. Inside is a traditional Northamptonshire skittles room and a comfortably furnished bar, with a log fire in season, offering the same menu as the 16-seater dining room, as well as its own snacks at lunchtime. Casseroles are a mainstay, featuring perhaps duck in white wine, with apples and calvados; mixed game with Grand Marnier; wild boar with port and brandy; or devilled kidneys with red wine, port and paprika. Alongside these are a few conventional pub dishes such as scampi, lasagne, chilli, grilled trout, and mushroom stroganoff, and desserts of spotted dick and cheesecake. Real ales might include Greene King IPA and Abbot Ale, Everards Tiger Best, Ruddles Best and County, or Wells Bombardier. Four wines are served by the glass from the 15-bottle list, and three by the half-carafe. SAMPLE DISHES: garlic pâté with melba toast and plum preserve £4.25; sausage Creole casserole £8.25; apple sponge pudding £3.50.

Licensees Paul and Jayne Kirkby (freehouse)
Open *12 to 2 (exc Mon; 3 Sat), 7 to 11, Sun 12 to 3, 7 to 10.30; bar food and restaurant Tue to Sat 12 to 1.30, 7 to 9, Sun 12 to 2*
Details *Children welcome Car park Wheelchair access (also WC) Garden No smoking in dining room No music No dogs Amex, Delta, MasterCard, Switch, Visa Accommodation: 5 rooms, B&B £30 to £50*

STOKE HOLY CROSS   Norfolk   map 6

Wildebeest Arms

82–86 Norwich Road, Stoke Holy Cross NR14 8QJ
TEL: (01508) 492497
from Norwich take A140 Ipswich road; directly after roundabout take the left turn signposted Stoke Holy Cross

Set in a quiet village, the Wildebeest is open-plan inside, with one part set for dining and the other mostly for drinking. The African-themed décor featuring weapons, masks and hanging carpets, as well as the logo of the eponymous herbivore which heads the menu, is not reflected in its content. In fact, the food is in large part Anglo-French with the odd toe dipped in the Mediterranean. Grilled smoked haddock and poached egg comes with chorizo, while saffron risotto accompanies grilled sea bass with aïoli and dressed rocket. Confit of duck with purée roots and shallot jus, and asparagus cappuccino show that today's metropolitan fashions are followed here too. Adnams Best and Courage Best Bitter are on draught; there's also Scrumpy Jack cider. The wine list is a well-balanced selection of about 40 fairly priced bottles; six are sold by the glass. SAMPLE DISHES: twice-baked Gruyère soufflé £5.75; roast duck breast with orange jus, lyonnaise beans and Parmentier potatoes £12.50; hot chocolate fondant with coconut ice cream £4.

Licensee Henry Watt (freehouse)
Open *11 to 11 (10.30 Sun); bar food and restaurant 12 to 2, 7 to 10, Sun 12 to 2.30, 7 to 9.30*
Details *Children welcome Car park Garden No smoking in dining area Background music No dogs Amex, Delta, Diners, MasterCard, Switch, Visa*

STOKENHAM   Devon   map 1

Tradesman's Arms   NEW ENTRY

Stokenham TQ7 2SZ   TEL: (01548) 580313
off A379 Kingsbridge to Dartmouth road, 5m E of Kingsbridge

The tradesmen the name refers to once collected their wares at the
port of Dartmouth and brought their donkeys on the bridle path
along the coast, using the inn as their first night's stopover. It is a
fifteenth-century thatched cottage pub with a simply furnished main
bar complete with stone fireplace, wood-burning stove and heavy
beams. A small dining room is rustic rather than formal in tone, and
the cooking echoes the style. One menu operates throughout,
supplemented by specials on a blackboard, with traditional roasts on
Sundays. Devilled mushrooms, or hot smoked mackerel with horseradish might fire up the taste buds to start, to be succeeded by seared
salmon fillet on a bed of leeks, or roast rack of lamb with redcurrant
sauce. Specials try out a few more experimental ideas: perhaps scallops flamed in brandy with a light onion sauce, or breast of wild
pigeon with chorizo in cream. Puddings are crowd-pleasers – apple
pie with clotted cream, or chocolate torte with vanilla ice cream –
but here, too, an inventive streak brings on creations such as pineapple with black pepper flamed in rum and served with coffee ice
cream. Adnams Southwold and Broadside ales are on handpump,
alongside a guest beer or two, and there's a cider called Ruddy
Turnstone from the Heron Valley. A wealth of single-malt Scotch is
kept, as is Sharpham Vineyard's Devon wine from a short list that
offers up to half a dozen by the glass. SAMPLE DISHES: fish soup with
garlic flutes £3.25; grilled Dover sole £13.50; lemon soufflé £3.50.

Licensees John and Elizabeth Sharman (freehouse)
Open *Wed to Fri and Sun 12 to 3 (2 or 2.30 winter), Tue to Sat 6.30 to 11
(10.30 some evenings winter); bar food 12 to 2, 6.45 to 9 or 9.30; closed 2
weeks some time during year (phone to check)*
Details *Children welcome in dining room lunchtimes only   Car park
Wheelchair access (not WC)   Garden   No-smoking area in bar   No music
Dogs welcome in bar   Delta, MasterCard, Switch, Visa*

STOKE ROW   Oxfordshire   **map 2**

Crooked Billet

Newlands Lane, Stoke Row RG9 5PU   TEL: (01491) 681048
WEB SITE: www.thecrookedbillet.co.uk
off B481 Reading to Nettlebed road, 5m W of Henley-on-Thames

Former customers of this off-the-beaten-track seventeenth-century
inn include Dick Turpin, who was romantically involved with the
landlord's daughter. Nowadays, it is an up-market dining pub
attracting a more salubrious clientele – actors are more likely than
highwaymen – but the rustic interior remains largely unchanged and
has plenty of atmosphere, especially in the evenings when candlelight
is used to good effect. Unusually, there is no bar counter and pints of
Brakspear are brought up from the cellar, where they are drawn
direct from the cask. The extensive, eclectic and adventurous
weekly-changing menu makes a real change from the usual 'pub
grub' without being pretentious about it: starters of chilli-roast baby
squid with coriander and mint on a Greek salad, or grilled goats'
cheese with artichoke hearts, sun-blushed tomatoes and sunflower
seeds might be followed by hake with pan-fried scallops on champ
with watercress and creamy white wine sauce, or roast venison with
spinach, haggis, roast figs and a port, redcurrant and juniper sauce.
Luxury ingredients such as lobster, oysters and caviar are common,
so it may come as a surprise to find that prices are reasonable.
Around 50 wines plus champagnes feature on a wine list, starting at
£12. Seven wines are served by the glass. Diverse live music events
have included jazz, flamenco and boogie-woogie evenings (note that
these usually attract a cover charge). SAMPLE DISHES: pan-fried pigeon
breasts with chorizo and spinach £6.75; confit of local rabbit with
olive oil and garlic mash and tarragon and mustard sauce £13;
Bakewell tart with custard £5.50.

Licensee Paul Clereheugh (Brakspear)
Open *12 to 3.30, 7 to 11.30, Sun 12 to 10; bar food 12 to 2.30, 7 to 10, Sun
12 to 10*
Details *Children welcome   Car park   Wheelchair access (also WC)   Garden
Live or background music   No dogs   MasterCard, Visa*

Hare Arms

Stow Bardolph PE34 3HT   TEL: (01366) 382229
off A10, 2m N of Downham Market

This large Georgian pub puts on a charming outer appearance, with
its improbably tall chimneys, creeper growing up its walls, and doves
populating an ornamental birdhouse on the front lawn. Enter
through the modern conservatory extension, which functions as a
no-smoking dining area, into the spacious main bar, an Aladdin's
cave of bric-à-brac: from prints of sports cars and photographs of
celebrities on the walls to an old spinning wheel and a big brass tele-
scope hanging from the ceiling. The atmosphere is as lively as the
décor, and the place can get very busy. A long menu comprises a
regular list of pub staples, such as lasagne, steak sandwich, and chilli,
plus a page of daily specials, which might include salmon fillet in a
herb crust with hollandaise, or steak and mushroom pie. There is
also a list of basic bar snacks, and no fewer than three blackboards of
desserts. The separate restaurant operates its own à la carte and set-
price menus in similar style. Well-kept beers are from Greene King
plus guests – Badger Tanglefoot, for example – and Much Marcle
Millennium Cider is also stocked. The extensively annotated wine
list runs to around 25 bottles, and six are served the glass. SAMPLE
DISHES: buffalo mozzarella on mixed leaves with tomatoes and basil
£7.50; whole lemon sole with parsley butter £9; apple and mincemeat Bakewell tart with custard £3.25.

Licensees David and Trish McManus (Greene King)
Open *10.30 to 2.30, 6 to 11, Sun 12 to 2.30, 7 to 10.30; bar food 12 to 2, 7
to 10; restaurant Sun 12 to 2, Mon to Sat 7.30 to 9.30; closed 25 and 26 Dec*
Details *Children welcome in family and dining rooms   Car park   Wheelchair
access (not WC)   Garden and patio   No smoking in conservatory; no smoking
in dining room before 10pm   No music   No dogs   Delta, MasterCard,
Switch, Visa*

▲ *Eagle and Child* ✿   NEW ENTRY

Digbeth Street, Stow-on-the-Wold GL54 1BN   TEL: (01451) 830670
WEB SITE: www.theroyalisthotel.co.uk
at junction of A429, A463 and A424, 8m W of Chipping Norton

The culture shock must have been enormous when Alan and
Georgina Thompson transplanted themselves from a trendy restaurant in the Fulham area of London to what has been certified as the

oldest inn in England, which served its first ale as long ago as 947. It now forms the pub arm of the Royalist Hotel, and can be accessed through the hotel reception. A small L-shaped bar and a room with bare stone walls and a flagstone floor have been extended with a conservatory dining area for days when it isn't pleasant enough to sit in the garden itself. 'Jolly good pub food' is what the proprietors set out to offer, and certainly the menu looks like a roll call of dishes answering to that description. Cotswold burger with chips and salad, steak and kidney pie made with Guinness, battered fish and chips with crushed (not mushy – this is Gloucestershire) peas, and locally made sausages with mash and onion gravy all appear to fit the bill. Raw materials are evidently very fine, and the presentation and careful cooking of the food announce that you are in the presence of an accomplished chef. A more ambitious dish such as pan-fried sea bream with saffron risotto and salsa verde only confirms it. You might begin a meal with a soup, such as cauliflower with truffle oil, or an omelette containing fresh crab and Brie, and end it with tarte Tatin with honey and ginger ice cream, or a platter of English farmhouse cheeses like the highly reputed Stinking Bishop and Oxford Blue. Local Hook Norton Best Bitter is on tap and is always joined by a guest beer, perhaps Brains Rev James Original Ale, or Shepherd Neame Spitfire Premium Ale. The wine list is a model of fair-minded concision, with just five whites and five reds, all at £2.95 a glass or £11.95 a bottle. SAMPLE DISHES: smoked haddock with a soft poached egg and pickled cucumber salad £5.25; game pie with champ and braised red cabbage £8; rice pudding with raspberry jam £3.50.

Licensees Alan and Georgina Thompson (freehouse)
Open *11 (12 winter) to 11, Sun 12 to 10.30; bar food 12 to 2.30 (3.30 Sun), 6.30 to 10*
Details *Children welcome   Wheelchair access (also WC)   Garden   No smoking in conservatory   No music   Dogs welcome   Amex, Delta, MasterCard, Switch, Visa   Accommodation: 10 rooms, B&B £45 to £170*

SUMMERHOUSE   Darlington   map 10

Raby Hunt Inn

Summerhouse DL2 3UD   TEL: (01325) 374604
on B6279, 6m NW of Darlington

Not far from Raby Castle you will find this unpretentious stone-built pub, which has been run by the same husband and wife team for nearly 25 years. A friendly atmosphere, excellent-value and uncomplicated lunchtime food (not on Sunday) are the order of the day in the bar. Starter options are limited to soup or pâté, and main courses are various pies, Cumberland sausage, and a roast of the day, plus a selection of daily specials, including a few more pies (steak, ale and Stilton, or game, for example) and perhaps cold poached salmon with salad and new potatoes. There are also salads, sandwiches, burgers and, to finish, things like peach melba, or apple pie with cream. On the real ale front, regular Marston's and Mansfield beers are accompanied by regularly changing guests from small local breweries. Four wines are offered by the glass from the short list. SAMPLE DISHES: ham and pheasant pie £4.75; chicken breast with mustard and mushroom sauce £4.75; banana split £2.25.

Licensees Michael and Barbara Allison (freehouse)
Open *11.30 to 3.30, 6.30 to 11, Sun 12 to 3, 7 to 10.30; bar food Mon to Sat 12 to 2*
Details *Children welcome   Car park   Wheelchair access (not* WC)   *Garden No music   Dogs welcome   No cards*

SUTTON GAULT   Cambridgeshire   **map 6**

▲ *Anchor Inn*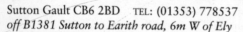

Sutton Gault CB6 2BD   TEL: (01353) 778537
off B1381 Sutton to Earith road, 6m W of Ely

Within 45 minutes of this pub, built in the mid-seventeenth century on the New Bedford River (aka the Hundred Foot Drain), are many attractive East Anglian destinations. Inside, it is so light and airy that on a summer's day it 'feels like eating al fresco'. Around 60 well-chosen wines include some stars (Henschke's Riesling, Château Grand Puy Lacoste Bordeaux) as well as some bargains (starting around the £13 mark). Five wines are listed by the glass and 14 by the half-bottle, and there's an excellent key to style (sweetness/dryness, heavy or light). Somerset cider and local apple juice supplement beers, which include Hobson's Choice from the City of Cambridge brewery, Nethergate IPA and seasonal specials. Starters on the daily-changing menu might take in herring fillets marinated with lemon grass, ginger and cucumber, or grilled dates wrapped in bacon with mushroom sauce. There is game in season – whole roast partridge with bread sauce and game chips, say – or perhaps steak, kidney and Guinness pie. Cheeses, mostly unpasteurised, can be ordered ahead for de-refrigeration, and sweet lovers could go for sticky toffee pudding, or blackcurrant cheesecake. The two-course weekday lunch, at £7.50, might include home-made faggot with sage mash and courgettes, while on Sunday three courses at £16.50 include roasts such as leg of Derbyshire pork, or topside of Dexter beef and Yorkshire pudding. SAMPLE DISHES: lobster ravioli with tomato and garlic dressing £6.50; roast breast of Barbary duck with blackberry sauce £14; organic Jersey cream ice creams £4.

Licensee Robin Moore (freehouse)
Open *12 to 3, 7 (6.30 Sat) to 11 (10.30 Sun); bar food and restaurant 12 to 2, 7 (6.45 Sat) to 9 (9.15 Sat)*
Details *Children welcome in family room   Car park   Wheelchair access (also WC)   Patio   No-smoking area in bar   No music   No dogs   Amex, Delta, MasterCard, Switch, Visa   Accommodation: 2 rooms, B&B £50 to £95*

SUTTON LANE ENDS   Cheshire   **map 8**

▲ *Sutton Hall*

Bullocks Lane, Sutton Lane Ends SK11 0HE   TEL: (01260) 253211
off A523, 2m S of Macclesfield

This must certainly be one of the grander addresses of any pub listed in the Guide. It is part of a sixteenth-century baronial mansion situated at the end of a long drive through lush parkland. Until a little over 30 years ago, the place was a convent, but it is now a hotel with a restaurant, an attractive lawn for outdoor dining, and a pub. However sceptical you might be at first as to its true identity, you will be reassured once through the door. Blackened beams, oak panelling and an ancient bar form the décor, together with a pair of vast open fireplaces, by one of which a suit of armour stands sentinel. Daily-changing blackboard specials, which include puddings, augment the choice on the printed menu. It is a style of homely country cooking that won't frighten the horses, no matter how grandiose the surroundings, offering French onion soup, Welsh rarebit, or chicken and leek pancake with a cheese sauce to start, followed by coq au vin, sirloin steak with mushrooms and onion rings, or mushroom stroganoff with basmati rice. Finish with crème brûlée, toffee and apple flan, or one of the cheesecake variations. Bass, Worthington and Marston are the roll call of familiar names among the draught ales, and four wines are served by the glass from an extensive list. SAMPLE DISHES: moules marinière £4.75; steak and kidney pie with smoked oysters £7; sherry trifle £3.

Licensee Robert Bradshaw (freehouse)
Open *12 to 12; bar food and restaurant 12 to 2.30 (2 Sun), 7 to 10*
Details *Children welcome in family and dining rooms   Car park   Garden Background music   Dogs welcome   Amex, Delta, Diners, MasterCard, Switch, Visa   Accommodation: 10 rooms, B&B £75 to £95*

Prices quoted in an entry are based on information supplied by the pub, rounded up to the nearest 25 pence. These prices may have changed since publication and are meant only as a guide.

Old Swan

Swan Bottom HP16 9NU   TEL: (01494) 837239
off A413, between Great Missenden and Wendover, just N of The Lee

The tiny hamlet of Swan Bottom enjoys its peaceful life partly because it is on a single-track road. The wavy line of the Old Swan's long roof hints at the pub's sixteenth-century origin, and the flag-stone-floored interior has a cosy atmosphere. The sign saying 'duck' hanging from a beam is not the Swan's homage to its relatives but valuable advice on safeguarding your head. It is a rural pub where locals drink and people come to lunch or dine in the green-carpeted eating area. The blackboard menu changes twice daily, and lunch dishes such as chicken liver and brandy pâté, or stir-fried marinated squid with herb and courgette salad can also be starters in the evening. More substantial lunch dishes might include deep-fried plaice fillets (fresh fish is a speciality), or, in winter, game pie. The dinner menu might offer pan-fried duckling breast in red wine and spiced plum sauce, or poached turbot with lemon hollandaise. Typical desserts are blackberry and apple crumble, and chocolate roulade with raspberry coulis. Adnams Best Bitter, Brakspear Bitter, and Hook Norton Generation are on draught, with guests including Shepherd Neame Spitfire. Belgian Hoegaarden wheat beer is kept too, and three wines are sold by the glass from a list of around 20 bottles. SAMPLE DISHES: tomato, mozzarella and basil salad £4.75; fillet of cod roasted in olive oil and rock salt on a bed of spinach with creamed potatoes £9.50; elderflower and rhubarb syllabub £3.

Licensees Sean and Katie Michaelson-Yeates (freehouse)
Open *Tue to Fri and bank hol Mon 12 to 3, 6 to 11, Sat 12 to 11, Sun 12 to 10.30 (8 winter); bar food (exc Sun evening) 12 to 2, 7 (6.30 summer) to 9*
Details *Children welcome in eating areas   Car park   Wheelchair access (also WC)   Garden   No smoking in dining room   Occasional live music   Dogs welcome exc in dining room   Delta, MasterCard, Switch, Visa*

Darby's 🍺

1–2 Elsing Road, Swanton Morley NR20 4NY
TEL: (01362) 637647

Dating from the early eighteenth century, Darby's has been a pub since the late 1980s, when it was converted from a pair of cottages. Inside it aims for a relaxed, family-friendly atmosphere, offering a no-smoking family room (there is also a children's adventure play area in the beer garden) as well as the traditional main bar, which is characterised by inglenooks and exposed ceiling beams. Plenty of fish and seafood appear on the menu, done up in a variety of styles: New Zealand mussels sautéed in garlic butter with cream and tomato, pan-fried trout, or a medley of prawns, melon and Parma ham with mint dressing, for example. There are also plenty of meaty offerings, ranging from chicken and cashew nuts in oyster sauce to pan-fried pigeon breast with red wine and mushroom sauce. Baguettes, vegetarian options and a children's menu are also possibilities. Beers are a fine selection comprising six regulars from Adnams, Badger, Woodforde's and Greene King as well as two guest ales. A short list of wines is reasonably priced, and there are three by the glass. SAMPLE DISHES: Zanzibar salad (avocado, prawns and mint on lettuce with vinaigrette and croûtons) £5; chargrilled pork steaks with mustard and mushroom sauce £7; lemon cheesecake £3.25.

Licensees John Carrick and Louise Battle (freehouse)
Open *Mon to Fri 11.30 to 3, 6 to 11, Sat 11 to 11, Sun 12 to 10.30; bar food and restaurant Mon to Fri 12 to 2.15, 6.30 to 9.15 (9.45 Fri), Sat 12 to 9.45, Sun 12 to 9*
Details *Children welcome in family and dining rooms   Car park   Wheelchair access (also WC)   Garden   No smoking in dining and family rooms   Live or background music   Dogs welcome in bar   Delta, MasterCard, Switch, Visa*

SWILLAND   Suffolk   map 6

Moon & Mushroom Inn 🍺 NEW ENTRY

High Road, Swilland IP6 9LR
TEL: (01473) 785320
*from Ipswich take B1077 N; pub on left
approx 1m past Witnesham*

VEGETABLES

The Goodalls bought this country pub ten years ago, when it was known as the Half Moon. It has a modest but attractive terrace with a couple of tables in front and a larger garden with overflow car park to the rear. The long, beamed main bar is decorated in rural style with cushioned benches, and there is a separate eating area just off it. Special events nights include gerbil racing (we kid you not) and a board is available on request for the playing of shove ha'penny, should anybody still be able to find one to shove. Good country cooking is the order of the day, and the drill is to go up to the counter, where it is served out to you, and then help yourself to vegetables. The latter – deemed 'excellent' by an inspector – might comprise seven choices, including broccoli in white sauce, Brussels sprouts, red cabbage and roast potatoes. These might accompany beef with dumplings, pork in Stilton sauce, minted lamb, halibut

Mornay or mushroom stroganoff. At lunchtimes, a variety of ploughman's platters is available, and the home-made puddings will bring
out the schoolboy or girl in most: ginger and toffee pudding with
butterscotch sauce and vanilla ice-cream is 'really yummy'. The same
might be said of the range of real ales on offer, which encompasses a
changing rollcall of East Anglia microbreweries. Nethergate Umbel
Ale, Buffy's Hopleaf and Norwich Terrier, Wolf Coyote Bitter, and
Woodforde's Wherry and Norfolk Nog have all been sighted,
dispensed straight from barrels behind the bar. In addition to that,
there is a list of nigh on 20 wines, of which nine may be had by the
glass, with the New World well represented. SAMPLE DISHES: smoked
mackerel ploughman's £3.50; goose breast casseroled with cranberries £6.75; treacle sponge with custard £3.

Licensees Clive and Adrianne Goodall (freehouse)
Open *Mon to Sat 11 to 2.30, Tue to Sat 6 to 11, Sun 12 to 2.30, 7 to 10.30;
bar food Tue to Sat 12 to 2, 6.30 to 8.15*
Details *No children   Car park   Wheelchair access (also WC)   Garden and
patio   No smoking in 1 room   No music   Dogs welcome on leads in bar area
only   No cards*

TADPOLE BRIDGE   Oxfordshire   map 2

▲ *Trout at Tadpole Bridge* ✿

Tadpole Bridge, Buckland Marsh SN7 8RF | NEW ENTRY |
TEL: (01367) 870382
*approx 1½m N of A420 Faringdon to Oxford road; follow signs to
Buckland Marsh; continue a further ½m beyond Buckland Marsh to
river*

The Trout is what one reporter termed a 'very bare-bones pub', the
plain exterior giving way to an equally unadorned bar. Despite being
located in a tiny village comprising only two buildings by a bridge
over the Thames, it is a popular place attracting a mixed clientele
and can get very busy. The atmosphere is clearly that of an old-fashioned pub, and most customers are there to drink, but food is not
what might be termed traditional pub grub – indeed, the chef is
noted for his fertile imagination. Among starters might be hot
smoked duck breast served with pickled apples, and equally inventive
main courses run to roast loin of lamb stuffed with chicken mousse,
served with wild mushrooms, redcurrant jus and couscous; more
conservative tastes are also catered for in the shape of chargrilled
sirloin of Aberdeen Angus with game chips and herb butter. Two
first-class regular real ales, Fuller's London Pride and Archers Village
Bitter, are joined by one or two guest ales. Eight house wines are
available by the glass or bottle; the full list offers a good selection
and prices are reasonable throughout; there are no half-bottles but

they are happy to open full bottles and only charge for what you drink. Other drinking options include home-made sloe gin, chilli vodka and cherry plum brandy. SAMPLE DISHES: deep-fried crispy scallops with Parma ham and chilli tartare sauce £6 or £12; Parmesan-crumbed chicken breast filled with mozzarella, basil and spinach with creamy pesto noodles £10.25; coffee parfait rolled in praline with blackcurrant coulis £4.

Licensee Christopher James Green (freehouse)
Open *11.30 to 3, 6 to 11.30, Sun 12 to 3.30, 7 to 10.30 (closed Sun evening Sept to Easter); bar food and restaurant 12 to 2, 7 to 9; Sun 12 to 2.30; closed Christmas to New Year*
Details *Children welcome   Car park   Wheelchair access (also WC)   Garden No smoking in dining room   Background music   Dogs welcome   Amex, Delta, MasterCard, Switch, Visa   Accommodation: 6 rooms, B&B £60 to £80*

TARRANT MONKTON   Dorset   map 2

▲ *Langton Arms* 🍺

Tarrant Monkton DT11 8RX   TEL: (01258) 830225
WEB SITE: www.thelangtonarms.co.uk
on Tarrant Valley thoroughfare, ½m off A354, 4m NE of Blandford Forum

---

With its peaceful location by the village church, this seventeenth-century thatched pub is 'everybody's idea of a traditional village inn'. The exterior is adorned with roses and hollyhocks in summer, while an inglenook adds to the charm of the rustic tiled lounge and public bars. The focus of the kitchen is meat, much of which comes from the farm run by the pub's owners, plus plenty of game in season. Wide choice is offered on the extensive printed menus and black-board, the range covering jacket potatoes, baguettes, and old favourites such as fish and chips, or steak and ale pie, as well as more interesting dishes: perhaps salmon with grain mustard and dill baked in filo, and wild rabbit with tarragon and mustard. The bistro in a converted stable block holds occasional theme evenings: game, Spanish, or Thai, for example. Beers are a regularly changing selection that might include Exmoor Wild Cat, Ringwood Old Thumper, and Hampshire Lionheart. Around half a dozen wines by the glass, written on a blackboard, also change often. The pub has a skittle alley, which functions as a family room at lunchtimes. SAMPLE DISHES: deep-fried breaded mushrooms £3.75; game pie with red wine and redcurrant gravy £8; banana split £3.

Licensees James and Barbara Cossins (freehouse)

Open *11.30 to 11, Sun 12 to 10.30; bar food 11.30 to 2.30, 6 to 9.45;*
restaurant Sun 12 to 2.30, Wed to Sat 6 to 9.45
Details *Children welcome in family room and dining room   Car park*
Wheelchair access (not WC)   Garden   No smoking in family room or dining
room   Jukebox   Dogs welcome in bar only   MasterCard, Switch, Visa
Accommodation: 6 rooms, B&B £50 to £70

TETBURY   Gloucestershire   map 5

▲ *Gumstool Inn*   NEW ENTRY

Calcot Manor, Tetbury GL8 8YJ   TEL. (01666) 890391
WEB SITE: www.calcotmanor.co.uk
on A4135, 3m W of Tetbury

'A great place to go when you want to relax, not dress up and eat
good food which is reasonably priced,' was how one regular summed
up the attraction of the pub part of Calcot Manor. The setting has
been described as 'divine', the sandy limestone buildings being
surrounded by rolling Cotswold countryside; the Gumstool is separate from the main house and has grand views of the mature formal
gardens. Inside, it sports contemporary décor – pale walls hung with
pastel prints and light wood furniture – though the flagstone floor is
a reminder of the true age of the place. The lengthy menu, also in a
modern eclectic style, changes regularly and always offers some
interesting specials, a 'wonderful' version of spaghetti and meatballs
for example. On the bar food menu typical starters might be grilled
portabello mushrooms topped with goats' cheese and ciabatta croûte,
or Thai spiced crab cakes with cucumber and crème fraîche,
followed by braised lamb shank with pickled lemon, tomato and
oregano, or Gloucestershire Old Spot pork and beer sausages with
spring onion mash. The separate Conservatory Restaurant has a
more formal setting, and its menu (also available in the bar) offers
dishes such as Cornish fish soup, or beef bresaola, followed by slow-
roasted confit duck, or grilled marinated filet mignon of yellow fin
tuna. Courage Best and Directors, as well as Wickwar Brand Oak
Bitter are the regular ales; these are joined by a seasonal guest. The
wine list is short but offers decent breadth of choice, and most wines
are also available in two sizes of glass. SAMPLE DISHES: spring roll
with shitaki, bok choy, noodles and plum sauce £5.25 or £7.50;
seafood paella £10.75; spotted Dick and custard £4.

Licensees Paul Sadler and Richard Ball (freehouse)
Open *Mon to Fri 11.30 to 2.30, 6 to 11, Sat and Sun 11.30 to 11; bar food*
Mon to Fri 12 to 2, 7 to 9.30, Sat and Sun all day; restaurant Mon to Fri 12
to 2, 7 to 9.30, Sat and Sun 12 to 9.30

Details *Children welcome   Car park   Wheelchair access (also WC)Garden and patio   No-smoking area in bar   Background music   No dogs   Amex, Delta, Diners, MasterCard, Switch, Visa   Accommodation: 28 rooms, B&B £120 to £190*

THELBRIDGE   Devon   map 1

▲ *Thelbridge Cross Inn*

VIEWS

Thelbridge EX17 4SQ   TEL: (01884) 860316
WEB SITE: www.westcountry-hotels.co.uk/thelbridgexinn
off B3137 from Tiverton, before Witheridge, take left fork on to B3042 for 2m

This ivy-covered stone and cob building, once a coaching inn, dates from the eighteenth century, and its elevated site provides fine views of Dartmoor. Modernisation inside combines open-plan areas with log fires and old photographs as decoration, and the restaurant tables have splendid deep-red cloths with white overcloths. The menu springs few surprises, and there are some pleasingly retro notions, such as prawn cocktail, salmon and a boiled egg with mayonnaise, veal in a Madeira and mushroom sauce, and peach melba. There are ploughman's, cheese melters, and lunchtime grills, with perhaps poached salmon with a shrimp sauce, or chicken breast with lemon cream sauce and asparagus among main courses. In addition, black-board specials may run to slowly roasted lamb shank with red wine and rosemary sauce and honeyed root vegetables. Among desserts might be lemon and ginger flan, or chocolate truffle torte. Butcombe Bitter and Bass are on draught; also Stowford scrumpy and organic ciders. House wines are sold by the glass along with country wines. SAMPLE DISHES: mussels in garlic butter £3.75; rabbit, bacon and mushroom pie £6.75; rum baba gâteau £3.

Licensees William and Ria Ball (freehouse)
Open *11.30 to 3, 6.30 to 11, Sun 12 to 3, 7 to 10.30; bar food and restaurant 12 to 2, 7 to 9; closed 26 Dec*
Details *Children welcome   Car park   Wheelchair access (also WC)   Garden No smoking in dining room   Background music   No dogs   Amex, Delta, Diners, MasterCard, Switch, Visa   Accommodation: 7 rooms, B&B £35 to £60*

If you disagree with any assessment made in the Guide, write to tell us why -- The Which? Guide to Country Pubs, FREEPOST, 2 Marylebone Road, London NW1 4DF.

THORGANBY   North Yorkshire   map 9

▲ *Jefferson Arms*

Main Street, Thorganby YO19 6DA
TEL: (01904) 448316
3m N off A163, 5m S of York

It's a far yodel from Zurich to this village where locals appreciate the
range of dishes offered by their Swiss chef-landlord, Adolf Rapp.
Rösti is a speciality, and 12 varieties of that potato dish feature in
both bar and restaurant menus with embellishments as different as
Swiss pork sausages and onion sauce in the St Galler version, to
prawns, herbs, green peppercorns and scrambled egg in the
Luzerner. Even more exotic are two ways with ostrich: the 'Tessiner'
version comes as mini-burgers with a mozzarella filling, while
'Strauss rösti' waltzes to the table sliced in a red wine and cranberry
sauce. The bar menu is more traditional, offering scampi or haddock
and chips, omelettes, burgers and sandwiches, although Euro-touches
appear in calamari, stuffed jalapeño peppers and lasagne verde. Five
or six wines are offered by the glass from French, Italian, Spanish,
German and New World selections. Home-based beers include Black
Sheep Best Bitter and John Smith's Bitter, while Hürlimann Stern
Brau lager represents Switzerland. Combining the hospitality of both
cultures is the warm welcome from Mrs Rapp and the friendly
customers of the unassuming, attractive, solidly brick-built pub.
SAMPLE DISHES: Swiss cheese croquettes £4; veal Zurich style £13;
crème caramel £3.

Licensee Margaret Rapp (freehouse)
Open *Tue to Sat 12 to 3, 6 to 11, Sun 12 to 10.30; bar food and restaurant
12 to 2, 6 to 9, Sun 12 to 2.30, 6 to 8.30*
Details *Children welcome in bar eating area   Car park   Wheelchair access
Garden and patio   No smoking in dining room and conservatory   Background
music   Dogs welcome exc in restaurant   Delta, Diners, MasterCard, Switch,
Visa   Accommodation: 2 rooms, B&B £35 to £55*

THORNBOROUGH   Buckinghamshire   map 5

Lone Tree   NEW ENTRY

Bletchley Road, Thornborough MK18 2DZ   TEL: (01280) 812334
*just off A421; approx 3m E of Buckingham pub is signposted on left;
do not go into village*

The Lone Tree is signposted just off the A421 connecting Milton
Keynes and Buckingham, and stands alone surrounded by fields
outside the village of Thornborough. Parts of it date back to the end

of the seventeenth century, although an extensive renovation – documented in photographs on the walls – was undertaken in the late 1990s. It owes its name to a tree that once stood in splendid isolation just near, but that was knocked down at the end of the Great War. Inside is one big open space with classical music quietly playing to a casual, well-heeled clientele. Old beams and a pair of old brick fireplaces, only one of which is functional, announce the age of the place. Printed and blackboard menus deal in traditional pub food, with the odd novelty popping up (DLT is a duck variation on the familiar sandwich). Thai fishcakes with a proper dipping sauce make an appealing starter or main dish, while the hearty of appetite might opt for a 16oz steak that comes in red wine gravy enriched with Stilton. For the rest, there are king prawns in garlic butter, lamb shanks in redcurrant and rosemary gravy with creamy leek mash, or pork glazed with honey and mustard. Vegetarians might go for stuffed mushrooms or a grilled goats' cheese salad, and all may well finish with apple and almond pie or banoffi cheesecake. The Hook Norton range of hand-pumped beers, as well as the handsomely named Lump Hammer, is kept, as is Weston's cider. Regularly changing guest beers are worth looking out for too. Six wines are served by the glass from a short, but cannily chosen list. SAMPLE DISHES: smoked salmon and prawn salad with lemon and dill vinaigrette £4.50; duck breast and crispy duck leg on dauphinoise potatoes with honey, apricot and Grand Marnier gravy £12; jam roly-poly and custard £3.

Licensees Pete Towler and Rebecca Szamlevski (freehouse)
Open *12 to 3, 6 to 11, Sun 12 to 3, 6.30 to 10.30; bar food 12 to 2.30, 6.30 to 9.30*
Details *Children welcome if eating   Car park   Wheelchair access (also WC) Garden and patio   No smoking in dining room   Background music   Dogs welcome by arrangement   Delta, MasterCard, Switch, Visa*

THORNHAM   **Norfolk**   map 6

▲ *Lifeboat Inn*

FISH

Ship Lane, Thornham PE36 6LT
TEL: (01485) 512236
WEB SITE: www.lifeboatinn.co.uk
follow A149 from Hunstanton; in Thornham turn left into Straithe Rd, then right into Ship Lane

---

Only intervening fields prevent the sea quite reaching the doors of this large, smart 'smugglers' ale house' (as the inn describes itself), but its harvest extends deeply into its bar menus. There you might find crab and ginger filo parcels, lemon sole, fishcakes, cod and chips, and a pie of prawns, smoked haddock, salmon and cod. The speciality is Brancaster mussels poached in white wine and cream, with garlic and onions. But it's not all fish, for Lifeboat chicken liver and garlic pâté is another speciality starter, and roulade of chicken breast, pork ribs, venison sausages plus a variety of steaks, are offered too. Children get a decent choice, and puddings of the day might include banoffi pie. Short walks to the beach, and longer ones along it and the dunes, pine woods and cliff tops, plus a warm welcome, all make it a favourite for dogs and their owners. Surviving sixteenth-century comforts inside include open fires. There is a walled patio garden, and beside it a conservatory with a vine said to thrive on Greene King Abbot Ale: lucky because this is one of the real ales kept, along with that brewery's IPA, Woodforde's Wherry, Adnams Bitter and a guest. About two dozen wines feature on the serviceable list, and four house wines – one red and three white – are served by the glass. The separate restaurant offers two- and three-course meals in the evenings, from £18. SAMPLE DISHES: whitebait £4.75 or £7.50; fried Whitby wholetail scampi and chips; £8 fruit crumble with custard £3.50.

Licensees Charles Coker and Julia Galligan (freehouse)
Open *11 to 11, Sun 12 to 10.30; bar food 12 to 2.30, 6.30 to 9.30; restaurant 7 to 9.30*
Details *Children welcome   Car park   Wheelchair access (also WC)   Garden and patio   Smoking in restaurant discouraged while others eat   Occasional live music   Dogs welcome exc in restaurant   MasterCard, Switch, Visa Accommodation: 12 rooms, B&B £40 to £86*

THORNTON　　West Yorkshire　　　　　　　　　　　map 8

Ring O' Bells 🏵 🍇

212 Hill Top Road, Thornton BD13 3QL　　TEL: (01274) 832296
WEB SITE: www.theringobells.com
just off B6145, 3m W of Bradford

It looks like the traditional country inn it is, but the many awards for food listed on menus and wine list confirm its intentions as a serious eating pub. A non-smoking conservatory was added since the last edition of the Guide, and in the bar area crimson and maroon colours provide a warm atmosphere attracting a mature clientele who appreciate the pleasant, unrushed service and the range and quality of the freshly prepared meals on offer. The long à la carte menu and daily specials are offered in both bar and restaurant. Specials might include white fish and sweet potato chowder, escalope of bacon loin on black pudding and cherry tomato hash with parsley sauce, and the day's pasta, pie and sausages. Reporters have enjoyed beef pie with onions, Guinness and oysters served in puff pastry with a rich, excellent gravy, and chicken breast stuffed with feta cheese and served with a red wine sauce and large sauté field mushroom. The menu might also run to more exotic dishes, such as fried marlin on coriander couscous with paw paw, mango and guacamole salad. Chips and vegetables have been highly praised. Desserts, says the menu, 'are made to order', and might take in school pud (steamed suet roly-poly with vanilla custard) or a duo of brandy-snap cones with vanilla ice cream in one and orange sorbet with a butterscotch sauce in the other. Beer lovers can happily choose from Black Sheep Best Bitter and Special Ale, and Webster's Green label, while care and attention to detail make for a particularly exciting wine list. From over 100 wines, the choice is as inspiring at the good-value £12 mark as it is for higher-echelon labels, and globally the options are superb. Ten wines are available by the glass, and as well as useful tasting notes, there's an excellent coding system to indicate the style of the wine and whether its organic, vegetarian or vegan. SAMPLE DISHES: goats' cheese, borlotti beans and walnut salad in a Parmesan basket £4.50; arni kleftico (slow-roasted lamb shoulder with mint and oregano) £12; warm sponge with dates, brown sugar, walnut and caramel sauce £4.25.

Licensee Ann L. Preston (freehouse)
Open *11 to 4, 5.30 to 11, Sun 11 to 4, 6.30 to 10.30; bar food and restaurant 12 to 2, 5.30 (6.30 Sat and Sun) to 9.30; closed 25 Dec*
Details *Children welcome Car park Wheelchair access (also WC) Patio No smoking in dining room and conservatory Background music No dogs Delta, MasterCard, Switch, Visa*

THORNTON WATLASS   **North Yorkshire**   map 9

▲ *Buck Inn* 🍺

Thornton Watlass HG4 4AH   TEL: (01677) 422461
off B6268 midway between Masham and Bedale

In summer you may see cricket being played in the shade of sycamore trees on the green in front of this stone-built pub; it is in one of Yorkshire's prettiest villages, which also features an eleventh-century church. Inside, it is comfortably furnished in traditional style, and the décor is a mixed bag of foxes' and otters' heads, old bottles and cartoons. 'Masham rarebit', made with local ale and Wensleydale cheese and topped with good bacon, typifies the cooking style: 'plain but done well' was one reporter's verdict. Also listed on the blackboard menu, which serves both bar and dining room, might be mussels in creamy pesto sauce, lamb hotpot, and deep-fried Whitby cod – it largely depends on what local produce is available. The more elaborate dinner menu might also take in Singapore noodles with prawns, or spicy roast duck breast with soy and honey sauce, while Sunday lunch brings on a traditional roast with

Yorkshire pudding. Handpumped real ales are from Yorkshire breweries Black Sheep, Theakston, John Smith's and Tetley, plus a guest
from a local independent such as Hambleton or Cropton. There are
also about 30 wines, five of which come by the glass, and a range of
more than 40 Scotch single malts, including many of the more
unusual brands. SAMPLE DISHES: chicken livers in garlic £4; beef and
beer curry £7.25; sticky toffee pudding £3.

Licensee Michael Fox (freehouse)
Open 11 to 11, Sun 12 to 10.30; bar food and restaurant 12 to 2, 6.30 to
9.30; closed evening 25 Dec
Details Children welcome   Car park   Wheelchair access (also WC)   Garden
No smoking in dining room   Live or background music   No dogs   Amex,
Delta, Diners, MasterCard, Switch, Visa   Accommodation: 7 rooms, B&B £38
to £58

THORPE LANGTON   Leicestershire   map 5

Bakers Arms

Thorpe Langton LE16 7TS   TEL: (01858) 545201
off B6047, 4m N of Market Harborough

The Bakers Arms, a sixteenth-century thatched cottage inn with a
garden at the back with picnic tables, is at the heart of the tranquil
village of Thorpe Langton. The atmosphere within is convivial and
welcoming, with many little nooks and alcoves where you can install
yourself. The blackboard menus advertise the kind of cooking that
goes with this ambience: home-made pâté with chutney and toast,
fishcakes with tartare sauce, roast shank of lamb with colcannon and
roast parsnips, or Stilton-crusted fillet steak served with a selection
of mushrooms. More mushrooms might go into a filo parcel together
with spinach and ricotta to make a vegetarian main course, and a
meal concludes with the likes of bread-and-butter pudding, or winter
fruits served warm with Greek yoghurt. Tetley is pretty much the
only game in town when it comes to handpumped ale, but one of the
winter specialities is hot mulled wine. Around half a dozen wines are
served by the glass from a 40-strong list. SAMPLE DISHES: warm salad
of new potatoes, bacon and black pudding £4; duet of salmon and
monkfish with crevettes and a prawn jus £12.25; apricot tarte Tatin
with cream £3.75.

Licensee Kate Hubbard (freehouse)
Open Sat and Sun 12 to 3, Tue to Sat 6.30 to 11; bar food 12 to 2 (3 Sun),
6.30 to 9.30
Details No children   Car park   Wheelchair access (not WC)   Garden   No-
smoking area in bar   Occasional live music   No dogs   Amex, Delta,
MasterCard, Switch, Visa

THRESHFIELD   North Yorkshire   map 8

▲ Old Hall Inn

Threshfield, Grassington BD23 5HB   TEL: (01756) 752441
on B6265, 1m W of Grassington

Like most of the houses in this tiny Dales village the old coaching inn
is stone-built with a steep, tiled roof. The atmosphere is traditional,
the décor not quite, for it includes chamber pots hanging from the
bar ceiling, some old maps, and good new local paintings, and by the
fireplace with its wood-burning range an elegant wooden cigarette
machine offers Woodbines for one shilling per packet. A conservatory leads to the garden, and at the other end of the building is the
main dining area with wooden furniture, and dried flowers in the
fireplace. An inspector was impressed by the service and 'very good-
quality home cooking' of food, which is mainly English in style,
although chicken curry, and nasi goreng (Indonesian fried rice) have
crept in. Large, meaty Cumberland sausages came on 'equally tasty'
mustard mash, and steak and mushroom pie contained very good
meat in 'delicately flaky' pastry. A good way to finish is treacle
sponge pudding with custard, which was 'polished off with enthusiasm' by a visitor. Five regular ales and a guest might include Timothy
Taylor Landlord and Best, Theakston's XB and Cool Cask, and John
Smith's Cask Bitter. There are six wines by the glass from a short list.
SAMPLE DISHES: grilled black pudding with bacon and a horseradish
cream sauce £4.50; grilled gammon with egg or pineapple £7; apple
pie £3.45.

Licensees Mr and Mrs R.C. Matthews (Pub Enterprises)
Open *11.45 to 3, 6 to 11.30, Sun 12 to 3, 6 to 10.30; bar food and
restaurant 12 to 2.30, 6 to 9*
Details *Children welcome in dining room   Car park   Wheelchair access (also
WC)   Garden and patio   Background music   Dogs welcome   MasterCard,
Switch, Visa   Accommodation: 3 rooms, B&B £20 to £40*

TILFORD   Surrey   map 3

The Hankley 🍺   NEW ENTRY

Tilford Road, Tilford GU10 2DD   TEL: (01252) 792236

Situated in the heart of well-heeled Surrey, The Hankley is a white-
painted country pub with a big garden, a terrace and children's play
area. It is a mere stone's throw from the Hankley Common golf
course, if you fancy a round before lunch – an unimpeachably Home
Counties setting that even the presence of a palm tree and pampas
grass in the grounds does nothing to dispel. Inside is a large L-shaped

room with small windows and gingham curtains, an embalmed fish in a glass case and, apparently undaunted by its proximity, some live goldfish drifting about in their tank. The printed menus advertise a varied mixture of tried-and-true pub dishes, from chicken liver pâté with onion marmalade and French bread, to sirloin steak with chips, and from Madras chicken curry with poppadums and chutney, to classic cottage pie. A good range of sandwiches at lunchtime takes in ham with Dijon mustard as well as crispy Chinese duck with hoisin sauce, spring onions and cucumber. Blackboard fish specials might well be beer-battered cod or scampi with chips. A lunchtime bacon and scallop salad followed by beef, Guinness and mushroom pie under a puff pastry top was rated very highly by one visitor. Choose from favourite desserts such as lemon tart, crème brûlée, or sticky toffee pudding. Around six real ales are offered, including Hog's Back TEA, Harvey's Sussex Best, and fff Alton Pride, plus Thatcher's cider. Hoegaarden and Riegele lager (the genuine article) are also served, as are four wines by the glass. SAMPLE DISHES: warm goats'-cheese salad with toasted pine-nuts £5; Lancashire hotpot £7.50; chocolate torte £3.75.

Licensee William Redford (freehouse)
Open *11.30 (12 winter) to 11, 12 to 11; bar food 12 to 2.30, 7 to 9.30, Sun 12 to 3.30*
Details *Children welcome   Car park   Wheelchair access (not WC)   Garden and patio   Occasional live music, or background music   Dogs welcome MasterCard, Switch, Visa*

TILLINGHAM   Essex   map 3

▲ *Cap & Feathers* 🍺   NEW ENTRY

South Street, Tillingham CM0 7TJ   TEL: (01621) 779212
on B1021, 5m NE of Burnham-on-Crouch

On the quiet main street of Tillingham, an out-of-the-way village of clapboard and brick houses, is the Cap & Feathers, also clapboard, once three cottages, the oldest dating from the mid-fifteenth century. Bend low to enter a 'lovely, old real pub', with old beams, brickwork and wooden sideboards, tables, chairs and benches. This is one of two pubs owned by the local Crouch Vale Brewery, so two or three of its beers are always on draught – Gold, Best or IPA – plus a couple of guests, and Thatcher's scrumpy. Everything is very friendly and informal; food ordered at the bar is brought to the table by one of the chefs. The blackboard menu offers mainly conventional pub food, described by a reader as fresh and well cooked, and served in generous portions. Mixed grill includes calf's liver, kidney, gammon, pork chop and rare steak, all accurately timed, and a wedge of

Tillingham pie, with beef cooked in Crouch Vale beer, is accompanied by 'brilliant' chips. There are regular fish nights when the menu might include spicy prawns on naan bread, or salmon carpaccio followed by grilled sea bass with soft egg noodles, or whole plaice marinière. SAMPLE DISHES: smoked salmon with avocado and prawns £5; whole-tail scampi with chips and salad £6.25; orchard pie with custard £2.50.

Licensee Anthony Burdfield (Crouch Vale Brewery)
Open *Mon to Fri 11 to 3, 5.30 to 11, Sat 11 to 11, Sun 12 to 10.30; bar food and restaurant 12 to 2.15, 7 to 9.30 (9 Sun)*
Details *Children welcome in family room   Car park   Wheelchair access (not WC)   Garden and patio   No smoking in dining room   No music   Dogs welcome   Delta, MasterCard, Switch, Visa   Accommodation: 3 rooms, B&B £30 to £40*

TILLINGTON   West Sussex   map 3

▲ *Horse Guards Inn* ✿

Tillington GU28 9AF   TEL: (01798) 342332
WEB SITE: www.horseguardsinn.co.uk
just off A272, 1m W of Petworth

No, it is not named in honour of members of the regiment who play polo at Cowdray Park or on the other nearby fields. The name is much older than polo in England and may go back to the Napoleonic period. But polo players do come here, as do many others looking for fine food and drink in an elegant well-kept inn with original pine panelling, antique furniture and open fires. Flowers and candles on the tables, and the question on entering, 'Have you a reservation?', confirm that this is a dining pub. As well as sandwiches, lunchtime snacks include ham with bubble and squeak and fried eggs, and savouries such as Welsh rarebit with bacon or soused herrings on toast. The sophisticated à la carte menu might offer pan-fried scallops and pancetta with a garlic and herb leaf salad, or assiette of marinated fish with celeriac rémoulade, while calves' liver and bacon is lifted by beignets of sage. The day's specials might include such fish as skate wing with raspberry beurre noisette and, in season, game such as roasted partridge 'properly garnished'. Pudding lovers will find around ten on offer, mostly along traditional lines, from perhaps lemon meringue pie to pear and apple crumble. Badger Best Bitter and Wadworth 6X are on tap. The 46-strong wine list offers ten 'fruit-first' house wines by the large glass (from £2.95) and ten 'classics' by the half-bottle. There are also full tasting notes and winery profiles to browse through. SAMPLE DISHES: grilled sardines £5.25; pan-fried duck breast with spicy sausage and date sauce £15.75; steamed treacle sponge pudding £4.25.

Licensee Aidan F. Nugent (freehouse)
Open *11 to 3, 6 to 11, Sun 12 to 3, 7 to 10.30; bar food and restaurant 12 to 2, 7 to 10*
Details *Children welcome in bar eating area; no children under 7 evenings Small car park   Garden and patio   No smoking in dining room   No music Dogs welcome in 1 bar area only   Amex, Diners, MasterCard, Switch, Visa Accommodation: 3 rooms, B&B £72 to £82*

TIPTON ST JOHN   Devon   map 1

▲ *Golden Lion Inn*   NEW ENTRY   **RIVERSIDE**

Tipton St John EX10 0AA   TEL: (01404) 812881
village signposted off B3176 between Ottery St Mary and Sidmouth

Standing in the village centre, beside the River Otter, this plain white-painted inn dates from 1903, and was once a railway pub with the line running through the garden. There is a rear terrace with a pergola and seating, while inside it is very traditional with dark wooden tables. The Lion is part of a small group whose flagship is the Anchor at Cockwood (see entry), and the formula takes in a long list of real ales, and an even longer menu, laid out according to main ingredients. It lists, for example, eight mussel dishes; seven sorts of fishcake and scallops; six meat and game suet puddings; and five ways each of venison, pheasant, duck, rabbit and lobster. Starters, bar snacks, steak, pork, chicken, lamb, and fish dishes fill another page or two. And in case that's not a wide enough choice, a blackboard provides five daily specials – maybe Irish rabbit stew, or seafood omelette. On draught are Bass, Fuller's London Pride, Wadworth 6X, Old Speckled Hen plus Scrumpy Jack cider. A shortish wine list, with ten by the glass, is backed by a 'reserve list' of hundreds more, and there are 25 malt whiskies. SAMPLE DISHES: lamb's liver pâté £4; pigeon pie £5.50; raspberry jam roly-poly (or 11 other varieties) £3.

Licensee T. Morgan (Heavitree Inns)
Open *summer 11 to 11(10.30 Sun), winter 11 to 3, 6 to 11 (10.30 Sun); bar food and restaurant 12 to 2.30 (Sun lunch available 'all afternoon'), 6.30 to 9.30*
Details *Children welcome up to 9pm   Car park   Wheelchair access (also WC) Garden   No smoking in dining room   Background music   Dogs welcome exc in restaurant   Amex, Delta, Diners, MasterCard, Switch, Visa Accommodation: 2 rooms, B&B £20 to £40*

TIRRIL   Cumbria   map 10

▲ *Queens Head*

BREW PUB

Tirril CA10 2JF   TEL: (01768) 863219
WEB SITE: www.queensheadinn.co.uk
on B5320, 2m S of Penrith

Dating from 1719, this large, whitewashed roadside inn was once
owned by Wordsworth – it has a signed debenture on display in the
bar to prove the fact. Among its other attractions is the Tirril
Brewery, opened on the premises in October 1999, exactly 100 years
since the original Tirril Brewery was closed. Under the guidance of
landlord Chris Tomlinson, it produces John Bewsher's Best Bitter
(named after the man who bought the pub from the Wordsworths),
Thomas Slee's Academy Ale, and Charles Gough's Old Faithful; a
local guest beer is also usually on offer. Food here is also above average, the lunchtime bar menu offering a wide range of snacks, from
jacket potatoes to stuffed pitta breads, pasta dishes and main courses
such as Thai chicken curry. The restaurant menu, which changes
every six months and is also available in the bar, goes in for grilled
black pudding with mustard sauce, chicken breast stuffed with
Cumberland sausage, and brewer's pudding (a suet pudding filled
with steak and ale). To finish, there might be peach crème brûlée, or
you could try the selection of local cheeses. Most of the 20 wines are
under £15, and eight more, including a pudding wine, are available
by the glass. SAMPLE DISHES: smoked chicken salad £3.75; shoulder of
Lakeland lamb with redcurrant gravy £9.25; steamed chocolate
pudding £3.

Licensees Chris and Jo Tomlinson (freehouse)
Open *Mon to Fri 12 to 3, 6 to 11, Sat 12 to 11, Sun 12 to 10.30; bar food
and restaurant Mon to Sat 12 to 2, 6 to 9.30, Sun 12 to 2, 6.30 (7 winter)
to 9*
Details *Children welcome   Car park   Patio   No smoking in dining room
Occasional live or background music; jukebox   Dogs welcome in bar only
Amex, Delta, MasterCard, Switch, Visa   Accommodation: 7 rooms, B&B £30
to £50*

TITLEY   Herefordshire   map 5

▲ *Stagg Inn* 🏵🏵 🍺 🍇   NEW ENTRY

Titley HR5 3RL   TEL: (01544) 230221
on B4355, NE of Kington
WEB SITE: www.kc3.co.uk/stagg

LOCAL PRODUCE

In a charming, picturesque village, the Stagg Inn has a warm and welcoming atmosphere, and staff are friendly and efficient. The lower bar area is strong on natural colours, with a wood-burning stove, half-timbered walls and closely set ceiling beams thickly hung with mugs, while a log fire burns in the upper area, reached via a couple of steps. Chef and co-owner Steve Reynolds was trained by the Roux brothers, and he applies his considerable skills to the excellent produce of Herefordshire: organic pork, bacon and sausages come from small local farms, as do duck, free-range poultry and lamb, and fish and seafood are delivered twice a week from Cornwall. Beers are from Hobsons brewery in nearby Cleobury Mortimer, supplemented by guests such as Tomos Watkin Cwrw Haf. The main menu is chalked up on blackboards in both bar and restaurant, and the cooking style is appealing, sophisticated and modern. A typical day's options might include salmon fishcakes with preserved lemons and chive beurre blanc, rack of lamb with fennel and garlic purée, or Trelough duck breast with caramelised grapefruit. There are also more straightforward steaks, and the bar has a list of lighter meals, such as prawn and smoked salmon risotto, crispy duck leg with cider sauce, or steak sandwich with chips and garlic mushrooms. Finish with a selection from the board of 12 unpasteurised British cheeses, mostly local, some organic; otherwise opt for a dessert such as warm spiced compote of winter fruits with creamed rice. Eight house wines at £1.70 a glass kick off a very reasonably priced wine list. There's an additional page of slightly more expensive chef's selections, and those with deeper pockets won't be disappointed by what's on offer. Over 60 wines on the main list, including around a dozen half-bottles, offer plenty to choose from, from Château Kirwan Margaux to Trapiche's oak cask Malbec, with some older vintages adding complexity. SAMPLE DISHES: seared scallops with creamed leeks and black pepper oil £5.50; hare confit with Madeira sauce and beetroot gratin £12.50; brown sugar hazelnut pavlova with banana and butterscotch £3.50.

Licensee Nicola Holland (freehouse)
Open *Tue to Sat 12 to 3, 6.30 to 11, Sun 12 to 3, 7 to 10.30; bar food (exc Sat evening and Sun lunchtime) 12 to 2, 6.30 to 10; restaurant 12 to 2, 6.30 to 10; closed first week Nov*
Details *Children welcome Car park Garden No smoking in dining room No music Dogs welcome in bar exc Sun lunchtime Delta, MasterCard, Switch, Visa Accommodation: 2 rooms, B&B £30 to £70*

TORCROSS Devon map 1

Start Bay Inn

FISH

Torcross TQ7 2TQ TEL: (01548) 580553
on A379 Dartmouth to Kingsbridge coast road

Paul Stubbs is approaching his quarter-century at the Start Bay Inn, a period in which he has never tired of diving for scallops and fishing for such things as plaice and bass, so that the denizens of Torcross may be plentifully supplied with the freshest seafood. This is the rock-solid reputation of this thatched, white-fronted inn positioned beside the beach at the southern end of Slapton Sands, opposite a freshwater lagoon and bird sanctuary. Variously furnished inside with old oak benches, a brick fireplace and black-painted beams, it may not be the most elegant place, but it is the quality of that fish that has people flocking here from miles around. Crab and prawn cocktails, deep-fried squid, and various species of white fish either lightly battered or fried in garlic butter are the mainstay of the menus, while posher things such as turbot, skate, red mullet or John Dory are becoming more frequent. High rollers might opt for one of the mixed seafood platters with mixed salad, potato salad and coleslaw, while those not so inclined might try one of the steaks, or one of the Italian- or Indian-style vegetarian dishes. Snacks and a children's menu are also available, as are the likes of spotted dick and treacle sponge to finish. Ciders from Addlestone's and Heron Valley sit alongside Flowers and Bass ales on draught, and there is a serviceable international wine list, with seven by the glass. SAMPLE DISHES: smoked mackerel with salad garnish £3.50; monkfish tails in garlic butter £7.25; chocolate sponge pudding with chocolate sauce £3.

Licensee Paul Stubbs (Heavitree)
Open *11.30 to 11 (11.30 to 2.30, 6 to 11 winter), Sun 12 to 2.30, 6 to 10.30; bar food summer 11.30 to 10.30, winter 11.30 to 2, 6 to 9.30*
Details *Children welcome in family room Car park Patio No-smoking area in bar, no smoking in dining room Jukebox Dogs welcome No cards*

TREBURLEY Cornwall map 1

Springer Spaniel

Treburley PL15 9NS TEL: (01579) 370424
on A388 halfway between Launceston and Callington

This unassuming cream-painted roadside pub is a warm and friendly place offering above-average food, and readers also praise it for its relaxing and convivial atmosphere. A wood-burning stove in a large recessed fireplace warms the neat and tidy bar, which has a parquet floor and is furnished and decorated simply but comfortably, with rustic benches and tables, and prints on cream walls. Another room has a sofa, easy chairs and various games, and a couple of steps from the bar lead to the beamed dining area. One menu, running to several pages, is offered throughout. Among fish dishes might be scallops sautéed with bacon and shallots, or salmon with parsley sauce; pastry dishes have included Cornish crab pasty, and steak and kidney pie. Other main-course options might feature pan-fried duck breast with apple and blackcurrant sauce, or grilled lamb chops with mint and redcurrant sauce. There are also various salads and vegetarian options and a blackboard of daily specials, such as lambs' kidneys with grain mustard sauce. On the drinks front, Springer Ale is brewed specially for the pub by Cornish brewery Sharp's; their Doom Bar Bitter is also available. The wine list runs to approximately 40 bottles from around the world, with nine served by the glass. SAMPLE DISHES: soused Orkney herrings £4.50; pan-fried sirloin steak in Stilton and cream sauce £10; lemon mousse £4.

Licensees Colin and Jackie Philips (freehouse)
Open *11 to 3.30, 5.30 to 11, Sun 12 to 3.30, 6 to 10.30; bar food and restaurant 12 to 2, 6 to 9*
Details *Children welcome   Car park   Wheelchair access (also WC)   Garden No smoking in dining room before 10pm   No music   Dogs welcome in bar Delta, MasterCard, Switch, Visa*

TREEN   Cornwall   map 1

▲ *Gurnard's Head Hotel*   NEW ENTRY

Treen TR26 3DE   TEL: (01736) 796928
WEB SITE: www.cornwall-online.co.uk/gurnards-head
on B3306 approx 6m NW of St just

SETTING

The hotel is in spectacular moorland, close to the coastal footpath, making it a much-used and welcome stop for walkers. On the walls inside are photographs showing the pub before modernisation: now it's still an inviting and unpretentious place, with free live music some nights of the week, but neither Muzak nor fruit machines. Efficient, friendly service adds to the feel-good factor. The same menus are available in the large bar area and the separate dining room that leads off it. Bar specials might include venison terrine with beetroot confit, or 'extremely fresh' Cornish crab claws with garlic mayonnaise, while the printed regular menu offers Cornish seafood broth (a house speciality), and minted haloumi cheese, followed by pigeon breasts pan-fried with bacon, onions and mushrooms, or eponymous gurnard fillets grilled with fennel butter. Sauté lamb's liver and bacon with rosemary jus was 'a great winter-evening dish', and mainly local cheeses are an alternative to exciting desserts such as 'thunder and lightning' (vanilla ice and black treacle with clotted cream). On tap are well-kept Truro-brewed Skinner's Knocker Ale, Flower's Original and Scrumpy Jack cider. Two wines of the month and five of the 16 on the list, most of them priced below £13, are offered by the glass. SAMPLE DISHES: rillettes of pork £4.50; whole grilled Megrim sole £11; special bread-and-butter pudding £4.

Licensees Ray and Joy Kell (freehouse)
Open *12 to 3, 6 to 11, Sun 12 to 4, 7 to 10.30; open Aug usually all day; bar food and restaurant 12 to 2.30, 6.30 to 9.15 (food available usually all day Aug); closed 25 Dec evening*
Details *Children welcome in dining-room Car park Garden and patio No-smoking area in bar Live music Dogs welcome Amex, MasterCard, Switch, Visa Accommodation: 6 rooms, B&B £20 to £60*

TRISCOMBE Somerset map 2

Blue Ball Inn ❧ NEW ENTRY

Triscombe, TA4 3HE TEL: (01984) 618242
signposted off A358 between Taunton and Minehead

This eighteenth-century pub on the edge of the Quantocks with views over the Vale of Taunton has been refurbished and improved since the new licensees took over in 1998. Originally three thatched cottages, it offers a warm welcome in its low-beamed, carpeted main bar, which has a large inglenook in which you can sit. Well-behaved children are welcomed, as are 'not too dirty' dogs. There is no separate restaurant but attractive menus and good cooking based on largely locally sourced ingredients: game comes from local shoots, beef, eggs and herbs from local farms, and fish from Brixham. Baguettes are available at lunchtimes, and regularly changing blackboards at lunch and dinner might veer towards the classic simplicity of fish and chips, or lamb loin with whortleberry sauce, or offer more imaginative dishes. Reporters have been impressed by hand-dived scallops with different sauces, as well as roast monkfish in Parma ham, and grilled black bream with olive and coriander tapénade. Meat eaters might consider roast partridge with Seville orange, juniper and thyme; or fillet steak Béarnaise; and home-made desserts might take in treacle and lemon tart or vanilla-bean ice cream. Service is 'friendly, chatty and nothing-too-much-bother'. Cotleigh Tawny Bitter is on tap, along with two guests which might include Young's Special, Bass or Hop Back Summer Lightning, as well as local farm cider. All wines under £20 on the 400-strong list are available by the glass – there are many to choose from. On the main list,

Petaluma Chardonnay and Pewsey Vale Riesling are good examples
of the excellent wines available from Australia; Italian Masi Amarone
proves there's an eye on wine trends as well; and Opus One from
Napa shows determination to include even the fashionable, hard-to-
get Californian wines. SAMPLE DISHES: Jerusalem artichoke and mushroom soup £3; Triscombe pheasant breasts with caramelised apples
and a calvados sauce £8.75; prune and Armagnac tart £3.25.

Licensees Paddy Groves and Sally Harvey (freehouse)
Open *12 to 3, 7 to 11, Sun 12 to 2.30, 7 to 10.30; bar food 12 to 1.45, 7 to
9; closed 25 Dec and evenings 26 Dec and 1 Jan*
Details *Children welcome   Car park   Garden   Occasional live music   Dogs
welcome by arrangement   No cards*

TROUTBECK   Cumbria   map 8

▲ *Queens Head Hotel* ✿ 🍺

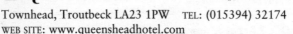

Townhead, Troutbeck LA23 1PW   TEL: (015394) 32174
WEB SITE: www.queensheadhotel.com
at start of Kirkstone Pass, 2½m from junction of A591 and A592

The grey slate roofs and white walls of this old coaching inn look
dramatic, but its views over the Troutbeck Valley and Applethwaite
Moors are even more striking. On the walls of the maze of rooms
and cosy alcoves are interesting old local photographs, while a
carved four-poster bed is part of the bar counter. Bar meals are
served at lunch and dinner, and the Mayor's Parlour Restaurant –
where tables can be booked – is open evenings only; the same menus
operate throughout. On the set-price three-course menu you might
find teriyaki chicken with carrot and leek julienne, followed by
salmon in garlic and herb cream on fettuccine. The dishes on the
carte and the daily specials are similarly ambitious. Typical are
smoked duck breast on tabbouleh with sweet grain mustard dressing,
grilled red bream fillet on buttered balsamic lentils with herb and
garlic ricotta, or Barbary duck breast on creamed celeriac with blackberry and plum jus. Desserts are listed on blackboards, and at
lunchtime baguettes are also on offer. A good choice of real ales –
normally four or five are 'on' at any one time – includes Coniston
Bluebird, Boddingtons Bitter, Jennings and guests. Wine lovers will
find plenty of well-priced bottles among the 30 listed. Around half a
dozen are offered by the small or large glass (£1.80 and £2.50
respectively), and just about every wine producing country is represented. SAMPLE DISHES: smoked and home-cured salmon layered with
filo with a honey and lemon dressing £5; spicy lamb meatballs with
rice and chilli dressing £6.25; passion-fruit and mango cheesecake
£3.75.

Licensees Mark Stewardson and Joanne Sherratt (freehouse)
Open *11 to 11, Sun 12 to 10.30; bar food 12 to 2, 6.30 to 9; restaurant 6.30 to 9; closed 25 Dec*
Details *Children welcome   Car park   Wheelchair access (not WC)   Patio No-smoking area in bar   Background music   Dogs welcome   Delta, MasterCard, Switch, Visa   Accommodation: 9 rooms, B&B £47.50 to £75*

TUCKENHAY   Devon   map 1

▲ *Maltsters' Arms* 🍺

WATERSIDE

Bow Creek, Tuckenhay TQ9 7EQ
TEL: (01803) 732350
off A381, 2½m S of Totnes

Long, winding, narrow country lanes lead to the remote but very attractive setting of this old stone inn right on the bank of Bow Creek. Inside, the main room is divided into two areas, one a traditional bar, the other given over to dining; beyond is a snug with a small log-burning fire, a collection of pewter tankards and prints of the Battle of Waterloo adding decorative touches. Real ale and cider are taken seriously here: the range includes Princetown Dartmoor IPA, Exe Valley Devon Glory and Heron Valley cider; while a dozen wines are available by the glass from a list of around 50. Colourfully decorated menus offer plenty of choice and variety. Starters range from squid sautéed in herbs, onion and sambuca to a platter of smoked duck and chicken with air-dried ham, while main courses run from traditional game casserole (albeit with non-traditional ostrich as well as pigeon, wild boar and venison) to roast monkfish tail with bacon and sun-dried tomatoes, and some fairly unusual dishes like mixed vegetable chilli with Pernod. The children's menu deserves special mention: in place of the usual chicken nuggets and fish fingers are grilled salmon fillet, cottage pie and pan-fried chicken breast. Regular 'events' at the pub have included a 'Tuckenhay Tandoori' evening, with a special Indian menu and live sitar music. SAMPLE DISHES: Dorset mussels and Armande clams in cream and vanilla £5; whole sea bass baked with olive oil and herbs £13.25; apple and apricot crumble £3.75.

Licensees Denise and Quentin Thwaites (freehouse)
Open *summer 11 to 11, Sun 11 to 10.30; winter Mon to Fri 11 to 2.30, 6 to 11, Sat 11 to 11, Sun 11 to 10.30; bar food and restaurant 12 to 2.30, 6.30 to 9.30 (all day July and Aug); open 25 Dec 12 to 2 (no food)*
Details *Children welcome in family room   Car park   Wheelchair access (not WC)   Patio   Occasional live music   Dogs welcome   Delta, MasterCard, Switch, Visa   Accommodation: 6 rooms, B&B £50 to £100*

Bull and Butcher 🍇

Turville RG9 6QU   TEL: (01491) 638283
between B480 and B482, 5m N of Henley-on-Thames

A walk up the hill to the windmill opposite should guarantee that you work up enough of an appetite to manage the generous portions of excellent pub food offered at this 'lovely little place' – and if the village looks familiar, it could be because it is the setting for TV's *The Vicar of Dibley*. The small seventeenth-century half-timbered inn is next to the thirteenth-century church, and tables and chairs set among the fruit trees on the front lawn provide the setting for occasional barbecues in summer. Although that suggests a degree of informality, the approach to food is serious and ambitious. The blackboard menus may not offer as much choice as some other establishments, but this is a case of quality over quantity. Reporters have commended 'excellent' sausages and 'absolutely delicious' liver and bacon, and the star of one meal was a starter of chargrilled squid on a mound of crunchy peppers, carrot, radish and tomatoes with lots of garlic, oil and balsamic vinegar. 'It would have graced a good London restaurant.' Regular beers are from the Brakspear range, plus Coniston Bluebird Bitter and a couple of Westons ciders. Every wine on the 36-strong list is offered in two sizes of glass, as well as by the bottle from just under £10. It's all there, from classic claret to Casablanca Chilean Chardonnay, well-presented, and with a few less-ordinary choices besides. SAMPLE DISHES: beef pastrami on rye bread £6; breast of duckling with sweet chilli sauce, rösti and vegetables £13; summer pudding and clotted cream £4.

Licensee Nicholas Abington Abbott (Brakspear)
Open *11 to 3, 6 (6.30 Sat) to 11, Sun 12 to 5, 7 to 10.30; bar food 12 to 2.30 (2 Mon and Tue), 7 to 9.45, Sun 12 to 4*
Details *Children welcome by arrangement   Car park   Garden   No-smoking area in bar   No music   Dogs welcome   Delta, MasterCard, Switch, Visa*

Three Crowns Inn   NEW ENTRY

LOCAL PRODUCE

Ullingswick HR1 3JQ   TEL: (01432) 820279
off A465 between Hereford and Bromyard

'Set back from a lane in the middle of nowhere, not even in Ullingswick', writes a reporter of this attractive small pub. The front is half-timbered and red brick, with cider presses in the forecourt. It is fresh and pleasing inside, with dried hops strung on big old beams and little else to clutter the simple rooms. An up-market dining pub, it offers no bar snacks beyond Monkland cheese ploughman's. Other lunch dishes might be omelette Arnold Bennett, or grilled cod with curry butter. Starters on the blackboard could include ambrosia of chicken liver with morels and grapes, or mussels with ginger, black beans and spring onions. Much use is made of produce from local sources, as in rosemary-crusted Marches lamb with creamed garlic and a bacon and leek quiche, or roast partridge with Puy lentils. Vegetables are organic, and puddings might run to lemon tart with mascarpone. Hobsons Best Bitter is kept, plus guests from local microbreweries such as Teme Valley and Wye Valley; Bulmers Traditional is supported by local ciders such as Dunkertons and a bottled still cider. Up to a dozen wines are sold by the glass. SAMPLE DISHES: scallop, crab and mussel pithiviers £5; beef, stout and mustard sausages with mash £6; chocolate and prune soufflé cake £4.

Licensees Derrick and Sue Horwood, and Brent Castle (freehouse)
Open *Wed to Mon 12 to 2.30 (3 Sun), 7 to 11 (10.30 Sun); bar food 12 to 2, 7 to 9.30 (9 Sun); closed 2 weeks from 25 Dec*
Details *Car park   Wheelchair access (also WC)   Garden and patio   No-smoking area in bar   Occasional live music   No dogs   Delta, MasterCard, Switch, Visa*

ULVERSTON **Cumbria** map 8

▲ *Bay Horse Hotel* 🏵 🍇

Canal Foot, Ulverston LA12 9EL   TEL: (01229) 583972
WEB SITE: www.thebayhorsehotel.co.uk
off A590, 8m NE of Barrow-in-Furness, take Canal Foot turn in Ulverston, then next signposted left turn following lane to pub

The restaurant is at the heart of this highly professional operation, a seventeenth-century inn on the Leven estuary with lovely views over Morecambe Bay. Bar food is served only at lunchtimes amid a preponderance of pictures, brass and copper. The menu goes well beyond pub standards, however, with soups, pâtés, or perhaps mushrooms in tomato, cream and brandy sauce on a peanut butter croûton for starters. Main courses might include smoked salmon, leek and water chestnut quiche, chicken, chive and Stilton sausage with Cumberland sauce, and a puff pastry pie of braised lamb, apricots and ginger. Readers have praised simple beef and mushroom pie and kedgeree from the daily specials board. Real ales are from Jennings, Marston's, Theakston and Thwaites, and the long and interesting wine list bases itself on the New World, with particular attention paid to Australia and South Africa. There's plenty of choice around the £15 a bottle mark, and while Meerlust Chardonnay, Vasse Felix Shiraz, Thelema Cabernet Sauvignon might be more threatening to the bank account, their presence makes a welcome sight. Six wines are served by the glass. SAMPLE DISHES: Galia melon with air-dried ham and Cumberland sauce £6.25; venison burger with onion marmalade, sage and apple sauce £9; orange and Grand Marnier crème brûlée £4.50.

Licensee Robert Lyons (freehouse)
Open *11 to 11, Sun 12 to 10.30; bar food Tue to Sun 12 to 2; restaurant Tue to Sat L 12 to 1.30, all week D 7.30 for 8 (1 sitting)*
Details *Children welcome in bar eating area   Wheelchair access (also WC) Garden   No smoking in dining room   Background music   Dogs welcome MasterCard, Switch, Visa   Accommodation: 9 rooms, D,B&B £90 to £170*

UMBERLEIGH   Devon   map 1

▲ *Rising Sun*   [NEW ENTRY]

Umberleigh EX37 9DU   TEL: (01769) 560447
on A377 9m S of Barnstaple

This substantial seventeenth-century inn is in a peaceful village on the River Taw. The accommodation is regularly full of anglers fly-fishing for salmon and trout, but local drinkers and diners also lend solid support. Simple furnishings and an open fire are found in the main bar, together with the expected fishing memorabilia, and there is also a separate dining room. It would be odd indeed if some of those river fish didn't end up on the menu, and, sure enough, there are salmon fishcakes with ginger and spring onion to start, followed perhaps by whole grilled trout filled with almonds and fresh herbs. Specials on a blackboard in the bar might well include carrot, orange and coriander soup, beef bourguignon with tagliatelle, a generous portion of grilled goats' cheese and pepper bruschetta, or maybe a hot Thai curry with prawns and cod. Lunchtime snacks, such as sandwiches, jacket potatoes and ploughman's, are dealt with on a separate menu. Puddings plough the sticky toffee, lemon posset and apple crumble furrow to good effect. Bass is on handpump plus a guest, which might be Cotleigh Tawny Bitter, Barum XTC or the Clearwater Brewery's Cavalier Ale, while the outward-looking wine list, which includes eight by the glass, makes a strong feature of New World wines. SAMPLE DISHES: baked pear filled with goats' cheese and wrapped in prosciutto £5.50; fillet of smoked haddock on creamed spinach with a poached egg and chive butter sauce £9.50; crème brûlée £3.75.

Licensees Charles and Heather Manktelow (freehouse)
Open *to 11, Sun 12 to 10.30; bar food and restaurant 12 to 2, 7 to 9; closed 25 Dec*

Details *Children welcome in bar eating area Car park Wheelchair access (not WC) Patio No smoking in dining room Background music Dogs welcome in bar Delta, MasterCard, Switch, Visa Accommodation: 9 rooms, B&B £40 to £77*

UPTON   Nottinghamshire   map 5

French Horn

Main Street, Upton NG23 5ST   TEL: (01636) 812394
on Southwell to Newark road, 5m from Newark

In the centre of an attractive village where National Trust-owned Upton House has pictures by Stubbs, Canaletto and El Greco, this local was a farmhouse when it was built in the eighteenth century. As proof, look at the back garden, a paddock with rustic benches and farmland views. The restaurant is upstairs in the pantiled former barn, and its menu is available in the bar, but not the converse. The bar offers lunchtime sandwiches and jacket potatoes, or main dishes along the lines of chicken and cashew nut stir-fry, steak and ale pie, or deep-fried fillet of cod with mushy peas. Dishes on the restaurant menu bring together some unusual combinations, such as fillet of pork rubbed in garlic and thyme on sauté potatoes with tomato coulis, or roast venison with basil and orange sauce on fried spring onion mash. Daily specials include a fish catch of the day, and there are five vegetarian dishes. Adnams and Marston's Pedigree are regular ales, and the guest might be Old Speckled Hen. Six wines are offered by the glass. SAMPLE DISHES: crab claws sautéed with shallots £4.75; wild boar steak £9.50; bread-and-butter pudding £3.

Licensee Joyce Carter (Pubmaster)
Open *11 to 11, Sun 12 to 10.30; bar food and restaurant Mon to Sat 12 to 3, 6.30 to 9.30, Sun 12 to 9*
Details *Children welcome Car park Garden Occasional background music No dogs MasterCard, Switch, Visa*

UPTON BISHOP   Herefordshire   map 5

Moody Cow

Upton Bishop HR9 7TT   TEL: (01989) 780470
WEB SITE: www.moodycow.co.uk
at crossroads of B4224 and B4221, 4m NE of Ross-on-Wye

Two swallows don't make a summer and two moody cows don't make a herd, but this and her younger sister at the Wykham Arms in Sibford Gower (see entry) make waves locally. The stone-built pub's

flowery patio is good for dining in fine weather; otherwise choose
between the carpeted bar, the wooden-floored Fresco or the two-
level restaurant in a former barn, which the owners describe as
having a 'church-like ambience'. Daily specials include fresh fish,
such as whole plaice with prawns, and perhaps 'a beautifully
presented, generous portion' of roast local turkey with apricot and
chestnut stuffing. The long menu is common to both bovines. There
are no bar snacks, but you can browse on a small portion of pasta, or
another starter, perhaps deep-fried Brie with cranberry and red wine
sauce. Main dishes include slow-roasted half-shoulder of lamb, and
veal escalope cordon bleu. Ales kept are Arkell's 2B, Hook Norton
Best Bitter and a guest, and there is also Stowford Press cider. Nine
house wines are served by the glass. SAMPLE DISHES: seafood chowder
£4; cod and chips (served in newspaper on request) £8.75; steamed
syrup sponge with custard £4.50.

Licensee James Lloyd (freehouse)
Open *Tue to Sat 12 to 2.30, Mon to Sat 6.30 to 11, Sun 12 to 3, 7 to 10.30;*
bar food and restaurant (exc Sun and Mon evenings) 12 to 2, 6.30 to 9.30
Details *Children welcome   Car park   Wheelchair access (also WC)   Patio*
No smoking in dining room   Occasional live or background music   Dogs
welcome in bar   Amex, Delta, Diners, MasterCard, Switch, Visa

UPTON SCUDAMORE   Wiltshire   map 2

▲ *Angel Inn* ❦   NEW ENTRY

Upton Scudamore BA12 0AG   TEL: (01985) 213225
Upton Scudamore signposted off A350 Warminster to Westbury road

Hidden away in a tiny village just off the A350 and A36, this
sixteenth-century coaching inn, restored in the late 1990s, ranks well
among the new breed of modern dining pubs. A walled terrace has
attractive wooden tables and benches under umbrellas, and, inside,
the main bar area is light, airy and spacious, with high beamed ceilings, terracotta-coloured walls and scrubbed pine tables with a
mixture of chairs, while the lower dining area is equally tasteful.
Well-trained and friendly staff take meal orders at table and serve
innovative pub food. For example, you might find buttered asparagus with a soufflé of 'smelly' (the menu's description) French cheese,
smoked haddock boudin with light curry sauce, a tart of Gruyère,
leeks and mushrooms with orange and saffron salsa, and salt-roasted
cod with pancetta and lemon-scented carrots. An inspector enjoyed
crème brûlée of goats' cheese with a 'pesto' of smoked salmon
followed by 'delicious' duck confit with garlic mash. The lunch menu
runs from baguettes to smoked haddock fishcakes with parsley
butter, merguez sausages with mash, and steak, egg and chips.

Butcombe and Wadworth 6X are kept, plus guests such as Bath Gem
Bitter, or Tisbury Archibald Beckett. Seven house wines are available
by the glass (two sizes), beginning with an appealing-sounding
Chilean Sémillon at £1.90 for 125ml, and going on to an interesting
Gamay Noir from the trendy Fairview estate in South Africa. The
main list stays mostly under £20 and has an interesting range of
food-friendly choices from France and New Zealand in particular.
SAMPLE DISHES: chicken tikka salad with banana chutney £5; breast of
guinea fowl with calf's liver, bacon and swede purée £11.50; cherry
custard tart with apricot sauce £4.

Licensees Charlie Barkshire and Sharon Scott (freehouse)
Open *12 to 3, 6 to 11, Sun 12 to 3, 7 to 10.30; bar food 12 to 2, 7 to 9.30
(9 Sun); closed 25 Dec*
Details *Children welcome   Car park   Wheelchair access (not WC)   Garden
No-smoking area in dining room   Occasional live or background music   Dogs
welcome in bar   Delta, MasterCard, Switch, Visa   Accommodation: 9 rooms,
B&B £49.50 to £70*

WADDESDON   Buckinghamshire   map 3

▲ *Five Arrows Hotel* 🍇

Waddesdon HP18 0JE   TEL: (01296) 651727
WEB SITE: www.waddesdon.org.uk/accomm.html
on A41 between Bicester and Aylesbury

The original purpose of this unusual-looking Grade II listed hotel was
to cater for workers who were building nearby Waddesdon Manor
for Baron Ferdinand de Rothschild in 1887. Its name refers to a
feature on the coat of arms of that famous dynasty, and its style –
ornate timbers, mullioned windows and fancy wrought ironwork –
reflects the opulence for which the family is known. Inside, the stylish
and comfortable décor fits the period, with features including timeworn leather armchairs, wall hangings and old prints. Though it aims
to be relaxed and informal, it still feels more like eating in a restaurant, thanks to full table service and a modern, cosmopolitan menu –
albeit listed on blackboards – that is fairly up-market by pub standards. Diverse starters might include pumpkin and roasted garlic soup
alongside smoked king scallops with grape jelly dressing, while mains
range from sirloin steak with peppercorn sauce to seared marlin with
a sweet pepper and caper salsa. To finish there may be hazelnut
meringue with warm chocolate sauce. The stable yard is an attractive
outdoor eating area, and the formal gardens are worth a look. Fuller's
London Pride is the real ale offered. A striking wine list starts off with
four bottled especially for Waddesdon Manor (the hotel's imposing
neighbour), their labels inspired by the famous Rothschild range. It

then goes on to list 22 from the Rothschild vineyards themselves, including Chateau Lafite-Rothschild 1991 (£90 a bottle). The rest of the list covers the rest of the world, stays mostly well below £20, and has eight wines by the glass. SAMPLE DISHES: roast boned quail stuffed with wild rice and apricots £6; pan-fried rump of lamb with aubergine caviar £12; brioche bread-and-butter pudding £4.25.

Licensees Julian Alexander-Worster and Fabia Bromovsky (freehouse)
Open *11.30 to 11, Sun 12 to 10.30; bar food 12 to 2.15, Sun 12.30 to 2; restaurant 12 to 2.15, 7 to 9.15, Sun 12.30 to 2, 7.30 to 9*
Details *Children welcome   Car park   Wheelchair access (also WC)   Garden and patio   No smoking in dining room   Live or background music   No dogs MasterCard, Switch, Visa   Accommodation: 11 rooms, B&B £65 to £150*

WALBERSWICK   Suffolk   map 6

▲ *Bell Inn*

Ferry Road, Walberswick IP18 6TN   TEL: (01502) 723109
WEB SITE: www.blythweb.co.uk/bellinn
on B1387, off A12, S of Southwold

You may catch glimpses of the sea from this upmarket 600-year-old inn by the village green, and the beach is only a stone's throw away. It is set in a peaceful, rural part of Suffolk not far from Southwold, so it is hardly surprising that Adnams ales, including seasonal beers such as Fisherman, are available in the bar. The wine merchant arm of Adnams also supplies the reasonably priced wines, including six house selections at £7.50 a bottle, or £1.60 per glass. The menu is supported by daily blackboard specials, and fish and seafood are in plentiful supply on both – options range from traditional battered cod with chips and peas to modern ideas such as pan-fried tuna with chilli and coriander salsa. Meat dishes likewise could be as simple as steak with chips and onion rings, or as exotic as duck breast with grapefruit and ginger sauce. The ambience throughout is relaxed and informal, and the place is furnished comfortably in a typically traditional style. As well as Southwold, local attractions include Minsmere bird sanctuary, and the cathedral at Blythburgh. SAMPLE DISHES: warm potato, duck liver and chorizo salad £4.75; pan-fried barracuda with roasted vegetables £9; sticky toffee pudding £3.

Licensee Sue Ireland-Cutting (Adnams)
Open *11 to 3, 6 to 11, Sun 12 to 3, 7 to 10.30 (11 to 11 all week Jul and Aug); bar food 12 to 2, 7 (6 in Jul–Aug) to 9, Sun 12 to 2.30; restaurant Fri and Sat 6 to 9*
Details *Children welcome in family and dining rooms   Car park   Wheelchair access (also WC)   Garden and patio   No smoking in dining room   Occasional live music   Dogs welcome exc in dining room   Delta, MasterCard, Switch, Visa   Accommodation: 6 rooms, B&B £40 to £90*

WAMBROOK   Somerset   map 2

▲ *Cotley Inn*

Wambrook TA20 3EN   TEL: (01460) 62348
off A30, just W of Chard

Off a T-junction in the village, the Cotley is built of local stone, with
small windows and a wide flight of steps leading up to the entrance.
Inside, it is a quiet place, with a log-burning fire and red velour seating lending a traditional, welcoming feel. In an extension is a bowling alley. Staff are friendly, and food is taken seriously, with
blackboards supplementing written menus. The kitchen aims to
cover all bases, from bar snacks such as sandwiches and jacket potatoes to full meals which might begin with king prawns with garlic
mayonnaise, or Brie filo with a fruit sauce, and proceed to main
courses of various sizes of steak with port and Stilton or bordelaise
sauces, or whole trout stuffed with apple and celery. A blackboard
special might be chicken in apricot and brandy sauce, or pepper
steak. Well over a dozen of 'big meaty eats' vie for attention with
around a dozen chicken and fish dishes. Vegetarians, too, have a
good choice: maybe vegetable minty pie, or sweet-and-sour vegetable
stir-fry. Oakhill Best Bitter and Boddingtons head up the beer-drink-
ing, and there is a list of over two dozen wines split equally between
European and New World listings. Three wines are offered by the
glass. SAMPLE DISHES: crispy whitebait £4; chicken in ginger and
cream sauce £8.50; banoffi pie £3.50.

Licensees David and Susan Livingstone (freehouse)
Open *11 to 3, 7 to 11; bar food and restaurant 12 to 2.30, 7 to 10*
Details *Children welcome   Car park   Garden   No smoking in dining room
No music   Dogs welcome in bar only   MasterCard, Switch, Visa
Accommodation: 2 rooms, B&B £35 to £45*

WARDLOW MIRES   Derbyshire   map 8

Three Stags Heads 🍺

WALKS

Wardlow Mires SK17 8RW   TEL: (01298) 872268
at junction of B6465 and A623, 2m E of Tideswell

It's not that there's a dress code, says an inspector, it's just that
anything except walking clothes wouldn't work for visiting this
plain, no-frills place in the middle of nowhere. It's on several major
walking routes. 'Brilliant, simple, unassuming, good-humoured' are
some of the words used to describe what the owners call a 'small,
traditional country pub'. It looks well worn, and you may find regu-

lars roasting chestnuts on the coal-burning range, but the welcome is warm and the beers are excellent. On draught are Broadstone Charter Ale and, from Abbeydale Brewery, Matins, Absolution and Black Lurcher. An occasional guest is Abbeydale Last Rites, which at an astonishing 11 per cent abv should perform miraculous resuscitations. Bottled beers include St Peter's Ales, Traquair House, Jacobite Bear Ales, Export Guinness, Belgian Gueuze and Chimay, and fruit beers. Opening hours are limited, so it's wise to phone before making a special journey. The menu is short, but the food has been described as 'hearty, fresh and home-cooked'. Starters might be soup, or tuna salad, with main dishes along the lines of pasta with tomato and vegetable sauce, cottage pie, rump steak, pigeon breasts, or 'really good, very gamey' rabbit in mustard with herbs. They don't do puddings any longer because few people wanted them. Note the pub is open only on Fridays, Saturdays, Sundays and bank holidays. SAMPLE DISHES: split pea and ham soup £3.50; steak and kidney pie £7.50; venison stew £10.50.

Licensees Geoffrey and Pat Fuller (freehouse)
Open *Fri 7 to 11, Sat 12 to 11, Sun 12 to 10.30 (also open Christmas and New Year weeks); bar food Fri 7.30 to 9.30, Sat and Sun 12.30 to 3.30, 7 to 9.30*
Details *No children Car park Garden Live music Dogs welcome No cards*

WARHAM ALL SAINTS　　　**Norfolk**　　　　　　　　map 6

Three Horseshoes

Bridge Street, Warham All Saints NR23 1NL
TEL: (01328) 710547
off A149 or B1105, 2m SE of Wells-next-the-Sea

A charmingly old-fashioned atmosphere pervades this rambling flint and brick inn in the centre of a small village. You enter a small bar area with a tiled floor and Victorian fireplace; beyond this is the carpeted dining area, though you can eat in either. Both are similarly furnished with sturdy old scrubbed pine furniture, and both are similarly decorated with a jumble of old beer advertising paraphernalia, stuffed birds and old cigarette boxes in cases, and even a grandfather clock and old slot machines. Blackboard menus hanging over the bar offer a wide range of interesting items, many of which are traditional recipes from Mrs Beeton. Pies are a strong suit, made with good home-made pastry and generously filled with things like garlic lamb, or rabbit and chicken in rich, tasty gravy. Light lunches take in variations on the ploughman's theme, and fish options might include soused herrings, or cod in cheese sauce. Beers are another strength:

regular Woodforde's Wherry Best Bitter, Greene King IPA, and Buffy's Polly's Folly and IPA are joined by a guest served direct from the cask, which might be Bull Best Bitter from Blanchfields of Fakenham. Wines are a limited but reasonably priced selection; there is also a selection of country wines. The pub offers guest accommodation in the old post office next door. SAMPLE DISHES: shellfish cheese bake £4.25; Norfolk beef pie £8; spotted dick £2.75.

Licensee Mr I.P. Salmon (freehouse)
Open *11.30 to 2.30, 6 to 11, Sun 12 to 3, 6 to 10.30; bar food 12 to 1.45, 6.30 to 8.30; no food 25 and 26 Dec*
Details *Children welcome in bar eating areas   Car park   Wheelchair access (also WC)   Garden   No-smoking area in bar   No music   Dogs welcome   No cards   Accommodation: 4 rooms, B&B £24 to £52*

WATH-IN-NIDDERDALE   North Yorkshire   map 8

▲ *Sportsman's Arms*

Wath-in-Nidderdale HG3 5PP
TEL: (01423) 711306
off B6265, 2m NW of Pateley Bridge

Nidderdale is an Area of Outstanding Natural Beauty where sportsmen bearing firearms or fishing rods pursue their interests on the moors and rivers, while bird-watchers can enjoy the sanctuary at Gouthwaite Reservoir. The bar décor reflects this theme, but the more formal restaurant has white-clothed tables and gleaming silver and glass. Although this is a hotel and restaurant, beer drinkers will find Theakston Best Bitter on draught, and frozen vodka is a speciality. The long wine list suits both those seeking French classics and pupils of New World schools of wine-making. Prices are reasonable for such quality, although the house recommendations cost a tad more than most house wines. At least six are offered by the glass. Neither the restaurant menu nor the bar boards are overlong, and they differ mainly in the restaurant's more elaborate preparations and garnishes, as in peppered fillet steak on rösti with balsamic button onions and Dijon mustard sauce. Fish and seafood are delivered daily from Whitby, and might turn up in the bar as scallops with asparagus and pasta, monkfish provençale, or roast sea bass on onion mash. Pâté du tête with mustard dressing is time-honoured Yorkshire bar fare, despite its foreign name, while fine local produce might appear as pheasant breast with a bacon and olive sauce, or venison casserole with parsnip mash. SAMPLE DISHES: jambon du pays from Toulouse £5.50; fillet of roasted turbot on caramelised red onions with artichokes and sun-dried tomatoes £13.50; baked rice with rum-soaked prunes £3.75

Licensee Ray Carter (freehouse)
Open *12 to 2.30, 7 to 11; bar food and restaurant 12 to 2, 7 to 9 (8 Sun); closed 25 Dec*
Details *Children welcome in eating areas   Car park   Wheelchair access (not WC)   Garden   No smoking in dining room   Occasional background music   Dogs welcome   MasterCard, Switch, Visa   Accommodation: 12 rooms, B&B £45 to £95*

WATTON-AT-STONE   Hertfordshire   map 3

George & Dragon

High Street, Watton-at-Stone SG14 3TA   TEL: (01920) 830285
on A602, 5m SE of Stevenage

Everything expected of a traditional country inn is found inside the pink-washed, half-timbered walls of this one – whether it's blackened beams, old hunting prints, copper and brass, Windsor chairs or velvet-covered settles. The landlord and landlady have been here over 25 years, and their skilful stewardship is matched by pleasant service. The menu is shared by the bar and the discreet dining room. Among lighter dishes are Chinese-style crispy duck with noodles, and poached lemon sole fillet, while main courses include steaks, roast breast of duck with apple and calvados sauce, and roast salmon fillet with garlic and chilli butter. Blackboard starters might see avocado filled with salmon and dill mousse, and fried herring roes, with main dishes of grilled bacon steak with a fried egg, bobotie, or poached halibut with a white wine, watercress and crème fraîche sauce. Greene King IPA and Abbot Ale, Ruddles County, Old Speckled Hen and Badger Tanglefoot are among regular and guest ales, while of 20-odd wines five are offered by the glass. SAMPLE DISHES: pickled herring fillets with apple and red onion £4.75; pot-roast lamb shank £10; strawberry and blackberry Pimm's tart £3.25.

Licensees Kevin and Christine Dinnin (Greene King)
Open *Sun to Fri 11 to 2.30, 6 to 11 (10.30 Sun), Sat 11 to 11; bar food and restaurant (exc Sun evening) 12 to 2, 7 to 10; closed evenings 25 and 26 Dec*
Details *Children welcome in eating areas   Car park   Garden and patio   No smoking in dining room   No music   No dogs   Amex, Delta, Diners, MasterCard, Switch, Visa*

WENLOCK EDGE   Shropshire   map 5

▲ *Wenlock Edge Inn*

Hilltop, Wenlock Edge TF13 6DJ
TEL: (01746) 785678
WEB SITE: www.wenlockedgeinn.co.uk
on B4371, 4½m S of Much Wenlock

Built in around 1700 as quarrymen's cottages, this limestone inn makes an excellent base for visiting Ludlow, Shrewsbury and the Ironbridge Gorge and is an equally good stopping-off point for walkers on Wenlock Edge. There are fine views from the pub, and once inside you can enjoy the warmth of the Waring family's hospitality, augmented, when needed, by a comforting cast-iron stove in one of the small bars. The short menu is written on boards for both restaurant and bar. The food is straightforward and traditionally English, the nearest to an interloper being organic Greek yoghurt offered as an alternative to cream or ice cream with pies, crumbles, and sponge puddings made with seasonal fruit. Typical starters, which come with home-made organic rolls, might be leek and carrot soup, or bradan rost – hot-smoked Loch Fyne salmon with dill and crème fraîche. Roast leg of lamb with garlic and mint, and chicken breast with leeks and smoked bacon in wine sauce are both served with freshly prepared vegetables. Well-kept beers are Hobson's Best Bitter and Town Crier. Only one of the 30 wines breaks the £20 barrier, and six are sold by the glass. SAMPLE DISHES: devilled chicken wings £3.50; venison pie £7.75; hot chocolate fudge pudding £3.50.

Licensee Stephen Waring (freehouse)
Open *Tue to Sat 11.30 to 2.30, Mon to Sat 6.30 to 11, Sun 12 to 2.30, 6.30 to 10.30; bar food and restaurant 12 to 2, 7 to 9*
Details *Children welcome in eating areas   Car park   Patio   No smoking in dining room   No music   Dogs welcome in bar   Amex, Delta, MasterCard, Switch, Visa   Accommodation: 3 rooms, B&B £40 to £75*

WENTNOR   Shropshire   map 5

▲ *Crown Inn*

Wentnor SY9 5EE   TEL: (01588) 650613
off A489, 6m NE of Bishop's Castle

A tricky drive along narrow country lanes with no passing places means this is not the most accessible of pubs, though once there the setting is attractive enough. The exterior is enlivened by hanging baskets and climbing roses, and a small patio at the rear is decked out with lots of hydrangeas. Inside, the bar is one large open space with a mix of seating, including comfortable sofas, and has a generally domestic feel. Menus, displayed on blackboards, offer a mostly familiar range of traditional pub food, from cottage pie or gammon, egg and chips to rump steak with onion rings, mushrooms and tomatoes, although more adventurous items may crop up: perhaps panfried pork fillet with herb stuffing, or chicken breast in white wine and cream with sun-dried tomatoes and tarragon. Worth noting are the interesting vegetarian options: baked Brie layered with apricots and onions, for example. House wines and wines of the month are sold by the glass, and there's a short, straightforward list. Four real ales include Hobsons Best Bitter and Salopian Shropshire Gold. SAMPLE DISHES: smoked salmon parcel £4; half a Gressingham duck with rich plum sauce £13; banana and sultana loaf £3.

Licensees Simon and Joanna Beadman (freehouse)
Open *12 to 3, 7 to 11 (10.30 Sun); bar food and restaurant 12 to 2, 7 to 9 (6.30 to 9.30 Sat)*
Details *Children welcome in bar eating area   Car park   Garden and patio No smoking in dining room   Background music   No dogs   Delta, MasterCard, Switch, Visa   Accommodation: 3 rooms, B&B £27.50 to £53*

WEST BEXINGTON   Dorset   map 2

Manor Hotel

Beach Road, West Bexington DT2 9DF
TEL: (01308) 897616
WEB SITE: www.themanorhotel.com
on B3157, 3m NW of Abbotsbury

This stone-built, slate-roofed manor house has been weathered for 900 years by winds blowing in from the vast Chesil Beach only half a mile away. Enjoy the sea view from the garden before descending a few steps to the low-ceilinged cellar bar, with its small ground-level window. The conservatory, built on to the main building, is a nosmoking extension of the bar. The restaurant menu, not available in the bar, is a two- or three-course set-price meal of mostly English dishes with a few French tweaks, such as chicken breast with a cream and Pernod sauce, or monkfish tails in a claret and mushroom sauce. The bar menu, written on blackboards, is even more English, except for vegetarian lasagne and moussaka. There are sandwiches, ploughman's and a wide choice of main dishes, from scallops with bacon to spicy crab and fish pie, or seafood thermidor. Meat lovers' options include cottage pie, or rabbit casserole, while starters or snacks might be prawns with garlic bread, or crab cakes with lime and chilli mayonnaise. Eldridge Pope Hardy Country and Royal Oak are on draught, together with Scrumpy Jack. More than 100 wines are

available in both restaurant and bar, with five served by the glass.
SAMPLE DISHES: moules marinière £6.75; Murphy's steak and kidney
pudding £8.75; bread-and-butter pudding £4.

Licensee Richard Childs (freehouse)
Open *11 to 11; bar food and restaurant 12 to 2, 7 to 10; closed evening 25
Dec*
Details *Children welcome   Car park   Garden   No-smoking area in bar
Occasional background music   Dogs welcome exc in dining room   Amex,
Delta, Diners, MasterCard, Switch, Visa   Accommodation: 13 rooms, B&B
£57 to £100*

WEST ILSLEY   **Berkshire**   **map 2**

Harrow Inn ✿

West Ilsley RG20 7AR   TEL: (01635) 281260
1½m off A34, 10m N of Newbury

Travellers between Oxford and Winchester may like to know of the
Harrow Inn. It is a whitewashed pub set a little apart from the main
road opposite the village cricket pitch and duck pond – a setting that
could hardly be more English pastoral if it tried. A pair of rooms,
one of which houses the bar, is decorated with equestrian memorabilia, prints of racehorses and a timetable of meetings at Newbury.
Simple, foursquare furnishings and some uncommonly fine cooking
are also to be discovered here. Blackboard and printed menus offer
the likes of twice-baked Roquefort soufflé with apple and walnut
salad, wild mushroom risotto with Parmesan and herb oil (which
may be taken as starter or main), baked Whitby cod on creamy mash,
or venison sausages with dauphinois potatoes and onion gravy. It all
seems pretty adventurous in the context, but is notably well
supported by local people. Chocolate soufflé, sticky toffee pudding,
or caramelised orange tart are the sorts of desserts to expect. This is
a Greene King pub, and so Abbot Ale appears on handpump, alongside Morland Original Bitter and Old Speckled Hen. Eight wines are
available by the glass. SAMPLE DISHES: avocado and pancetta salad
with garlic dressing £5.50; braised shoulder of English lamb on
bubble and squeak with a rosemary jus £10.25; pear and almond tart
with Guernsey cream £4.50.

Licensee Emily Hawes (Greene King)
Open *Tue to Sat 11 to 3, 6 to 11, Sun 12 to 4; bar food and restaurant 12 to
1.45 (2 Sun), 7 to 8.45*
Details *Children welcome   Car park   Wheelchair access (also WC)   Garden
No-smoking area in dining room   No music   Dogs welcome exc in dining
room   Delta, MasterCard, Switch, Visa*

WESTLETON Suffolk map 6

▲ *Crown*

Westleton IP17 3AD   TEL: (01728) 648777
WEB SITE: www.westletoncrown.com
on B1125, 8m N of Saxmundham

Westleton is not far from the coast, halfway between Southwold and Aldeburgh, and not far from Minsmere RSPB Reserve. The village has a long and colourful history, much of which is centred on goings-on at the inn, which has existed on this site in one form or another since the twelfth century. The present building is at least a few hundred years old and was restored to its current fine condition by the present owners, who are also responsible for landscaping the gardens. The Crown also has its own collection of animals, including budgies, hens, pot-bellied pigs and horses, which will keep the children happy; there is also a baby-changing area to keep parents happy. Four eating areas – conservatory, brew room, parlour and bar (note than a small cover charge applies to non-residents eating in the brew room or conservatory) – are served by one menu, and the modern cooking style shows a wide range of influences: cured Spanish sausage with pepper and bean salad, belly of Suffolk pork with bubble and squeak, and pan-fried monkfish on sauté Chinese cabbage, for instance. Desserts might include warm apple and almond cake with raspberry sauce. On handpump are Greene King Abbot Ale and IPA, Mauldons Dickens Bitter, St Peter's Brewery Organic Bitter, and Nethergate Suffolk Bitter, and there are 85 malt whiskies. Seven house wines are available by the glass, starting at £1.95. The main list spans a range of prices and vineyards, with some particularly good choices from Australia and a selection of interesting half-bottles too. SAMPLE DISHES: rocket and potato soup £3; pan-fried sea bass on butter bean purée £12.50; marinated oranges on Grand Marnier parfait £4.

Licensees Richard and Rosemary Price (freehouse)
Open *11 to 3, 6 to 11, Sun 12 to 3, 7 to 10.30; bar food and restaurant 12 to 2.15, 7 to 9.30*
Details *Children welcome   Car park   Wheelchair access (also WC)   Garden Background music   No smoking in 2 rooms   Dogs welcome in bar   Amex, Diners, MasterCard, Visa   Accommodation: 19 rooms, B&B £59.50 to £119.50*

All details are as accurate as possible at the time of going to press, but pubs often change hands, and it is wise to check beforehand by telephone anything that is particularly important to you.

WEST WYCOMBE Buckinghamshire map 3

▲ *George & Dragon*

High Street, West Wycombe HP14 3AB
TEL: (01494) 464414
WEB SITE: www.george-and-dragon.co.uk
on A40, 3m W of High Wycombe

Recent developments at the George & Dragon have seen the owners delving into the world of wine-importing, and the opening of a wine shop on the premises. The list offered in the pub is exclusively French but has been carefully selected to provide something out of the ordinary. Also unusual is the fact that everything on the list is available by the glass, and bottle prices start at a remarkably good-value £7. Nor are ale drinkers overlooked, the beer range taking in Fuller's London Pride, Charles Wells Bombardier and Greene King Abbot Ale. If that isn't reason enough to pay the George & Dragon a visit, there is also the well-equipped children's play area in the large garden to consider, and an attractive menu of traditional English food, featuring local game and cheeses, and lamb from the nearby estate, which might appear as a leg steak with rosemary and garlic. Influences from further afield are also apparent, as in a Mediterranean vegetable brochette, or chicken tikka masala. The pub itself – an eighteenth-century coaching inn, entered through a cobbled archway from the high street – is a charming setting for all this, which perhaps explains why it is reportedly the chosen haunt of Sukie, the ghost of a beautiful social climber. SAMPLE DISHES: spicy Cajun chicken wings £4.50; steak and wild mushroom pie £8; caramel cream pot £3.

Licensee Philip Todd (Inntrepreneur)
Open *11 to 2.30 (3 Sat), 5.30 to 11, Sun 12 to 3, 7 to 10.30; bar food 12 to 2, 6 to 9.30, Sun 12 to 2.15, 7 to 9*
Details *Children welcome in family room Car park Garden No smoking in dining room No music Dogs welcome Amex, Delta, Diners, MasterCard, Switch, Visa Accommodation: 11 rooms, B&B £68 to £72; hotel closed 24 Dec to 3 Jan*

WHITCHURCH Hampshire map 2

Red House ✿

21 London Street, Whitchurch RG28 7LH   TEL: (01256) 895558
on A34 between Basingstoke and Andover

In a large commuter village between Newbury and Winchester, this warmly hospitable country pub is just a little misleadingly named: it's white, not red. Round-backed chairs and stolid tables reinforce a sense of 'pubbyness' inside despite massive mirrors that make the place feel bigger than it is and shelves laden with home-made flavoured oils, pickles and chutneys. Pots Ale from the Cheriton Brewhouse is the real ale on handpump, as well as one From Itchen Valley, and the thoughtfully chosen wine list offers seven bottles by the glass. The kitchen produces some ambitious modern cooking, turning out starters such as chicken and cashew-nut terrine with Mexican salsa, or crab and Parma ham salad with beetroot aïoli, and main courses of artichoke and goats' cheese fritters with chilli salsa, or pan-fried mahi mahi with asparagus and crayfish coulis. Portions tend to be on the mountainous side, but if you've room, pavlova with fresh berries, or Key lime pie, might be a good way to finish. SAMPLE DISHES: oat-crusted Thai salmon fishcakes with lemon and parsley sauce £5; Cajun pork loin with chorizo sausage and chickpeas £9.50; white chocolate crème brûlée £3.25.

Licensees Caroline and Shannon Wells (freehouse)
Open *11.30 to 3, 6 to 11, Sun 12 to 3, 7 to 10.30; bar food and restaurant 12 to 2, 6.30 (7 Sun) to 9.30; closed 25 Dec*
Details *Children welcome in dining room   Car park   Garden and patio   No smoking in dining room   Occasional live music; jukebox   Dogs welcome in public bar   Delta, MasterCard, Switch, Visa*

WHITEWELL   Lancashire   map 8

▲ *Inn at Whitewell* ❦

Whitewell, Forest of Bowland BB7 3AT
TEL: (01200) 448222
off B6243 Clitheroe to Longridge road, 6m NW of Clitheroe

The Inn at Whitewell, a remote hamlet in the Forest Of Bowland, is more than a pub: it also sells wine and coffee and has fishing rights on the River Hodder, which flows alongside. Coal fires, flagged floors, oak beams and a plethora of prints and photographs set the tone inside. On the restaurant menu – also available in the bar – are original dishes such as slow-roast belly pork glazed with maple syrup (a starter), and main courses of perhaps calf's liver fried with Parma ham and sage served on chorizo and chive potato cake, or roast breast of Goosnargh duckling with orange marmalade. Simplicity rules in the bar, with seafood chowder, or Bury black pudding with a poached egg, followed by fish pie, beef bourguignon, or grilled Norfolk kipper. Service is competent and relaxed. Marston's Pedigree and Boddingtons Bitter are on draught. Wine buffs will appreciate the encyclopedic list of French classics, with shorter but impressive selections from other

European and New World countries. Prices are reasonable, with house wines starting at £9.90. Ten are offered by the glass. SAMPLE DISHES: roast stuffed quail £5.75; Cumberland bangers with champ £7.50; fig and almond tartlet with vanilla sauce and fudge brownie ice cream £3.75.

Licensee Richard Bowman (freehouse)
Open *10 to 3, 6 to 11, Sun 12 to 3, 7 to 11; bar food and restaurant 12 to 2, 7.30 to 9.30*
Details *Children welcome Car park Garden No music Dogs welcome Amex, Delta, Diners, MasterCard, Switch, Visa Accommodation: 17 rooms, B&B £57 to £114*

WHITLEY Wiltshire map 2

Pear Tree Inn ✿ NEW ENTRY

Top Lane, Whitley SN12 8QX TEL: (01225) 709131
from Bath take A365 at Box; just after Atworth take left turning sign-posted to Whitley

---

Looking more like a farmhouse than a pub, this modest mellow stone house on a straggling country lane is 'definitely worth a detour'. Inside, the rustic décor brings out the best of the place while avoiding country pub clichés (though the requisite quota of flagstone floors and exposed stone walls are in place), and there is a 'refreshing lack of formality and pretension' in the air. Though the restaurant is the main focus of the business, drinkers are equally welcome in the bar to enjoy pints of Wadworth 6X or one of the three guest ales, which might come from the local Oakhill or Stonehenge breweries. One menu serves both dining room and bar, but the approach is flexible (starters may be taken as main courses), and the style ranges from modern bar food staples, such as Thai fishcakes, to fancier-sounding 'restaurant' dishes like braised lamb shank with herb polenta and green peppercorn sauce, or roast breast of corn-fed chicken with creamed leeks and a bacon and almond sauce. An inventive streak is evident in such combinations as pan-fried salmon fillet with sun-dried tomato mash and star anise saffron cream, though puddings are generally more conventional. The home-baked bread has come in for special praise. Ten wines are available by the glass from the list of over 40 bottles. SAMPLE DISHES: pumpkin and red wine risotto with caramelised red onion and Parmesan tuile £5.25; fillet of sea bass with rosemary and red onion marmalade, sauté ceps and bordelaise sauce £12.75; cinnamon and apple crème brûlée with cinnamon and brown sugar biscuits £5.

Licensee Martin Still (freehouse)
Open 11 to 3, 6 to 11, Sun 12 to 3, 7 to 10.30; bar food and restaurant 12 to 2, 6.30 to 9.30 (10 Fri and Sat), Sun 12 to 2.30, 7 to 9
Details *Children welcome Car park Wheelchair access (also WC) Garden and patio No smoking in dining room No music Dogs welcome in bar only Delta, MasterCard, Switch, Visa*

WHITNEY Herefordshire

map 5

▲ *Rhydspence Inn*

Whitney HR3 6EU TEL: (01497) 831262
off A438 Hereford to Brecon road, 4m E of Hay-on-Wye

The stream that runs past the bottom of the garden of this half-timbered fourteenth-century manor house marks the border between England and Wales, though really the Rhydspence is in the middle of nowhere. The pub is on an old drovers' route and still attracts passing travellers to this day, who come for the traditional bar and the smart restaurant with views of the Wye Valley. The country-house style of cooking means starters like chicken liver and bacon pâté, or Thai king prawns, followed by half a roast Aylesbury duck with orange and Grand Marnier sauce, while the specials board might include chargrilled tuna with chargrilled vegetables and raspberry dressing. Real ales are from Robinson's and Bass, and Dunkerton cider is also available. The list of about 50 wines includes a decent number of half-bottles and house wines by the bottle, half-litre or litre carafe. The resident ghost 'is very friendly and loves playing with children', apparently. SAMPLE DISHES: smoked salmon with lime and strawberry vinaigrette £7.50; sizzling Cajun chicken with stir-fried rice and naan £8.50; chocolate and pecan tart £4.25.

Licensee Peter Glover (freehouse)
Open 11 to 2.30, 7 to 11; bar food and restaurant 12 to 2, 7 to 9.30; closed 2 weeks Jan
Details *Children welcome in eating areas Car park Garden and patio No smoking in dining room No music No dogs Amex, Delta, MasterCard, Switch, Visa Accommodation: 7 rooms, B&B £32.50 to £75*

WIDECOMBE IN THE MOOR   Devon   map 1

Old Inn

Widecombe in the Moor TQ13 7TA   TEL: (01364) 621207
from Bovey Tracey take Haytor road and continue to Widecombe in the Moor, 5m NW of Ashburton

This fourteenth-century moorland pub certainly draws the crowds, often by the coachload. The ambience is warm in the small rooms, with open log fires and dark wooden furniture. There is no separate restaurant, but the menu runs to several pages. Grills range from eight-ounce steaks to a mixed one that includes a lamb chop, kidney, rump steak, sausage, egg, bacon, mushrooms, onions, chips and peas. An even greater tribute to Devon appetites is 'the butcher's delight', which adds a spare rib chop, gammon, chicken breast and black pudding. The standard menu offers ploughman's with cheese, beef or prawns, open sandwiches, home-made pies and curries. Appetisers (which at busy times are only available when followed by a main course) are conventional enough except for haggis, neeps and tatties. Specials of the day and desserts are on blackboards, and a regular speciality is roast lamb in a redcurrant and gin sauce. Wadworth ales include 6X and Henry's Original IPA, and there are Teignworthy ales and Gray's Farmhouse Cider too. Only two of the bottles on the wine list of 30-plus bins (plus guests) are over £15 and seven are available by the glass. SAMPLE DISHES: deep-fried Brie £4; poached Devon salmon steak £8; meringue filled with ice cream and raspberry sauce £2.75.

Licensees Alan and Susie Boult (freehouse)
Open *11 to 3 (2.30 winter), 6 (7 winter) to 11, Sun 12 to 3, 7 to 10.30; bar food 11 to 2.30 (2 winter, 2.30 Sun), 6.30 (7 winter) to 10 (9.30 winter, 10 Sat winter)*
Details *Children welcome   Car park   Wheelchair access (also WC)   Garden and patio   Occasional background music   Dogs welcome   Delta, MasterCard, Switch, Visa*

WINCLE   Cheshire   map 8

Ship Inn

Wincle SK11 0QE   TEL: (01260) 227217
1m S of A54, between Congleton and Buxton, 5m SE of Macclesfield

This small, stone-built sixteenth-century pub, set in the beautiful Dane Valley, attracts walkers from the wealth of nearby footpaths. Inside, a warm and friendly ambience prevails, with no intrusive music or games to spoil it. Although traditional items appear on the menu – venison fillet with port and cranberry sauce, and home-made steak and ale pie, for example – you also may find wild mushrooms tossed in garlic and pesto cream, or smoked salmon and dill pâté. Typical main dishes are Brie and leek parcels with mustard cream sauce, chicken breast stuffed with mozzarella and sun-dried tomatoes with provençale sauce, and monkfish with a mild cumin sauce. In addition are daily specials: maybe guinea fowl with armagnac and prune sauce, and a variety of seafood – Wednesday is the day for fish fresh from Grimsby. All these, plus sandwiches and baguettes, are available in both bar and restaurant. Boddingtons Bitter and a weekly-changing guest beer are on tap, and among the hundred guests entertained in a year you might find Timothy Taylor Landlord or beers from Wye Valley or Beartown breweries. Bottled choices include fruit beers from Belgium, and four wines are sold by the glass. SAMPLE DISHES: filo prawns with a chilli dip £3.50; pan-fried duck breast glazed with honey and thyme £11; rhubarb crumble £3.

Licensees Steven and Sally Simpson (freehouse)
Open *Tue to Sun 12 to 3, 7 to 11 (10.30 Sun); bar food and restaurant 12 to 2 (2.30 Fri to Sun), 7 to 9 (9.30 Fri and Sat)*
Details *Children welcome in family room   Car park   Wheelchair access (not WC)   Garden and patio   No smoking in dining room   No music   Dogs welcome   Delta, MasterCard, Switch, Visa*

WINFORTON   Herefordshire   map 5

▲ *Sun Inn*

Winforton HR3 6EA   TEL: (01544) 327677
on A438 Hereford to Brecon road, 6m S of Kington

This whitewashed old inn is set amid the beautiful rolling country-side of Welsh border country. Inside, it has a rustic feel, with rough stone walls, big chunky beams, a wood-burning stove and horse paraphernalia adorning the walls. A long menu is chalked up on blackboards and features plenty of local produce – notably Marches lamb and game – as well as a decent selection of vegetarian and fish dishes; there are also lighter dishes (such as venison sausages or cod and chips) and a children's menu. The style is somewhat eclectic, starters ranging from Carew mussels with leeks, bacon and ginger sauce, or smoked Bavarian ham and three-cheese bake, to minted lamb kebabs with yoghurt dip. Main courses might take in lamb and apricot pie, fillets of red mullet with green sauce, or half a guinea fowl with port and redcurrant sauce. Wood Parish Bitter, Buckley's Best Bitter and Hook Norton Best Bitter are the regular real ales, and cider comes from Stowford Press. A large selection of wines includes four by the glass. SAMPLE DISHES: Thai-style prawn parcels £5; oxtail braised in cider with herbs £9.75; banoffi crumble tart £4.25.

Licensees Brian and Wendy Hibbard (freehouse)
Open *Wed to Mon 11 to 3, 6 (7 Sun) to 11; bar food 12 to 2, 6.45 to 9.30*
Details *Children welcome in bar eating area   Car park   Wheelchair access
(not WC)   Garden   No-smoking area in bar, no smoking in dining room
Occasional live music   No dogs   No cards   Accommodation: 3 rooms, B&B
£32 to £60*

WING   Rutland   map 6

▲ *King's Arms*

Top Street, Wing LE15 8SE   TEL: (01572) 737634
WEB SITE: www.thekingsarms-wing.co.uk
off A47, 4m SE of Oakham

The oldest part of this village pub, which dates from 1649, is the bar
where an inspector chose to dine and enjoy 'the wonderfully atmospheric feel, helped by an impressive log fire burning under an open
copper canopy'. Adding to the ambience are deal tables, exposed
stone, pewter mugs hanging from beams, and soft lamplight, while
the large restaurant area has a comfortable but more conventional
feel, with white and pink tablecloths and oil lamps. Both bar and
restaurant menus are listed on chalkboards and are available
throughout. The former offers crusty baguettes, pasta – perhaps with
a cream, chive, and smoked salmon sauce – and grilled local sausages
with garlic mash, while the latter extends choice and ambition
considerably. There might be pan-fried kidneys chasseur, or crab
cake with saffron mayonnaise, followed by spring onion and artichoke risotto with Parmesan, or seared tuna steak with garlic and
tomato sauce. You might also consider breast of guinea fowl
wrapped in Parma ham, or baked Rutland Water trout, plus traditional pub desserts along the lines of sticky toffee pudding. On
draught are Batemans XB, local Grainstore Triple B, and two guest
ales each week. Four house wines and up to half a dozen specials are
offered by the glass, with a further 15 by the bottle, starting at
£8.95. SAMPLE DISHES: Brie and grape tartlet with red pepper coulis
£4; honey-baked ham with egg and chips £8; pear and calvados
parfait £4.50.

Licensees Neil and Karen Hornsby (freehouse)
Open *all week (except Sun evening and Mon lunchtime) 12 to 12 (12 to 2.30,
6 to 12 winter); bar food (exc Sat evening) and restaurant 12 to 2, 6.30 to
9.30 (9 winter)*
Details *Children welcome   Car park   Wheelchair access (not WC)   Garden
and patio   No smoking in dining room   Occasional live or background music
No dogs   Amex, Delta, Diners, MasterCard, Switch, Visa   Accommodation: 8
rooms, B&B £35 to £100*

De La Pole Arms 🍺

Wingfield IP21 5RA   TEL: (01379) 384545
off B1118 Framlingham to Diss road, just N of Stradbroke

Beautifully situated next to the village church, this sensitively restored seventeenth-century pub attracts both locals and temporary locals from Wingfield College. Its appeal is based on food, which is efficiently and attentively served in the restaurant, bar and split-level lounge, with its tiled floor, log fire and many exposed beams. The restaurant menu is also offered in the bar (but not the other way round). The bar menu lists about 15 dishes, with no distinction between starters and main dishes – but a reader found that all portions are of main-course size. They include bowls of mussels or mixed seafood, halibut and basil crumble on a bed of spinach, wild rabbit casserole, and black pudding and chicken livers with 'delicious, crisp lardons of locally smoked bacon' accompanied by a salad of leaves and black olives. St Peter's Best Bitter and Strong Ale, and Wheat Beer, in summer, or seasonal Winter Ale are on draught, with a full range of the brewery's bottled beers. The list of 30-plus wines includes Oak Hill from nearby Fressingfield, and five are offered by the glass. SAMPLE DISHES: fishcakes with crème fraîche and salad £6.75; Irish stew with parsley dumplings £8.75; syrup sponge and custard £3.75.

Licensee Terence Mulqueen (St Peter's)
Open *11 to 3, 6 to 11, Sun 12 to 3, 7 to 10.30; bar food and restaurant 12 to 2, 7 to 9 (9.30 Fri and Sat)*
Details *Children welcome   Car park   Wheelchair access (also WC)   Patio No smoking in dining room   Background music   Dogs welcome in bar Delta, MasterCard, Switch, Visa*

▲ *Royal Oak Inn*

Winsford, Exmoor National Park TA24 7JE
TEL: (01643) 851455
WEB SITE: www.royaloak-somerset.co.uk
off A396, 5m N of Dulverton

A 'Come to Britain' advertisement might feature a picture of this old (parts of it date from the twelfth century) cream-walled, thatched pub facing the village green in a beautiful valley in Exmoor National Park. A smart but comfortable ambience, with cloths and candles on the restaurant tables, greets the visitor upon entering. Restaurant and bar both offer à la carte menus, which are more expensive and elaborate in the restaurant. In the bar you might choose a ham, beef or BLT sandwich, or a full meal starting with grilled goat's cheese with roasted tomatoes and olives, basil and garlic dressing, or a special of soused mackerel with honey and mustard dressing. Main courses veer towards the traditional – venison sausages and mash, local game pie, and liver and bacon, for example – though a daily special might include a chicken curry. Puddings such as cheesecake are home-made too. Thirty mainly classic wines are offered in the restaurant, while nine bar wines are mostly New World, with only three by the large or small glass. Beers on draught include brown ales and Harrier SPA from the local Cotleigh Brewery as well as Exmoor Ale from (again local) Gordon Hill Brewery; Stowford Press Cider is available too. SAMPLE DISHES: baked cheese mushrooms with leek sauce £4.50; steak and kidney pudding £8.50; Bakewell tart £3.

Licensee Charles Steven (freehouse)
Open *11 to 3, 6 to 11, Sun 12 to 3, 7 to 10.30; bar food 12 to 2, 6.30 to 9; restaurant Sun 12 to 1, all week 7.30 to 9*
Details *Children welcome in bar eating area Car park Wheelchair access (also WC) Garden and patio No music Dogs welcome Amex, Delta, Diners, MasterCard, Switch, Visa Accommodation: 14 rooms, B&B £89 to £120*

WINTERTON-ON-SEA Norfolk map 6

▲ *Fishermans Return* 🍺

The Lane, Winterton-on-Sea NR29 4BN TEL: (01493) 393305
on B1159, 8m N of Great Yarmouth

A welcoming host, a pleasant atmosphere and proximity to beaches and nature reserves make this converted row of 300-year-old brick and flint fishermen's cottages a popular venue for holidaymakers in summer. Indeed, whether or not you are a fisherman, it is an ideal place to return to after a bracing walk across the dunes or after a day on the Broads. What you will find when you arrive are two homely, simply furnished bars, both with wood-burning stoves and a décor of local prints and old photographs. A selection of excellent real ales and ciders is served, including Wherry Best Bitter and Norfolk Nog from Woodeforde's, Broadside and Fisherman from Adnams, and James White Suffolk Cider. There is also a menu of straightforward pub food, plus a blackboard of home-cooked specials, such as bacon and lentil soup, a medley of salmon and plaice with caper and mushroom sauce, or pork loin stuffed with apricots and pine nuts with a red wine sauce. Five wines are available by the glass from short but well-chosen and reasonably priced list. SAMPLE DISHES: salmon and sun-dried tomato pâté £4.50; monkfish on a bed of spinach and wild rice with mild curry sauce £8.75; baked sponge pudding with custard £2.75.

Licensee John Findlay (freehouse)
Open *Mon to Fri 11 to 2.30, 6.30 (7 winter) to 11, Sat and Sun 11 to 11; bar food 12 to 2, 6.30 (7 winter) to 9.30 (9 winter)*
Details *Children welcome in family and games room   Car park   Wheelchair access (not WC)   Garden and patio   No smoking in lounge and family room Occasional background music; jukebox   Dogs welcome   Amex, Delta, MasterCard, Switch, Visa   Accommodation: 3 rooms, B&B £30 to £60*

WISWELL　　Lancashire　　　　　　　　　　　map 8

Freemasons Arms

8 Vicarage Fold, Wiswell BB7 9DF
TEL: (01254) 822218
1m off A680 near Whalley

The tiny village of Wiswell is at the foot of Pendle Hill, and this homely pub is at its centre on an unmade lane. Originally a row of three cottages, it has not changed much since it was converted, and the bar area is split into two simply and neatly furnished rooms decorated with brasses and various prints and furnished with copper-topped tables. A friendly atmosphere is generated by the crowds of locals who gather regularly to enjoy the food and drink here. A straightforward but extensive menu is offered, with local black pudding, or spinach pancakes among a dozen starters, and main courses covering a wide range of meat and fish dishes, such as lasagne and cottage pie. Desserts might include trifle, or sticky toffee pudding. Real ales come from Jennings and Black Sheep, 80 whiskies are available, and there is a list of around 20 wines, of which four are served by the glass. (The pub was unable to supply sample dishes and prices before the Guide went to press.)

Licensee Pauline Livesey (freehouse)
Open *Wed to Sat 12 to 2.30, 6.30 to 11, Sun 12 to 2.30, 6 to 10.30; bar food and restaurant Wed to Sat 12 to 2, 6.30 to 9.30, Sun 12 to 2.30, 6 to 9; closed 25 and 26 Dec*
Details *Children welcome in dining room   Background music   No dogs Delta, MasterCard, Switch, Visa*

The Guide is totally independent, accepts no free hospitality and carries no advertising.

WITHYHAM   East Sussex   map 3

Dorset Arms

Withyham TN7 4BD   TEL: (01892) 770278
WEB SITE: www.dorset-arms.co.uk
on B2110, 2m E of Hartfield

On a tiny village green near Ashdown Forest, the white-painted, tile-hung Dorset Arms is popular with locals, who appreciate the warm welcome in this well-run pub. Sit in one of the bar areas or in the restaurant: the same menus apply throughout except on Friday and Saturday evenings, when bar food is not available in the restaurant. A restaurant starter such as deep-fried Camembert with port and redcurrant sauce might precede whole sea bass baked with spring onions, or half a roast duckling with cherry and brandy sauce. Bar food includes a wide choice of sandwiches and ploughman's, plus a full menu that encompasses a soup, whitebait, cod and chips, or steak with onions. Among nearly 20 blackboard specials might be griddled plaice fillets with parsley butter, lamb chop in rich Shrewsbury sauce, and the intriguingly named drunken bull – chunks of steak with mushrooms and onions in rich red wine sauce. A reporter found that crushed sea salt and black pepper on a thick, moist piece of salmon with hollandaise gave it a 'fresh and lively taste', while roast beef at Sunday lunchtime has been thick, rare and tender, and served with good, simple vegetables. Desserts include fresh strawberry pavlova, and autumn pudding with apricot brandy. This is a Harveys pub and on draught are the brewery's Sussex Best Bitter, Pale Ale and Old Ale, plus other seasonal brews. The short, basic wine list includes one from England; three house wines are £12.60 per litre, and £2.50 per 175ml glass. SAMPLE DISHES: smoked salmon with brown bread £4; filo-topped cod and prawn pie £6.25; dark chocolate truffle torte £3.75.

Licensee John Pryor (Harveys)
Open *Mon to Fri 11.30 to 3, 5.30 to 11, Sat 11 to 3, 6 to 11, Sun 12 to 3, 7 to 10.30; bar food and restaurant all week 12 to 2, Tue to Sat 7 to 9.30*
Details *Children welcome in dining room and lounge area   Car park Wheelchair access (not WC)   Garden and patio   No smoking in dining room Occasional background music   Dogs welcome in bar   Amex, Delta, Diners, MasterCard, Switch, Visa*

Food mentioned in the entries is available in the bar, although it may be possible to eat in a dining room.

Three Horseshoes NEW ENTRY

Wixford B49 6DG TEL: (01789) 490400
*from A46 at Alcester roundabout follow A435 towards Redditch; left
on to A422, then left following signs for Wixford*

Wixford is a somewhat sprawling little village, the sort of place that
tourists exploring the byways of Shakespeare country might come
across, and at its heart is this brick-built, creeper-covered pub with
an extension to one side, and quite a reputation hereabouts as a
dining destination. Inside is an open-plan dining area adjoining the
main bar, with a separate family room for busy periods. A warm
terracotta colour scheme and an open fire ensure that nobody need
feel cold, and the bustling, convivial atmosphere is instantly infec-
tious. Lighter lunch dishes are listed on a printed menu, but the day's
main offerings are chalked up on a large blackboard. You might start
with pan-fried black pudding with a sauce of Stilton, apple and
cream, or perhaps with smoked salmon roulade filled with avocado
and cream cheese mousse, before going on to one of the interestingly
sauced main dishes. These have included lambs' liver with orange
and Worcester sauce gravy, or a combination of cod and salmon
with smoked bacon and a rosemary jus. Finish with pecan pie with
white chocolate sauce, or orange tart with raspberry coulis. Beers
offer a good selection of Shepherd Neame Master Brew Bitter,
Marston's Pedigree and Tetley, as well as a guest beer (perhaps
something from the Church End Brewery at Shustoke), while wines
in three basic styles are served by the glass from a list of 25. SAMPLE
DISHES: sauté field mushrooms in pastry with rosemary and garlic
cream sauce £3.50; pot-roast lamb shank with minted mash and red
wine sauce £10.25; chocolate fudge pudding £4.25.

Licensee Simon Dearden (freehouse)
Open *summer 12 to 11, Sun 12 to 10.30; winter 12 to 2.30, 6.30 to 11, Sun
12 to 2.30, 6.30 to 10.30; bar food 12 to 2 (2.30 Sun), 6.30 to 9 (9.30 Fri
and Sat)*
Details *Children welcome Car park Wheelchair access (also WC) Garden
and patio No-smoking areas in bar Live or background music Dogs
welcome by arrangement Delta, MasterCard, Switch, Visa*

🏆 *indicates a pub serving outstanding bar food, backed up by all-
round excellence in other departments, such as service, atmosphere
and cleanliness.*

WOOBURN COMMON   **Buckinghamshire**   map 3

▲ *Chequers Inn* ❦ ❦

Kiln Lane, Wooburn Common HP10 0JQ   TEL: (01628) 529575
just S of M50 junction 2

Though the oak beams and flagstone floor in the bar confirm the
seventeenth-century origins of this large brick-built hotel, it is the
thoughtful decorative touches that give the Chequers its comfortable,
homely character. The clientele of locals and passing business people
also endow the place with a lively atmosphere, and it is always busy.
On fine days, sit outside in the attractive garden or on the patio in
front of the pub; when the weather is not so good, bag a place by the
log fire in the bar, where an enticing range of snacks and more
substantial dishes is offered. Typically, the daily-changing menu
takes in options as diverse as home-made beefburgers topped with
bacon and cheese, chargrilled tuna loin with niçoise salad, and Swiss
cheese soufflé with garlic cream sauce. Among the lush palm trees
and period advertising posters in the restaurant, it is possible to
sample classical Anglo-French cuisine with some inventive modern
twists: witness tian of crab, avocado and tomato with gazpacho
sauce, or a tart of oxtail, kidney and girolles with a port jus. Drinkers
are equally well catered for: Wadworth 6X, Greene King IPA and
Abbot Ale, and Morland Original are served in the bar, and the
nicely presented wine list is set out by country, with strongest
emphasis on France. Prices average around the £20 mark, but a hefty
smattering of good names and top growers (Drouhin, Chapoutier,
Dopff & Irion, Simonsig, Rothschild) provide the likely explanation
for this. Helpful notes aid selection, and around half a dozen wines
are available by the glass. SAMPLE DISHES: deep-fried calamari with
sweet chilli dressing £8; pan-fried calf's liver, tomato salad and
balsamic jus £11; summer fruit tart £3.50.

Licensee Peter J. Roehrig (freehouse)
Open *10am to 11pm, Sun 10am to 10.30pm; bar food and restaurant Mon
to Fri 12 to 2.30, 6.30 to 10, Sat and Sun 12 to 10*
Details *Children welcome   Car park   Wheelchair access (not WC)   Garden
No smoking in dining room   Background music   No dogs   Amex, Delta,
Diners, MasterCard, Switch, Visa   Accommodation: 17 rooms, B&B £72.50
to £102.50*

WOODHILL Somerset map 2

▲ *Rose and Crown*

Woodhill, Stoke St Gregory TA3 6EW TEL: (01823) 490296
between A361 and A378, 8m E of Taunton, via North Curry

This 300-year-old cottage-style pub is tucked away in a tiny basket-making hamlet on the Somerset Levels. Outside is a flower-filled patio for summer use; inside, the décor is bright, if a little dated, and walls are cluttered with old prints, photographs, signs and posters, some of which even make it on to the ceiling. A laminated menu lists a wide range of mostly standard pub grub, predominantly grills: liver and bacon, skate wings, and lamb cutlets, for example. A board highlights fresh fish, which might include brill, haddock and sea bass, and also a pair of daily specials: perhaps game pie, and local pork chops. If it sounds a little unexciting, note the crowds who return time and again. In the evening, a lengthy fixed-price menu, with supplements charged for some items, offers even greater choice. Exmoor Ale and Thomas Hardy Royal Oak are the regular real ales, joined by guest beers and Thatcher's cider. Wines include six by the glass and a varied list of three dozen bottles. SAMPLE DISHES: plaice stuffed with prawns £6.50; half a roast chicken £6.50; banoffi pie £2.75.

Licensees Ron and Irene Browning (freehouse)
Open *11 to 3, 6.30 to 11, Sun 12 to 3, 7 to 10.30; bar food and restaurant 12 to 2, 7 to 10*
Details *Children welcome Car park Wheelchair access (not WC) Garden and patio No smoking in dining room No music Dogs welcome exc in dining room Delta, MasterCard, Switch, Visa Accommodation: 6 rooms, B&B £25 to £50*

WOOLHOPE Herefordshire map 5

▲ *Butchers Arms*

Woolhope HR1 4RF TEL: (01432) 860281
off B4224, 7m SE of Hereford

The Butchers Arms dates from the fourteenth century, and certainly looks its age. It is in an isolated position, just outside the village, by a stream amid orchards, hop fields and vineyards, and prettily adorned with hanging baskets. In the very traditional bar even short people will have to duck to avoid the low beams. Food is like everything else: reminiscent of a bygone era. Deep-fried whitebait and chicken liver pâté are typical starters, three varieties of ploughman's are offered, and main courses are along the lines of local wild rabbit and cider pie, venison sausage with mash and gravy, or chilli con carne with crusty bread. Vegetarian options are better than average. Shepherd Neame Spitfire Premium Ale and Hook Norton Best Bitter and Old Hooky are the real ales on handpump; Stowford Press cider is also stocked. Four wines are available by the glass from the list of 34 bottles. SAMPLE DISHES: leek and hazelnut terrine with wild berries £5; salmon fishcakes with creamy cheese sauce £8; autumn pudding with Chantilly cream £3.

Licensee Mrs S. Vallely (freehouse)
Open *11.30 to 3, 6.30 to 11, Sun 12 to 3, 7 to 10.30; bar food and restaurant 12 to 2 (2.30 Sun), 6.30 to 9.30*
Details *Children welcome in bar eating area   Car park   Wheelchair access (also WC)   Garden and patio   No smoking in dining room   No music   No dogs   Amex, Delta, MasterCard, Switch, Visa   Accommodation: 2 rooms, B&B £30 to £39*

Crown Inn
Woolhope HR1 4QP   TEL: (01432) 860468

The younger of the village's pubs is still plenty old enough, dating from the mid-eighteenth century. It is a white-painted stone building in the centre of this scattered village high above the Wye Valley, next to the church, and there is a neat lawn at the front with picnic benches. The well-kept and spotlessly maintained interior is divided into three sections, each decorated with pictures of country scenes and wildlife, with a warming log fire in the central area. The atmosphere is relaxed and informal, and the clientele is a mixture of locals and day trippers. The menu runs to several pages, opening with more than a dozen starters ranging from grilled sardines with garlic, to deep-fried Brie with raspberry sauce, or bacon and cheese crumpet. Main courses are divided into grills, fish and 'home-made', the last comprising dishes like steak, stout and mushroom pie, or faggots in onion gravy. Even the vegetarian section is longer than some pubs' entire range. Real ales are Wye Valley Bitter and Smiles Best, and the real cider comes from Stowford Press. Eight wines are offered by the large or small glass, and the full list offers variety and good value. SAMPLE DISHES: prawn cocktail £3.75; rabbit pie £7; blackberry and apple fool £3.25.

Licensees Neil and Sally Gordon (freehouse)
Open *12 to 2.30, 6.30 (7 winter) to 11 (10.30 Sun); bar food and restaurant 12 to 2, 6.30 (7 winter) to 10; closed evening 25 Dec*
Details *Children welcome   Car park   Wheelchair access (not WC)   Garden and patio   No smoking in dining room   Occasional background music   No dogs   Delta, MasterCard, Switch, Visa*

WOOTTON RIVERS Wiltshire   map 2

▲ *Royal Oak*

Wootton Rivers SN8 4NQ   TEL: (01672) 810322
off A346, 3m NE of Pewsey

In a smart and prosperous village that is way off the beaten track –
approach it down single-track roads – the Royal Oak is a white-
fronted thatched pub dating from the sixteenth century. Inside is an
L-shaped bar/dining room with white walls and dark beams, alongside a spacious public bar. Fifteen malt whiskies, Somerset brandy,
and good cognacs lend authority to the range of speciality drinking,
which is founded on handpumped ales from Wadworth and an imaginative wine list that includes seven by the glass. The kitchen
produces some accomplished cooking. Fish is good, maybe local pink
trout with lemon, or sea bass roasted with lime, and the free-range
pork, if available, is not to be missed. Starters include a good showing of pub favourites, along the lines of avocado stuffed with prawns
or crab, deep-fried whitebait with tartare sauce, and smoked salmon
with brown bread, while puddings indulge with the likes of banana
split, hot chocolate fudge cake, or treacle tart with cream. SAMPLE
DISHES: chicken liver and brandy pâté with wholemeal toast £4.75;
roast rack of English lamb with Cumberland sauce £13.50; kiwi fruit
meringue with vanilla ice cream £3.75.

Licensee J.C. Jones (freehouse)
Open *10 (12 Sun) to 3, 6 to 11; bar food and restaurant 11.45 to 2.30, 6.45
to 9.30, Sun 12 to 3, 6.30 to 9.30*
Details *Children welcome Car park Patio No-smoking area in dining
room Jukebox in 1 bar Dogs welcome Amex, Delta, Diners, MasterCard,
Switch, Visa Accommodation: 5 rooms, B&B £25 to £55*

WORFIELD Shropshire   map 5

Dog Inn 🍺 NEW ENTRY

Main Street, Worfield WV15 5LF   TEL: (01746) 716020
village signposted off A454 NE of Bridgnorth

The proprietors of the Munslow Inn (formerly the Crown) at
Munslow (see entry) have added this second string to their bow,
reopening it after extensive refurbishment. It is a fairly plain red-
brick building, with a small garden at the back, in a trim, up-market
village that contains some handsome properties (including an interesting church that's worth a look), close to the River Worfe and not
far from Bridgnorth. A modern tiled floor, light pine furnishings and
some fetching floral prints on the walls give a neat, clean impression

inside, and the place is divided into a bar and a dining area with a wood-burning stove. A simple lunchtime snack menu lists baguettes, cauliflower cheese, ratatouille and the like, and children get to choose from their own range, all served with chips and beans, with ice cream to follow. For the seniors, a choice of fixed-price or à la carte is offered, the latter dealing in Thai beef salad, anchovies in garlic dressing, fillet steak with olives and tomatoes, and chicken breast poached with lemon and herbs. A bowl of authentically home-made minestrone soup scored well for one visitor on a chilly winter lunchtime, while the vegetarian main-course option might be mushrooms cooked in red wine with walnuts and garlic. Puddings are listed on a blackboard. Cask-conditioned beer is treated with the same respect as at the owners' other venue. Here are listed Courage Directors, Wells Bombardier Premium Bitter and own-brew Butcher's Best, supported by constantly changing guest ales, which might well include something like Batemans Champagne Charlie. Just three wines by the glass are picked out from a compact but appreciably well-chosen list. SAMPLE DISHES: chicken livers bonne femme £4; beef Marie (strips of rump steak with mushrooms and cream) £9.50; banoffi pie £3.

Licensee Victor Pocock (freehouse)
Open *12 to 2.30 (3 Sun), 7 (6 Sat) to 11, Sun 12 to 3, 7 to 10.30; bar food and restaurant 12 to 2, 7 to 9*
Details *Children welcome   Car park   Wheelchair access (also WC)   Patio No smoking in dining room   Background music   Dogs by arrangement Amex, Delta, MasterCard, Switch, Visa*

WRIGHTINGTON   Lancashire   map 8

Mulberry Tree ✿   NEW ENTRY

9 Wrightington Bar, Wrightington WN6 9SE
from M6 junction 27, take Mossy Lea road

One of the modern breed of gastro-pubs, concentrating more on food than drinks, this Victorian pub nevertheless provides a pleasantly informal environment, with an open-plan bar and separate dining room. The cooking combines traditional ideas with an eclectic modern style and makes good use of local produce. Lancashire brawn might appear next to nettle and lovage soup, or local game terrine with pear chutney among starters, while main courses range from steak and kidney pudding to grilled confit duck leg with black pudding and pancetta, or baked fillet of salmon with parsley and Lancashire cheese crust. International influences also show up in the shape of Thai fishcakes, and penne arrabbiata with Parmesan. The menu sounds appealing enough in itself, but the food on the plate confirms that Mark Prescott is a chef of some merit, with reports commending the timing and flavours. As well as the bar menu, the dining room menu and a separate list of daily specials are also available in the bar. The real ale selection is limited to Flowers IPA, but Hoegaarden beer adds a note of interest to the drinks line-up. Three house wines are sold by the glass, and the full list offers a decent range of styles and quality. SAMPLE DISHES: Lancashire pork terrine with piccalilli £5; roast suckling pig with apple and sage £14; red fruits in mulled red wine jelly £4.

Licensees Mark and Annie Prescott (freehouse)
Open *12 to 11 (10.30 Sun); bar food and restaurant Tue to Sun 12 to 2 (2.30 Sun), 6 to 9 (10 Fri and Sat, 8.30 Sun); closed 26 Dec, 1 Jan*
Details *Children welcome in bar eating area   Car park   Wheelchair access (not WC)   Patio   No smoking in dining room   Live or background music No dogs   Delta, MasterCard, Switch, Visa*

WYMONDHAM   Leicestershire   map 5

Berkeley Arms 🏵 NEW ENTRY

Main Street, Wymondham LE14 2AG   TEL: (01572) 787587
off B676 between Melton Mowbray and Colsterworth

The drive through this especially sumptuous stretch of countryside is worthwhile in itself, thought a reporter, and the Berkeley Arms is a good landmark to set a course for. Built of honey-coloured stone, the inn is on the only road through this attractive village, with picnic tables at the front and a garden at the back. The main bar is spacious, with terracotta tiles, beams, hop garlands and exposed stonework, and retains the true feeling of a place where local people go to drink as well as eat. There is a separate restaurant area with carpeting and a no-smoking rule, but you may eat in either part. A short, keenly priced printed lunchtime menu lists such dishes as carefully cooked seared medallions of salmon with hot pepper marmalade and crème fraîche raita, or boiled collar of bacon with mustard sauce, along with baguettes and salads. On the blackboard might be pan-fried pigeon breast with sauté winter greens, or wild mushroom risotto with Parmesan. Main courses have included fillet of plaice on tomato fondue with roast garlic, calf's liver on horseradish and cabbage mash with caramelised onion gravy, and beef tournedos with a Stilton and mushroom crust. Desserts roll out the luxuries with chocolate truffle with hot chocolate sauce, or hot banana with Tia Maria and rum and raisin ice cream. Tetley Bitter, Marston's Pedigree and a regularly changing guest beer are supported by a shortish but reasonably comprehensive wine list, with three by the glass. SAMPLE DISHES: tomato and red pepper soup with pesto bread £4.25; slow-roast belly pork with Thai curry risotto £6.50; passion-fruit charlotte £4

Licensees Nick and Cathy McGeown (Pubmaster)
Open *12 to 2.30 (3 Sat), 6.30 (6 Fri and Sat) to 11, Sun 12 to 3, 7 to 10.30; bar food and restaurant Tue to Sun (exc Sun evening) 12 to 2, 6.30 to 9*
Details *Children welcome Car park Wheelchair access (also WC) Garden No smoking in dining room Background music No dogs MasterCard, Switch, Visa*

YARMOUTH   Isle of Wight   map 2

King's Head

Quay Street, Yarmouth PO41 0PB   TEL: (01983) 760351
opposite harbour

A sixteenth-century fort stands opposite the King's Head, adding a sense of security perhaps to this convivial pub. The interior is spacious and well decorated, and the sense of hospitality brought to the place by the Jacksons is such that children (who have their own menu to peruse) are as welcome as their parents. Filled baguettes, such as bacon and mature Cheddar, or sausage and fried onions, are a welcome proposition at chilly lunchtimes, when you will find the log fire roaring. Equally warming might be one of the speciality spicy dishes, such as chicken fajita, chilli con carne burrito, or blackened Cajun ribeye steak. These are supplemented by old favourites like prawn cocktail, deep-fried whitebait with tartare sauce, and steak and ale pie with a shortcrust pastry top. Burgers, pizzas and ice creams with liqueurs poured over are also available. For quality drinking, there are real ales, such as Flowers, Boddingtons Bitter and Old Speckled Hen, and Scrumpy Jack cider and a bottled German wheat beer in the shape of Erdinger. The short, well-selected wine list includes half a dozen by the glass. SAMPLE DISHES: nachos with salsa and sour cream £4.25; sirloin steak au poivre £11; chocolate ice cream with Cointreau £4.

Licensees Robert and Michelle Jackson (Whitbread)
Open *11 to 11, Sun 12 to 10.30; bar food 12 to 9.30*
Details *Children welcome in family room and bar eating area Garden No smoking in dining room Occasional background music Dogs welcome exc in eating areas No cards*

Licensing hours and bar food times are based on information supplied by each establishment and are correct at the time of going to press.

▲ *Royal Oak* ✿

The Square, Yattendon RG18 0UG   TEL: (01635) 201325
off B4009, 5m W of Pangbourne

The Royal Oak was once a row of terraced brick cottages, though
nowadays you can scarcely see the join behind its wisteria-covered
façade. With its smartly furnished guest bedrooms, a stylish lounge
and a very smart restaurant, you might feel that this is a pub in name
only, although the bar at the back is where people can just take a
drink without needing to have booked for dinner. And if you do eat,
you'll find the napkins are paper, so perhaps the transition is not
quite complete. Service is superbly well drilled, even bringing the
blackboard to your table so that you can see what the specials are.
Stuffed baby squid with tomato and olive emulsion, the fish itself
perfectly tender, makes an agreeable starter, while goats'-cheese
mille-feuille, or pigeon salad with chicken livers in a Marsala jus, are
alternatives. Main courses try out some bold ideas: Jamaican jerk
chicken with saffron risotto and bang-bang sauce, for example, or
pan-fried sea bass fillet with crayfish, lettuce, asparagus and shellfish
essence. Vegetables are charged extra. Prune and armagnac soufflé,
or hot chocolate fondant with orange sorbet, might be among the
luxurious ways to round off a meal. Boddingtons Bitter and
Wadworth 6X are on handpump, and a handful of carefully chosen
wines ranges from the crisp and light to the full and fruity while
staying firmly under the £25 mark. Geoff Merrill's Grenache Rosé is
just one of the great food wines among them. Four wines are served
by the glass. SAMPLE DISHES: rockfish soup with rouille and Gruyère
£5.25; confit of lamb shoulder with Dijon mustard crust and polenta
chips £13; banana parcels with roasted nuts and banana and passion-
fruit ice cream £5.

Licensees Corinne MacRae and Charles Holmes (freehouse)
Open *12 to 3, 6 to 11; bar food and restaurant 12 to 2 (2.30 Fri to Sun), 7 to
9 (9.30 Fri to Sun)*
Details *Children welcome   Car park   Garden   No smoking in dining room
Occasional background music   Dogs welcome   Amex, Delta, Diners,
MasterCard, Switch, Visa   Accommodation: 5 rooms, B&B £95 to £125*

---

*If you disagree with any assessment made in the Guide, write to tell
us why -- The Which? Guide to Country Pubs, FREEPOST, 2
Marylebone Road, London NW1 4DF.*

YEALAND CONYERS   Lancashire   map 8

New Inn 🍺

40 Yealand Road, Yealand Conyers LA5 9SJ
TEL: (01524) 732938
off A6, 2m N of Carnforth

In winter, locals are joined by diners and hardy walkers to enjoy the blazing log fire and the warm welcome at this stone-built pub just down the road from Leighton Hall. The walls of the bar, which has a stone-fronted counter, bear sepia photographs, plates and small farming paraphernalia, and in the entrance hall a large horned gramophone sits on a harmonium. Menus start with a long list of baguettes, sandwiches and jacket potatoes, but grilled sardines are drizzled with lime juice and olive oil, steaks are served with a choice of five sauces, and beef is stewed in Uncle Tom ale. Fish, vegetarian and vegan dishes are among daily specials, as were Cajun potato slices that happily complemented a reporter's Cumberland sausage with apricot and smoked bacon and flavourful onion gravy. Puddings might include banana split, while cheese – Lancashire, Stilton and Brie, with a slice of beetroot and sliced plums – could make a satisfying lunch in itself. On draught are Hartleys XB, Robinson's Frederics and Best Bitter and, in winter, Old Tom. The wine list, approaching 40 bottles, is fairly priced; four come by the glass. Some 40 malt whiskies are also kept. SAMPLE DISHES: chicken liver pâté £4; poached salmon fillet with creamy Chardonnay and chive sauce £8; lemon posset £3.

Licensee David Wrigley (Frederic Robinson)
Open *11 to 11, Sun 12 to 10.30; bar food and restaurant 12 to 9.30*
Details *Children welcome   Car park   Wheelchair access (not WC)   Garden*
No smoking in dining room   Background music   Dogs welcome in bar
Delta, MasterCard, Switch, Visa

SCOTLAND

APPLECROSS Highland   map 11

▲ *Applecross Inn*

Shore Street, Applecross IV54 8LR   TEL: (01520) 744262
off A896, 18m W of Loch Carron

Magnificent views of Raasay, Skye and Ben Nevis are the reward for
those who make the trek over Bealach na Ba, the highest mountain
pass in Britain, to reach Applecross. But even on those days when
bad weather obscures the views, the white-painted inn, which stands
hard by the shore, would make the journey worthwhile. Fish and
seafood are the stars on the daily bar menu. Starter/snack options
might take in plainly served local oysters, a half-pint of prawns, or
smoked salmon, alongside hot and spicy squat lobster with chilli and
pepper oil, and burgers include a venison version. For main course
try Applecross Bay crab salad, local scallops in creamy mushroom
and tarragon sauce with wild rice, or battered monkfish with chips
and peas. Thai chicken curry, or steak and onion pie might be among
meat options. Finish perhaps with cranachan, or apple and bramble
crumble. No real ales are served, but bottled versions of the Isle of
Skye Brewery's range are available, as well as Fraoch Heather Ale, a
range of over 50 single malts, and Scottish Cairn O'Mohr wines,
which come in flavours such as elderflower or oak leaf. Up to half a
dozen wines are sold by the glass. SAMPLE DISHES: haggis flambé in
Drambuie £5; Scottish salmon fillet marinated in olive oil, wine, lime
and coriander £7; boozy bread-and-butter pudding £2.50.

Licensee Judith Fish (freehouse)
Open *11.30 to 11.30 (1am Fri, all week 12 to 11 winter); bar food 12 to 9;
restaurant 6.30 to 8.30; closed 25 Dec, 1 Jan*
Details *Children welcome before 8.30pm   Car park   Wheelchair access (also
WC)   Garden and patio   No-smoking area in bar, no smoking in dining room
Occasional live music; jukebox   Dogs welcome exc in dining room
MasterCard, Switch, Visa   Accommodation: 7 rooms, B&B £25 to £60*

ARDFERN Argyll & Bute   map 11

▲ *Galley of Lorne*

Ardfern PA31 8QN   TEL: (01852) 500284
on B8002, reached from A816 N of Lochgilphead

On fine days it is possible to take meals and drinks on the terrace of
this traditional eighteenth-century inn, and enjoy the beautiful
scenery, which includes views over Loch Craignish. When the
weather is not so kind, the friendly atmosphere and log fires in the
Galley Bar provide a welcome alternative setting. The lengthy bar

menu offers down-to-earth but appealing fare that ranges from traditional Scottish delicacies like haggis with cream and whisky to spicy Mexican chicken. In between come sweet-cured pickled herrings, deep-fried sole fillet, cheesy pasta, and moules marinière, with hot lemon pudding, or sticky ginger pudding with toffee sauce to finish. There is also a blackboard of daily specials, which might include braised shank of lamb, or monkfish provençale. The restaurant occupies the inn's former stables and has fine views of the loch from its glass doors, which open on to the terrace. Fresh local seafood is the speciality, which might mean kipper pâté, pan-fried large Islay scallops with herb and garlic butter, or poached Loch Etive salmon with salad. Real ales are not served, owing to the pub's remote location, but there is a short wine list, and around 20 or so malt whiskies are offered. SAMPLE DISHES: smoked salmon, bacon and chive pâté £5; venison escalopes with redcurrant gravy £9.75; cranachan £3.25.

Licensee Susana Garland (freehouse)
Open *summer 11 to 11, Sun 12 to 11, winter Mon to Fri 11 to 2.30, 5 to 11, Sat 11 to 11, Sun 12 to 11; restaurant Easter to Nov 6.30 to 9.15; closed weekday afternoons winter, 25 Dec*
Details *Children welcome in bar eating area   Car park   Wheelchair access (also WC)   Garden and patio   Occasional live or background music   Dogs welcome* MasterCard, Switch, Visa   Accommodation: 7 rooms, B&B £35 to £80

BOWMORE   Argyll & Bute   map 11

▲ *Harbour Inn*

The Square, Bowmore, Isle of Islay PA43 7JR
TEL: (01496) 810330
WEB SITE: www.harbour-inn.com

LOCAL PRODUCE

A visit to the Harbour Inn is worth it for the locality alone. It sits out on a limb in the Western Isles among the whisky distilleries of Islay. The local single malt, Bowmore, takes pride of place among the range on offer, but the whole complement of the smoky, peaty whiskies the island specialises in is available behind the bar. The proprietors also support local produce in their cooking, with red meats and seasonal game from both hereabouts and from neighbouring Jura the centrepieces. Seafood, too, is celebrated, perhaps in the form of fish chowder with garlic croûtons, a fishcake of crabmeat with lime and sweet pepper dressing, or oysters from Loch Gruinart served plain with sea salt and lemon or gratinated under local cheese on a bed of creamed leeks. For main course, Lagavulin scallops are seasoned with ginger, soy and honey, baked whole sea bass is served with provençale vegetables and herbs, and venison is accompanied by wild mushrooms and rosehip jelly. For what is billed as 'the finale', expect chilled coconut risotto with grilled pineapple and dark rum caramel sauce, or summer berries with lemon bavarois. No real ales are served, but the interesting wine list has much to offer under £15, and eight are available by the glass. SAMPLE DISHES: pan-fried scallops on dauphinois potatoes £6; beef fillet and Stornoway haggis with a shallot and Bordeaux sauce £15; steamed apricot and orange nutty pudding with orange custard £3.75.

Licensee Scott Chance (freehouse)
Open *11am to 1am; bar food and restaurant all week (exc Sun lunchtime) 12 to 2.30, 6 to 9; closed lunchtime 1 Jan*
Details *No children Wheelchair access (not WC) No smoking in dining room Occasional background music Dogs welcome Amex, Delta, MasterCard, Switch, Visa Accommodation: 8 rooms, B&B £37.50 to £75*

BRIG O'TURK Stirling   map 11

Byre Inn

Brig o'Turk FK17 8HT   TEL: (01877) 376292
on A821 Callander and Aberfoyle

'Bridge of the Wild Boar' is the English translation of the name of this hamlet in the Trossachs, though that may seem a touch exotic when you see this tiny inn. Inside, bare stone walls and dark beams are the order of the day, and the place feels cosy and friendly, thanks to a huge fire in winter and the equally warm welcome from the host. In winter, the clientele are mostly locals, but in summer the pub is popular with walkers and tourists. At lunchtime, food is simple, and in the evening the nearest thing to pub grub might be soup with chunky bread, and Toulouse sausages with mash. Otherwise the extensive menu might offer tom yum soup, navarin of lamb with couscous, and duck breast with kumquats. Drinking options include Fraoch Heather Ale, a reasonably priced wine list of 20-plus bottles (with three by the glass), and a decent range of whiskies. Prices are considered reasonable for the quality of the food, and, as a reader commented, the pub earns 'full marks for achieving this standard while remaining an honest local'. Note that winter lunchtime opening may be a bit erratic and it is best to check in advance. SAMPLE DISHES: steamed West Coast mussels in curry cream £4.25; Cajun salmon with avocado salsa and gazpacho sauce £9.50; crème brûlée £4.

Licensee Jean-François Meder (freehouse)
Open *Tue to Sat 12 to 3, 6 to 11 (12 Fri and Sat), Sun 12 to 10.30; bar food and restaurant Tue to Sun 12 to 2, 6 to 9*
Details *Children welcome Car park Wheelchair access (also WC) Garden No smoking in dining room Background music No dogs Switch, Visa*

CLACHAN Argyll & Bute map 11

▲ *Tigh-an-Truish*

Clachan Seil, Isle of Seil PA34 4QZ   TEL: (01852) 300242
on B844, 12m S of Oban

Seil is linked to the mainland by an elegant bridge, which can be seen from this eighteenth-century stone-built pub. 'Homely if a little spartan' was how a reporter described the two bar areas, one popular with locals, the second a traditional snug where those with children can be accommodated. Likewise, cooking is 'simple but effective' and doesn't try to innovate but produces some good dishes in hearty portions: leek and potato soup, 'delicious' sweet-cured pickled herring, pork chops in grain mustard sauce, moules marinière, lasagne, baked potatoes, and various filled baguettes. Regularly changing guest ales might include Courage Directors or Wells Bombardier Premium Bitter, and a basic wine list includes three by the glass. In front of the pub is a patio with tables where you can sit and enjoy the view in summer. SAMPLE DISHES: locally smoked salmon £4.50; seafood pie £6.50; apple crumble £2.

Licensee Miranda Brunner (freehouse)
Open *summer 11am (12.30 Sun) to midnight; winter Mon to Thur 11 to 2, 5 to 11.30, Fri and Sat 11 to 11.30, Sun 12.30 to 11.30; bar food 12 (12.30 Sun) to 2, 6 to 8.30*
Details *Children welcome in family room   Car park   Garden and patio   No smoking in dining room   Background music   Dogs welcome   No cards Accommodation: 2 rooms, B&B £45*

CRINAN Argyll & Bute map 11

▲ *Crinan Hotel* ✿ NEW ENTRY

Crinan PA31 8SR   TEL: (01546) 830261
WEB SITE: www.crinanhotel.com
take B841 off A816 6m NW of Lochgilphead

'The Crinan Hotel,' commented a visitor, 'is set in heaven.' Indeed, you might well feel that you had left terra firma behind when sitting in the rooftop seafood restaurant here, but the view from the bar across the loch to the hills beyond is quite as breathtaking. In the foreground, just outside the window, boats can be seen negotiating the complex lock system. The hotel is a shimmering white presence on the western edge of Argyll, the bar an elegant, wood-panelled room with pictures of marine wildlife and a pleasantly relaxed atmosphere. The bar food is perfectly simple, and yet a combination of fine raw materials and care in presentation elevates it out of the ordinary. Top-quality pork sausages come with 'rich, unctuous' mash flecked with chives and an intense onion gravy, Arbroath smokie is tender and delicately smoked, served with a sharp-tasting tomato butter sauce and good chips, and the ten-ounce Aberdeen Angus sirloin steak with chips, salad and spot-on béarnaise sauce could scarcely be bettered. Start with a bowl of home-made soup with crusty bread, or smoked wild salmon, and round things off with dessert of the day or one of the Orkney ice creams. A list of carefully chosen wines offers only a pair of house wines by the glass, but there are a fair few half-bottles to consider. Only bottled beers are stocked, which seems a shame given the class exuded by the rest of the operation. SAMPLE DISHES: Loch Etive mussels with garlic and cream £8.50; locally smoked wild Scottish salmon with caper-berries and shallots £12.50; Scottish farmhouse Cheddar with fig chutney £4.50.

Licensee Nick Ryan (freehouse)
Open *11 to 11; bar food 12 to 2.30 (2 winter), 7 to 9 (8.30 winter); restaurant Tue to Sat 7 to 9; closed Christmas*
Details *Children welcome   Car park   Wheelchair access (also WC)   Patio No smoking in dining room   Occasional live music   Dogs welcome exc in dining areas   Amex, MasterCard, Switch, Visa   Accommodation: 20 rooms, D,B&B £75 to £220*

CROMARTY   Highland   map 11

▲ *Royal Hotel*

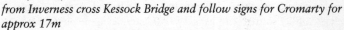

SEASIDE

Marine Terrace, Cromarty IV11 8YN
TEL: (01381) 600217
from Inverness cross Kessock Bridge and follow signs for Cromarty for approx 17m

---

Overlooking the beach from behind a sea wall, this large white-painted hotel with black woodwork also overlooks the Ross-shire mountains from its lounge and sun porch. Inside, it is bright and colourful enough to compensate for any greyness in the sky, and the equally bright menu portrays some intriguing forays from the ordinary. Highland pâté is made according to 'a slightly secret' recipe, locally smoked salmon is accompanied by cream cheese and aspara-gus, deep-fried mushrooms come with a light curry mayonnaise, while battered haggis balls offer the added pleasure of a Drambuie sauce. 'Trout tantaliser' is garnished with prawns, pineapple, apple and nuts, tagliatelle sutors is pasta in cream sauce with smoked salmon, prawns and herbs, while the farmer's mixed grill adds 'a few surprises' to steak and escalope. Real ales stocked are John Smith's Bitter, Tetley Smooth and Belhaven Best, and over 25 malts are kept. Two wines from the thirty-strong list are offered by the glass. SAMPLE DISHES: prawn and apple boat £5; seafood crêpe £7.75; sherry trifle £3.25.

Licensee John Shearer (freehouse)
Open *10 to 12; bar food 12 to 2, 5.30 (6 restaurant) to 9*
Details *Children welcome   Car park   Wheelchair access (also WC)   Garden and patio   No-smoking area in bar   Occasional live or background music; jukebox   Dogs welcome in bar   Amex, Delta, MasterCard, Switch, Visa Accommodation: 10 rooms, B&B £30 to £60*

DRYMEN   Stirling   map 11

Clachan Inn 🍺

2 Main Street, Drymen G63 0BP   TEL: (01360) 660824
off A811, 20m W of Stirling

This old pub is what an inspector calls a traditional 'couthy' Scottish place. For non-Scottish readers the dictionary defines this is as friendly, kindly, comfortable, snug – and, indeed, she found it offered a genuine and warm welcome to natives, children and strangers. Décor may be somewhat basic, but the appeal lies in the great atmosphere and the 'lashings of basic pub grub in old-fashioned portions' at reasonable prices. 'Splendid' steaks have included Lamlash sirloin with Arran whisky and mustard, haggis has been 'tasty', and lasagne comes with a rich Cheddar cheese sauce. Belhaven Best and St Andrew's Ale, and Caledonian Deuchars IPA are 'well kept and skilfully hand-pumped' and there is wide range of whiskies. House wines are said to be 'decent', and so are tea and coffee from a cappuccino and espresso machine. SAMPLE DISHES: leek and potato soup £2; chicken fillet stuffed with haggis £7.50; caramel apple pie £2.25.

Licensee Elizabeth Plank (freehouse)
Open *11 to 12, Sun 12.30 to 12; bar food and restaurant 12 to 4, 6 to 10 (12.30 Sun); closed 25 Dec and 1 Jan*
Details *Children welcome in dining-room   Wheelchair access (also WC) Background music   Dogs welcome on leads in bar   MasterCard, Switch, Visa*

Old Rectory Inn

West Quality Street, Dysart KY1 2TE   TEL: (01592) 651211
off A955 Methil road, N of Kirkaldy

Located in a picturesque village, a short walk from the harbour, this pub may have a plain exterior but that is countered by the warm welcome inside. Indeed, service is attentive, friendly and particularly good with children. The décor makes much use of empty cigar and wine boxes, but what draws visitors and the canniest of Scots is the good food in 'frighteningly large portions' at 'ridiculously cheap' prices. Despite including chicken curry, and pasta, the menu otherwise rarely strays far from home. Even 'vegetable Swiss fondue' turns out to be a large Yorkshire pudding filled with diced vegetables. However the restaurant à la carte menu (also available in the bar) does offer some more exotic items such as sweet-and-sour sauce with baby black pudding fritters. Of the bar dishes and daily specials, reporters have enjoyed beef and tomato soup with 'a wonderfully rich beef flavour', and smoked haddock Mornay. Main courses might include a fish stew of prawns, mussels, scallops and cockles; or Tyrolean steak with tomato and onion sauce, and onion rings. Hot puddings are £1.95 but those based on ice cream, such as knicker-bocker glory, are a pound more. Bottled Calders Cream is the main beer, but the continually updated wine list has five reds by the glass and four whites, and prices that stay resolutely below the £20 mark. Wines have been selected for easy-drinking approachability – they'll be pretty good with food too. SAMPLE DISHES: flash-fried sardines £3.50; boiled leg of ham £6; chocolate brownie £2.

Licensee David North (freehouse)
Open *Tue to Sat 12 to 5, 7 to 11, Sun 12.30 to 4; bar food and restaurant 12 to 2, 7 to 9.30, Sun 12.30 to 3; closed 1 week mid-Jan, 2 weeks mid-Oct, 1 week early July*
Details *Children welcome in eating areas   Car park   Wheelchair access (also WC)   Garden   No music   Guide dogs only   Amex, Delta, MasterCard, Switch, Visa*

▲ *Courtyard*

Eaglesfield DG11 3PQ   TEL: (01461) 500215
off A74(M), 3m E of Ecclefechan

The village of Eaglesfield consists of not much more than a row of houses, though it is close to several tourist hotspots, including

Gretna Green and Ecclefechan, birthplace of Thomas Carlyle. At the
centre of the village is this relaxed and welcoming pub, which
consists of a series of rooms starting with the main bar where locals
gather to drink, then a dining area and beyond that the restaurant –
it can be busy, so those wishing to eat, whether in bar or restaurant,
may be advised to book. Food is good value if not over-ambitious:
crispy mushrooms with garlic dip, deep-fried Brie with redcurrant
jelly, pork fillet with creamy mustard sauce, loin of lamb in sherry
sauce, and mild and fruity chicken curry are typical of the style. Real
ales are not a strong suit, but wines are a decent choice of fairly
priced bottles with three by the glass. SAMPLE DISHES: grilled king
prawns in garlic butter £3.75; duck breast with cranberries and
Glayva £8.75; sticky toffee pudding £2.75.

Licensee Michael Mason (freehouse)
Open *12 to 2.30, 6.30 to 12; bar food and restaurant Tue to Sun 12 to 2, 7
to 9; closed Mon winter*
Details *Children welcome in bar eating area   Car park   Wheelchair access
(also WC)   Garden and patio   No smoking in dining room   Background
music   Dogs welcome exc in dining room   MasterCard, Visa
Accommodation: 6 rooms, B&B £21 to £40*

ELIE   Fife   map 11

Ship Inn

The Toft, Elie KY9 1DT   TEL: (01333) 330246
on A917, 5m W of Anstruther

Where many country pubs have a village green, the Ship has a beach
stretching out before it. And like the traditional village green, the
beach is where the pub's cricket team plays in summer, with crowds
watching from the relative comfort of the sea wall. Also in the
summer you will find a barbecue in the beer garden turning out
burgers, sausages, steaks and a variety of seafood. The interior is
simply decorated and furnished, and often crowded with day trippers from Edinburgh as well as with locals and holidaymakers. A
short and varied menu deals mostly in pub stalwarts, many with a
Scottish theme, such as haggis, tatties and neeps. Fish options are
plentiful: moules marinière, for example, grilled whole Dover sole,
and haddock and chips with good batter and 'excellent' home-made
tartare sauce. Real ales such Deuchars IPA and Theakston Best Bitter
are available in the summer months, and a short list of wines
includes four by the glass. Golf fans should note that Elie has its own
golf course, and St Andrews is only 11 miles away. SAMPLE DISHES:
chicken and avocado £4.50; steak and Guinness pie £7.50; apple pie
with custard £3.50.

Licensees Richard and Jill Philip (freehouse)
Open *11am to midnight (1am Fri and Sat, 11pm winter), Sun 12.30 to midnight (11 winter); bar food Mon to Sat 12 to 2.30 (2 winter), 6 to 9.30 (9 winter exc Fri and Sat), Sun 12.30 to 3 (2.30 winter); closed 25 Dec*
Details *Children welcome in eating areas Wheelchair access (also WC) Garden and patio No music Dogs welcome Delta, MasterCard, Switch, Visa*

GLENDEVON   Perthshire & Kinross   map 11

▲ *Tormaukin Hotel*

Glendevon FK14 7JY   TEL: (01259) 781252
WEB SITE: www.tormaukin.co.uk
on A823, 6m SE of Auchterarder

In the Ochil Hills on a quiet country road, the setting of this eighteenth-century drovers' inn can truly be called rural and idyllic. The interior is very pleasant, too, with blazing fires warming the comfortably furnished bars and oak-beamed family room in winter. Eclectic would be a good way to sum up the bar menu: among starters may be dishes like haggis and black pudding fritters, but this could be followed with something more exotic, such as Thai chicken, or spiced Moroccan lamb. Children and vegetarians have their own sections on the menu. The alternative eating option is the relaxed dining room, which has its own menu of fine Scottish fare, including Perthshire lamb, wild venison, and salmon with scallops and mussels. By Scottish standards, the selection of real ales is well above average, including Harviestoun Brooker's Bitter & Twisted and Timothy Taylor Landlord. A good wine list, strong on French bottles, and not always cheaply priced, has the bonus of 16 half-bottles, including two champagnes. Around eight wines are served by the glass. The pub arranges special events, such as wine and whisky tastings, live jazz and quiz nights. SAMPLE DISHES: mussel, onion and potato chowder £4; minced steak and kidney bridies £8; sticky gingerbread pudding £4.

Licensee Isadura Simpson (freehouse)
Open *11 (12 Sun) to 11; bar food Mon to Sat 12 to 2, 5.30 to 9.30, Sun 12 to 9.30; restaurant 12 to 2, 5.30 to 9.30; closed 8 to 11 Jan*
Details *Children welcome in eating areas Car park Wheelchair access (also WC) Patio Live or background music No dogs Amex, Delta, Diners, MasterCard, Switch, Visa Accommodation: 10 rooms, B&B £30 to £55*

The Guide is totally independent, accepts no free hospitality and carries no advertising.

GLENELG   Highland   map 11

▲ *Glenelg Inn*

Glenelg, by Kyle of Lochalsh IV40 8JR   TEL: (01599) 522273
WEB SITE: www.glenelg-inn.com
at head of Sound of Sleat, off A87 at Loch Duich

A lively atmosphere pervades the bar of this traditional Highland
inn, where you may hear traditional singing and fiddle or pipe music
being performed by local folk groups in the evening. The dining
room has a quieter atmosphere. Simple lunch fare might be lentil and
vegetable soup followed by smoked chicken salad, roast loin of pork
with a herb stuffing, or one of the assorted sandwiches and toasties
offered. Bar food in the evening is along similar lines, with, perhaps,
a main course of baked halibut with vine tomatoes. In the restaurant
at dinner the format is a four-course set-price meal: cream of mushroom soup, perhaps, followed by pan-fried Scotch beef with baked
peppers and onions and a Burgundy sauce, or a dish using local
seafood (oysters, mussels, prawns and wild salmon all feature regularly in season). Finish with bananas baked in syrup and rum, and
then 'help yourself to cheese'. Other ingredients from Scotland's
natural larder include local venison and lamb. There are no real ales,
but two wines are available by the glass from a list of about ten, and
Fraoch Heather Ale is available in bottles. Boat trips can be arranged
for those who wish to explore the sea lochs, with their unspoilt
beaches and coves. SAMPLE DISHES: smoked mackerel and peppers
with herb bread £3.50; game pie £7; strawberry cheesecake £3.

Licensee Christopher Main (freehouse)
Open *summer Mon to Sun 12 to 2.30, 5 to 11; winter Mon to Sat 5 to 11;
bar food and restaurant 12.30 to 2, 7.30 to 9*
Details *Children welcome   Car park   Wheelchair access (also WC)   Garden
No smoking in dining room   Live or background music   Dogs welcome exc in
dining room   Delta, Diners, MasterCard, Switch, Visa   Accommodation: 6
rooms, B&B and dinner from £50 per person*

HOWGATE   Midlothian   map 11

The Howgate 🍇

Howgate EH26 8PY   TEL: (01968) 670000
WEB SITE: www.howgate.f9.co.uk
on A6094 Leadburn to Auchendinny road, 1½m SE of Penicuik

Set in rural woodland a couple of miles from Penicuik (and only ten
from Edinburgh), The Howgate is a converted row of agricultural
workers' cottages now housing a bar/bistro and a restaurant. A chan-

delier hangs from a panelled ceiling in the bar/bistro, where polished wood tables are set for dining, while the main restaurant is softly lit, with bare floorboards and whitewashed stone walls, and the tables are set with crisp napery and good glassware. Separate menus of some length operate in the two eating areas (though the restaurant menu is available throughout), but both seem to be doing their level best to avoid the clichés of pub catering. Thus, in the bar/bistro, you might progress from warm honeyed chicken and cashew-nut salad with lime and ginger dressing to lamb meatballs with garlic and coriander, tagliatelle and a red wine and tomato sauce. Restaurant visitors get through seared pigeon breast with a stir-fry of spinach and sultanas, followed by olive-crusted sea bass with saffron and mascarpone risotto. Vegetarian choices are equally well conceived, and classically sauced chargrilled steaks are a speciality. To finish, try sauté strawberries in Drambuie syrup with cracked pepper ice cream, or coconut and pistachio parfait with coffee syrup. A Belhaven beer is on draught, and eight wines by the glass conclude a lively and well-priced list, arranged by grape variety. Cru Classé Margaux sits easily among Chilean and Australian Cabernets and Merlots, and Sauvignon Blanc and Grenache get good billing too. If you want fruity, full-on New World flavour then there's lots to tempt here under £20. A clutch of good cognacs adds lustre to after-dinner drinking. SAMPLE DISHES: filo basket of haggis with king prawns £6; roast pork fillet with apple, ginger and thyme with lemon couscous and red wine glaze £11.50; citrus cheesecake with mixed berry compote £4.50.

Licensee Nigel Hogg (freehouse)
Open *12 to 2.30, 6 to 11; bar food and restaurant 12 to 2.30, 6 to 9.30; closed 25 and 26 Dec, 1 and 2 Jan*
Details *Children welcome   Car park   Wheelchair access (also WC)   Patio No smoking in dining room   Background music   No dogs   Amex, Delta, Diners, MasterCard, Switch, Visa*

INNERLEITHEN   Borders   map 11

▲ *Traquair Arms* 🍺

Traquair Road, Innerleithen EH44 6PD   TEL: (01896) 830229
off A72, 6m SE of Peebles

Fans of Sir Walter Scott will know Innerleithen better as St Ronan's Well, the name he gave the village in his Waverley novels. It has changed little since Scott's day, and that includes this comfortable and welcoming hotel. On handpump are Bear Ale and sometimes others from the eighteenth-century brewery in nearby Traquair House, as well as brews such as Greenmantle and Merlin from the local Broughton Ales brewery. Food is served in the bar and lounge, both warmed by blazing log fires, or in the restaurant or tea room. One menu is offered throughout, and the cooking is in mostly traditional vein: moules marinière, or deep-fried garlic mushrooms for starters, and main courses of Finnan savoury (smoked haddock with Ayrshire cheese), baked sole with chilli sauce, grilled lamb chops, and various steaks. A good-value wine list includes three house selections in two sizes of glass or by the bottle. SAMPLE DISHES: chicken liver pâté £3.50; venison casserole £6.25; cranachan £2.75.

Licensee Dianne Johnston (freehouse)
Open *11 to midnight, Sun 12 to 11; bar food and restaurant 12 to 9; closed 25 and 26 Dec, 1 to 4 Jan*
Details *Children welcome   Car park   Wheelchair access (not WC)   Garden and patio   No smoking in dining room   Background music   Dogs welcome exc in dining room   Amex, Delta, MasterCard, Switch, Visa   Accommodation: 10 rooms, B&B £45 to £80*

KILMELFORD   Argyll & Bute   map 11

▲ *Cuilfail Hotel*

Kilmelford PA34 4XA   TEL: (01852) 200274
WEB SITE: www.cuilfail.co.uk
on A816 at head of Loch Melfort, 12m S of Oban

Cuilfail is Gaelic for 'sheltered corner', an appropriate name for this old drovers' inn at the foot of the Argyll hills, close to the shore of Loch Melfort. Most of the present structure dates from Victorian times, although the building has much older origins. Prime Highland produce is put to good use in the kitchen, and the centrepiece of the Tartan Puffer restaurant is the indoor barbecue, which is used to cook beef, lamb, pork and venison, as well as local fish and seafood. A typical selection might take in duck breast, dived scallops, or fillets of wild salmon from the loch, all served in various combinations, including 'surf 'n' turf', with a selection of sauces. For starters, there may be haggis fritters, or grilled smoked trout, and to finish you could try barbecued bananas, or poached pears with Bailey's-flavoured toffee. The same menu is available for those eating in the bar. Beers are an uninspiring selection, but wine drinkers are offered a list of 16 to choose from, including house red and white at £11.95. Between two and four wines are available by the glass. In addition, there are 100 whiskies to try. SAMPLE DISHES: mussels and bacon kebabs £5; best end of Scotch lamb £9; stem ginger and kiwi cheesecake £4.

Licensee David Birrell (freehouse)
Open *11 to 11 (12 to 2.30, 6.30 to 11 winter); bar food 12 to 9 (6 winter); restaurant 6.30 to 9.30*
Details *Children welcome   Car park   Wheelchair access (also WC)   Garden Occasional live or background music   Dogs welcome   Delta, MasterCard, Switch, Visa   Accommodation: 12 rooms, B&B £25 to £70*

KINNESSWOOD   Perthshire & Kinross   map 11

▲ *Lomond Country Inn*

Kinnesswood KY13 7HN   TEL: (01592) 840253
on A911, 4m SE of Milnathort

Panoramic views of Loch Leven are one of the draws of this 100-year-old inn. On the one hand it functions as the local pub, and on the other it is a place for visitors to stay at, whether touring the area or partaking in the many sporting activities that the region provides: fishing, golf and riding, for example. Bar menus have a familiar ring to them, with options such as chicken liver pâté, or Caesar salad among starters, and main courses of beef and ale pie, deep-fried haddock with lemon and caper mayonnaise, or goats' cheese and broccoli quiche with warm couscous salad. A more up-market menu operates in the separate restaurant. Typical dishes might be smoked venison carpaccio with thyme and lemon vinegar, followed by roast crown of pheasant on braised red cabbage with smoked bacon and apples. A small selection of real ales includes Deuchars IPA and Tetley Bitter; more variety is shown on the reasonably priced wine list, with four served by the glass. SAMPLE DISHES: deep-fried potato wedges with garlic and herb mayonnaise £4.50; chargrilled tuna steak on roasted Mediterranean vegetables £8.50; blackcurrant mousse £3.75.

Licensee Martin Bald (freehouse)
Open *Mon to Thur 11 to 11, Fri and Sat 11 to 11.45, Sun 12.30 to 11; bar food and restaurant Mon to Sat 12.30 to 2, 6.30 to 9, Sun 12.30 to 9*
Details *Children welcome   Car park   Wheelchair access (also WC)   Garden and patio   No-smoking area in bar, no smoking in dining room   No music Dogs welcome exc in dining room   Amex, Delta, Diners, MasterCard, Switch, Visa   Accommodation: 12 rooms, B&B £32.50 to £74*

All details are as accurate as possible at the time of going to press, but pubs often change hands, and it is wise to check beforehand by telephone anything that is particularly important to you.

▲ Cross Keys

Main Street, Kippen FK8 3DN   TEL: (01786) 870293
on B822, 10m W of Stirling

This village inn, dating from the beginning of the eighteenth century, has climbing roses outside, a garden at the back and a mixture of rooms within. These comprise a public bar, a family room and a low-ceilinged, beamed restaurant area, all plainly decorated but comfortable. It changed hands shortly before the Guide went to press, and early reports suggest that the Scotts are well capable of maintaining the high standard set by their predecessors. The fruit machine and jukebox have now vanished from the public bar, which will be music (or not) to the ears of many. The same daily-changing menu applies throughout the pub, listing comfort food of the likes of chicken liver and orange pâté, herrings marinated in sherry, and prawn cocktail to start. These may be followed by highly rated steak pie, accurately cooked lambs' liver and bacon, smoked salmon omelette, or Irish stew, all accompanied by 'excellent' vegetables. Sandwiches are available all day. The desserts (gâteaux, profiteroles and ice creams) are mostly bought in, but home-made bread-and-butter pudding is worth investigating. A constantly changing pair of guest beers might well include something like Belhaven 80/- or the ominously named Brooke's Bitter & Twisted from the Harviestoun Brewery. Five wines from a list of around 20 come by the glass. SAMPLE DISHES: watercress soup £2; fillet of haddock £6.25; cheesecake £3.

Licensee Gordon Scott (freehouse)
Open *Mon to Thur 12 to 12, Fri and Sat 12 to 1, Sun 12.30 to 12; bar food and restaurant 12 (12.30 Sun) to 9 (12 to 2.30, 5.30 to 9 winter); closed 1 Jan*
Details *Children welcome   Car park   Wheelchair access (also women's WC) Garden and patio   No smoking in 1 dining room   Live or background music Dogs welcome in bar   Delta, MasterCard, Switch, Visa   Accommodation: 3 rooms, B&B £21.50 to £43*

Ship Inn 🍺

VIEWS

Halketts Hall, Limekilns KY11 3HJ
TEL: (01383) 872247
on N bank of Firth of Forth, 2m W of Inverkeithing

From this pub on the north side of the Firth of Forth there are splendid views of the water, and downstream to the bridges crossing it. Inside it is welcoming and homely, and child friendly too, with shipping artefacts and books, and different books and toys for the children. Menus have a nice balance between the slightly exotic, such as prawn parcels with soy dip, and the traditional, as in haggis Creggin, shepherd's pie (made with 'nicely flavoured minced lamb in a tomato-y base'), and home-made ice cream. Prices are very reasonable, and there's a children's menu too. Affable, prompt and informal service is commended, particularly the bringing to table of samples of the two house wines, to taste and choose. The house wines change every couple of months, and are the only ones on the short list to be served by the glass. A good choice of real ales includes Belhaven St Andrews and 80/- Ale, Orkney Dark Island, and Houston St Peter's Well. Live folk music or karaoke feature on Saturday evenings. The pub has no car park, but parking is available along the sea front. SAMPLE DISHES: fish chowder £3.50; beef enchiladas £6; fruit crumble £3.

Licensee Jane Karan (freehouse)
Open *Mon to Wed 11 to 11, Thur to Sat 11am to midnight, Sun 12.30 to 12; bar food 11.30 to 6, Sun 12.30 to 6; closed 25 Dec*
Details *Children welcome   Wheelchair access (also WC)   Garden   Live music or background music   Dogs welcome   Delta, MasterCard, Switch, Visa*

MELROSE   Borders   map 11

▲ *Burts Hotel* ❦

Market Square, Melrose TD6 9PL
TEL: (01896) 822285
WEB SITE: www.burtshotel.co.uk
on A6091, midway between Galashiels and St Boswells

Melrose is a popular base for tourists exploring the Scottish Borders country, its attractions including the remains of the twelfth-century abbey, believed to be the burial place of the heart of Robert the Bruce. Burts is much more recent, having been built in 1722 on the picturesque market square as the home of a local dignitary, but for more than 30 years it has been run as a friendly hotel with a formal restaurant and relaxing lounge bar. The bar menu has a Scottish feel but also shows wider influences, so quenelles of pigeon and haggis pâté come with red onion marmalade and peppered mango dressing, while Loch Fyne mussels in mushroom and garlic cream, and grilled Scottish Border lamb cutlets are likely to appear alongside seared tuna on oriental salad with basil, and stir-fried beef with pasta and hoisin. Appealing options on the restaurant menu might include galantine of quail with strawberry, grape and pecan salad, and Barbary duck breast with sauté cabbage and Parma ham. Drinkswise, this is whisky heaven, with no fewer than 80 single malts on offer. Alternatively, Caledonian 80/- and Deuchars IPA are the regular beers, while the guest ale might be Fuller's London Pride. Of the 100 or so wines listed there's a serious tranche of French classics that are not to be skipped past as starting prices are very reasonable. Fans of New World fruity flavours will not be disappointed either as Chardonnay, Shiraz and the other varietal favourites are all listed too. Four wines by the glass, and house wines around the £12 mark, allow some breathing space for those not looking to spend a fortune. SAMPLE DISHES: terrine of salmon and monkfish wrapped in smoked salmon £4; chargrilled lamb burgers with yellow tomato chutney £6.75; coffee and Tia Maria crème brûlée with cappuccino ice cream £4.25.

Licensee Graham Henderson (freehouse)
Open *11 to 2, 5 to 11, Sun 12 to 2, 6 to 11; bar food and restaurant 12 to 2, 6 to 9.30; closed 26 Dec*
Details *Children welcome   Car park   Garden   No smoking in 1 lounge   No music   Dogs welcome in bar   Amex, Delta, Diners, MasterCard, Switch, Visa Accommodation: 20 rooms, B&B £50 to £88*

MINNIGAFF   Dumfries & Galloway   map 11

▲ *Creebridge House Hotel* 🍺

Minnigaff DG8 6NP   TEL: (01671) 402121
WEB SITE: www.creebridge.co.uk
off A75, just N of Newton Stewart

Formerly a residence of the Earls of Galloway, now a comfortable country hotel, this attractive stone building stands in three acres of gardens and woodland. The primary eating option is the Garden Restaurant, which offers a fixed-price menu of dishes as varied as seared salmon with tomato pasta and lobster sauce, and Chinese-style stir-fried pork. The style and atmosphere are more informal in the brasserie, though dishes can be complex: prawn cocktail becomes a timbale of prawns and smoked salmon dressed with marie-rose sauce and basil oil and garnished with scallops, for instance. Galloway lamb is a highlight, perhaps in filo parcels with onion confit and port jus, or a roast shoulder stuffed with mushrooms and walnuts; steaks come in various cuts and weights with a choice of sauces. Unusual variations on the lunchtime sandwich theme include home-baked naan filled with curried chicken, and further choice is offered by the daily specials board. Wash the food down with real ales from the small Sulwath Brewers, which is just down the road in Castle Douglas: Criffel, Cuil Hill and Knockendoch are regularly stocked. Around 30 wines are listed, with an impressive 10 to 20 by the glass. Great care and attention have gone into the selection, but you'll have to dig deep into your pockets to appreciate it fully. SAMPLE DISHES: seared king scallops and mussels gratin £5.75; steak and ale pie £6.50; hot chocolate and orange bread-and-butter pudding £3.

Licensee Chris Walker (freehouse)
Open *12 to 2.30, 6 to 11 (12 Sat and Sun); bar food and restaurant 12 (12.30 Sun) to 2, 6 to 9; restaurant closed Nov to Mar; closed 26 Dec*
Details *Children welcome   Car park   Wheelchair access (not WC)   Garden No smoking in dining room   Live or background music   Dogs welcome exc in eating areas   Amex, Delta, MasterCard, Switch, Visa   Accommodation: 19 rooms, B&B £49 to £79*

NETHERLEY   Aberdeenshire   map 11

Lairhillock Inn

Netherley AB39 3QS   TEL: (01569) 730001
on B979, 4m S of Peterculter

Despite being only a short drive from the centre of Aberdeen, this 200-year-old inn is surrounded by nothing but countryside for miles. The centrepiece of the bar and lounge is a charming log fire, and a conservatory with fine views is popular with families. Ale drinkers will appreciate a range that includes Timothy Taylor Landlord, Marston's Pedigree, Courage Directors plus a fortnightly-changing guest, and bottled 'Lairie's Ale', which is brewed for the inn by the Isle of Skye Brewery. More than 50 malt whiskies are also available. The bar menu, supplemented by daily specials on a blackboard, offers an extensive and varied range – from spicy spare ribs, or home-made venison sausages, to steak and ale pie, or whole baked haddock with lightly curried rice. An old-fashioned feel is aimed for in the Crynoch Restaurant, where a pianist plays most evenings. Its menu is based on local produce and a classical cooking style, typi-cally offering medallions of venison with a port and tarragon sauce, and sauté scallops with grilled salmon fillet and a mustard and leek sauce. The lengthy restaurant wine list is a serious tome; a shorter version is offered in the bar, along with guest wines, by the bottle or glass, displayed on a blackboard. SAMPLE DISHES: chunky seafood chowder £4; braised lamb shank with rosemary and red wine sauce £9.75; banana and butterscotch sundae £4.

Licensee Roger Thorne (freehouse)
Open *Mon to Fri 10.30 to 2.30, 5 to 11 (12 Fri), Sat 11am to 11.45pm, Sun noon to 10.45; bar food 12 to 2, 6 to 9.30 (10 Fri and Sat); restaurant Sun 12 to 1.45, Wed to Mon 7 to 9.30; closed 25 and 26 Dec, 1 and 2 Jan*
Details *Children welcome in dining room and conservatory   Car park Wheelchair access (also WC)   Garden   No-smoking area in bar   Background music   Dogs welcome in snug   Amex, Delta, Diners, MasterCard, Switch, Visa*

PLOCKTON   Highland   map 11

▲ *Plockton Inn*

SEAFOOD

Innes Street, Plockton IV52 8TW
TEL: (01599) 544222
WEB SITE: www.plocktoninn.co.uk
off A87, 5m NE of Kyle of Lochalsh

The harbour is not quite in sight of the pub, or its little terrace, although it's only 100 yards down the road. But the menu pays tribute to its proximity with generous netfuls of seafood in the restaurant and in the bar. Supplementing the printed menu are blackboard dishes of the day that always include a vegetable-based soup, another based on meat or fish; and a vegetarian main course. Among sandwiches made to order are spiced beef, and salmon with home-made mayonnaise. But locals as well as visitors are often tempted by Plockton prawns (to the French they are langoustines) from Lochcarron, or a platter of seafood from the smokery which might include mussels, trout, sprats, even squat lobster. These are offered as starters or main courses. Queenie scallops, lemon sole and skate wing with traditional black butter, come from specified waters, while meat might include beef, lamb or venison. Those resistant to the appeal of such desserts as brown bread ice-cream can opt for the four Scottish cheeses, Strathdon blue, Craig Mhaol, oak-smoked Orkney, and caise cruin from the local Achmore dairy. Two real ales are always on tap: perhaps Marston's Pedigree, Old Speckled Hen, Isle of Skye Blaven, Caledonian 80/-, Fuller's London Pride or Greene King Abbot Ale. SAMPLE DISHES: smoked trout pâté £3.50; red snapper with salsa verde £10; strawberry and almond roulade £3.25.

Licensee Kenneth Gollan (freehouse)
Open *11am to midnight (11.30 Sat), Sun 11 to 11; closed 25 Dec; bar food and restaurant 12 to 2.30, 6 to 10 (9 winter)*
Details *Children welcome   Car park   Wheelchair access (also WC)   Garden and patio   No smoking in dining room   Live or background music   Dogs welcome   Delta, MasterCard, Switch, Visa   Accommodation: 6 rooms, B&B £23 to £58*

STRACHUR Argyll & Bute map 11

▲ *Creggans Inn*

Strachur PA27 8BX   TEL: (01369) 860279
WEB SITE: www.creggans-inn.co.uk
on A185, to N of village

Marvellous views across water to hills are what most inspire visitors
to put pen to paper to report on this small white-painted pub on the
shore of Loch Fyne. They also commend the food, which features
plenty of the fine seafood from the loch: a plate piled high with the
freshest langoustines, for example. Also on the modern British-style
menu in the long dining room might be rack of lamb with dauphinois potatoes, king scallops with tomato and rocket salad, poached
halibut with asparagus, and breast of duck with celeriac cream. In
the comfortable, smartly panelled bar, by the warmth of a real fire,
simpler food is offered, such as half a dozen oysters, Rothesay
smoked salmon, or a sirloin steak sandwich. Courage Directors and
Boddingtons Bitter are the real ales dispensed, and the interesting
wine list has plenty of half-bottles and six by the glass. SAMPLE
DISHES: grilled goats' cheese and roast vegetable salad £4.75; roast
pork chops with grain mustard mash £6.50; lemon tart £3.50.

Licensee Alex Robertson (freehouse)
Open *11 to 11 (12 Fri and Sat); bar food and restaurant 12 to 2.30, 6 to 9*
Details *Children welcome   Car park   Garden   No smoking in dining room
Occasional live or background music   Dogs welcome in bar   Delta,
MasterCard, Switch, Visa   Accommodation: 14 rooms, B&B£55 to £170*

SWINTON Borders map 11

▲ *Wheatsheaf* ❁ ❦

Main Street, Swinton TD11 3JJ
TEL: (01890) 860257
on A6112, Coldstream to Duns road

This stone-built country inn facing the village green can be considered a gastro-pub or, as the Reids describe the operation, a restaurant-with-rooms. The interior has an upmarket feel, but is warm and
inviting, with well spaced-out tables and an open log fire. A stream
of favourable reports unanimously note friendly and extremely efficient service and praise Alan Reid's cooking. Typical of starters are
deep-fried squid with garlic mayonnaise, or sauté mushrooms and
bacon in a filo pastry basket. Main dishes might be Eyemouth
smoked fish and potato pie, or roast Scottish pork tenderloin with

cider sauce, with summer pudding with (local) Whitsome berries, or Scottish cheeses to follow. Broughton Bramling Cross and Greenmantle, as well as Caledonian 80/- and Deuchars IPA are kept. A well-balanced range of 99 wines starts with a house selection of six at £10.65, or £2.30 a glass, and continues the good work with choice from all over the world, mostly under the £20 mark. The 18-strong half-bottle selection finishes with a rare treat: Austrian *Trockenbeerenauslese*. SAMPLE DISHES: baked avocado with seafood and cheese £5.25; sauté lambs' liver with bacon and shallots £7; iced cranachan parfait with Drambuie and raspberries £4.

Licensees Alan and Julie Reid (freehouse)
Open *Tue to Sun 11 (Sun winter 12.30) to 2.30, 6 to 11; bar food and restaurant 12 to 2.15, 6 to 9.30 (residents only Mon evening); closed Sun evening in winter, 2 weeks Jan*
Details *Children welcome   Car park   Wheelchair access (not WC)   Garden and patio   No smoking in dining room   No music   Dogs welcome in bedrooms only   Delta, MasterCard, Switch, Visa   Accommodation: 8 rooms, B&B £50 to £98*

TAYVALLICH   Argyll & Bute   map 11

Tayvallich Inn

 SEAFOOD

Tayvallich PA31 8PL   TEL: (01546) 870282
WEB SITE: www.tayvallich.com
on B8025, off B841, reached from A816 N of Lochgilphead

A pleasant drive along the shore of Loch Sween brings you to the small, pretty village of Tayvallich, which stands on a perfectly formed bay. You will have to keep your eyes out for the inn, which doesn't have a sign. Inside, the bar has a wood-burning fire, terra-cotta-tiled floor and a slightly nautical feel, thanks to flags and pennants, photographs of sailing boats and local artwork. Picture windows make the best of the views across the bay. The inn holds an annual festival of local seafood, but the produce of the loch can be enjoyed at most other times too: perhaps oysters *au naturel*, or mussels marinière. For main course there may be a salad of smoked haddock and prawns, or you could go the whole hog and opt for the seafood platter. The printed menu also offers several meaty options, such as home-made chilli burgers, or beef curry. The restaurant menu follows similar lines. No real ales are served, only keg beers, and the wine list is fairly limited, but a wide range of Islay malt whiskies is available. SAMPLE DISHES: pickled herring with dill and mustard mayonnaise £3.75; grilled scallops with sweet chilli sauce and crème fraîche £14.50; raspberry cheesecake £3.25.

Licensee Jilly Wilson (freehouse)
Open *summer Sun to Thur 11 to midnight, Fri and Sat 11am to 1am; winter Mon to Sat 11 to 2.30, 5 to 11 (1am Fri and Sat), Sun 12 to 2.30, 5 to 12 winter; bar food 12 to 2, 6 to 8; restaurant (exc Sun to Thur Nov to Easter) 12 to 2, 7 to 8.30; closed 25 and 26 Dec, 1 and 2 Jan*
Details *Children welcome   Car park   Wheelchair access (not WC)   Garden No smoking in eating area of bar during meal times   Occasional live music Dogs welcome exc during meal times   Delta, MasterCard, Switch, Visa*

WEEM   **Perthshire & Kinross**   **map 11**

▲ *Ailean Chraggan*

Weem PH15 2LD   TEL: (01887) 820346
on B486, ½m N of Aberfeldy

In two acres of grounds at the foot of a steep forested slope, this small hotel's garden and two terraces with views of the River Tay are an incentive to dine outside. The bar décor features the landlord's photographs of the locality, and the atmosphere is unstuffy and friendly. The menu, available throughout, is supplemented by daily specials. Local produce comes in the form of venison casseroled in red wine with apricots, prawns from Loch Etive, or a super-platter of seafood, comprising prawns, mussels, oysters, smoked salmon pâté, smoked trout, and scallops in bacon. Scottish beef might turn up as a traditional roast with Yorkshire pudding at Sunday lunch, or as fillet steak with garlic butter. Some desserts come with home-made ice cream, such as caramel with caramel cheesecake, or Irn Bru in a brandy-snap basket. There are no draught ales, but interesting drinking includes bottled Fraoch Heather Ale and Grozet Gooseberry Ale – and over 80 malt whiskies. Of the 40-odd reasonably priced wines, eight are in half-bottles; four are sold by the glass. SAMPLE DISHES: seafood soup with rouille £4.25; chicken breast in a creamy wild mushroom and brandy sauce £8.50; profiteroles £3.50.

Licensee Alastair Gillespie (freehouse)
Open *11 to 11; bar food 12.15 to 2, 6.30 to 9.15; closed 25 and 26 Dec, 1 and 2 Jan*
Details *Children welcome   Car park   Wheelchair access (not WC)   Garden and patio   No smoking in dining room   Dogs welcome exc in dining areas MasterCard, Switch, Visa   Accommodation: 5 rooms, B&B £38.50 to £77*

After the main section of the Guide is the special 'Out and about' section listing additional pubs that are well worth a visit. Reports on these entries are most welcome.

W·A·L·E·S

ABERCYCH   Pembrokeshire   map 4

Nag's Head Inn NEW ENTRY

Abercych SA37 0HJ   TEL: (01239) 841200
off B4332 between Cenarth and Boncath

A preacher whose father once owned the Nag's Head is responsible
for the biblical inscription on the sign – you have to be a Welsh-
speaker to understand it, but that accounts for a fair portion of the
clientele. The building was once the village courtroom, and has also
been a blacksmith's forge, but it is now a characterful pub with its
own microbrewery: the house beer is Old Emrys; weekly-changing
guest ales have included Smiles Heritage, Otter Ale and seasonal
brews such as Dorothy Goodbody Autumn Delight. The pub, painted
a cheerful shade of orange, is in an attractive valley. Inside, a wood-
burning stove provides warmth in the beamed, flagstoned bar, and
an impressive international collection of bottled beers adorns shelves
around the walls. The bar menu extends to several pages. Under
House Specialities you will find steak and ale pie, and smuggler's
chicken (marinated in brandy with herbs and garlic); from the char-
grill come steaks, and gammon with egg and pineapple; further
pages are devoted to seafood, curries, vegetarian dishes, and children's meals. The wine list is short and simple, with three house
selections by the glass. This is 'a real family pub', as a note on the
menu proclaims and a reporter testifies. SAMPLE DISHES: crispy whitebait £3.75; Welsh lamb and leek pie £6.50; tiramisù £2.75.

Licensee Steven Jamieson (freehouse)
Open *11.30 to 3, 5.30 (6 winter) to 11, Sun 12 to 2, 6 to 9; bar food and
restaurant 12 to 2, 6 to 9; restaurant closed weekdays winter*
Details *Children welcome   Car park   Wheelchair access (not WC)   Garden
No smoking in dining room   Occasional background music   Dogs welcome
No cards*

ABERDOVEY   Gwynedd   map 7

▲ *Penhelig Arms Hotel* ✿ ❦

Aberdovey LL35 0LT   TEL: (01654) 767215
on A493 Tywyn to Machynlleth road, opposite Penhelig station

Fine views across the Dovey estuary are one of several attractions of
this charming harbour-side hotel, which dates from the eighteenth
century and was originally known as Y Dafarn Fach (The Little Inn).
Comfortable guest accommodation and an award-winning restaurant
add to its allure; there is also the Fisherman's Bar, an unspoilt traditional pub in a self-contained part of the hotel, with slate walls,

wood panelling and open fire, and décor featuring a collection of toby jugs. Bar food comes from the same kitchen that serves the restaurant and is somewhat more sophisticated than run-of-the-mill pub grub. Crab-filled tomatoes with lemon mayonnaise, or Stilton pâté with pear and walnut salad are typical starters, while main courses might feature monkfish with roast pepper and tomato sauce, roast breast of Gressingham duck with apricot sauce, or Thai-spiced chicken breast with yoghurt and cucumber relish. Poached nectarines with raspberry sauce and vanilla ice cream is one of the appealing dessert options. A regular line-up of Tetley, Bass, Wadworth 6X, and Greene King Abbot Ale is joined by guest ales such as Brains SA. About ten house wines are available by the glass, but it's worth delving into the widely sourced main list for the Hugheses' enthusiastic recommendations. There are over 100 well-priced wines in all, with special focus on Italy. On warm days it is possible to have your meal outside and enjoy the view from the small patio by the sea wall. SAMPLE DISHES: fritto misto with tartare sauce £4.75; chargrilled swordfish steak with aïoli £9.50; raspberry frangipane tart £3.

Licensees Robert and Sally Hughes (freehouse)
Open *11 to 11 (11 to 3, 6 to 11 winter); bar food 12 to 2.30, 6.30 to 9.30; restaurant 7 to 9.30; closed 25 and 26 Dec*
Details *Children welcome   Car park   Patio   No-smoking area in bar, no smoking in dining room   No music   Dogs welcome   Delta, MasterCard, Switch, Visa   Accommodation: 10 rooms, B&B £34.50 to £79*

AFON-WEN   Flintshire   map 7

Pwll Gwyn

Denbigh Road, Afon-Wen CH7 5UB   TEL: (01352) 720227
off A541, 10m NW of Mold

This old coaching inn in a scattered hamlet near Offa's Dyke Path has a picturesque interior. Collections of brass spoons and horse brasses, old photographs on the walls, and oak captain's-chairs, together with very friendly service, make for a warm pubby ambience. Although there is a separate restaurant, its menu and the one in the bar are available throughout. Starters vary from simple chilled melon with ginger, or avocado filled with prawns, to smoked mussels with smoked cheese and cream. Main dishes may be plain grills or cold roasts from the restaurant menu, but bar specials are more exciting, including perhaps sliced roast duckling breast in ginger and spring onion sauce, Rosie's pie (lamb cooked in red wine with garlic and rosemary), or baked blue-nose sea bass fillet marinated in lemon juice and sherry. Jamaican dream – banana with meringue, rum and cream – or home-made bread-and-butter and rice puddings may be among desserts. The regular real beer on draught is Tetleys, which is joined by two guests which might include Old Speckled Hen, Greene King Abbot Ale, Tolly Cobbold Original or Marston's Pedigree. Three wines are sold by the glass. The opening hours listed below may vary: best to check before setting out. SAMPLE DISHES: black pudding with curried apple and barbecue sauce £3.75; half a local pheasant in red wine and port sauce £7.50; fresh pineapple meringue with Malibu £2.50.

Licensee Andrew Davies (freehouse)
Open *summer 12 to 2, 7 (6.30 Fri, 6 Sat) to 11, Sun 12 to 2, 6 to 10.30 (all day Sun in high season); winter 12 to 2, 7 (6.30 Fri, 6 Sat) to 11 (10 Mon, 10.30 Sun); bar food and restaurant 12 to 2, 6 or 7 (depending on opening time) to 9; closed 26 Dec and 1 Jan*
Details *Children welcome   Car park   Wheelchair access (also WC)   Garden and patio   No smoking in dining room   Background music   No dogs   Amex, Delta, MasterCard, Switch, Visa*

BEAUMARIS   Isle of Anglesey   map 7

▲ *Ye Olde Bulls Head* ✿ NEW ENTRY

Castle Street, Beaumaris LL58 8AP
TEL: (01248) 810329

HISTORY

The present incarnation of this Grade II listed pub dates from 1617, though an inn has stood on the site since the late fifteenth century. It earns a place in the history books thanks to events of 1645, when Cromwell's General Mytton used it as his base while laying siege to thirteenth-century Beaumaris Castle. The bar at the front remains very much in traditional pub vein, serving beers from Hancock's, Bass and Worthington by the warmth of an open fire. Adjacent to the bar is a modern conservatory extension that houses the brasserie, the more informal of the two eating areas, where you can eat as much or as little as you like, from a sandwich or a simple pasta dish to a three-course meal: perhaps snails in garlic and parsley butter, followed by chargrilled brochette of turkey with roast Mediterranean vegetables and pesto, and then chocolate and pecan fudge brownie with blueberry ice cream. The separate restaurant has its own menu. A short selection of wines can be found on the back of the brasserie menu; the full restaurant list (not available in the brasserie) runs to over 180 bins. Ten wines come by the glass. SAMPLE DISHES: whole smoked quail with salad and walnut oil £6; beef and root vegetable hotpot £6.25; poppy seed parfait with black cherry coulis £3.

Use the maps at the back of the book to plan your trip.

Licensee David Robertson (freehouse)
Open *11 to 11, Sun 12 to 10.30; brasserie 12 to 2, 6 to 9; restaurant Mon to Sat 7 to 9.30; closed evening 25 Dec; no food 25 and 26 Dec, 1 Jan*
Details *Children welcome; no children under 7 in restaurant   Car park Wheelchair access (also WC)   No-smoking area in brasserie   Occasional live or background music   No dogs   Amex, Delta, MasterCard, Switch, Visa Accommodation: 15 rooms, B&B £55 to £97*

BETWS-Y-COED   Conwy   map 7

▲ *Ty Gwyn Hotel*

Betws-y-coed LL24 0SG   TEL: (01690) 710383
WEB SITE: www.tygwynhotel.co.uk
on outskirts of village, at junction of A5 and A470 by Waterloo Bridge

---

This welcoming and cosy roadside inn with real character boasts a thoroughly homely interior awash with bric-à-brac and low-beamed ceilings. Outside is a fantasia of colour in summer when tubs and hanging baskets come into their own. Two bar areas have comfortable chairs and plenty to look at, and the hotel also has its own dining room. Local Welsh Smooth, Boddingtons and Wadworth 6X are available on tap, as is Scrumpy Jack cider, and three wines may be had by the glass from the list of European and New World offerings. From an extensive menu, you might try marinated herrings with shallots and sweet Madeira to start, or a pairing of grilled black pudding and salami with peppercorn sauce, before going on to sauté king prawns with stir-fried Singapore noodles, or medallions of fillet steak in a dressing of garlic, ginger, chilli, soy, and tomato. Braised pheasant and stuffed goose have also been known to crop up. You might finish with fresh fruit pavlova, or home-made apple pie. Fast-paced, cheerful service adds to the sense of contentment. SAMPLE DISHES: whole boneless quail stuffed with wild rice, apricots, and sultanas £4; Conwy salmon with dill and Dubonnet velouté £12; forest fruit charlotte £3.

Licensee James Ratcliffe (freehouse)
Open *12 to 3, 6 to 11; bar food and restaurant 12 to 2, 6.45 to 9 (9.30 Sat, 8.30 Sun to Thur winter); closed Mon to Wed Jan*
Details *Children welcome   Car park   Wheelchair access (also WC)   No smoking in dining room   Background music   No dogs   Amex, Delta, MasterCard, Switch, Visa   Accommodation: 12 rooms, B&B £17 to £90*

Prices quoted in an entry are based on information supplied by the pub, rounded up to the nearest 25 pence. These prices may have changed since publication and are meant only as a guide.

CAPEL CURIG   Conwy   map 7

▲ *Bryn Tyrch Hotel*

VEGETARIAN

Capel Curig LL24 0EL   TEL: (01690) 720223
on A5, 5m W of Betwys-y-coed

'Cragging and paddling' are two of the principal activities that visitors to these parts get up to, according to the Bryn Tyrch literature, these parts being the heart of the Snowdonia National Park. The hotel offers special rates for walking and cycling clubs, and it knows its constituency well enough to proclaim itself arguably the most proficient vegetarian and vegan caterer in North Wales. In the main bar, a Continental feel prevails, with customers seated at plain wooden tables. There is a smaller public bar with a pool table, while the Caffi Bryn dining room is watched over by an old grandfather clock. Wadworth 6X, Castle Eden Ale and Flowers IPA lend pedigree to the drinking options, as does the range of fruit wines, such as plum, elderberry and gooseberry. The ordinary grape stuff includes French house wines by the glass, and one or two more interesting items such as the Anglesey Shiraz that isn't, it turns out, a local speciality, but comes from Australia. The meat-free cooking is inventive and satisfying, taking in beer-battered courgettes with teriyaki dipping sauce, cider nut roast with Italian tomato sauce, and chickpea and vegetable curry with rice and poppadoms. For the rest, there might be salmon and broccoli lasagne, or homely lunchtime specials like sausages, chips and baked beans, or cod, chips and peas. If chips are all you want, have them on a butty for £2. Puddings include the intriguingly named raspberry scrunch, as well as Mövenpick ice creams. SAMPLE DISHES: vegetable samosa with mango chutney £3.75; carrot, courgette and lentil cottage pie with potato wedges and salad £6.75; rhubarb crumble £3.25.

Licensee Rita Davis (freehouse)
Open *12 to 11; bar food and restaurant 12 to 9.30; closed Christmas*
Details *Children welcome   Car park   Garden   No-smoking area in bar, no smoking in dining room   Occasional live music   Dogs welcome exc in eating areas   MasterCard, Switch, Visa   Accommodation: 15 rooms, B&B £24.50 to £49*

CAREW Pembrokeshire

map 4

Carew Inn

Carew, SA70 8SL   TEL: (01646) 651267
off A477, 4m E of Pembroke

The twelfth-century Carew Castle with its Tudor add-ons is no more than a ruin, but the nineteenth-century tidal mill, rare everywhere, and the last one left in Wales, is complete, and open to visitors on summer afternoons. Both of them, and a ninth-century stone cross, are in view of the pub's terrace and garden, in which you can eat and drink, and where there is a children's play area. Within, there is a warm and welcoming ambience, where colourful walls, beams, local prints and various settles give a rustic and characterful feel. Besides a pleasant lounge bar and adjacent small dining room, there is a public bar and, upstairs, another dining room. One modestly priced menu is offered everywhere, and while it sticks mainly to traditional pub favourites, a few dishes have come in from East and West – for example tarragon and lime chicken, red Thai chicken curry, and chilli con carne, all noted as home-made. Specials widen the choice, turning up perhaps Greek salad, braised Moroccan lamb shank, or local trout fillet with leek and almond sauce, plus puddings along the lines of pineapple upside-down cake. On draught are Worthington Best Bitter, Brains Reverend James, and a summer guest such as Skinner's Figgy Brew. Three wines are available by the glass from a short list. SAMPLE DISHES: chicken liver pâté £4; leg of lamb with redcurrant sauce £10; sticky toffee pudding £3.

Licensee Mandy Hinchliffe (freehouse)
Open *summer 11 to 11, winter Mon to Fri 11 to 2.30, 4.30 to 11, Sat 11 to 11, Sun 12 to 10.30; bar food 12 to 2.30, 6 to 9.30 (6.30 to 9 winter); closed 25 Dec*
Details *Children welcome in eating areas   Car park   Garden and patio   No smoking in upstairs dining room   Live or background music   Dogs welcome in public bar only   Delta, MasterCard, Switch, Visa*

CLYTHA Monmouthshire

map 2

▲ *Clytha Arms* ✿ 🍺 🍇

Clytha NP7 9BW   TEL: (01873) 840206
off old Abergavenny to Raglan road, S of A40, 6m E of Abergavenny

This former dower house, with its small leaded windows and slate roof, stands in its own grounds in a delightfully pastoral setting. The rural style is confirmed in the main bar, which has an old-fashioned wood-burning stove, pews of stripped wood, and old posters on the walls. In the lively public bar locals play darts and other pub games, and enjoy excellent beers at the same time. These include frequently changing guests which join regulars Caledonian Deuchars IPA, Felinfoel Double Dragon and draught Bass; or there's Old Rosie cider, and a good choice of malts, cognacs and calvados. Blackboard specials, mostly fish, shellfish and game, supplement the à la carte menu which tempts many into the more sedate restaurant. There are temptations also in the bar menu, with its sandwiches and salads along with more substantial dishes such as bacon, laverbread and cockles, black pudding with apple and potato mash, or wild mushroom ragoût with pasta. Service is friendly but may be stretched at busy times. The list of over 100 wines covers all options from Bordeaux to Barossa with imaginative flare, and doesn't miss out on local Welsh wine either. It's just £1.80 for a glass of house wine (£9.95 for a bottle) and there are 11 good ones to choose from. SAMPLE DISHES: croque madame (with egg) £3.75; grilled mixed shellfish £8; lime and mascarpone tart and pecan ice cream £4.

Licensees Andrew Canning and Beverley Canning (freehouse)
Open *Tue to Fri 12 to 3, 6 to 11, Sat 11 to 11, Sun 12 to 4, 7 to 10.30; bar food and restaurant Tue to Sat (and restaurant Sun) 12.30 to 2.15, Tue to Fri (and restaurant Sat) 7 to 9.30; closed 25 Dec*
Details *Children welcome   Car park   Garden and patio   No smoking in dining room   Occasional live music   Dogs welcome on leads only   Amex, Delta, Diners, MasterCard, Switch, Visa   Accommodation: 4 rooms, B&B £45 to £80*

CREIGIAU   Cardiff   map 4

Caesar's Arms

Creigiau CF15 9NN   TEL: (029) 2089 0486
2m N of M4 junction 33

On a winding country lane a few miles from Cardiff, this large whitewashed building gives the impression of being more restaurant than pub, though as well as the large, plainly furnished dining area there is a spacious lounge bar where the usual range of drinks is served by a friendly barman. The formula for eating is the same as ever: simply choose what you like the look of from the display of fish and meat in chilled cabinets and someone will take it off to be cooked to your liking (you are charged according to the weight). Choices may include hake, wild salmon, monkfish, and sea bass baked in rock salt. Meat options usually take in Welsh black beef and Welsh lamb, and starters might include wild mushroom risotto, and local dressed crab. Hancock's HB is the only real ale offered, but the range of malt whiskies, ports, liqueurs and bottled beers is claimed to be vast. Although no wine list was sent to the Guide, the pub tells us they have 180 wines, displayed on various blackboards, and ten wines by the glass. SAMPLE DISHES: Bajan fishcakes £4; honeyed crispy duck £11; strawberry mille-feuille £3.75.

Licensee Mark Sharples (Whitbread)
Open *12 to 4 (6 Sun), 6 to 11.30; bar food and restaurant (exc Sun evening) 12 to 2.30 (3.30 Sun), 7 to 10.30*
Details *Children welcome in bar eating area   Car park   Wheelchair access (also WC)   Garden and patio   Background music   No dogs   Amex, Delta, Diners, MasterCard, Switch, Visa*

CRICKHOWELL   Powys   map 4

▲ *Bear Hotel* ♣ 🍇

High Street, Crickhowell NP8 1BW   TEL: (01873) 810408
WEB SITE: www.bearhotel.co.uk
on A40, 6m NW of Abergavenny

Many a venerable old coaching inn is still doing service as a country pub and hotel, and the Bear is among the more aged. The original building dates from the early fifteenth century. It is a whitewashed edifice on three floors at one side of a T-junction, with an absolute warren of public rooms on the ground floor, all done in warm colours and highly comfortable. The cooking is built around pub standards but with plenty of more modern ideas popping up here and there, and it displays a distinctly accomplished edge. Starters and light one-plate dishes include chargrilled aubergine slices wrapped around cumin-spiced lamb with apricots in a sauce of tomatoes and black olives, all under a topping of cheese. Mains take in faggots and peas, juniper-flavoured venison burger on bubble and squeak with parsnip crisps, plaice fillets in 'parsley and dill fish custard', and linguine tossed with crabmeat, coriander and chilli. Round things off with caramelised leaves of puff pastry interlaced with fresh fruits on a lemon-grass sauce, or a rich terrine of dark chocolate and Bailey's topped with white chocolate ice cream. Alternatively, the selection of fine Welsh cheeses looks to be worth a punt. Hancock's HB, Old Speckled Hen and Bass, along with guests such as Felinfoel Double Dragon Ale, lend distinction to the beer side, while ten grape-led wines by the glass get you into the swing of the enterprising and well-chosen wine list. These come in two sizes, priced from £1.70 (125ml), to £7.02 for a large (250ml) measure of Brands Laira Australian Cabernet-Merlot. The rest of the 30 or so wines available take in familiar flavours – Chardonnays, Chablis, Cabernets and Fleuries – and have useful tasting notes and an eye for good value. SAMPLE DISHES: tartlet of smoked haddock and Puy lentils with grain mustard and lemon dressing £4.50; Thai-marinated chicken breast with coconut rice £8.50; home-made ice creams and sorbets £3.

Licensee Mrs J.L. Hindmarsh (freehouse)
Open *10 to 3, 6 to 11, Sun 11 to 3, 7 to 10.30; bar food 11 to 2, 6 to 10, Sun 12 to 2, 7 to 9.30; restaurant 11 to 2, 6 to 10, Sun 12 to 2*
Details *Children welcome in bar eating area   Car park   Wheelchair access (also WC)   Garden and patio   No-smoking area in bar   No music   Dogs welcome exc in dining room   Amex, Delta, MasterCard, Switch, Visa Accommodation: 35 rooms, B&B £49.50 to £120*

▲ *Nantyffin Cider Mill Inn* ✿ 🍺 🍇

Brecon Road, Crickhowell NP8 1SG
TEL: (01873) 810775
WEB SITE: www.cidermill.co.uk   **LOCAL PRODUCE**
1½m W of Crickhowell at junction of A40 and A479

Enjoying a fine setting amid the Brecon Beacons National Park, the Nantyffin is a large, sprawling building with equally expansive car-parking space. Within its walls are a main bar area and two areas for eating, one an informal bistro-like room and the other a more grandiosely scaled dining-room with plum-coloured walls. Gilt cherubs peer down from cross-beams, and the wine racks that occupy the lower half of one end-wall are encouragingly laden. That the Inn is often packed to the gills is ample sign of its popularity among locals and those from further afield drawn by the kitchen's skills. Food is often based on local produce which might then be given international treatment. Grilled Welsh ribeye steak might come with horseradish fondant onions, mustard mash and a tarragon butter sauce, while salmon cured in vodka and dill might be followed by pot-roasted balsamic chicken. Sticky toffee pudding and raspberry semifreddo have been among crowd-pleasing desserts. Rotating guest beers join Brains SA, Reverend James and Buckley's IPA, as well as Marston's Pedigree and micro-ciders such as Old Rosie, Mendip Magic and Thatcher's Premium Press. An extensive wine list is composed exclusively of New World offerings, with many fine selections from the Americas in particular. Prices might seem a little steep, but are an accurate indicator of quality; there are a number of choices around and under the £15 mark – enough to keep the bargain-hunter happy too. Four house wines, plus four monthly-changing wines, are served by the glass, from £2.30. SAMPLE DISHES: grilled Welsh goats' cheese with sauté leeks and red wine dressing £5.25; Welsh lamb confit with herb mash and rosemary and garlic sauce £9; pear and almond tart with sauce anglaise £4.25.

Licensees Sean Gerrard and Glyn Bridgeman (freehouse)
Open *Tue to Sat 12 to 3, 6 to 11, Sun 12 to 3, 7 to 11; bar food and restaurant Tue to Sun 12 to 2.15, 6.30 to 10*

Details *Children welcome   Car park   Wheelchair access (also WC)   Garden*
No smoking in dining room   Occasional background music   Dogs welcome
by arrangement in bar area only   Amex, Delta, MasterCard, Switch, Visa
Accommodation: 22 rooms, B&B £50 to £95

CWMDU   Powys   map 4

▲ *Farmers Arms*

Cwmdu NP8 1RU   TEL: (01874) 730464
WEB SITE: www.thefarmersarms.com
on A479, 4m NW of Crickhowell

The Farmers Arms is a converted white cottage in a small village set
in good walking country and just a short drive from Tretower Court
and Castle. The flagstone-floored bar with its log-burning stove
preserves a rustic feel. As well as basket meals in adult and child-
sized portions, and bar meals like beef Madras, or chicken, ham and
leek pie, there is a full-scale blackboard restaurant menu, also available in the bar, that essays some interesting turns and makes
resourceful use of local produce. Welsh dragon pâté is made of chil-
lied venison and is served with a fruity chutney and granary toast,
while filo pastry moneybags are filled with tarragon-scented creamed
leeks and Llanboidy cheese. For mains, there might be chargrilled
tuna with pesto, poached halibut on samphire sauced with white
wine and saffron, or herb-crusted rack of Brecon lamb with
Cumberland sauce, before lemon tart on raspberry coulis with
lemon-curd ice cream, or a selection of pedigree Welsh cheeses.
Handpumped real ales rotate and might include Old Speckled Hen,
Buckley's Rev James Original or Uley Pig's Ear. Thatcher's cider is
also on draught, and the wine list – short and to the point – majors
in New World bottles. SAMPLE DISHES: salmon, laverbread and chive
soufflé £5; Indian-spiced chicken fillet on tomato and parsley couscous £10; two-tone chocolate terrine with chocolate sauces £4.

Licensees Andrew Lawrence and Susan Brown (freehouse)
Open *12 to 2.30 (4 Sat), 6.30 to 11, Sun 12 to 4, 7 to 10.30; bar food and*
restaurant 12 to 2, 7 to 9.30 (10 Sat), Sun 12 to 3, 7 to 9; closed Mon and
Tue lunchtimes Oct to Mar
Details *Children welcome   Car park   Wheelchair access (not WC)   Garden*
No smoking in dining room   Background music   Dogs welcome in bar area
only   Delta, MasterCard, Switch, Visa   Accommodation: 3 rooms, B&B £15
to £40

Licensing hours and bar food times are based on information supplied
by each establishment and are correct at the time of going to press.

DRAETHEN   Caerphilly   map 4

Hollybush Inn   NEW ENTRY

SETTING

Draethen, Lower Machen, NP10 8GB
TEL: (01633) 441326
off A468 Newport to Caerphilly road, about 1m from main road; pub is signposted

This substantial stone house in a tiny village has a terraced garden with fine views of wooded hills and surrounding farming country, and a strongly rushing stream running all round it adding to the charm of the setting. After taking over in early-summer 2000, the licensees have refurbished the interior in a light airy style, installing huge picture windows in the restaurant, while successfully preserving an attractive pub ambience elsewhere through sensitive restoration. Lightly beamed ceilings, open stonework, carefully chosen pictures and artefacts, country-style furniture and carpet throughout, plus friendly and helpful staff, make a visit here both welcoming and comfortable. The pub draws those wishing to eat and locals who've come for a chat and a drink. On the bar menu all main meals are priced under £6, and dishes such as roast lamb shank, or fettuccine, tomato and chilli fondue with mushrooms and Parmesan, demonstrate the ambition. Visitors have praised coq au vin – 'a large, appetising and filling dish' – and 'beautifully cooked' lamb's liver. Desserts might include sticky toffee pudding, crème caramel or an excellent version of crème brulée with mango ice cream. The more extensive restaurant menu, not available in the bar, produces the likes of fillet of Welsh beef with black pepper, and roast breast of wild duck. Brains Bitter and SA, plus a guest such as Marston's Pedigree or Shepherd Neame Spitfire, are the real beers on tap, while wine drinkers can choose from 20. Two wines, both French, are available by the glass. Note that there is no bar food on Sunday, though the restaurant is open for Sunday lunch. SAMPLE DISHES: prawn salad £5.25; beef and ale pie £6; chocolate marquise £3.

Licensee Paul Verallo (Punch Taverns)
Open *summer 12 to 3, 5 to 11, Sun 12 to 10.30; winter 12 to 4, 7.30 to 10.30; bar food Mon to Sat 12 to 2.30, 6 to 9; restaurant Mon to Sat 6 to 9, Sun 12 to 3*
Details *Children welcome   Car park   Wheelchair access (not WC)   Garden and patio   No smoking in dining room   Background music   No dogs   Delta, MasterCard, Switch, Visa*

All details are as accurate as possible at the time of going to press, but pubs often change hands, and it is wise to check beforehand by telephone anything that is particularly important to you.

FELIN FACH   Powys   map 4

▲ *Felin Fach Griffin* | NEW ENTRY |

Felin Fach LD3 0UB   TEL: (01874) 620111
WEB SITE: www.eatdrinksleep.ltd.uk
on A470, NE of Brecon

The terracotta paint on this sprawling building tones in with the
sandstone soil of the area, and the same colour is used inside. Total
renovation and refurbishment have been sensitively accomplished,
retaining character and old-world charm. In the main bar area, an
old piano, comfortable leather easy chairs and sofas encourage a
relaxed approach: sip a pint, read the papers provided and perhaps
give an ear to the piped pop music. An open wood fire divides this
from the main eating area. Order at the bar and efficient and friendly
staff bring the food to the table. The half-dozen or so dishes on the
lunchtime menu might include salmon and leek tart with crisp shortcrust pastry, or what a reader has described as a 'rive-gauche bistro
dish' of 'tender and moist' minute steak with crisp fries and thick
béarnaise sauce. On the slightly longer evening menu, starters might
include pigeon salad, or imam bayaldi, with main dishes of roast
chicken breast with champ and tarragon butter, or chargrilled tuna
with noodles, chard, and sesame and ginger oil. Ales on tap are
Tomas Watkin OSB and BB, and the fairly priced wine list is supplemented by a blackboard of specials, mostly available by both glass
and bottle. SAMPLE DISHES: eggs Benedict £4.25; bangers and mash
£7; glazed lemon tart £3.25.

Licensees Huw Evans Bevan and Charles Inkin (freehouse)
Open *Tue to Sat 12 to 3, 6 to 11, Sun 1 to 11; bar food Tue to Sun 12.30 (1
Sun) to 2.30, 7 to 9.30 (9 Sun); closed last week Jan, first week Feb*
Details *Children welcome   Car park   Wheelchair access (also WC)   Garden
No smoking in dining room   Background music   Dogs welcome   Delta,
MasterCard, Switch, Visa   Accommodation: 7 rooms, B&B £49.50 to £73*

GLANWYDDEN   Conwy   map 7

Queen's Head ✿

Glanwydden LL31 9JP   TEL: (01492) 546570
just off B5115 Colwyn Bay to Llandudno road

PUDDINGS

Judging by outward appearances, the Queen's Head is a simple but
attractive and well-maintained pub. Inside, it has a warm and
welcoming atmosphere, aided by a wood-burning stove in a stone
fireplace. Despite the unassuming style of the place, food is well
above average. Separate menus operate at lunchtime and in the

evening, both opening with a selection of hot and cold starters, such as smoked breast of goose with fig and kumquat chutney (cold), or crispy duck leg with red onion marmalade (hot). The rest of the menu is divided into pastas and salads, chef's specials (Glanwydden lamb cutlets with plum, blackberry and port sauce, for example), vegetarian dishes, and fish options, the last supplemented by an additional board of daily specials. Try the seafood platter, comprising local smoked and fresh seafood with new potatoes and marie-rose sauce; poached salmon with parsley cream sauce; or large field mushrooms stuffed with crab and topped with hollandaise and almonds. At lunchtime there is also a selection of open rolls and sandwiches, and the list of home-made desserts runs to half a dozen each of hot and cold options: sticky toffee pudding among the former, fresh oranges in Cointreau among the latter. To drink, there are Tetley Bitter and weekly guest ales, 20 single malts, and a list of over 40 wines, of which six are available by the glass. SAMPLE DISHES: smoked salmon and trout mousse £4.75; roast loin of pork with apple and mint preserve £7.75; cherry Bakewell tart £3.25.

Licensee Robert Cureton (Punch Group)
Open *11.30 to 3, 6 to 11, Sun 11.30 to 10.30; bar food 12 to 2.15, 6 to 9, Sun 12 to 9; closed 25 Dec*
Details *No children under 7 Car park Wheelchair access (not WC) Patio No smoking area in dining room Background music No dogs Delta, MasterCard, Switch, Visa*

GRESFORD   Wrexham   map 7

Pant-yr-Ochain 🍺 NEW ENTRY

Old Wrexham Road, Gresford LL12 8TY   TEL: (01978) 853525
take Gresford turning off A483 Wrexham bypass

Ochain was a thirteenth-century Welsh warlord, but the licensees at this Dutch-gabled, cream-coloured inn are much more welcoming to strangers than its namesake would have been. Hard by a lake and a miniature railway, it is quite as quirky within as without, boasting a book-lined room as well as hordes of nostalgic memorabilia, from seaside postcards to vintage advertising posters. The choice of real ales is very good, with Plassey, Boddingtons Bitter, Flowers Original and Timothy Taylor Landlord on tap plus a guest such as Rudgate Viking, and there is a refreshingly imaginative wine selection, grouped by grape variety and offering a generous ten by the glass. Drawing inspiration from diverse corners of the globe, the food, which is ordered at the bar, might take in a well-composed salad of Thai-style beef with vegetables and cashew nuts; porcini ravioli with rocket, roast peppers and pesto; grilled Bury black pudding with champ and bacon; or crispy duck confit with stir-fried vegetables, noodles and spicy plum sauce. To tempt the sweet of tooth might be treacle and sultana tart with honeycomb ice cream, or profiteroles with dark chocolate sauce. SAMPLE DISHES: ham hock terrine with home-made chutney £4.75; sesame-coated tiger prawns with caramelised peppers, oriental greens and coconut and chilli sauce £15; crème brûlée £4.

Licensees Graham Arathoon and Linsey Prole (freehouse)
Open *12 to 11; bar food 12 to 9.30 (9 Sun)*
Details *Children welcome before 6pm   Car park   Wheelchair access (also WC)   Garden   No smoking in dining room   Background music   No dogs Amex, Delta, MasterCard, Switch, Visa*

HAY-ON-WYE   Powys   map 4

▲ *Old Black Lion*

26 Lion Street, Hay-on-Wye HR3 5AD   TEL: (01497) 820841
WEB SITE: www.hay-on-wye.co.uk/blacklion/welcome.htm

With some three dozen places at which to buy second-hand and antique books, and an annual literary festival to boot, Hay-on-Wye is clearly a must-do for the bookishly inclined. It also boasts this ancient (with origins around the thirteenth century) whitewashed inn and a colourful history: it was one of the stopovers where Oliver Cromwell billeted himself during a spot of hard besieging in the Civil War. Choose from the King Richard (the Lionheart) Bar or the Cromwell Restaurant to eat in. In the former you might enjoy a plate of grilled sardines with garlic and herb butter, followed by spicy venison casserole served on parsnip mash, while in the restaurant a slightly more extensive choice takes in dishes such as roast monkfish wrapped in bacon with rosemary and garlic butter, or duck breast on oyster mushrooms with a red berry sauce. Each menu has a couple of vegetarian choices, and desserts aim to indulge with the likes of Tia Maria meringue, or chocolate pudding with warm chocolate sauce. Look at the blackboard for daily specials. Wye Valley Butty Bach and a guest beer, plus Bulmers Original Cider, are among the hand-pumped offerings, and the commendable wine list delves about in Europe and the New World to produce some tempting bottles. Only three are available by the glass, but there are ten half-bottles. SAMPLE DISHES: laverbread with cockle cakes £5.75; wild boar steak on sauté potatoes with cider and mustard-seed sauce £13; lemon crème brûlée £4.

Licensee Vanessa King (freehouse)
Open *11 to 11 (10.30 Sun); bar food and restaurant 12 to 2.30, 7 to 9.30; closed 25 and 26 Dec*

Details *Children over 5 welcome in eating areas   Car park   Patio   No smoking in dining room   No music   No dogs   MasterCard, Switch, Visa Accommodation: 10 rooms, B&B £30 to £75*

LAMPHEY   Pembrokeshire   map 4

▲ *Dial Inn*

Ridgeway Road, Lamphey SA71 5NU
TEL: (01646) 672426
just off A4139 Tenby to Pembroke road

Squash courts (bookable) and picnic tables are in a modern extension to the rear of this former dower house of Lamphey Court, converted into a pub in the 1960s. Flowers in window boxes and hanging baskets add colour to the white building at the village centre. It is near the ruins of the Bishop's Palace, a large mural of which is above the fireplace in the main room, which is otherwise decorated with photographs and blue and white plates on a shelf. The atmosphere is cheerful and welcoming, and staff compensate in friendliness for any slow service at busy times. The menu offers imaginative, sensible variations on such classics as melon (with apricot and ginger coulis and seasonal fruits), and duck breast (baked with smoked bacon and almonds, served with a whisky and butter jus). The same menu, as well as daily specials featuring fish – maybe baked sea bass stuffed with asparagus – is served throughout. So, too, is the 'And Also' menu of simple pub food with the accent on quality. Starters include pâté and soup, with main courses of pasta, Welsh steaks and, for vegetarians, Glamorgan cheese sausages with plum chutney, or falafel with Arabic bread and mint mayonnaise. Home-made desserts might include pineapple upside-down pudding, or hazelnut meringue. Draught Bass, Hancock's HB, Worthington Bitter and a guest beer are offered, along with a short wine list. Around ten wines are available by the glass. SAMPLE DISHES: salmon and crab cakes with seafood sauce £4.25; Pembrokeshire pork and leek sausages with onion gravy £7; strawberry pavlova £3.50.

Licensees Granville and Ruth Ann Hill (freehouse)
Open *11 to 12.30am, Sun 12 to 3, 7 to 11; bar food and restaurant 12 to 2.30, 6.30 to 9.30*
Details *Children welcome in eating areas and family room   Car park Wheelchair access (also WC)   Patio   No smoking in dining room   Background music   No dogs   Delta, MasterCard, Switch, Visa   Accommodation: 5 rooms, B&B £20 to £50*

Recommendations for good country pubs will be very welcome.

Swan Inn

Point Road, Little Haven SA62 3UL TEL: (01437) 781256
off B4341, 6m W of Haverfordwest

This unpretentious, friendly pub, in a beautiful location by a sea wall
overlooking a sandy cove, is a good-value lunch location, and a cut
above most of the local competition. The unspoilt interior is in the
vein of bare stone walls, high-backed settles and oak tables, and
window tables make the best of the views. Eating is a straightforward
affair, both in the bar and restaurant, with local fish and seafood to
the fore. In the bar, soups, ploughman's, pâtés and sandwiches make
up a large part of the menu, along with main dishes such as ham
salad, or 'Swan Upper' (sardines, spinach and egg, topped with
mozzarella and grilled). Lobster salad is always available with 24
hours' notice. Added to this in the slightly more formal restaurant
are things like steak, whole Dover sole, and crispy roast duck with
blackcurrant sauce. Wash the food down with Young's Special,
Wadworth 6X, Brains Rev James Original Ale, or one of the wines
by the glass. SAMPLE DISHES: crab and mayonnaise bake £5; chicken
korma £6; chocolate roulade £2.75.

Licensee Glyn Davies (Narbarth)
Open *Mon to Fri 11 to 3 (2.30 winter), 6 (7 winter) to 11, Sat 11 to 11 (11
to 2.30, 7 to 11 winter), Sun 12 to 3, 7 to 10.30; bar food 12 to 2; restaurant
Wed to Sat 7 to 9.30; closed evening 25 Dec*
Details *No children Wheelchair access (not WC) Patio No cigars/pipes in
dining room No music No dogs No cards*

▲ West Arms

Llanarmon Dyffryn Ceiriog LL20 7LD TEL: (01691) 600665
WEB SITE: www.hotelwalesuk.com
*off A5 LLangollen to Oswestry road at Chirk, then follow B4500
for 11m*

Geoff Leigh-Ford is a friendly host, in keeping with the unstuffy
atmosphere of this old-fashioned rural inn. It is well off the beaten
track, at the foot of a broad valley, and has been a hotel since 1670 –
which may well explain the low ceilings, slate floors, massive
inglenooks and ancient blackened timbers that give the bar its character. Bar menus have some enterprising touches: grilled local trout

with almonds, pancakes filled with chicken and sweetcorn, or wild mushroom strudel with a brandy sauce, which might follow starters of moules marinière, or West Arms pâté. There are also mixed-cheese ploughman's, various sandwiches, and chicken nuggets and the like for children. The separate restaurant menu follows a more upmarket route, taking in chicken marinated in grenadine with citrus fruit, duck breast on caramelised pear and shallot, and medallions of pork in a garlic sauce. Alongside Whitbread Trophy and Stowford Press cider, drinkers are offered a selection of whiskies and vintage ports, and an extensive wine list; this includes own-label house wines at £11.50 and three by the glass. SAMPLE DISHES: Ceiriog Valley salad £5.50; braised shoulder of Welsh lamb £8.25; lemon and lime bavarois £3.35.

Licensees Gill and Geoff Leigh-Ford (freehouse)
Open *11 to 11; bar food and restaurant 12 to 2, 7 to 9; sandwiches and cream teas available afternoons*
Details *Children welcome Car park Wheelchair access (also WC) Garden No smoking in dining room Background music Dogs welcome MasterCard, Switch, Visa Accommodation: 16 rooms, B&B £41.50 to £57.50*

LLANDWROG   Gwynedd   map 7

▲ *Harp Inn* 🍺

Ty'n Llan, Llandwrog LL54 5SY   TEL: (01286) 831071
WEB SITE: www.users.globalnet.co.uk/~theharp
off A499, 5m SW of Caernarfon

This solid, stone-built inn is located between the beach and the mountains of Snowdonia, and walking is the activity to which it is devoted: they run organised walking holidays for visitors. There is also the national sailing school nearby. Two- or four-wheeled travellers are welcomed as well as those on foot, and all mix easily with locals in the bar, and at pool, darts and shove half-penny in the games room. The mostly traditional cooking runs from sausages or fish and chips or steaks to pies with beef and beer or lamb and leek. Choice runs to bargain weekday lunches and three courses plus coffee on Sundays for £8.95 (children £6). Daily specials may include a curry or local fish. Beer lovers will find draught Bass usually on tap plus several guests: perhaps Plassey Bitter, Spinning Dog Chase Your Tail, local Flannery Brewery's Four Thumbs, or Celtic Ale. Over 30 malt whiskies are stocked, with Islay malts a speciality. Wines on the short, global list include one from Wales, and seven wines are available by the glass. SAMPLE DISHES: pâté de campagne £4; lamb and leek pie £7; gâteau of the day £3.25

Licensee Colin Downie (freehouse)
Open *Oct to mid-July Tue to Fri 12 to 2, 6 to 11, Sat 12 to 11, Sun 12 to 3;
mid-July to Sept Mon 6 to 11, Tue to Sun 12 to 11; closed 1 Jan; bar food and
restaurant Tue to Sun 12 to 2, Tue to Sat 6.30 to 8.30; meals also available
Sun and Mon evenings in summer*
Details *Children welcome in eating areas and games room   Car park
Wheelchair access (also WC)   Garden and patio   No smoking in dining room
Background music; jukebox   Dogs welcome exc in bedrooms or restaurant
Delta, MasterCard, Switch, Visa   Accommodation: 4 rooms, B&B £24 to £46*

LLANFIHANGEL-NANT-MELAN   Powys   map 4

▲ *Red Lion Inn* ✿

LOCAL PRODUCE

Llanfihangel-nant-Melan LD8 2TN
TEL: (01544) 350220
on A44 Rhayader to Kington road, 3m W of New Radnor

This particular Red Lion is a long, low building of whitewashed
stone sitting close enough to the A44 that what traffic there is sails
past within a few feet of the conservatory extension. The bar and
lounge areas are tiny, although a big fireplace with a log fire will
attract the hungry visitor, not least because the blackboard menu
hangs on the wall above it. Good-value cooking using the freshest
local ingredients has always been the touchstone of the kitchen here,
and David and Annie Browne, who took over in May 2000, are
continuing the good work. The bar menu regularly includes various
curries, steak and mushroom pie, and scampi and the like, while the
more formal restaurant menu turns up Penrhyn mussels with prawn
cream, Welsh wild boar with chestnuts, mushrooms and smoked
bacon, and rack of Welsh lamb with dauphinois potatoes. Salmon
goujons with lemon mayonnaise made a good starter special for a
reporter, and fish fanciers may well go on to roast hake with
Penclawdd cockles and samphire to follow. Finish with chocolate
and brandy truffle terrine, banana split, or a selection of British
farmhouse cheeses, with Welsh ones strongly to the fore. Cider
comes in the form of Stowford Press or Ralph's – a local brew – and
the single handpumped ale is from Hook Norton. Wales is represented on the international wine list, where five listings are sold by
the glass. SAMPLE DISHES: organic Charentais melon fan with
Pembrokeshire damson sorbet £3; breast of chicken stuffed with
prawns and mushrooms £9.50; white chocolate and pistachio slice
with fruit coulis £3.25.

Licensee David Browne (freehouse)
Open *12 to 2.30, 6 to 11 (10.30 Sun); bar food and restaurant 12 to 2, 6 to
9.45*

Details *Children welcome   Car park   Wheelchair access (not WC)   Garden*
No smoking in dining room   Occasional background music   Dogs welcome in
bar   Delta, MasterCard, Switch, Visa   Accommodation: 5 rooms, B&B £25 to
£50

LLANGATTOCK   Powys   map 4

Vine Tree Inn

The Legar, Llangattock NP8 1HG
TEL: (01873) 810514
off A40, SW of Crickhowell

Enviably sited in the Usk Valley (right by the river, in fact), and
facing the medieval bridge that links Llangattock to Crickhowell, this
well-established dining pub is an amalgam of a row of low knocked-
through cottages fronted by picnic benches and a fine magnolia. The
interior is distinguished by old exposed stonework in the walls and
many a snug little alcove to install yourself in, and a large blackboard
by the bar gives notice that there is a very industrious kitchen behind
it all. Food is ordered from the bar and then brought to your table,
turning up perhaps hot curried prawns or smoked venison with cranberry sauce to start, and then apricot-stuffed pork, rabbit cooked in
wine with celery and almonds, or one of the variously sauced steaks
to follow. Portions can be gargantuan (the rump steaks are over a
pound in uncooked weight), so work up an appetite. If you feel you
can manage a pudding, then rejoice in the oldfangled likes of
Bakewell tart or spotted dick. Children have their own menu and
may well be tempted by the prospect of potato smiley faces with
their main courses. Vegetarians might go for a bake, nut roast, pasta
or curry. Wadworth 6X and Fuller's London Pride are on draught,
and the largely French wine list covers all the main bases, with four
served by the glass. SAMPLE DISHES: mushrooms in garlic and chilli
butter £4; lamb chops in a garlic, rosemary and marsala cream sauce
£9; rum and raisin cheesecake £3.

Licensee Ian Lennox (freehouse)
Open *12 to 3, 6 to 11, Sun 12 to 3, 7 to 10.30; bar food and restaurant 12*
to 2.30, 6 to 10
Details *Children welcome   Car park   Patio   No music   No dogs   Delta,*
MasterCard, Switch, Visa

LLANGYNIDR Powys map 4

▲ *Coach & Horses*

Cwm Crawnon Road, Llangynidr NP8 1LS
TEL: (01874) 730245
off B4558, 4m W of Crickhowell

Visitors, and locals too, cruise down the Monmouth Canal, or tread the towpath, to this pub's garden on the edge of the canal, with moorings opposite for your narrow-boat. It is ideally located for trekking, too, with the Black Mountains and the Brecon Beacons in view above the Usk Valley village, and inside there is respite for you and your walking boots. It's a simple, unpretentious place, with the public bar a venue for pub games and pool while the open lounge and carpeted restaurant are comfortably but simply furnished. There is just the one menu, but it is quite long and everything is claimed to be home made. Vegetarians will find deep-fried vegetables with garlic as a starter, and a vegetable moussaka among the main dishes. Others may turn to prawns in garlic butter; tagliatelle with smoked chicken, mushrooms and pesto; chicken Llangynidr; or pork Napoleon. Homely desserts include cheesecake, apple pie and tiramisù. On Sunday only roasts are served. Real ales on draught are Bass, Old Speckled Hen and Hancocks HB, and five wines from the 28-strong list are available by the glass. SAMPLE DISHES: goujons of plaice with tartare sauce £4; venison steak £11; sherry trifle £3.50.

Licensee Anthony Jukes (freehouse)
Open *11 to 11, Sun 12 to 10.30; bar food and restaurant 12 to 2, 6.30 to 9.30, Sun 12 to 2, 7 to 9.30*
Details *Children welcome   Car park   Wheelchair access (also WC)   Garden Background music   Dogs welcome exc in restaurant   Amex, Delta, MasterCard, Switch, Visa   Accommodation: 3 rooms, B&B £22.50 to £50*

LLANVAPLEY Monmouthshire map 2

Red Hart 🍺

Llanvapley NP7 8SN   TEL: (01600) 780227
on B4233, 4m E of Abergavenny

'In my view, this is the essence of what a country pub should be,' said a satisfied visitor to this family-run cottagey hostelry, a large whitewashed building opposite the village church on the Abergavenny to Monmouth road. Views over farmland and across fields and woods from the verandah are among its attractions, along with a pretty garden with picnic tables. Inside, there are two rooms on either side of a central bar, one of which serves as a family room.

Exposed-stone walls are adorned with decorative china, countryside artefacts, horse brasses, and Royal Navy memorabilia, reflecting the owner's former profession. Furniture is a mixture of comfortable chairs, sofas and settles, and log fires add to the atmosphere. Menus comprise a printed list of standards plus a handwritten section of daily specials, which might include Cajun chicken, spinach and ricotta lasagne, lamb curry, and the house speciality of steak pies. Beers are draught Bass, brews such as Golden Arrow from the Cottage Brewing Company in Somerset, plus a changing seasonal guest ale, and three wines are served by the glass. SAMPLE DISHES: salmon braised in wine and basil £7.25; spicy cinnamon lamb with salad and pitta bread £8.25; Henry's pudding £3.25.

Licensees Mrs J. Sharpe and Mrs G.M. Cattroll (freehouse)
Open *Wed to Sun 12 to 3 (4 Sun), Tue to Sat 6 to 11; bar food and restaurant 12 to 2 (2.30 Sun), 7 to 9*
Details *Children welcome in eating areas   Car park   Wheelchair access (not WC)   Garden   No smoking in dining room   Occasional background music Dogs welcome   No cards*

LLANYRE   Powys   map 4

▲ *Bell Inn*

Llanyre LD1 6DY   TEL: (01597) 823959
just off A3081, 1m W of Llandrindod Wells

Evening visitors to this seventeenth-century grey-stone inn will probably spot it from some way off, thanks to green fluorescent lights in the gables. Inside, the atmosphere is as cheerful and bright as this external feature may lead you to expect – one visitor used the word 'jazzy' to describe the décor. Bar menus comprise a list of 'lite bites' and 'not such lite bites'. Among the former are various filled jacket potatoes and sandwiches, garlic baguettes, and chicken liver pâté with chilli and herbs; the latter take in traditional dishes such as turkey and ham pie, cod in beer batter, and braised liver with bacon and onions. The restaurant has its own menu, offering steaks, garlicky chicken breast pan-fried with prawns, and grilled lemon sole with herb sauce. Hancock's HB and Worthington Bitter plus a guest are the real ales offered; wine drinkers will find a list of 40 bottles, most under £20, with four by the glass. SAMPLE DISHES: garlic baguette with chorizo and melted cheese £2.75; chicken with asparagus in creamy sauce £6.50; hot chocolate sponge pudding £3.25.

Licensee Dave Jones (freehouse)
Open *11.30 to 3, 6 to 11, Sun 12 to 3, 6 to 10.30; bar food (exc Sun lunchtime) and restaurant 12 to 2, 6.30 to 9.30; closed evening 25 Dec*
Details *Children welcome in bar eating areas   Car park   Wheelchair access (not WC)   Patio   No smoking in dining room   Background music   No dogs MasterCard, Switch, Visa   Accommodation: 9 rooms, B&B £35 to £60*

LLYSWEN   Powys   map 4

Griffin Inn

Llyswen LD3 0UR   TEL: (01874) 754241
WEB SITE: www.griffin-inn.co.uk
on A470 Builth Wells to Brecon road

The name over the doorway of this fifteenth-century fishing inn is almost submerged under the burgeoning creepers which cover its walls; and the warm hospitality of the Stockton family who own it is sometimes nearly submerged under its huge popularity. From their upper Wye Valley location they find and cook many local ingredients: Welsh Black beef, Welsh lamb, salmon and occasionally sewin, as well as cheeses, in menus which demonstrate a knowledge of modern cuisine combined with respect for the conventional. Menus are common to bar and restaurant, and as well as the printed menu there are blackboard daily specials of fish, meat and game. Among starters at lunch might be smoked cod and Welsh cheeses wrapped in bacon; or hot smoked salmon with Glanwye sauce. Lunch or dinner main dishes usually take in much praised Black beef daube or braised lamb knuckle, and several vegetarian options. A wide-ranging, well-priced wine list is cleverly organised into different food categories ('full reds for rich roasts, casseroles, etc.', for example). Six wines are served by the 175ml glass (£3). For beer drinkers Elgood's Golden Newt, Flowers IPA, Kingdom Bitter and Young's Special Brew are stocked; there's also Stowford Press cider. SAMPLE DISHES: house pâté and terrines £5; trout fillets with smoked bacon £11; chocolate and brandy biscuit cake £4.

Licensees Richard and Di Stockton (freehouse)
Open *12 to 3, 7 to 11, Sun 12 to 2.30, 7 to 10.30; bar food and restaurant Mon to Sat 12 to 2, 7 to 9, Sun no bar food, restaurant open 1pm (1 sitting); closed 25 and 26 Dec*
Details *Children welcome   Car park   Wheelchair access (not WC)   Patio No smoking in dining room   Occasional live music   Dogs welcome   Amex, Delta, Diners, MasterCard, Switch, Visa   B&B 9 rooms, £45 to £80*

Recommendations for good country pubs will be very welcome.

MACHYNLLETH   Powys   map 4

▲ *Wynnstay Hotel* ❀ ❦   NEW ENTRY

Machynlleth SY20 8AE   TEL: (01654) 702941
WEB SITE: www.wynnstay-hotel.com

This rambling Georgian coaching inn can be found right at the heart
of this lively small town just to the south of Cader Idris. Inside are
several interconnecting bar areas with original oak floors, plus two
lounges at the front; the main dining room is at the rear. At the time
of going to press, extensive renovation was under way, making any
description of the décor redundant, but early work had already
uncovered and restored the original stone fireplace in the main
room, and the atmosphere among staff and customers is cheerful.
Bar food is considered far better than average, and, according to a
reporter, 'good enough for a reputable restaurant'. This is hardly
surprising, given the pedigree of chef Gareth Johns, who spent nine
years at the highly rated Red Lion in Llanfihangel-nant-Melan (see
entry). He applies his skills to fine local produce, including beef,
lamb, veal, fish and game, producing an appealing and varied menu
that ranges from old favourites, such as Welsh cheese ploughman's,
or cod with chips and peas, to blackened salmon with tomato, chilli
and coriander salsa, or linguine with roasted vegetables and
Parmesan. The set-price restaurant menu, available in the bar, also
features a mix of old and new, with oxtail soup alongside chargrilled
vegetable terrine with basil dressing. Regularly changing real ales
might include Timothy Taylor Landlord, Brains Bitter and Greene
King Abbot Ale, and the 40-strong wine list has six choices available
by the glass and four by the half-bottle. In addition, a useful tasting
guide makes it easy to work out a wine's weight and sweetness
before you make your decision. Italy and Argentina show particularly well on this list, with some nice food wines selected. Bottle
prices start at £9.75 and are, on the whole, very reasonable. SAMPLE
DISHES: Richie's rarebit £3; pheasant breast with sweet plum sauce
£9; mango cheesecake £3.25.

Licensees Charles Dark, Nigel Edwards and Kathryn Vaughan (freehouse)
Open *11 to 11, Sun 12 to 10.30; bar food and restaurant 12 to 2, 6.30 to 9*
Details *Children welcome   Car park   Garden   No-smoking area in bar, no
smoking in dining room   Occasional live or background music   Dogs
welcome   Amex, Delta, Diners, MasterCard, Switch, Visa   Accommodation:
23 rooms, B&B £45 to £70*

❀ *indicates a pub serving outstanding bar food, backed up by all-
round excellence in other departments, such as service, atmosphere
and cleanliness.*

MONKNASH   Vale of Glamorgan   map 4

Plough and Harrow 🍺   NEW ENTRY

Monknash CF71 7QQ   TEL: (01656) 890209
WEB SITE: www.publive.com
off B4265 from Llantwit Major

'Why have themed pubs when you can have the real thing?' mused a
visitor to this friendly, unpretentious local – a solid, unprepossessing
building dating from the twelfth century. It is somewhat off the
beaten track, on a narrow lane that leads to the sea and coast path.
Outside is a patch of grass crammed with picnic tables and an old
sailing boat, while inside are two stone-walled bars with huge wood-
burning fireplaces, black beams, old photographs and prints, swags
of hops, hanging hams, and a display of old musical instruments in
an inglenook. The place has a real buzz, thanks to a lively crowd
ranging from farmers in wellies to parents with children, but
outsiders are made to feel just as welcome. The menu, chalked up on
a beam, makes no attempt at modernity: spaghetti bolognese, faggots
and peas, and beef in Guinness are typical. Portions are enormous,
and ingredients are fresh and appetising. Beers are the real stars of
the show. The wide range, dispensed from handpumps or direct
from the cask, changes by the hour (or so it seemed to a reporter).
Seven regulars are supplemented by up to nine guest ales, perhaps
including Cottage Our Ken, Bullmastiff Son of a Bitch, and Organic
Lizard Point. Old Rosie cider is also served, plus four wines by the
glass. SAMPLE DISHES: ham, egg and chips £2; chicken curry £5.50;
spotted dick £2.50.

Licensee Andrew Davies (freehouse)
Open *12 to 11 (10.30 Sun); bar food (exc Sat and Sun evenings) 12 to 2, 6 to
9*
Details *Children welcome in eating areas before 8pm   Car park   Garden and
patio   Live or background music   Dogs welcome exc during eating times*
MasterCard, Switch, Visa

PEMBROKE FERRY   Pembrokeshire   map 4

Ferry Inn
                                              WATERSIDE
Pembroke Ferry SA72 6UD   TEL: (01646) 682947
off A477, N of Pembroke at southern end of Cleddau Bridge

Prime views of all the comings and goings on the Cleddau estuary –
whether from the waterside terrace on fine days, or sitting by the
coal fire in the friendly atmosphere of the traditional bar – are a
major draw for this creeper-covered pub. Food on the printed menu

is mostly old-fashioned pub grub, but a note reminds visitors that 'our specials board always includes fresh local fish', which is another good reason to pay the Ferry a visit. Options might take in whole sewin, skate wing with caper butter, local crab or lobster in a salad, or a seafood platter, while other local ingredients to get a look-in include lamb chops, which are marinated in honey and mint, or pork tenderloin, which comes with a paprika, cider and sweet chilli sauce. Vegetarians usually have around four choices, and puddings might include lemon brûlée. Beers are from Bass plus a weekly guest ale (Timothy Taylor Landlord or Greene King Abbot Ale, for example), and four wines from the list of around a dozen are offered by the glass, at £1.50. SAMPLE DISHES: smoked mackerel with horseradish and crusty bread £4; poached salmon with hollandaise sauce £8; Irish coffee meringue £2.75.

Licensee Colin Williams (freehouse)
Open *11.30 to 2.45, 6.30 to 11, Sun 12 to 2.45, 7 to 10.30; closed 25 and 26 Dec; bar food and restaurant 12 to 2, 7 to 10 (9 Sun)*
Details *Children welcome   Car park   Wheelchair access (also WC)   Patio No smoking in dining room   Occasional live or background music   Dogs welcome on terrace only   Delta, MasterCard, Switch, Visa*

PENALLT   Monmouthshire   map 2

Boat Inn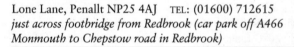

Lone Lane, Penallt NP25 4AJ   TEL: (01600) 712615
just across footbridge from Redbrook (car park off A466 Monmouth to Chepstow road in Redbrook)

Boats are usually surrounded by water, and this one in its 350 years has often been in, not beside, the River Wye. The pub's appeal to walkers and the less energetic doesn't end with its location and views. Inside, quarry-tiled floors and stone walls, simple furniture, and old photographs of floods as decoration provide a homely and welcoming atmosphere, enhanced by the notably friendly service – and by the live music on Tuesday and Thursday evenings. In casks behind the bar are well-kept beers, including regular Wadworth 6X and Greene King IPA and Abbot Ale, plus guests such as Theakston Old Peculier, Wye Valley Butty Bach and Old Speckled Hen. Thatcher's ciders are available too, as well as farmhouse ciders in summer, and there are a dozen or so country wines. The bar menu offers traditional fare such as pasta, filled jacket potatoes, steak and Guinness pie, and haddock and chips, together with some exotic dishes. These might be curries, Greek stifado, or Scottish pan haggerty, a dish of onions and garlic layered with cheese and sliced potatoes, and in its non-vegetarian form with diced bacon too.

Desserts include Tennessee grasshopper pie and Alabama fudge cake.
SAMPLE DISHES: bacon and Stilton melt £2.50; lamb and leek pie £5;
woodland fruit pie £2.25.

Licensees Don and Pat Ellis (freehouse)
Open *11 to 11, Sun 12 to 10.30; bar food 12 to 2.30, 6 to 9.30 (9 winter)*
Details *Children welcome in family room   Car park   Garden and patio
Occasional live music   Dogs welcome   MasterCard, Switch, Visa*

PONTARDDULAIS   Swansea   map 4

▲ *Fountain Inn*

111 Bolgoed Road, Pontarddulais SA4 1JP   TEL: (01792) 882501
WEB SITE: www.fountaininn.com

Though the setting is not blessed with bucolic charm, the decorative
theme inside this large, rambling, black and cream building on the
eastern outskirts of Pontarddulais is decidedly rural. A decent selection of real ales is offered (generally four in winter, three in
summer), including Old Speckled Hen, Fuller's London Pride and
Bateman XXXB, and four wines are sold by the glass. Menus are
wide-ranging and tend to stick to a tried and tested culinary style,
though with some modern ideas: feta, tomato and olive salad might
appear alongside things like minted Barnsley chops, steak and ale
pie, and steak and mushroom stroganoff. There is also a daily
specials board, which is weighted towards the catch of the day. The
restaurant, on a raised area at one end of the main room, is named
Rebecca and is decorated to show the history of the town. It has a
separate menu of mostly traditional dishes, some of authentic Welsh
origin (laverbread with bacon and cockles, for example). SAMPLE
DISHES: duck pâté with orange, port and redcurrant sauce £3.50;
prawn, chicken and snow pea pasta with creamy pesto sauce £8;
bread-and-butter pudding £3.25.

Licensee Adrian Smith (freehouse)
Open *12 to 2.30, 5 to 11, Sun 12 to 3.30, 6 to 10.30; bar food (exc Sun
lunchtime) and restaurant 12 to 2, 5 to 9.30, Sun 12 to 2.30, 6 to 8.30;
closed 25 Dec*
Details *Children welcome in bar eating areas   Car park   Wheelchairaccess
(also WC)   Garden   No-smoking area in bar and restaurant   Background
music   No dogs   Amex, Delta, MasterCard, Switch, Visa   Accommodation:
10 rooms, B&B £19.95 to £42.50*

---

*Report forms are at the back of the book; write a letter if you prefer,
or email your pub report to whichcountrypubs@which.net.*

PONTARGOTHI Carmarthenshire map 4

Salutation ✿ ♥ | NEW ENTRY |

Pontargothi SA32 7NH TEL: (01267) 290336
on A40 between Llandeilo and Carmarthen

Despite the unprepossessing outer appearance of this black and
white roadside inn, the kitchen here produces food that is far ahead
of run-of-the-mill pub grub. As you enter, it becomes immediately
apparent that the place is geared up for people eating rather than
drinking. Several dining areas feature exposed-stone walls and
beams, though there is also a cosy and atmospheric central bar area
where you can enjoy beers from the local Felinfoel Brewery by an
open fire. Plenty of enticements are found on the extensive menu,
listed on a blackboard, from old-fashioned dishes like deep-fried
Brie, or chargrilled sirloin steak, to more modern offerings, such as
bacon and goats'-cheese won tons, and beef fillet with pesto and
mozzarella. Among dishes to receive praise have been mildly spiced
Thai fishcake containing plenty of salmon, and tender loin of pork
on garlic mash. To finish, there may be brown bread-and-butter
pudding, 'a good example of its genre', with crème anglaise. If the
style seems somewhat traditional, this may be due to the fact that the
Potters (Sera Potter runs front-of-house while husband Richard is in
charge of the kitchen) both trained at London's Savoy; unlike the
Savoy, the Salutation offers on Tuesday evenings fish and chips with
mushy peas to eat in or to take away. Around 30 wines are listed,
with six by the glass, and a useful style guide (1–9 for sweetness in
whites; A–E for fullness in reds) keeps you fully in the picture. Bottle
prices range from a thoroughly reasonably £8.50 to around £21 for
the Flagship wines (two New Zealanders, a Châteauneuf-du-Pape
and a Pouilly-Fuissé). SAMPLE DISHES: laverbread and prawn filo
parcel £5; délices of cod with chorizo £10.25; deep-fried strawberry
and black pepper sandwich with caramelised pineapple £4.

Licensee Richard Potter (freehouse)
Open *12 to 3, 6 to 11, Sun 12 to 3, 7 to 10.30; bar food and restaurant 12
to 2 (3 Sun), 6 to 9 (9.30 Sat)*
Details *Children welcome   Car park   No smoking in dining room   No music
No dogs   MasterCard, Switch, Visa*

PORTHGAIN   Pembrokeshire   map 4

Sloop Inn

Porthgain SA62 5BN   TEL: (01348) 831449
off A487, 4m W of Mathry

Here indeed be dragons: one the real Welsh ale noted below, the other a hot chicken curry called tan y ddraig, or dragon's fire. But the connections here are more maritime, for the pub houses relics from a shipwreck off Porthgain, and the patios are hung with lobster pots and floats. Local crab may appear on the menu along with Welsh black beef sirloin steaks, Pembrokeshire ham salad, and Llangloffan cheese ploughman's. Otherwise it's mainly conventional fare but, given its setting by the harbour, with an appropriate emphasis on the sea: moules marinière, home-made macaroni and seafood bake, and fish specials from the blackboard. Real ales are Brains SA Best Bitter, Felinfoel Double Dragon Ale, Old Speckled Hen and Worthington Bitter, and three wines are sold by the glass. SAMPLE DISHES: chicken liver pâté £3.75; steak, kidney and mushroom pie £6.50; granny's hot apple and caramel pie £3.

Licensee Matthew Blakiston (freehouse)
Open *11 to 11, Sun 12 to 3.40, 5.30 to 10.30; bar food 12 to 2.30, 6 to 9.30*
Details *Children welcome   Car park   Garden   No-smoking area in bar Occasional live or background music; jukebox   No dogs   Amex, Delta, Diners, MasterCard, Switch, Visa*

PWLLGLOYW   Powys   map 4

▲ Seland Newydd ✿

Pwllgloyw LD3 9PY   TEL: (01874) 690282
on B4520, 4m N of Brecon

Despite no longer having antipodean connections, this unassuming seventeenth-century roadside inn has not changed its name (Welsh for New Zealand), and evidence suggests that high standards have also been maintained. The long, narrow bar is divided into three areas and has a cosy and informal feel, thanks to a wood-burning fire in a brick hearth, and settees and easy chairs in one section. It is not a drinkers' pub – though Brains Dark and Wye Valley Bitter are available, plus a guest such as Butty Bach (also from Wye Valley) – as the main focus is on food, presented on a large blackboard by the bar. Baguettes (filled with hot Welsh beef and horseradish, or smoked bacon and Welsh rarebit, for example) should suit those looking for a snack, while pan-fried ribeye with black pudding and spicy potato wedges caters for those after something more substantial. The separate restaurant has its own menu, which is also available in the bar. Among its appealingly varied options might be whole roast partridge with crusted new potatoes, thyme and garlic, or seared salmon with saffron risotto. Chef Paul Thomasson, the son of one of the owners, 'displays quite a flair', thought a satisfied luncher who praised a 'light, refreshing and tasty' Parma ham and vine tomato tart, and an attractively presented and richly flavoured confit duck leg on a bed of haggis and mustard-flavoured mash. A good-value, international wine list opens with three house wines at £1.75 a glass and £8.95 or £9.50 a bottle. SAMPLE DISHES: duck liver parfait with beetroot chutney on toasted brioche £4.25; duo of sausages: Welsh dragon and tomato and basil, with mustard mash and honey-roasted root vegetables £7.50; vanilla and toffee crème brûlée with fruits of the forest ice cream £4.50.

Licensee Anthony Savage (freehouse)
Open *12 to 2.30, 7 to 10.30 (all day Sat summer); bar food and restaurant Tue to Sun (exc Sun evening) 12 to 2.30, 6.45 to 9 (9.30 Thur to Sat); closed evening 25 Dec*
Details *Children welcome   Car park   Wheelchair access (also WC)   Garden No smoking in dining room   Background music   No dogs   Delta, Diners, MasterCard, Switch, Visa   Accommodation: 3 rooms, B&B £25 to £50*

RED WHARF BAY   Isle of Anglesey   map 7

Ship Inn 🍺

Red Wharf Bay LL75 8RJ   TEL: (01248) 852568
off A5025, 6m N of Menai Bridge

SEASIDE

A spectacular setting, looking out over a wide sandy bay filled with boats from a promontory on the east coast of Anglesea, makes this whitewashed sixteenth-century pub popular for al fresco lunches in summer. Make sure you arrive early to beat the crowds. Rustic seating in the shade of an ash tree makes the most of the views, but if conditions are unfavourable for sitting outside then the homely, unspoilt bar, with shelves of toby jugs, hunting cartoons and open fires in winter, is an attractive alternative. A wide range of culinary influences produces a modern, eclectic style of cooking: seared citrus and chilli lamb with noodles and yoghurt dressing, and smoked trout and salmon salad are typical starters. Daily-changing main courses, listed on a blackboard, might be as traditional as pan-fried lambs' liver with onion gravy or as unusual as chilli and coriander meatballs with pineapple curry sauce. Those looking for something lighter can choose from a range of baguettes and sandwiches. No fewer than five real ales are on handpump in summer (maybe just two weekdays in winter and four weekends), and these might include Burton Ale, Marston's Pedigree, Tetley Mild, plus Robinson's Best Bitter, or (in winter) Friary Meaux Bitter. Wines are an international selection, with six by the glass. SAMPLE DISHES: sauté king prawns with mango and coriander salsa £5; Thai-style fillet of sea bass with yoghurt dressing £9; peach and basil crème brûlée £3.75.

Licensee A.L. Kenneally (freehouse)
Open *summer 11 to 11; winter Mon to Fri 11 to 3.30, 6 to 11, Sat 11 to 11, Sun 12 to 11; bar food Mon to Sat 12 to 2.30, 6 to 9.30, Sun 12 to 9; restaurant Fri and Sat 6 to 9.30, and Sun winter 12 to 2.30*
Details *Children welcome in bar eating areas   Car park   Wheelchair access (not WC)   Garden and patio   No-smoking area in bar, no smoking in dining room   Occasional background music   No dogs   Delta, MasterCard, Switch, Visa*

RUTHIN   Denbighshire   map 7

▲ *Ye Olde Anchor Inn*

Rhos Street, Ruthin LL15 1DX   TEL: (01824) 702813
WEB SITE: www.anchorinn.co.uk
at junction of A525 and A494

Located in a very pretty Welsh market town, this eighteenth-century coaching inn is kitted out inside with a wealth of old-world accoutrements: gleaming horse brasses and copper pots, coaching horns and ancient guns and rifles, along with low oak beams and inglenooks, and sepia-toned photographs of stern Victorian townsfolk. Clientele include a mix of locals and those coming for the attractively presented, well-above-standard pub grub on offer. The bar menu applies only at lunchtime and in the early evening; after that the restaurant menu kicks in everywhere. From the bar food menu, reporters have enjoyed starters of well-flavoured broccoli and almond soup, and equally fine mushrooms stuffed with smoked bacon and garlic and topped with Cheddar, as well as main courses of beef lasagne, and richly sauced chicken and leek pie. Otherwise there are filled baked potatoes, several vegetarian options (maybe mixed bean and lentil chilli), savoury pancakes and crèpes, and sandwiches. 'Unmistakably home-made' vanilla ice cream, or 'just right' crème brûlée might be good ways to end a meal. The restaurant menu revs up a notch or two to offer the likes of devilled lambs' kidneys, steaks, or Indonesian pork fillet, plus chef's specials: Stilton-stuffed chicken with a red wine and wild mushroom jus, for example. Friendly service enhances the care taken in the kitchen. Bass and Flowers are the draught ales, and three wines are offered by the glass. SAMPLE DISHES: tuna and egg with korma mayonnaise £3.75;

seafood pancake with mustard sauce £5; poached pears in spiced orange syrup £4.

Licensee Rod England (freehouse)
Open *11 to 11 (10.30 Sun); bar food 12 to 2, 5.30 to 7; restaurant 12 to 2, 7 to 10*
Details *Children welcome   Car park   Wheelchair access (also WC)   Garden No smoking in dining room   Background music   Dogs welcome   Amex, Delta, Diners, MasterCard, Switch, Visa   Accommodation: 26 rooms, B&B £24.50 to £37.50*

ST GEORGE   Conwy   map 7

Kinmel Arms

St George LL22 9BP   TEL: (01745) 832207
off A55, 2m SE of Abergele

There is a charming rural look about this stone-built seventeenth-century pub with its leaded windows, and inside, although décor in the bar area is somewhat basic, the welcome is warm and genuine and service efficient. In the more elaborately done-out restaurant, setting the scene are walls hung with reproduction paintings, and the odd nude brass statue. Menus for bar (on blackboards) and restaurant (printed) are available throughout. What the pub describes as 'basic sandwiches' (rare roast beef or tuna mayonnaise perhaps) and 'designer sandwiches' (for example, 'Hamlet', with home-baked ham, lettuce, tomato, mayonnaise and mustard; or 'Napoleon', with Brie, bacon and cranberry sauce) are available lunchtime only. Larger appetites might choose specials of confit of Barbary duck with char-grilled apples and a spice sauce, and then seared pink tuna with a tomato and red pepper salsa, while printed menus might offer Bury black pudding with cider and mustard sauce, or king prawns flamed with brandy, chillies and garlic butter, followed by lasagne, steak and ale pie; or cod in beer batter with chips. Thwaites Best Bitter is on draught plus guests such as Marston's Bitter and Pedigree, and a handful of wines are served by the glass. SAMPLE DISHES: smoked cod and cheese tartlet £3.75; gammon steak with egg and chips £7.50; lemon tart with fruit coulis £3.

Licensee Gary Edwards (freehouse)
Open *12 to 3, 7 to 11; bar food and restaurant 12 to 2, 7 to 9.30; closed 25 Dec*
Details *Children welcome in bar eating area   Car park   Wheelchairaccess (not WC)   Garden   No smoking in dining room   Background music   No dogs Delta, MasterCard, Switch, Visa*

ST HILARY   Vale of Glamorgan   map 4

Bush Inn

St Hilary CF71 7DP   TEL: (01446) 772745
WEB SITE: www.downourlocal.com/thebushinn
off A48 Cardiff to Bridgend road

Old but not old-fashioned sums up the appeal of this sixteenth-century inn, a long, low stone building with a thatched roof opposite the Norman church in the quiet village of St Hilary. Inside, as may be expected, flagstones and heavy beams set the atmosphere, and if you are lucky you may also encounter the ghost of a former customer of the inn: one Ianto Ffranc, a highwayman who was hanged. If not, you can at least be sure that the place will be busy at all times. Bar food follows a tried and tested route, with a menu of traditional favourites such as deep-fried Brie with redcurrant jelly, or garlic mushrooms in cream sauce for starters, and things like baked ham with parsley sauce, plaice or cod (grilled or fried), or chicken curry to follow. Blackboard specials, such as Cajun steak, feature at weekends, while desserts might include lemon cheesecake, or bread-and-butter pudding. The restaurant menu is in a similar vein, with a few more up-market ideas, such as tournedos Rossini, or breast of duck with caramelised blackberry and kumquat sauce. Drinkers are offered Old Speckled Hen, Hancock's HB, Worthington BB, Old Rosey cider, and Vat cider. Three house wines, at £8.95, open a varied list, and four wines are available by the glass. SAMPLE DISHES: laverbread and bacon £3.25; steak and ale pie £5.50; raspberry trifle £3.25.

Licensee Sylvia Murphy (Punch Taverns)
Open *11.30 to 11, Sun 12 to 10.30; bar food and restaurant 12 to 2.30, 6.45 to 9.45, Sun 12.15 to 3; closed evening 25 Dec*
Details *Children welcome in bar eating area   Car park   Wheelchair access (not WC)   Garden and patio   No smoking in dining room   Occasional background music   No dogs   Delta, MasterCard, Visa*

STACKPOLE   Pembrokeshire   map 4

Armstrong Arms

Stackpole SA71 5DF   TEL: (01646) 672324
off B4319, 3m S of Pembroke

The peaceful village of Stackpole is at the heart of the National Trust-owned Stackpole Estate. Its proximity to the coast and the Pembrokeshire Coast Path makes the local hostelry, a pair of converted seventeenth-century cottages, a popular venue for passing walkers, but it also draws in visitors who come for the consistently good food. Inside is a warren-like series of interconnected rooms, with smart pine furniture and some areas laid up for dining. A straightforward approach on the lunch menu produces things such as a pint of prawns with crusty bread and mayonnaise, or crab and spring onion cakes with French bean salad. In the evening, sage-crusted rack of Welsh lamb with courgette and tarragon cream is more typical, while local fish and seafood show up well: sewin, John Dory, monkfish and turbot, among others. Home-made puddings – among them perhaps lemon and lime cheesecake, and profiteroles – are listed on a blackboard. As well as around twenty wines are a red and a white wine of the month, and four house wines are sold by the litre, half-litre, bottle (£7.45) and two sizes of glass. Beer drinkers are offered Buckley's Best, Brains Rev James Original and SA, and Wadworth 6X, and a large range of whiskies is kept. SAMPLE DISHES: home-made beefburger with roasted sweetcorn, chilli and tomato salsa £7; medallions of pork with apple and calvados sauce £8.50; amaretti and raspberry trifle £3.50.

Licensees Margaret and Valerie Westmore (freehouse)
Open *11 to 3.30 (3 winter), 6 (7 winter) to 11, Sun 12 to 3, 7 to 10.30; bar food and restaurant 12 to 2.15, 7 to 9.15; closed Sun evening, all day Mon Feb*
Details *Children welcome   Car park   Wheelchair access (also WC)   Garden No smoking in dining room   Occasional background music   Dogs welcome exc in restaurant   Delta, MasterCard, Switch, Visa*

TYN-Y-GROES   Conwy   **map 7**

▲ *Groes Inn*

Tyn-y-Groes LL32 8TN   TEL: (01492) 650545
4m S of Conwy; from mini-roundabout at Conwy Castle take B5106 towards Trefriw for 2m

---

First licensed in 1537 and offering traditional hospitality ever since, the Groes Inn enjoys a spectacular location with views of the Conwy Estuary in one direction and the peaks of Snowdonia in the other. The well-maintained exterior is as pretty as a picture, with small shuttered windows, creepers, hanging baskets, trees and shrubs. Inside, the ambience is as might be expected from a pub of this age, and warmth is provided by a wood-burning stove in an inglenook with a huge beam hung with pots. The décor is in the familiar vein of polished brass and copper, plus varied prints and a shelf laden with old books; a separate modern dining room extension is in similar style. Food in the bar is listed on a blackboard, while a fixed-price menu is offered in the dining room. Choice is wide, covering traditional and modern styles, and many of the first-rate ingredients are local: salt-marsh lamb, for example, and fish and seafood from the waters around Anglesey, notably Conwy mussels in various forms. Typical offerings include rabbit casserole with smoked bacon and juniper, and a seafood mixed grill comprised of codling, skate, and plaice, or whatever has been freshly caught. Tetley Bitter is provided for real ale drinkers, and there are six wines by the glass. SAMPLE DISHES: grilled big field mushrooms with Stilton £4.75; braised local pheasant with Indian spices and yoghurt £7.50; bara brith bread-and-butter pudding £3.70.

Licensee Dawn Humphreys (freehouse)
Open *12 to 3, 6 to 11; bar food and restaurant 12 to 2.15 (2.30 Sun winter, 3 Sun summer), 6.30 to 9*
Details *Children welcome in family room   Car park   Wheelchair access (also WC)   Garden   No-smoking areas in bar and dining room   Background music No dogs   Amex, Delta, Diners, MasterCard, Switch, Visa   Accommodation: 14 rooms, B&B £64 to £115*

WOLF'S CASTLE   Pembrokeshire   map 4

▲ *The Wolfe* ✿ ❦

Wolf's Castle SA62 5LS   TEL: (01437) 741662
WEB SITE: www.pembrokeshire-online.co.uk/wolfe
on A40, 7m S of Fishguard

The austerity of the grey stone walls of this large old pub on a main road through beautiful countryside is offset by the colourful creepers and hanging flower baskets outside, and more importantly by the warm, friendly welcome inside provided by Gianni and Jacqueline di Lorenzo and their staff. There are three pleasant dining rooms and a patio. An Italian influence shows in the drinks on offer, which include interesting Italian wines, and an extensive choices of aperitifs and grappas. The bar menu takes in comforting pub standards such as bangers and mash with onion gravy, lamb's liver and bacon, and steak, kidney and ale pie; plus some a little more exotic, such as creamy garlic mushrooms in a crispy filo basket, or Thai-style chicken curry with a choice of rice or 'Welsh fries'. Chef's specials and fresh fish of the day are marked out on blackboards, while restaurant dishes (also available in the bar) might include flash roasted saddle of venison on red cabbage with orange and port syrup, or guinea-fowl stuffed with apricots and celery and served with mushroom cream sauce. Draught Worthington is on tap, and the very reasonably priced wine list has a 'round the world' selection of 11 house wines almost all under £10. The rest of the 40-strong selection offers similar good value and focuses on France and Italy.

Eight wines are available by the glass and six by the half-bottle. SAMPLE DISHES: savoury pancake with filling of the day £5.75; chicken breast cooked with garlic and lemon £7; chocolate and amaretti terrine with brandy £4.

Licensee Gianni di Lorenzo (freehouse)

Open *summer Mon to Sat 11 to 11, Sun 11 to 3; winter Tue to Sun 11 to 3, Tue to Sat 6 to 11; bar food and restaurant 12 to 2, 6.30 to 9*

Details *Children welcome in bar eating area   Car park   Wheelchair access (also female WC)   Garden and patio   No smoking in dining room Background music   Dogs welcome in bar only   Delta, MasterCard, Switch, Visa   Accommodation: 3 rooms, B&B £30 to £40*

OUT AND ABOUT

Country pubs have all kinds of attractions, and people use them for all kinds of reasons. Pubs in 'Out and About' are a mixed bag, but each has some special quality that makes it well worth visiting.

Some of the pubs listed here are superlative outlets for real ale; others have fascinating history and architecture. There are hostelries close to public gardens, castles, rivers and canals; walkers, bird-watchers, climbers and fishermen will also find plenty of establishments serving their own interests. Many places are also excellent family venues, and some may offer decent accommodation.

Most of these pubs serve food, although that is not the main reason for their inclusion in 'Out and About'. Food is often incidental to the proceedings, and some places provide only limited snacks; a few serve no food at all.

Pubs are listed on the basis of readers' recommendations, backed up in many cases by inspectors' reports. Further feedback on these places is most welcome.

ENGLAND

ABBOTS BROMLEY

Staffordshire   map 5

Bagot Arms

Bagot Street,
Abbots Bromley WS15 3DB
TEL: (01283) 840371

on B5104, 6m W of Uttoxeter

New licensees took over in early 2000 and keep up the pub's tradition of special events by staging a monthly 'Classic Car Meet'. Participants receive a free Sunday lunch, so dust off those fenders. Marston's Pedigree, Banks's Mild and Mansfield Class are the real ales on offer, and all 16 wines on the imaginative list are available by the glass. Potato skins or mussels might provide a light snack, and there is a comprehensive list of pub favourites from various curries, for example, to chicken wrapped in bacon with Stilton sauce.

Open *Mon to Fri 12 to 2.30, 5.15 to 11, Sat 12 to 11, Sun 12 to 10.30*

AINSTABLE

Cumbria   map 10

New Crown

Ainstable CA4 9QQ
TEL: (01768) 896273

take A6 from M6 junction 41, follow signs to Armathwaite, then 2m to Ainstable

This family-run, white-painted inn offers a comfortable place in which to relax after a walk in the Eden Valley or a visit to the nearby Roman camp. Ales on draught include Tetley's, and guests such as Black Sheep and Jennings Cumberland Ale. As well as snacks, there is a menu of full-size meals (for example, grilled marinated halibut steak, or duckling with orange sauce) and children's 'small bites' with free ice cream. Overnight accommodation is available.

Open *12 to 3, 6 to 11; winter closed evenings Mon to Thur*

ALDEBURGH

Suffolk   map 6

Ye Olde Cross Keys Inn

Crabbe Street, Aldeburgh IP15 5BN
TEL: (01728) 452637

on A1094, 8m E of A12

With its three guest rooms, the Cross Keys is ideally situated for the beach, for visits to nearby Southwold (home of Adnams) and of course for the Festival. Adnams beers are on handpump here, and the wine list, from which six are available by the glass, is also from that company. They accompany some classic seafood cookery, including moules marinière, scallops in bacon, fresh crab, Dover sole or cod, with sticky toffee or summer puddings to conclude, depending on the season.

Open *11 to 3, 5.30 to 11, Sun 12 to 3, 7 to 10.30 (summer 11 to 11)*

ALMONDSBURY

South Gloucestershire   map 2

Bowl Inn

16 Church Road, Lower
Almondsbury BS32 4DT
TEL: (01454) 612757

on A38, 7m N of Bristol

The name refers to the local topography of the Severn estuary, which may be viewed from this whitewashed stone inn. Licensed since 1550, the cluster of cottages was built to house the monks who constructed the twelfth-century church next door. Some enticing modern food is served, from tiger prawn brochettes wrapped in streaky bacon to black pudding in lager batter on apple and onion marmalade, and seasonally changing cask ales such as Bass and Rebellion Smuggler are offered alongside an extensive wine list. Thirteen guest rooms are available.

Open *11 to 3, 5 to 11, Sun 12 to 3, 7 to 10.30*

ALSTON

Cumbria   map 10

Turk's Head Inn

Market Place, Alston CA9 3HS
TEL: (01434) 381148
*at junction of A686/A689/B6277, 16m
NE of Penrith*
Alston is said to be the highest market
town in England, lying not far from the
Pennine Way and surrounded by
wonderful moorland landscape. This
inn forms part of a terrace of
commercial premises overlooking the
square. It offers Boddingtons Cask,
Flowers IPA and Trophy Bitter on
draught plus pies, steaks and casseroles
for hungry walkers. Children are
welcome.
Open *11 to 3.30, 6.30 to 11, Sun 12
to 3.30, 7 to 10.30; closed evening 25
Dec*

ALVESTON

Warwickshire   map 5

Ferry Inn

Ferry Lane, Alveston CV37 7QX
TEL: (01789) 269883
*off B4056, between Stratford-upon-
Avon and Wellsbourne*
Charlecote Park (NT) is nearby and the
birthplace of the Bard only a couple of
miles away. While on the tourist trail,
make time for a pint of Adnams or
Fuller's London Pride at this charming
village inn, where a varied menu might
tempt you with Caesar salad, spaghetti
puttanesca, shoulder of lamb braised in
red wine, rosemary and redcurrants, or
halibut with salsa verde. Two wines are
served by the glass.
Open *12 to 3, 6 to 11, Sun 12 to 3*

ANICK

Northumberland   map 10

Rat Inn

Anick NE46 4LN
TEL: (01434) 602814
just N of A69, 1½m NE of Hexham
In a peaceful location with outstanding
views across the Tyne valley, the Rat is
an unassuming grey stone pub offering
several real ales, including Old
Speckled Hen, Theakston Best,
Marston's Pedigree and Mordue Five
Bridges. Four wines are available by the
glass. In addition to the printed menu
of bar food staples, there are
blackboard specials such as pork
medallions with sweetcorn and olive oil
relish, or loin of lamb with mint,
cucumber and garlic salsa. Children are
welcome throughout the pub, which
also has a garden.
Open *11 to 3, 6 to 11, Sun 12 to 3, 7
to 10.30*

APPLEBY

Cumbria   map 10

Tufton Arms

Market Square, Appleby CA16 6XA
TEL: (017683) 51593
Set in the centre of the medieval
market town of Appleby-in-
Westmorland, this former Victorian
coaching inn is now a family-run hotel,
with a restaurant in the conservatory
overlooking a mews courtyard. Tufton
Arms ale (brewed by Tetley) is
available, together with an extensive
wine list (160 bins). The cooking
features local produce. Children are
welcome throughout the pub.
Open *11 to 11, Sun 12 to 3, 7 to
10.30*

APPLETON ROEBUCK

North Yorkshire   map 9

Shoulder of Mutton

Chapel Green,
Appleton Roebuck YO23 7DP
TEL: (01904) 744227
*3m SE of A64 Leeds to York road; turn
off at Colton Lane End*
Travellers along the A64 might well
take a detour to this tiny village where
this Samuel Smith's pub overlooks the
village green. Here, real ales are drawn
straight from the wood, and you will
also find bottled organic beer and
lager, plus a menu that includes such
modern dishes as aubergine black
pudding tower and the mysteriously
named chicken mahogany.
Open *11 to 3, 6.30 to 11, Sun 12 to 3,
7 to 10.30*

ASHBURNHAM

East Sussex   map 3

Ashtree Inn

Ashburnham TN33 9NX
TEL: (01424) 892104
just off B2204 (off A271), 4m W of Battle

Homely sixteenth-century local tucked away down narrow country lanes in an isolated hamlet close to the town of Battle and Ashburnham Park. Cosy beamed bars with three inglenook fireplaces, old settles, exposed brickwork, and evening candlelight. Expect Harveys Best as well as Old Speckled Hen on handpump, and a short selection of hearty country dishes listed on blackboards and a printed menu. Children are welcome.
Open *12 to 3, 7 to 11*

ASHBY ST LEDGERS

Northamptonshire   map 5

Olde Coach House Inn

Ashby St Ledgers CV23 8UN
TEL: (01788) 890349
off A361, 4m N of Daventry

The local manor house has connections with Guy Fawkes and his fellow conspirators. Ivy-clad and built of stone, this former farmhouse has a cavernous, rambling interior containing both large family tables and small, intimate dining areas. As well as regular Flowers Original and Fuller's London Pride there are three guest ales, and from the list of 35 wines nine are offered by the glass. Game usually features on the menu. Children are welcome inside and out (there is a baby changing room and a garden play area), and six en-suite rooms are available.
Open *12 to 2.30, 6 to 11, Sat 12 to 11, Sun 12 to 10.30*

ASHLEWORTH

Gloucestershire   map 5

Boat Inn

The Quay, Ashleworth GL19 4HZ
TEL: (01452) 700272
off A417, 5m N of Gloucester

For five centuries this riverside pub, near the spot where the old chain ferry used to cross the Severn, has been quenching the thirst of boatmen. Arkell's 3B, RCH Pitchfork and Wye Valley ales are on tap – at least four at any one time – plus traditional ciders. The food is confined to a selection of filled baps, but in summer services extend to a coffee house offering drinks and cakes.
Open *11 to 2.30, 6 (7 winter) to 11, Sun 12 to 3, 7 to 10.30; closed Wed lunchtime, 25 Dec*

AYOT ST LAWRENCE

Hertfordshire   map 3

Brocket Arms

Ayot St Lawrence AL6 9BT
TEL: (01438) 820250
off B656/B651, 2m W of Welwyn

George Bernard Shaw's home (NT) is in the village and the pub, dating from the fourteenth century and reputedly haunted by the ghost of a priest tried and hanged here during the Reformation, probably hasn't changed much since his day. It was once the quarters of monks attached to the village's Norman church, which now stands in ruins. The real ales are Greene King's Abbot Ale and IPA, Fuller's London Pride, Adnams Broadside and Young's IPA, and are joined by guests, perhaps Gale's HSB. Eight wines are available by the glass, and the menus might include local game in season. The large walled garden is a sun-trap in summer, and accommodation is available.
Open *11 to 11*

BADBY

Northamptonshire   map 5

Windmill

Main Street, Badby NN11 3AN
TEL: (01327) 702363
on A361 Daventry to Banbury road, 2m S of Daventry

A charming thatched inn established in the seventeenth century, the Windmill is on the main street of this attractive village. Nearby are excellent walks, Canon's Ashby (NT), Althorp (home of the Spencers) and Sulgrave Manor, where George Washington's family lived. Inside the mellow stone walls are flagstone floors, log fires and cask-conditioned ales including Flowers, Wadworth 6X and Boddingtons. Children are welcome where food is served, including the little garden at the front. A hotel extension has been built at the rear, with a separate entrance.

Open *12 to 3, 5.30 to 11*

BAINBRIDGE

North Yorkshire　　map 8

Rose & Crown Hotel

Bainbridge DL8 3EE
TEL: (01969) 650225
on A684, between Hawes and Leyburn, 4m E of Hawes

Look for the green – complete with stocks – in this attractive Wensleydale village of charming mellow stone houses and you will find this long, white-painted coaching inn, which bears the date 1445. At the bar are ales from Black Sheep, Webster's Yorkshire Bitter and John Smith's, and a range of wines. Hearty dishes feature on the bar menu, including some locally produced items, and the dinner menu in the restaurant changes regularly. The hotel has 12 rooms.

Open *10.30 to 11*

BARBON

Cumbria　　map 8

Barbon Inn

Barbon LA6 2LJ
TEL: (01524) 276233
just off A683, 3m N of Kirkby Lonsdale

Walking, mountain biking, riding, fishing in the River Lune or golf at Kirkby Lonsdale are all within easy reach of the pub; they will even lend you a dog for company. The less energetic will appreciate this seventeenth-century coaching inn's secluded beer garden, and its restaurant; bar food is available all day. Beers include Theakston Best, Dent Aviator, Courage Directors and several from Bushes.

Open *12 to 3, 6 to 11.30*

BARHAM

Suffolk　　map 6

Sorrel Horse

Barham IP6 0PG
TEL: (01473) 830327
off A14 at Claydon, 5m N of Ipswich

This pink-washed seventeenth-century inn, situated opposite Shrublands Park health farm, has a spotlessly refurbished and modernised interior, with oak beams, an open log fire and a friendly atmosphere. Local Tolly Cobbold ales, competently cooked food, notably the daily blackboard specials, and the extensive rear garden with children's play area are particular attractions. A converted barn houses eight *en suite* bedrooms.

Open *Mon to Fri 11 to 3, 5 to 11, Sat 11 to 11, Sun 11 to 10.30*

BARTHOMLEY

Cheshire　　map 5

White Lion

Barthomley CW2 5PG
TEL: (01270) 882242
off Alsager road, from M6 junction 16, 4m SE of Crewe

The charm of this seventeenth-century black-and-white timbered building lies in the simplicity of its timeless interior. Three traditional rooms feature quarry-tiled floors, heavy oak beams, wonky walls, scrubbed tables and benches, and the sound of crackling log fires and lively conversation – no piped music or electronic games here. An inn since 1614 and with only 18 landlords since that time, it is a peaceful retreat in which to enjoy a pint of Burtonwood Bitter or Top Hat. Simple, good-value lunchtime food.

Open *11.30 to 11 (Thur 5 to 11), Sun 12 to 10.30*

BECKLEY

Oxfordshire　　map 2

Abingdon Arms

High Street, Beckley OX3 9UU
TEL: (01865) 351311
off B4027, 5m NE of Oxford

As you enter this traditional village pub, note the curious door-closing mechanism operated by the weight of

an old cider flagon. The menu is more modern but equally imaginative; among the specials might be skate wing, or braised veal shin with herb risotto, as well as a pasta, pizza, curry, sausage, steak and dessert of the day. Brakspear Bitter and seasonal ales are on draught.

Open *11 to 3, 6 to 11, Sun 12 to 10.30*

BEER

Devon map 2

Anchor

Beer EX12 3ET
TEL: (01297) 20386
off A3052, between Seaton and Sidmouth
This Anchor is firmly planted on a hillside, and the white-painted pub – now owned by Old English Inns – overlooks the harbour and beach. There is a family room and the large restaurant offers a conventional bar menu with fresh fish specials. Courage Best, Otter and Directors are the draught ales, and there are 12 wines by the glass.

Open *11 to 11, Sun 12 to 10.30*

BERKSWELL

West Midlands map 5

Bear Inn

Spencers Lane, Berkswell CV7 7BB
TEL: (01676) 533202
off A452, 6m W of Coventry
Food options at this large village inn include a bar snacks menu of things like open ciabatta sandwiches and prawns by the pint, and a long main list featuring everything from sausage with bubble and squeak to half a duck with honey and pink peppercorn sauce. Regular Theakston Best Bitter and Courage Directors are joined by two guest ales: Exmoor Gold and Robinson's Best Bitter, for example. All 16 bottles on the wine list are offered by two sizes of glass.

Open *11 to 11, Sun 12 to 10.30*

BERRYNARBOR

Devon map 1

Ye Olde Globe

Berrynarbor EX34 9SG
TEL: (01271) 882465
off A399, 4m E of Ilfracombe
First licensed in 1675, this converted row of ancient cottages probably dates from about 400 years before then. Inside, it is full of interesting antiques and curios. Children enjoy a special menu, the garden, and a large family room, which 'is partially non-smoking'. On tap are Ushers Best and Courage Directors, plus a guest ale. There are also West Country country wines, and ten 'real' wines by the glass.

Open *11.30 to 2.30, 6 (7 winter) to 11*

BEST BEECH

East Sussex map 3

Best Beech Inn

Mayfield Lane, Best Beech TN5 6JH
TEL: (01892) 782046
on B2100, midway between Mark Cross and Wadhurst
Dating in part back to 1680, this tile-hung and largely Victorian building stands on a sandstone ridge at the foothills of the Ashdown Forest. The interior consists of a series of comfortably rustic rooms, where you will find Harveys Sussex Best Bitter and Adnams Best Bitter on tap and a good choice of dishes on both the bar and restaurant menus. Overnight accommodation is available.

Open *11 to 3, 6 to 11, Sun 12 to 3, 7 to 10.30*

BETCHWORTH

Surrey map 3

Dolphin

The Street, Betchworth RH3 7DW
TEL: (01737) 842288
off A25, 2m W of Reigate, in centre of Betchworth
A fully functioning blacksmith's forge is something of a rarity these days, even out in the wilds, but there is one just opposite this sixteenth-century village inn. The Dolphin is a Young's house serving their Bitter, Special, Triple A and Winter Warmer, alongside a compact list of ten wines. Food is traditional pub fare, namely liver pâté,

lasagne, steaks, scampi or gammon. Finish with jam roly-poly.

Open *11 to 3.30, 5.30 to 11, Sat 11 to 11, Sun 12 to 10.30*

BEWDLEY

Worcestershire   map 5

Little Packhorse

31 High Street, Bewdley DY12 2DH
TEL: (01299) 403762

3m W of Kidderminster

Dating from the fifteenth century and reputedly the oldest pub in this attractive riverside town, the Little Packhorse is an atmospheric and oddly eccentric drinkers' pub. The tiny interior is adorned with bric-à-brac, from old clocks and advertising signs to fascinating tools. Now an Innspired Inn (part of Ushers), it serves Ind Coope Burton Ale and Ushers ales on draught. Food is hearty and traditional, and the menu still features the famous Desperate Dan (steak and ale) pie.

Open *Mon to Fri 12 to 3, 6 to 11, Sat 12 to 11, Sun 12 to 10.30*

BILBROUGH

North Yorkshire   map 9

Three Hares

Main Street, Bilbrough YO2 3PH
TEL: (01937) 832128

off A64, between Tadcaster and York

Ownership of the Three Hares changed in 1998 and again in late 2000 but as a coaching inn its old world ambience has survived intact for a long time, and will surely be maintained. Daily-changing menus are fit for the twenty-first century but also traditional enough to offer Yorkshire pudding as a starter. The wine list runs to 40 pages; hand-pulled ales are from Black Sheep and Timothy Taylor, plus a guest.

Open *Tue to Sat 12 to 3, 7 to 11, Sun 12 to 3*

BLACKAWTON

Devon   map 1

Normandy Arms

Chapel Street, Blackawton TQ9 7BN
TEL: (01803) 712316

off A381 and B3207, 5m W of Dartmouth

A base for bird-watching, or sea fishing, this fifteenth-century inn has a long, low-priced menu, mainly of familiar pub favourites. The speciality is rump steak done six ways, including Blackawton (with local beer, dark brown sugar and herbs). The regular ale is Young's Special Bitter, and Blackawton Brewery supplies up to three guests, such as 44 Special or Headstrong. Wine from the local Sharpham vineyard is listed too.

Open *Mon to Fri 12 to 2.30, 7 to 11, Sat 12 to 11, Sun 12 to 2.30, 7 to 10.30*

BLAISDON

Gloucestershire   map 5

Red Hart Inn

Blaisdon GL17 0AH
TEL: (01452) 830477

off A4136, 2m from Huntley

The dark interior of this sixteenth century pub contrasts with the pleasures of the large sloping garden, and a stone patio complete with brick barbecue. The bonus in the garden is the welcome from a family of tame rare breed pigs living there. Regular ales are Hook Norton Best and Tetley's cask, joined by three guests from local breweries, perhaps Wickwar, Uley, Bath Ales or Goff's. The local cider is Weston's. The traditional bar menu is supported by a specials board, and there is a separate restaurant.

Open *11.30 to 2.30, 6 to 11.30, Sun 12 to 3, 7 to 11*

BLAKENEY

Norfolk   map 6

King's Arms

Westgate Street,
Blakeney NR25 7NQ
TEL: (01263) 740341

on A149, 5m W of Holt

This Grade II listed pub dates from 1760, which answers the obvious question people ask when they see that date written in tiles on the roof. It offers a good selection of real ales, including Marston's Pedigree and Woodforde's Wherry Best Bitter, and a menu that specialises in local seafood, notably crab, mussels and whitebait, and meat from local butchers.

Open *11 to 11 (10.30 Sun)*

BLETCHINGLEY

Surrey   map 3

Prince Albert

Outwood Road,
Bletchingley RH1 4LR
TEL: (01883) 743257

on A25, 2m W of Godstone
A 500-year-old building in the Surrey
countryside, the Prince Albert offers
outdoor seating in the summer in an
attractive garden at the back. Bar food
is served during all opening hours, and
there is a separate restaurant. Pork
medallions or tournedos Rossini might
be followed by bread-and-butter
pudding or pancakes doused in rum.
Young's Special and Wadworth 6X are
on tap, and there are two bottled house
beers.
Open *11 to 3.30, 5.30 to 11, Sun 12
to 10.30*

William IV

Little Common Lane,
Bletchingley RH1 4QF
TEL: (01883) 743278

A brick-and-tile inn set in a leafy Surrey
byway, the William IV was originally a
couple of nineteenth-century cottages.
It has a child-friendly policy, and an
appealing secluded garden. The handpumped beers change regularly, but are
likely to include Wadworth 6X,
Adnams, Young's Special and Harveys,
and four wines are available by the
glass. Food is standard pub fare.
Open *11 to 3, 6 to 11, Sun 12 to 3, 7
to 10.30*

BLICKLING

Norfolk   map 6

Buckinghamshire Arms

Blickling NR11 6NF
TEL: (01263) 732133

*off B1354, from A140, 2m NW of
Aylsham*
This splendid seventeenth-century
coaching inn was built for guests and
servants of Blickling Hall (now owned
by the National Trust), which is said to
be haunted by Ann Boleyn. On draught
are Greene King Abbot Ale and IPA,
and the house beer, Blickling Bitter
brewed by Woodforde's of nearby
Woodbastwick. Game and Cromer
crabs are specialities on a menu that
emphasises the use of fresh local
produce and combines modern and
traditional fare.
Open *11 to 3, 6 to 11 (open 11 to 11
some days in summer)*

BODICOTE

Oxfordshire   map 5

Plough

Bodicote OX15 4BZ
TEL: (01295) 262327

just off A4260, 2m S of Banbury
The Blencowe family have presided
over this welcoming, two-roomed
village pub since 1957 and have been
brewing beer on the premises since
1982. The range includes Bitter and
No. 9, plus more powerful winter ales
like Triple X and Old English Porter.
The varied bar food runs from
sandwiches and filled baguettes to
roasts, casseroles and steaks. Children
are welcome in the eating area only.
Open *11 to 3, 6 to 11, Sun 12 to 3, 7
to 10.30*

BOLTER END

Buckinghamshire   map 3

Peacock

Bolter End, Lane End HP14 3LU
TEL: (01494) 881417

on B482 Marlow to Stokenchurch road
Wooden pews, china plates, old
advertising posters, prints and photos
abound in this old-style pub. As well as
a genuinely warm welcome, it offers
Brakspear Bitter and Fuller's London
Pride on draught, six red and six white
wines by glass and bottle, plus freshly
pressed orange juice among a range of
soft drinks. For diners, a few
blackboard specials (chicken fajitas, for
example) supplement the
straightforward printed menu, and
patrons appreciate the large, value-for-
money portions served.
Open *11.45 to 2.30, 6 to 11, Sun 12
to 3*

BOROUGHBRIDGE

North Yorkshire　　　　　　　map 8

Black Bull

6 St James Square,
Boroughbridge YO51 9AR
TEL: (01423) 322413

on B6265, ½m from A1(M) junction 48
This cheerful pub has new owners since
2000. They offer a long and
adventurous bar snack menu, including
Yorkshire pudding filled with lamb
casserole, and home made savoury pie,
as well as an à la carte menu in the no-
smoking restaurant. Regular ales are
John Smith's and Black Sheep, the
guest might be Timothy Taylor
Landlord; and there are at least a
dozen wines by the glass.
Open *11 to 11, Sun 12 to 10.30*

BOTTOM-OF-THE-OVEN

Cheshire　　　　　　　　　　map 8

Stanley Arms

Bottom-of-the-Oven, Macclesfield
Forest SK11 0AR
TEL: (01260) 252414

*just S of A537, between Buxton and
Macclesfield*
Close to Macclesfield Forest, the Peak
District National Park and miles of
open moorland, this isolated and
beautifully situated pub provides a
welcome refuge after an invigorating
walk. The small, cosy interior with
open fires in winter is the setting for
Marston's Bitter and Pedigree on tap,
and hearty, home-made soups and pies
on the traditional pub menu. Rear
terrace and garden afford good views.
Children are welcome in the lounge bar
until 7pm.
Open *Mon to Fri 12 to 3, 5.30 to 11,
Sat 12 to 11, Sun 12 to 10.30*

BOWNESS-ON-WINDERMERE

Cumbria　　　　　　　　　　map 9

Hole in't Wall

Lowside, Bowness-on-
Windermere LA23 3DH
TEL: (01539) 443488

*on A5074, on E shore of Lake
Windermere*
Champion wrestler Will Longmire was
landlord here during the 1800s and

Charles Dickens visited this unspoilt
tavern in the old part of the town. Full
of interest and character, with a lively
and chatty atmosphere, the rambling
series of rooms are crammed with
artefacts and curios, including old
farming implements, chamber-pots,
stuffed animals, and old pictures. Good
Robinson's ales such as Hartleys XB
and Robinson's Best. It can get very
busy, especially in the tourist season.
Open *11 to 11, Sun 12 to 10.30*

BRADFIELD

South Yorkshire　　　　　　　map 8

Strines Inn

Mortimer Road, Bradfield S6 6JE
TEL: (0114) 285 1247

*2m off A57 (not in village), 6m NW of
Sheffield*
Set in the Peak District National Park
overlooking a reservoir, this ancient
inn was built as a manor house in
1275, though most of it dates from the
1550s. Marston's Pedigree, Banks
Bitter, Old Speckled Hen and guest ales
such as Cameron's Famous Frigate are
on draught. A large selection of malt
whiskies and a few wines are available.
The menu features grills, pies and
pasta, plus blackboard specials.
Children will enjoy the play area in the
garden and the visitor-friendly animals.
As well as three rooms with four-
posters, accommodation includes a
family room.
Open *summer 10.30 to 11, winter
10.30 to 3, 5.30 to 11*

BREDON

Worcestershire　　　　　　　map 5

Fox and Hounds

Church Street, Bredon GL20 7LA
TEL: (01684) 772377

*from M5 junction 9, follow signs to
Tewkesbury then take B480 to Bredon*
Look for the outsized church with its
colossal spire in this tiny village, and a
couple of hundred yards away is the
Fox and Hounds. The large, open-plan
bar is geared up for eating, but should
you want a pint of real ale, there are
Banks's, Marston's Pedigree, and Old
Speckled Hen to choose from. Six
wines are served by the glass, and

might accompany smoked salmon and Camembert pancake, chicken breast filled with spinach, cheese and sweet basil, or a lamb shank glazed with honey and mint.
Open *9 to 3, 6.45 to 11, Sun 12 to 3, 7 to 10.30*

BRETFORTON

Worcestershire   map 5
Fleece Inn
The Cross, Bretforton WR11 5SE
TEL: (01386) 831173
on B4035, 4m E of Evesham
A living museum of the Victorian era, when it first became a pub, this striking, black and white former farmhouse in fact dates back to the early fourteenth century. Run by the Taplin family from 1848 until 1977, it was given by Lola Taplin, the last owner, to the National Trust on strict condition that the pub remained unaltered and potato crisps weren't sold. The pub is a fascinating time warp, where the Taplins' furniture, rare and valuable antiques and collections of pewter and Victorian measures grace the entirely original interior, namely the Brewhouse, the Dugout (originally the pantry) and the Pewter Room. This is also a drinker's paradise, offering five real ales and Weston's Old Rosie Cider on draught, and a range of fruit wines. Annual beer festival and a delightful orchard garden where Morris dancers perform in summer. Children are welcome.
Open *Mon to Fri 11 to 3, 6 to 11, Sat 11 to 11, Sun 12 to 10.30*

BRINDLE

Lancashire   map 8
Cavendish Arms
Sandy Lane, Brindle PR6 8NG
TEL: (01254) 852912
on B5256 between Leyland and Blackburn
Just a few miles from the Leeds and Liverpool Canal and the urban sprawl of Blackburn, this seventeenth-century hostelry enjoys a peaceful setting beside the parish church in one of Lancashire's oldest villages. The garden and small terrace are popular in summer and make the most of the pub's position. Inside, modern stained glass depicts medieval scenes. Burtonwood ales and a monthly-changing guest are on handpump. Children are welcome in the eating areas.
Open *Mon to Fri 12 to 3, 5 to 11, Sat 12 to 11, Sun 12 to 10.30*

BROAD CAMPDEN

Gloucestershire   map 5
Bakers Arms
Broad Campden GL55 6UR
TEL: (01386) 840515
off B4081, 1m SE of Chipping Campden
Good real ales are the main draw at this creeper-covered Cotswold-stone pub. Five are offered at a time, coming from breweries like Hook Norton, Donnington and Timothy Taylor. Sandwiches, ploughman's and filled Yorkshire puddings feature at lunchtimes; otherwise the menu runs to things like chicken curry, mariner's pie, or lasagne, and daily specials might be pork with apricots, or beef stroganoff.
Open *summer 11.30 to 11, Sun 12 to 10.30; winter Mon to Fri 11.30 to 2.30, 4.45 to 11, Sat 11.30 to 11, Sun 12 to 10.30; closed 25 Dec, evening 26 Dec*

BROADWAY

Worcestershire   map 5
Crown and Trumpet
Church Street,
Broadway WR12 7AE
TEL: (01386) 853202
off High Street (A44), on Snowshill road
The local Stanway Brewery produces two beers exclusively for this seventeenth-century Cotswold-stone pub: Cotterswold Gold in summer and Lords a-Leaping in winter; these are complemented by a good range of other real ales and eight wines by the glass. Food is in traditional English vein, a speciality being Evesham pie (beef in plum sauce), and a special menu of dishes containing local asparagus features in season.

Open *Mon to Thur 11 to 3, 5 to 11,*
Fri and Sat 11 to 11, Sun 12 to 11

BROCKHAM

Surrey   map 3
Royal Oak
Brockham Green,
Brockham RH3 7JS
TEL: (01737) 843241
just off A25, 2m E of Dorking
Right by the village green, the Royal
Oak has an attractive location, making
it an ideal summer venue. Whatever
time of year you drop in, though, you
can expect cask ales from Adnams,
Wadworth, Harveys and Fuller's, as
well as a varied selection of eight wines
by the glass. A straightforward bar
menu deals in chilli and rice,
Cumberland sausage, steak and kidney
pie and so forth, with daily specials on
a board.
Open *Mon to Thur 11 to 3, 5.30 to*
11, Fri to Sat 11 to 11, Sun 12 to 10.30

BROOKLAND

Kent   map 3
Woolpack
Brookland TN29 9TJ
TEL: (01797) 344321
just off A259, 5m W of New Romney
This atmospheric fifteenth-century pub
features old beams, a capacious
inglenook and a long Victorian table
with shove-penny carved at one end
and shove-ha'penny at the other. Water
jugs are a key element of the décor.
Ales on draught include Shepherd
Neame Masterbrew and Spitfire, and
simple pub fare served in very generous
portions at low prices.
Open *11 to 3, 6 to 11, Sun 12 to 3, 7*
to 10.30

BROOM

Bedfordshire   map 6
Cock
23 High Street, Broom SG18 9NA
TEL: (01767) 314411
on B658, 2m SW of Biggleswade
Three centuries have done little to
change this pub's four snug rooms,
with log fires, low ceilings, and tiled
floors. Bar snacks have changed a little

to include chicken in Cajun and balti
styles. Entirely traditional are Greene
King IPA, Abbot Ale, and Triumph
drawn straight from casks, which
would be behind the bar if they had
one. They are actually by the steps
leading to the cellar.
Open *Mon to Fri 12 to 3, 6 to 11, Sat*
12 to 4, Sun 12 to 5

BUCKLERS HARD

Hampshire   map 2
Master Builder's House Hotel
Bucklers Hard SO42 7XB
TEL: (01590) 616253
off B3054, just S of Beaulieu
Formerly the home of the master
builder Henry Adams, this carefully
refurbished eighteenth-century hotel is
on the bank of the Beaulieu River in a
fascinating preserved shipbuilding
village. The beamed and comfortably
rustic Yachtsman's Bar is popular with
yachtsmen and tourists alike, offering
welcome respite from the summer
crowds in the village, Courage ales on
tap, and soup, sandwiches and
ploughman's at lunchtime; limited
evening menu. Separate up-market
hotel and restaurant.
Open *11 to 11, Sun 12 to 10.30*

BURCOT

Oxfordshire   map 2
Chequers
Burcot OX14 3DP
TEL: (01865) 407771
on A415, 4½m E of Abingdon
Regular events at this old village inn
include themed menu nights (balti, for
example) accompanied by a pianist. At
other times the extensive blackboard
menus cater for a wide range of tastes,
from steak and kidney pudding to
escalope of chicken with fennel and
lemon grass; 'Mary's disaster cake'
sounds like an interesting pudding.
Beers are from Brakspear and
Wadworth, and three wines are sold by
the glass.
Open *11 to 2.30, 6 to 11, Sun 12 to 3,*
7 to 11

BURITON

Hampshire   map 2

Five Bells

High Street, Buriton GU31 5RX
TEL: (01730) 263584
off A3, 1m S of Petersfield
The bells in question are those of
Buriton church. Part of this fine village
pub, which dates from 1639, was once
a farrier's. It retains its rambling
sequence of rooms, heated by open
fires and wood-burning stoves. Badger
Best and Tanglefoot, Ballard's Best and
Gribble Inn Fursty Ferret are among
the real ales served, and a fair selection
of wines is also offered – a good many
by the glass. Children are welcome in
pub and garden, and accommodation is
available.
Open *11 to 2.30 (3 Fri and Sat), 5.30
to 11, Sun 12 to 3, 7 to 10.30*

BYWORTH

West Sussex   map 3

Black Horse

Byworth GU28 0HL
TEL: (01798) 342424
off A283, just S of Petworth
The Black Horse is an unspoilt,
traditional country pub serving a
limited but decent range of real ales
(including Cheriton Pots Ale) and a
more-interesting-than-average weekly-
changing bar menu. Smoked chicken
and avocado salad with mint to start,
for example, might be followed by
fresh herrings in oatmeal with mustard
sauce, or steak and kidney pudding,
with chocolate charlotte to finish.
Open *11 to 2.30, 6 to 11, Sun 12 to 3,
7 to 10.30*

CALVER

Derbyshire   map 8

Chequers Inn

Froggatt Edge, Calver S32 3ZJ
TEL: (01433) 630231
on B6054, off A623 6m N of Bakewell
This smartly appointed Peak District
inn, originally four eighteenth-century
stone cottages, is strikingly positioned
beneath the steep banks and woodland
of Froggatt Edge. It is a good base for
country walking and exploring nearby

attractions, notably Chatsworth House
and Haddon Hall. The pretty
landscaped beer garden is popular in
warm weather. One menu is served
throughout the relaxing and civilised
bar and adjoining dining area. New
licensees, so reports please.
Open *12 to 3, 5.30 to 11 (10.30 Sun)*

CARDINGTON

Shropshire   map 5

Royal Oak

Cardington SY6 7JZ
TEL: (01694) 771266
off B4371, 4m E of Church Stretton
Wood Shropshire Lad, with Hobson's
Best Bitter also among the real ales,
demonstrates this 500-year-old pub's
dedication to the cause of local
produce. Meat is locally sourced too,
though the dishes it is used in – in
terms of style anyway – could be from
anywhere: the extensive menu lists a
familiar range, from steak and kidney
pie to chicken tikka, plus ploughman's
and various baguettes at lunchtime.
Open *Tue to Sun and bank hol Mon 12
to 2.30, 7 (6 Fri) to 11 (10.30 Sun)*

CAREY

Herefordshire   map 5

Cottage of Content

Carey HR2 6NG
TEL: (01432) 840242
*between A49 and B4224, 6m SE of
Hereford*
A secluded setting in remote
countryside close to the River Wye has
preserved this delightful 500-year-old
pub, which is indeed aptly named. Oak
beams, open fires, ancient settles and
farmhouse tables in the tiny bars add to
the old-world charm. Daily dishes
listed on a chalkboard enhance the
standard printed menu. Hook Norton
and an occasional guest beer are on
draught, and there are 40 malt whiskies
to choose from. Children are welcome,
and the pub provides accommodation.
Open *12 to 3, 7 (6 Sat) to 11 (10.30
Sun)*

CASTLE HEDINGHAM

Essex   map 3

Bell

10 James Street, Castle
Hedingham CO9 3EJ
Tel: (01787) 460350

off B1058, 4m NW of Halstead

This sixteenth-century coaching inn has
retained some of its character of times
past. While they take beer seriously,
they are adamant that they do not
serve, and never will serve, chips.
Instead there may be green-lipped
mussels with port and Stilton sauce, or
tuna steak with chilli and lime sauce.
Nor do they have jukeboxes, fruit
machines or pool tables, but there is
often live music taking in Irish, folk
and modern jazz varieties. Greene King
IPA, Shepherd Neame Spitfire and
Adnams Best Bitter are stocked.

Open *11.30 to 3.30, 6 to 11, Sun 12
to 3.30, 7 to 10.30*

CAULDON

Staffordshire   map 5

Yew Tree

Cauldon, nr Waterhouses ST10 3EJ
Tel: (01538) 308348

*off A523 Leek to Ashbourne road at
Waterhouses, 6m NE of Cheadle*

Alan East clocks up 40 years as
landlord at the Yew Tree in 2001, an
accomplishment that you might
celebrate with him if you are in the
vicinity. Bar snacks are things like hot
pies and sandwiches or home-made
quiche, perhaps followed by apple
crumble made with apples from the
pub's own trees. Beers come from local
breweries such as Burton Bridge and
Titanic. A local folk band plays once a
month, and Alton Towers is less than
five miles away.

Open *10 to 2.30, 6 to 11, Sun 12 to 3,
7 to 10.30*

CERNE ABBAS

Dorset   map 2

New Inn

14 Long Street, Cerne
Abbas DT2 7JF
Tel: (01300) 341274

on A352, 7m N of Dorchester

The huge chalk figure of the Cerne
Abbas Giant is undoubtedly the most
prominent attraction hereabouts, but a
refreshing stopover at the New Inn
should also be considered. As well as
eight guest rooms, the sixteenth-
century inn with its own walled
orchard deals in Courage Directors,
Three Valleys Bitter and Thomas
Hardy ales. Eight wines, four in each
colour, are served by the glass. Food is
traditional pub fare.

Open *summer 11 to 11, winter Mon to
Fri 11 to 2.30, 6 to 11, Sat 11 to 11,
Sun 11 to 10.30*

CHACOMBE

Northamptonshire   map 5

George & Dragon

Silver Street, Chacombe OX17 2JR
Tel: (01295) 711500

off A361, just N of M40 junction 11

A friendly seventeenth-century inn
close to the village church, the George
& Dragon provides a choice of bar
areas and a couple of guest rooms.
Theakston Best and XB and Courage
Directors are drawn from handpumps,
and a selection of fruit wines is offered
alongside the trio of conventional
wines served by the glass. A typical
meal might run from a mélange of
smoked salmon, prawns and halibut in
an olive dressing, through collops of
pork with sherry, cream and jalapeño
peppers, to finish with baked Alaska.

Open *12 to 11, Sun 12 to 10.30*

CHALE

Isle of Wight   map 2

Wight Mouse Inn

Chale PO38 2HA
Tel: (01983) 730431

on B3399, 5m W of Ventnor

This devoted drinking pub serves food
all day every day, and stocks a whisky
for every day of the year, including

African, Argentinian, Indian and French examples. The six draught ales are Gale's HSB, Wadworth 6X, Boddingtons, Marston's Pedigree, Old Speckled Hen, and Fuller's London Pride, and there is a list of 30 wines from £8 to £16. Children's facilities include an indoor play area, bouncy castle and ice cream shop with a long menu.
Open *11 to 11.45, Sun 12 to 10.30*

CHARLTON

Wiltshire   map 2

Horse and Groom

The Street, Charlton SN16 9DL
TEL: (01666) 823904
on B4040 Malmesbury to Cricklade road, 2m E of Malmesbury
A couple of miles outside Malmesbury, this stone-built former coaching inn reflects its licensees' enthusiasm for motor-racing in the prints and photos on the walls. A freehouse hosting themed evenings for regulars, it has few frills but can offer several real ales (Wadworth 6X, Archer's Village, Smiles Best), plus a baker's dozen of wines by the glass. Food ranges from lobster filo parcels to beef, Stilton and Guinness pie. In good weather you can sit at the picnic tables on the lawn and in the wooded area of the garden, where children can have fun on the giant climbing frame. Three bedrooms are available for B&B.
Open *12 to 3, 7 to 11, Sat 12 to 11, Sun 12 to 10.30*

CHARTHAM HATCH

Kent   map 3

Chapter Arms

New Town Street, Chartham
Hatch CT4 7LT
TEL: (01227) 738340
turn off A28 2m S of Canterbury
In November 2000 Mr and Mrs Richards moved from the George at Newnham to this modern pub in a street of modern houses. This is a Shepherd Neame house serving Masterbrew, Spitfire and Bishops Finger. Bar snacks are substantial and the softly lit restaurant offers both table d'hôte and à la carte menus. Reports please.

Open *11 to 3, 6 to 11, Sun 12 to 3, 7 to 10.30*

CHEDINGTON

Dorset   map 2

Winyard's Gap

Chedington DT8 3HY
TEL: (01935) 891244
on A356, between Crewkerne and Dorchester, at Winyard's Gap
Ancient inn on a unique site on the edge of the Dorset Downs, with stunning views over the Axe Valley towards the Quantock Hills. The view inspired Thomas Hardy to write the poem 'At Winyard's Gap'. You can survey the prospect from the pleasantly modernised bar or from the front terrace over a pint of Wadworth 6X or one of two changing guest ales. A standard pub menu is served, with families welcome in a designated dining area.
Open *11 to 2.30, 6.30 to 11, Sun 12 to 2.30, 7 to 10.30; closed evenings 25 Dec and 1 Jan*

CHEDWORTH

Gloucestershire   map 5

Seven Tuns

Chedworth GL54 4AE
TEL: (01285) 720242
off A429, 5m N of Cirencester
Built 'circa 1690', this attractive old inn is not far from Chedworth Roman Villa (NT). Many visitors make a point of seeing the restored water wheel, always in operation, in the walled water garden. Beers from Smiles and Young's are always complemented by guest ales, plus Wes Englun cider. From an extensive wine selection (listed on the board) a dozen are available by the glass. The menu ranges from baguettes and pizzas to sophisticated but reasonably priced daily-changing mains and starters, such as pigeon breast on Puy lentils with smoked bacon and a sherry and rosemary sauce. Dogs always get a biscuit. Children are welcome throughout and there is a no-smoking room.
Open *summer 11 to 11, winter 11 to 3, 6 to 11, Sun all year 12 to 3, 7 to 10.30*

CHERITON BISHOP

Devon   map 1

Old Thatch Inn

Cheriton Bishop EX6 6HJ
TEL: (01647) 24204
*off A30, between Exeter and
Okehampton, 6m SW of Crediton*
This thatched, sixteenth-century Grade
II listed building is just off the A30,
providing a useful refreshment stop for
travellers heading west. The
comfortable beamed bar has a central
log fire and a rambling, carpeted dining
area. Three real ales come from smaller
independent breweries, perhaps
Branscombe Vale, Otter and Palmers.
Straightforward range of bar food, and
the pub offers overnight
accommodation. Children welcome in
the eating areas.
Open *11.30 to 3, 6 to 11, Sun 12 to 3,
7 to 10.30; closed 25 Dec*

CHIDDINGSTONE

Kent   map 3

Castle Inn

Chiddingstone TN8 7AH
TEL: (01892) 870247
off B2027, 4m E of Edenbridge
The 'Castle' in question is really an
adapted manor house, and this tile-hung
inn, established in 1730, stands opposite
the church and next to a cobbled
alleyway. The village itself is
exceptionally attractive, and old photos
of it can be seen inside the pub. Beers
are Larkin's Traditional, Harveys Best
and Young's Bitter, and a vast range of
wines is listed, of which three are
offered by the glass. The choice of food,
itemised on various printed menus, plus
a couple of blackboard dishes, recalls
what was in vogue in the 1970s.
Open *11 to 11, Sun 12 to 10.30*

CHILMARK

Wiltshire   map 2

Black Dog

Chilmark SP3 5AH
TEL: (01722) 716344
just S of B3089, 10m W of Salisbury
A classic fifteenth-century stone-built
pub that is worth tracking down for its
unspoilt atmosphere, appealing decor,
good real ales and promising food.

Drink draught Bass, Hopback GFB or
Wadworth 6X in the main bar, with its
black and terracotta tiled floor, sturdy
wooden tables and large fireplace, or
head for the huge rear garden on
warmer days. Children are welcome in
the dining areas and garden. A snack
menu might feature Black Dog burger,
and freshly baked baguettes, while the
short blackboard bar menu might
include chicken liver salad or fillet of
salmon topped with crab and wrapped
in filo pastry. Reports please.
Open *11 to 3, 6 to 11, Sun 12 to 3, 7
to 10.30*

CHURCHILL

N.W. Somerset   map 2

Crown Inn

The Batch, Churchill BS25 5PP
TEL: (01934) 852995
off A368, 3m S of Congresbury
Set beside a track at the base of the
Mendip Hills, this 400-year-old pub
was originally a coaching inn and once
housed the village grocer's and
butcher's shops. Both unspoilt bars
have flagstoned floors, stone walls,
heavy beams and open fires. Five
handpumps dispense Bass, Palmers and
more unusual local brews like the
Weston-super-Mare RCH Brewery's
Hewish IPA and PG Steam. Simple,
home-made lunchtime food and a
delightful walled front terrace for al
fresco drinking.
Open *11 to 11, Sun 12 to 10.30*

CHURCH KNOWLE

Dorset   map 2

New Inn

Church Knowle BH20 5NQ
TEL: (01929) 480357
off A351, 4m S of Wareham
Near Corfe Castle with views of the
Purbeck Hills from the garden, this
sixteenth-century inn draws walkers
and other visitors. The ambience is
pleasantly relaxed, with open fires and
Turkish carpets in three
interconnecting rooms. The long menu
features local produce – Blue Vinny
Cheese in a ploughman's and various
fresh fish as blackboard specials. Real
ales kept are Flowers Original,
Wadworth 6X and Old Speckled Hen.

Open *summer 11 to 3.30, 5.30 to 11, winter 11 to 3, 6 to 11; closed Mon Jan to mid-March*

CLYST HYDON

Devon   map 1

Five Bells

Clyst Hydon EX15 2NT
TEL: (01884) 277288
take B3181 to Clyst Hydon, then follow signs for Clyst St Lawrence
The landlord is a happy man who shares his good humour with customers of this sixteenth-century thatched Devon longhouse in a lovely rural setting. In the neat traditional bar drinkers can enjoy Otter Ale, Cotleigh Tawny and Wadworth 6X, or one of six wines by the glass. Fresh fish features in the menus and specials boards and one bar snack, fisherman's bake, has specially pleased reporters.
Open *11.30 to 2.30, 6.30 (7 winter) to 11, Sun 12 to 2.30, 6.30 (7 winter) to 10.30*

COMBE HAY

Bath & N.E. Somerset   map 2

Wheatsheaf

Combe Hay BA2 7EG
TEL: (01225) 833504
off A367, 3m S of Bath
Glorious views from the garden are a real plus here. Within, the bar has a more somber feel, though the no-smoking restaurant is a cheerful place. New licensees took over in autumn 2000, so new menus and wine list were being prepared as the Guide went to press. Courage Best and Old Speckled Hen are the draught ales and 40 wines are listed. Reports please.
Open *11 to 3, 6 to 10.30, Sun 12 to 3, 7 to 10.30*

CONDER GREEN

Lancashire   map 8

Stork Hotel

Conder Green LA2 0AN
TEL: (01524) 751234
Situated on the banks of the Conder and Lune estuary, the Stork looks out on mudflats with a large bird population – and at very high tides is on the water's edge. A large white-painted sixteenth-century coaching inn bedecked with window boxes in summer, it can be relied upon for well-kept ales, including Boddingtons, Timothy Taylor Landlord and various guest beers. The printed menu is supplemented by blackboard specials such as wild boar pie and seafood skewers with coriander sauce. Children welcome.
Open *11 to 11, Sun 12 to 9.30*

CONISTON

Cumbria   map 8

Black Bull

1 Yewdale Road,
Coniston LA21 8DU
TEL: (015394) 41335 or 41668
off A593, 6m SW of Ambleside
Built around the time of the Spanish Armada, this old coaching inn is now a pub, restaurant and 15-bedroom hotel with its own brewery. The home brews include Old Man ale (the big toe of the Old Man mountain, which overlooks the inn, is a large piece of stone set into the wall of the residents' lounge) and the award-winning Bluebird Bitter (Donald Campbell used Coniston for his water speed record attempts); plus Opium, Blacksmith's and Premium Bluebird. Guest ales and Saxon draught scrumpy are also available. An extensive range of food is offered, sometimes featuring local fish.
Open *11 to 11, Sun 12 to 10.30*

COOKHAM

Berkshire   map 3

Bel and the Dragon

High Street, Cookham SL6 9SQ
TEL: (01628) 521263
on A4094, off A404 just N of Marlow
Handy for the Thames Path and directly opposite the Stanley Spencer Gallery (which is worth a visit), this fascinating fifteenth-century inn takes its unusual name from one of the books of the Apocrypha. Cartoon-style drawings relating to the story decorate the bar area and the menu. A rambling series of well-refurbished, low-ceilinged rooms lead through to a galleried barn.

The modern bistro-style menu lists an interesting choice of contemporary British dishes, real ales are from Marston's and Brakspear, and a decent list of wines has ten available by the glass. Children welcome.

Open *11.30 to 11, Sun 12 to 10.30; closed evenings 25 and 26 Dec, 1 Jan*

CORFE CASTLE

Dorset   map 2

Fox Inn

West Street, Corfe
Castle BH20 5HD
TEL: (01929) 480449
on A351, SE of Wareham
Visitors to this unspoilt village inn will find the mature, sun-trap rear garden particularly appealing in summer, especially as it enjoys fine views of the dramatic ruined castle. Very snug little front bar and slightly less enchanting larger lounge with a thirteenth-century fireplace and a bustling, often smoky atmosphere. Enjoy Young's Special, Greene King Abbot Ale, Wadworth 6X, Fuller's London Pride and two guest ales, all tapped straight from the cask. Straightforward pub food. No children inside.

Open *11 to 3, 6 to 11, Sun 12 to 3, 7 to 11*

Greyhound Inn

The Square, Corfe Castle BH20 5EZ
TEL: (01929) 480205
on A351 in village centre
This sixteenth-century coaching inn in the pretty National Trust village of Corfe Castle is justifiably popular for the fine views of the impressive castle ruins, and the Purbeck Hills, that can be enjoyed from its rear garden. The characterful interior, with low beams, oak panelling, sturdy furnishings and cosy alcoves, is the setting for traditional pub meals and ales such as Flowers IPA and beers from the Ringwood or Hampshire breweries. Children are welcome throughout the pub.

Open *summer 11 to 11, Sun 12 to 10.30; winter Mon to Thur 11 to 3, 6 to 11, Fri and Sat 11 to 11, Sun 12 to 10.30*

CORFTON

Shropshire   map 5

Sun Inn

Corfton SY7 9DF
TEL: (01584) 861239
on B4368, 4m E of Craven Arms
Award-winning Corvedale ales are brewed by landlord Norman Pearce behind his seventeenth-century stone village pub, situated in perfect walking country between Ludlow and Much Wenlock. Follow a relaxing rural ramble through Corve Dale with a traditional pub meal and a fine pint of Norman's Pride in the welcoming bar. Much extended over the years, it offers good facilities for both children and the disabled.

Open *11 to 2.30, 6 to 11, Sun 12 to 3, 7 to 10.30; open all day bank hols*

COTHERSTONE

Co Durham   map 10

Fox and Hounds

Cotherstone DL12 9PF
TEL: (01833) 650241
on B6277, 3m NW of Barnard Castle
This eighteenth-century inn is set back from the road overlooking a village green. The location is ideal as a base for anyone exploring the scenic landscapes of Teesdale, and the 900-foot Percymire Rock is nearby. Children are welcome anywhere in the pub, which also has a garden and can provide overnight accommodation (three rooms and residents' lounge). Black Sheep Best and Special are on draught; three wines by the glass.

Open *11 to 3, 6 to 11.30 (10.30 Sun)*

COTTERED

Hertfordshire   map 3

Bull

Cottered SG9 9QP
TEL: (01763) 281243
on A507, between Buntingford and Baldock
A roaring fire provides a cheerful welcome to visitors at this whitewashed village pub in winter. The printed menu, supplemented by blackboards brought to the table, deals in pub standards such as jacket potatoes,

sandwiches and ploughman's, with heartier appetites catered for by steak, Stilton and Guinness pie, calf's liver and smoked bacon, or various burgers. Chocolate and Tia Maria cheesecake should send you away contented. Greene King IPA and Abbot Ale are on handpump, and three wines are available by the glass.

Open *12 to 2.30, 6 to 11, Sun 12 to 3, 7 to 10.30*

COTTESMORE

Rutland   map 6

The Sun

25 Main Street,
Cottesmore LE15 7DH
Tel: (01572) 812321
on B668 between Oakham and Stretton (A1), 4m NE of Oakham

This picture-postcard pub with whitewashed stone walls and thatched roof, dates from 1610 and makes the most of its name in its interior decoration. It will be interesting to see whether its considerable reputation for good food continues under its new management – reports, please. Along with Everards Original and Adnams Bitter, there is a short but carefully chosen list of wines concentrating on France and the New World (three are available by the glass); and a selection of malt whiskies and brandies. No children.

Open *11.30 to 2.30, 6 (6.30 winter) to 11*

CRANBORNE

Dorset   map 2

Fleur de Lys

5 Wimbourne Street,
Cranborne BH21 5PP
Tel: (01725) 517282
on B3078 in centre of Cranborne

Popular with ramblers and trout-fishers, this seventeenth-century inn cocooned in creepers has also been visited by Rupert Brooke and Thomas Hardy. Traditional pub food from devilled whitebait to ham cooked in cider and honey is offered; blackboard specials might include medallions of pork with mushrooms in brandy, or bacon-wrapped chicken breast stuffed

and sauced with Stilton. Seven wines by the glass, as well as good Badger Tanglefoot and Inch's cider, add to the attraction.

Open *summer 11 to 3, 6 to 11, Sun 11 to 3, 7 to 10.30; winter 11 to 3, 6.30 to 11, Sun 11 to 3, 7 to 10.30*

CRASTER

Northumberland   map 10

Jolly Fisherman

Craster NE66 3TR
Tel: (01665) 576461
off B1339, 6m NE of Alnwick

Food is served all day during the summer at this harbourside pub. The short menu continues to offer excellent value, with various sandwiches and rolls, simple snacks like crab soup or home-made Craster kipper pâté with toast, and light meals such as Texas burger, or a Geordie stottie cake pizza topped with ham, mushrooms and cheese. Beers are from Tetley and Theakston.

Open *summer 11 to 11, Sun 12 to 10.30; winter 11 to 3, 6 to 11, Sun 12 to 3, 6 to 10.30*

CRAY

North Yorkshire   map 8

White Lion

Cray BD23 5JB
Tel: (01756) 760262
off B6160, 2m N of Buckden

This rustic stone-built former drovers' inn has the distinction of being the highest pub in Wharfedale, and is situated beneath Buckden Pike and surrounded by open moorland and stunning scenery. The muddy-boot-friendly main bar, open fires, excellent real ales on handpump, including Moorhouses Premier and Black Cat, hearty, home-cooked food, and streamside tables make the White Lion a favoured walking destination. Accommodation is available for those intent on lingering longer.

Open *11 to 11 (10.30 Sun); closed 25 Dec*

CROSCOMBE

Somerset   map 2

Bull Terrier

Croscombe BA5 3QJ
TEL: (01749) 343658
*on A371, between Wells and Shepton
Mallet*
Originally a priory and first licensed to
sell ale in 1612, this attractive stone
village pub is reputedly one of
Somerset's oldest. There are three
welcoming bars: the Snug, the
Common bar, and the Inglenook,
which was the original medieval hall
and features fine Jacobean beams.
Winchester's Buckland Best Bitter is the
regular ale, joined by up to three
guests. To the rear, the elevated garden
backs on to the church and overlooks
the surrounding countryside. An
interesting walk leads across fields to
the Bishop's Palace at Wells.
Accommodation is available.
Open *12 to 2.30, 7 to 11 (10.30 Sun)*

CUMNOR

Oxfordshire   map 2

Vine Inn

11 Abingdon Road,
Cumnor OX2 9QN
TEL: (01865) 862567
off A420, 4m W of Oxford
This white-painted, vine-covered inn,
dating from 1743, attracts a youngish
crowd, many of them local families,
and has a pleasantly relaxed
atmosphere. The resident dogs have
been known to stake their claim to the
comfortable settees provided for
customers. Adnams Bitter, Wadworth
6X, and Old Speckled Hen are
available together with a varied
selection of wines (five by the glass).
The menu leans towards new-wave
cuisine (chargrilled tuna steak on wild
mushroom risotto with garlic butter,
for example) rather than traditional
pub fare. As well as a 'civilised' games
room inside for the grown-ups, there is
a climbing frame in the garden for
younger visitors.
Open *Mon to Thur 11 to 2.30, 6 to
11, Fri and Sat 11 to 11, Sun 12 to 3, 6
to 10.30*

DALWOOD

Devon   map 2

Tuckers Arms

Dalwood EX13 7EG
TEL: (01404) 881342
*1m N of A35, between Honiton and
Axminster*
Uneven stone floors, low beamed
ceilings and open log fires set the scene
at this flower-decked and part-thatched
thirteenth-century longhouse, situated
in the centre of a delightful Axe Valley
village. Formerly a manor house and
later a coaching inn on the old Exeter-
London road, it offers local Otter ales,
fresh fish and game dishes, and
overnight accommodation in four *en
suite* bedrooms. Well placed for the
Devon and Dorset coasts, and peaceful
rural walks.
Open *12 to 3, 6.30 to 11, Sun 12 to 3,
7 to 10.30; closed 26 Dec*

DENT

Cumbria   map 8

Sun

Main Street, Dent LA10 5QL
TEL: (015396) 25208
in Dentdale, 4m SE of Sedburgh
Standing in a Dales village street lined
with fifteenth- and sixteenth-century
cottages, this charming old white-
painted inn serves all the beers from
the Dent brewery, which was opened in
1990 by the Sun's licensee in a
converted stone barn at nearby
Cowgill: Bitter, Aviator and lager-style
Rambrau in cask, and three strong ales
in both cask and bottle. The pub
welcomes children and serves daily
specials in addition to a range of snacks
and bar meals. Four rooms are
available for B&B. Bar meals are not
available at weekends in winter;
indeed, the pub's opening hours are
unpredictable in winter, so please
phone to check.
Open *summer 11 to 11, Sun 12 to
10.30; winter Mon to Fri 11 to 2.30, 7
to 11, Sat 11 to 11, Sun 12 to 10.30*

DITCHLING

East Sussex   map 3

Bull Hotel

2 High Street, Ditchling BN6 8SY
TEL: (01273) 843147

*on B2112, midway between Haywards
Heath and Brighton*

The ambience of the Bull's long,
timbered bar reflects that of a village
whose antique attractions include Anne
of Cleves's sixteenth-century house, a
candle-maker's workshop and a
seventeenth-century dissenters' meeting
house. On the bar menu are locally
made bangers and mash, roast rack of
English lamb, and caramelised salad as
a starter. Flowers Original, Greene
King IPA and Harveys are the beers.
Open *11 to 11, Sun 12 to 10.30*

DOCKING

Norfolk   map 6

Pilgrims Reach

High Street, Docking PE31 8NH
TEL: (01485) 518383

on B1153, 11m W of Fakenham

This solid-looking cottagey roadside
pub, dating from 1731, is close to the
church in the centre of a small village.
Being near the coast, the pub has a
menu that is naturally focused on fish
and seafood, not least oysters and
mussels from nearby Brancaster, and of
course samphire from the marshes.
Highlights from the specials board
might include shellfish chowder with
coconut, and skate wing with sorrel
butter sauce. Real ales are from
Shepherd Neame and Greene King, and
the short wine list offers good value.
Open *Mon to Sat (exc Tue) 12 to 2.30,
6 (7 winter) to 11, Sun 12 to 30, 7 to
10.30; closed late Jan to early Feb*

DORSTONE

Herefordshire   map 5

Pandy Inn

Dorstone HR3 6AN
TEL: (01981) 550273

*off B4348 Hay-on-Wye to Hereford
road, 5m E of Hay-on-Wye*

Claiming to be the oldest inn in
Herefordshire, built in 1185 to cater
for the builders of Dorstone church,

the Pandy Inn offers typical pub fare
along with some South African dishes
introduced by the current landlady. An
enormous fireplace dominates the low-
ceilinged and rather dark interior,
which features exposed stone walls and
floor, and red plush seats. Although
this is very much a locals' haunt,
strangers are made welcome. Butty
Bach and Dorothy Goodbody ales from
the local Wye Valley brewery are
served, along with Stowford Press
cider. The brief wine list includes
several South Africans.
Open *Mon 6 to 11, Tue to Fri 12 to 3,
6 to 11, Sat 12 to 11, Sun 12 to 3, 6 to
10.30*

DUXFORD

Cambridgeshire   map 6

John Barleycorn

Moorfield Road, Duxford CB2 4PP
TEL: (01223) 832699

on B1379, close to M11 junction 10

An archetypal olde-English thatched
inn with roses around the door, this
former coaching-house was built in
1660 and stands on the main road
through the village, not far from
Duxford Air Museum. Background
music that will have the over-50s
'positively soggy with nostalgia' sets the
scene for drinking Greene King Abbot
Ale and IPA, Black Sheep and Old
Speckled Hen. Eat king prawns, black
pudding with gooseberries, chilli-spiced
beef, or bacon-wrapped chicken breast,
finishing with bread-and-butter
pudding or chocolate and orange
sponge.
Open *12 to 2.30, 6.30 to 11, Sun 12
to 10.30*

EARL SOHAM

Suffolk   map 6

Victoria Inn

Earl Soham IP13 7RL
TEL: (01728) 685758

on A1120, 3m W of Framlingham

Overlooking a tiny village green, this
cosy little pub, liberally endowed with
paintings and old photos, offers beers
from the Earl Soham brewery, which is
on the premises – Victoria Bitter and
Albert Ale, plus Gannet Mild and Sir

Roger's Porter – plus juices made from local apples, and four wines by the glass. Filling and very reasonably priced pub fare is joined by fish specials on Friday evenings. You can hear live folk music here, and children are welcome throughout the pub.

Open *11.30 to 3, 5.30 to 11, Sun 12 to 3, 7 to 10.30*

EAST BERGHOLT

Essex   map 3

Kings Head

Burnt Oak, East Bergholt CO7 6TL
TEL: (01206) 298190
off B1070, follow signs to Flatford Mill
Located in a beautiful part of Constable country, this pub offers a straightforward menu of home cooking that might include prawn and cucumber salad, or Stilton and mushroom pasta bake. On handpumps are Greene King IPA, Adnams, and Courage Directors, and an unusual English pub drink is cocoa – for those who know it's there, and ask for it. Six wines are available by the glass.

Open *12 to 3, 6.30 to 11, Sun 12 to 3, 7 to 10.30*

EASTBRIDGE

Suffolk   map 6

Eel's Foot Inn

Eastbridge IP16 4SN
TEL: (01728) 830154
off B1122, 2m N of Leiston
This oddly named Adnams pub attracts walkers, visitors to the nearby RSPB reserve at Minsmere and holidaymakers. The complete Adnams range is on tap, together with Batemans's Mild and a food menu, comprising standard pub dishes. Children are welcome throughout the pub, and three rooms are available on a B&B basis.

Open *summer exc July and Aug 11 to 3, 6 to 11 (10.30 Sun), July and Aug 11 to 11, Sun 12 to 10.30; winter 12 to 2, 7 to 11 (10.30 Sun); closed Mon in winter*

EASTGATE

Norfolk   map 6

Ratcatchers Inn

Easton Way, Eastgate NR10 4HA
TEL: (01603) 871430
10m NW of Norwich off B1149 Holt road, 1m SE of Cawston
Portions are generous in this dining pub, so you may appreciate the two-course 'light eaters lunch'. The full menu offers plentiful vegetarian options, home-made pies and rump steaks – 7 to 20 ounces. Daily special boards feature fish, as well as such rarities as goose breast; pike, salmon and prawn pancake; or baked duck egg. Real ales are Adnams, Greene King IPA and Hancock's HB.

Open *11.45 to 3, 6 to 11, Sun 11.45 to 3, 6.30 to 11*

EAST ILSLEY

Berkshire   map 2

Crown & Horns

East Ilsley RG16 0LH
TEL: (01635) 281545
just off A34, 9m N of Newbury
Here is refreshment for those who exercise by walking the Ridgeway path, those who exercise by watching horses running, and those whose preferred activity is skittles in the pub's alley. There's a good choice of bar snacks and real ales are changed fortnightly; you might find examples from Wadworth, Adnams, Bass, Hook Norton, Popes or Jennings. All 17 wines listed are available by the glass.

Open *11 to 11, Sun 12 to 10.30*

EAST LYNG

Somerset   map 2

Rose & Crown

East Lyng TA3 5AU
TEL: (01823) 698235
on A361, 5m NE of Taunton
In the low-beamed, stone-floored main bar a massive grandfather clock stands beside the warming oven and adjoining fireplace, which like much of the pub is constructed of red brick. The long, conventional bar menu offers few surprises except among desserts where speciality ice creams include

butterscotch chip, maple pecan fudge and Beaulieu blackberry. Draught ales are Butcombe Bitter, Gold and Royal Oak.

Open *11 to 2.30, 6.30 to 11, Sun 12 to 3, 7 to 10.30*

EAST PRAWLE

Devon   map 1

Freebooter Inn

East Prawle TQ7 2BU
TEL: (01548) 511208

Located close to a beautiful stretch of coastline in the southernmost village in Devon, the eighteenth-century inn is a welcome refuelling stop for walkers trekking the South Devon coast path. The homely open-plan bar has rug-strewn wooden floors, simple furnishings and three open fires. Limited lunchtime food includes soup and crusty bread, sandwiches and filled jacket potatoes. The more extensive evening menu is likely to feature local organic produce. Dartmoor Best Bitter and Greene King Abbot Ale are joined by a guest in the summer. Children are welcome. Credit cards are not taken.

Open *12 to 3, 6.30 to 11, Sun 12 to 2.30, 7 to 10.30; closed Mon lunchtime winter, and evening 25 Dec*

EGLOSHAYLE

Cornwall   map 1

Earl of St Vincent

Egloshayle PL27 6HT
TEL: (01208) 814807

on A389, just E of Wadebridge

Named after one of Nelson's admirals, this characterful fifteenth-century inn was originally the boarding house for the masons who built the nearby church. The pub resembles an Aladdin's cave, with antique china and pictures and merrily ticking clocks of all shapes and sizes, which create a warm and relaxing atmosphere. This is a St Austell house serving Tinners Ale, HSD and guest ales, plus a range of wines. Food is standard pub fare.

Open *11 to 3, 6.30 to 11, Sun 12 to 3, 7 to 10.30*

EXTON

Rutland   map 6

Fox and Hounds

19 The Green, Exton LE15 8AP
TEL: (01572) 812403

2m off A606, between Stamford and Oakham

The Viking Way passes the door and Rutland Water is just two miles away from this handsome seventeenth-century coaching inn overlooking the unusual village green. The stylish, high-ceilinged lounge is particularly attractive, while the more rustic public bar is where you will find Bass, Greene King IPA and Samuel Smith Old Brewery Bitter on handpump. Pretty rear lawns and overnight accommodation in three bedrooms. Homely, traditional bar food.

Open *11 to 3, 6 (6.30 winter) to 11, Sun 12 to 3, 7 to 10.30*

FADDILEY

Cheshire   map 7

Thatch Inn

Wrexham Road, Faddiley CW5 8JE
TEL: (01270) 524223

on A534, 3m W of Nantwich

This fifteenth-century inn lives up to its name. Inside, even the gents' has fitted carpets, but it still has rustic appeal in the shape of beams and exposed brickwork and a cornucopia of flowers at the front. An interesting, varied menu runs from dim sum parcels or jacket potato wedges with dips, to chicken curry with all the trimmings or a generously proportioned steak and pickle baguette. Cask-conditioned ales from Theakston are served, and there are guest beers and a short wine list.

Open *12 to 3, 6 to 11, Sun 12 to 10.30*

FALSTONE

Northumberland   map 10

Blackcock Inn

Falstone NE48 1AA
TEL: (01434) 240200

off B3620, 8m W of Bellingham

Walkers, and other less-energetic visitors to Kielder reservoir and forest, enjoy the warmth of this snug old-time

local with its traditional atmosphere.
Bar snacks are along familiar lines and
go well with the Blackcock ale brewed
specially for the pub by John Smith's,
whose Magnet is also kept. Guest ales
might be Courage Directors, Marston's
Pedigree, or Ruddles Best or County.

Open *summer 11 to 11, Sun 12 to
10.30, winter 7 to 11, Sun 7 to 10.30*

FARTHINGSTONE

Northamptonshire   map 5

Kings Arms

Farthingstone NN12 8EZ
TEL: (01327) 361604
off A5, 5m SE of Daventry
Excellent real ales on tap and hearty
country cooking at weekend lunchtimes
are among the attractions of this
handsome, Grade II listed building in a
sleepy village close to Canons Ashby
(NT). Homely bar area with log fire,
flagstones, simple tables and chairs, and
a range of traditional pub games. It
stands in the heart of good walking
country on the Knightley Way.

Open *Mon to Fri 7 to 11, Sat and Sun
12 to 3, 7 to 11; closed evenings 25 and
26 Dec*

FEERING

Essex   map 3

Sun Inn

Feering CO5 9NH
TEL: (01376) 570442
off A12, 5m NE of Witham
This historic sixteenth-century house
offers a varied, mostly traditional bar
menu but the speciality is a southern
Italian dish called braciole: stewed beef
olives. The real ales provide a taste of
heaven for beer lovers. Mauldons
Midwinter Gold, Swale Kentish Pride,
Crouch Vale Millennium Gold and
Wolf Woild Moild are some of the
more unusual beers that have appeared
in the ever-changing line-up of six.

Open *11.30 to 3, 6 to 11, Sun 12 to 3,
6 to 10.30*

FELSHAM

Suffolk   map 6

Six Bells

Church Road, Felsham IP30 0PJ
TEL: (01449) 736268
off A14, 7m SE of Bury St Edmunds
As long as your map-reading skills hold
out, when you find this old inn deep in
the country lanes of Suffolk you will be
rewarded with a friendly atmosphere
and constantly changing blackboard
menu of dishes such as Greek lamb,
leek and butter bean bake, and steak
and kidney pudding. This is a Greene
King pub serving IPA and Abbot Ale
plus guest beers including Badger
Tanglefoot, Adnams Bitter and
Bateman's XXXB. It also has a garden
and welcomes children in the areas of
the pub where food is served.

Open *Mon and Tue 6.30 to 11, Wed to
Sat 12 to 2.30, 6.30 to 11, Sun 12 to
2.30, 7 to 10.30*

FEN DRAYTON

Cambridgeshire   map 6

Three Tuns

High Street, Fen Drayton CB4 5SJ
TEL: (01954) 230242
This Greene King pub dates from the
fifteenth century and is believed to
have started life as the village guildhall.
Bar snacks are the usual suspects,
ranging from ploughman's to scampi
and chips or lasagne. The restaurant
menu offers more interest, with things
like pan-fried swordfish with spicy
salsa, and Barbary duck breast with
basil and mustard potatoes and a honey
balsamic jus. Five wines are offered by
the glass.

Open *12 to 3, 6 to 11 (7 to 10.30
Sun); closed evening 25 Dec*

FITZHEAD

Somerset   map 2

Fitzhead Inn

Fitzhead TA4 3JP
TEL: (01823) 400667
off B3227, 2m N of Milverton
Some rather luxurious cooking is going
on at this quirky pub, the menu taking
in such dishes as crab and prawn
andalouse, fillet steak stuffed with

mussels and Stilton, pheasant with bacon and Lancashire sausage in red wine sauce, and deep-fried ice-cream with mincemeat in filo pastry served with brandy butter. Exmoor Fox is a brew worth tasting, and there are also Fuller's London Pride and half a dozen wines by the glass.

Open *Mon and Tue 7 to 11, Wed to Sat 12 to 2.30, 7 to 11, Sun 12 to 3, 7 to 10.30*

FLAUNDEN

Hertfordshire   map 3

Bricklayers Arms

Long Lane, Hogspit Bottom, Flaunden HP3 0PH
TEL: (01442) 833322
3m SW of Hemel Hempstead; village signposted off A41

This charming, Virginia creeper-covered little pub offers robust food including Yorkshire puddings filled with sausage and onion, pork and cider, or chicken and mushroom. Fuller's London Pride, Bass and Ringwood Old Thumper are regular ales, with several guests and there are ten wines by the glass from the short list.

Open *11.30 to 3, 6 to 11, Sun 12 to 2.30, 6.30 to 10.30*

FOOLOW

Derbyshire   map 8

Bulls Head

Foolow S32 5QR
TEL: (01433) 630873
off A623 Chapel-en-le-Frith to Chesterfield road, 3m E of Tideswell

With its cosy, cottagey ambience and attractive location in prime walking country, the Bulls Head is a useful stop-off for walkers and a good base from which to explore the Peak District (B&B accommodation is offered). Ales on tap are from Tetley, Black Sheep and Marston's and the wine list focuses on France. Food is mostly along traditional lines: Barnsley chop with minted gravy, or steak, Guinness and kidney pie, for example. There is no garden, but children are welcome in most parts of the pub.

Open *12 to 3, 6.30 to 11 (10.30 Sun)*

FORD

Gloucestershire   map 5

Plough Inn

Ford GL54 5RU
TEL: (01386) 584215
on B4077, 4m E of Winchcombe

This sixteenth-century, slate-roofed Cotswold stone inn once did time as a courthouse, where those arraigned for sheep-stealing would be slung in what are now the cellars. Simple, homely food runs from fishy starters through steaks, pies and bowls of chilli, to English puds like mixed fruit crumble. Drinking centres on Donnington's ales, Addlestone's cider and half a dozen wines by the glass. Three guest rooms are available.

Open *11 to 11, Sun 12 to 10.30*

FORD

Wiltshire   map 2

White Hart

Ford SN14 8RP
TEL: (01249) 782213
on A420, 5m W of Chippenham

In its picturesque setting by a trout stream in the Wyvern Valley, this fifteenth-century coaching inn built of warm yellow stone oozes charm, especially in summer when you can sit at a waterside table. As well as Bass, Wadworth 6X, Marston's Pedigree and Worthington Royal Oak on draught, the pub has a respectable wine list including eight by the glass. Part of the large restaurant is in a sunny extension constructed over the stream. Hearty pub standards are served in the bar. Children are welcome, and a games room (which can be chilly) is provided. Eleven *en suite* rooms, mostly in the converted stables across the lane, are also available.

Open *11 to 3, 5 to 11, Sun 12 to 4, 7 to 11*

FORDCOMBE

Kent   map 3

Chafford Arms

Spring Hill, Fordcombe TN3 0SA
TEL: (01892) 740267

on B2188, off A264 East Grinstead to
Tunbridge Wells road, 4m W of
Tunbridge Wells

The immediate appeal of this attractive
pub, not far from Hever Castle and
Penshurst Place, lies in its colourful
garden brimming with flowers,
cascades of creeper and warm red tiles.
Larkins beers and Chafford cider are
available within, together with 11
wines by the glass and a bar and
restaurant menu, the latter including
some local fish. Children are welcome.
No food Sun and Mon evenings.

Open *Mon to Fri 11.45 to 3, 6.30 (6*
Fri) to 11, Sat 11.45 to 11, Sun 12 to
4, 7 to 10.30

FORTY GREEN

Buckinghamshire   map 3

Royal Standard of England

Forty Green HP9 1XT
TEL: (01494) 673382

off B474 out of Beaconsfield at Knotty
Green

Centuries fly by in this 900-year-old
inn named by Charles II for services
rendered, and full of intriguing
architectural and decorative details.
Only 40 years ago, stained-glass
windows from war-damaged London
churches were added. Even its ales are
historic, for Owd Roger, brewed in the
pub for over 300 years, is now made by
Marston's whose Pedigree is kept
alongside Old Speckled Hen, Brakspear
Bitter and Fuller's London Pride.

Open *11 to 3, 5.30 to 11, Sun 12 to 4,*
7 to 10.30

FOWNHOPE

Herefordshire   map 5

Green Man Inn

Fownhope HR1 4PE
TEL: (01432) 860243

on B4424, 6m SE of Hereford

This tall fifteenth-century inn has the
friendly atmosphere of an
unpretentious old-time pub, though as

a base for salmon-fishing on the Wye
with 20 bedrooms and a leisure
complex it is really more of a hotel. A
wide choice of simple pub food is
complemented by Marston's Pedigree,
Hook Norton Best and Courage
Directors. Children are welcome
throughout, and many areas are non-
smoking.

Open *summer 11 to 11, Sun 12 to*
10.30; winter 11 to 3, 5.30 to 11, Sun
12 to 10.30

FRILSHAM

Berkshire   map 2

Pot Kiln

Frilsham RG18 0XX
TEL: (01635) 201366

off B4009; in Yattendon take road
opposite church, left at next T-junction,
go over M4 motorway bridge and
straight on – do not turn right to
Frilsham

The West Berkshire Brewery is located
behind this traditional seventeenth-
century pub on a narrow country lane.
It produces Black Kiln Bitter and Gold
Star, which are served here alongside
Arkell's BBB. Hungry walkers are often
in evidence, eating the simple home-
cooked meals available from both a
printed menu and the blackboard.

Open *12 to 3, 6.30 to 11, Sun 12 to 3,*
7 to 10.30

FROXFIELD GREEN

Hampshire   map 2

Trooper Inn

Alton Road, Froxfield GU32 1BD
TEL: (01730) 827293

from Petersfield, follow signs to Steep
and continue climbing to Froxfield; pub
on right

Tiptop real ales, decent wines, hearty
food and a relaxed, laid-back
atmosphere draw the crowds to this
isolated and unpretentious roadside
inn. Beyond the plain exterior there's a
rustic, wooden-floored bar and two
dining areas, all fitted out with old pine
furnishings and interesting prints. Soft
candlelight enhances the convivial
evening atmosphere. Come on
Wednesday night for live jazz. The

landscaped garden makes the most of the open downland views.

Open *Tue to Sat 12 to 3.30, 6 to 12, Sun 12 to 2.30*

FULLER STREET

Essex   map 3

Square & Compasses

Fuller Street CM3 2BB
TEL: (01245) 361477
off A131 or A12, 5m W of Witham
Ramblers and walkers find this tucked-away rural pub more easily than motorists. Back and front gardens relieve pressure on space, as locals easily fill the two little bars, which have bare floorboards and walls covered with stuffed birds and hunting photographs. Food is 'hearty country' style, and ranges widely for the size of the place. Ridley's IPA and Nethergate Suffolk County are the beers on draught.

Open *11.30 to 3, 6.30 (7 winter) to 11, Sun 12 to 3, 7 to 10.30*

GARRIGILL

Cumbria   map 10

George & Dragon

Garrigill CA9 3DS
TEL: (01434) 381293
off B6277, 3m S of Alston
A welcome sight and a favoured retreat among Pennine Way walkers having negotiated Cross Fell – the highest part of the gruelling trail. Some 300 years old, the stone-built George & Dragon overlooks the green and offers sustaining food, liquid refreshment in the form of Theakston, Slaters and Marston's ales, and four bedrooms for weary travellers. The rustic interior has open fires, flagstone floors and old wooden furnishings.

Open *Mon to Fri 12 to 4 (3 winter), 6 (7 winter) to 11, Sat 12 to 11, Sun 12 to 4 (3 winter), 7 to 10.30*

GESTINGTHORPE

Essex   map 3

Pheasant

Gestingthorpe CO9 3AX
TEL: (01787) 461196
off B1058, from A131, 4m SW of Sudbury
Pale pink in colour, this bow-windowed locals' pub on the main street of this small village offers well-kept Old Speckled Hen, Adnams Bitter, and Greene King IPA on draught, and a short wine list. Children are welcome throughout, and the pub has a garden. A weekly-changing blackboard menu offers things like king prawns in chilli sauce and fillet steak in peppercorn sauce.

Open *12 to 3.30, 6 to 11, Sun 12 to 4.30, 6 to 10.30*

GLOOSTON

Leicestershire   map 5

Old Barn Inn

Andrews Lane, Glooston LE16 7ST
TEL: (01858) 545215
off A6, 6m N of Market Harborough
The focal point of the tiny backwater village is the cream-painted pub. Inside, the name seems appropriate with 'pubby' rooms extending back a long way. New owners since autumn 2000 offer a varied restaurant menu with five vegetarian choices, and a conventional bar menu with blackboard specials. Among the four regular ales and two guests might be Adnams Southwold Bitter, Fuller's London Pride, and Woodforde's Wherry.

Open *12 to 3.30, 6.30 to 11, Sun 12 to 3.30, 7 to 10.30*

GREAT BARRINGTON

Gloucestershire   map 2

Fox Inn

Great Barrington OX18 4TB
TEL: (01451) 844385
off A40, 3m W of Burford
Gas heaters are provided in the garden for those occasions when atmospheric conditions aren't sufficiently sizzling but you still wish to partake of the views of the River Windrush. Inside, Donnington's Bitter and Special Ale are

on tap, along with six wines by the glass. Blackboard menus offer the likes of prawn pâté, chicken and ham pie, leek, mustard and cream bake, or crème brûlée.

Open *11 to 11, Sun 12 to 10.30*

GREAT LANGDALE

Cumbria   map 8

Old Dungeon Ghyll Hotel

Great Langdale LA22 9JY
TEL: (015394) 37272
on B5343, 6m from Skelwith Bridge on A593

Miles from anywhere in magnificent surroundings at the foot of Langdale Pike, this former farmhouse is a magnet for serious walkers and climbers. Real ales include Theakston XB and Old Peculier, Jennings Cumberland, Black Sheep Special and Yates Bitter, and for cider drinkers there is Weston's Old Rosie. Filling pub fare is available, and children are welcome in both pub and garden. Spontaneous outbreaks of folk music have been known. The hotel has 14 rooms available for B&B.

Open *Mon to Fri 11 to 11, Sat and Sun 9am to 11pm (10.30pm Sun)*

GREAT OUSEBURN

North Yorkshire   map 9

Crown

Main Street, Great
Ouseburn YO26 9RF
TEL: (01423) 330430
4m S of Boroughbridge

North-west of York and close to the River Ouse, this warm and welcoming freehouse, with ancient beams and a massive log fire in the central bar, changed hands shortly before the Guide went to press – reports, please. As well as John Smith's and Black Sheep on draught, it offers eight wines by the glass, and a substantial list of blackboard specials – lobster thermidor, or fillet steak with Stilton and horseradish, for example – in addition to printed bar snacks and restaurant menus. The restaurant is non-smoking and children are allowed anywhere in the pub.

Open *Mon to Fri 5 to 11, Sat 11 to 11, Sun 12 to 10.30*

GRITTLETON

Wiltshire   map 2

Neeld Arms Inn

The Street, Grittleton SN14 6AP
TEL: (01249) 782470
from M4 junction 17 take A429 N and follow signs to Grittleton

Within easy reach of the M4 and standing opposite rambling Grittleton House in this former estate village, the Neeld Arms is an unpretentious seventeenth-century pub built of Cotswold stone. The rustic single bar is furnished in old pine, with Archers Best, Buckley's Best, Shepherd Neame Spitfire and Wadworth 6X on handpump, and an interesting, short blackboard menu. Typical dishes include salmon and prawn fishcakes and shoulder of lamb braised in red wine gravy. Accommodation is also available.

Open *Mon to Fri 5.30 to 11, Sat 11 to 3, 5.30 to 11, Sun 12 to 3, 6 to 10.30*

HAPPISBURGH

Norfolk   map 6

Hill House

Happisburgh NR12 0PW
TEL: (01692) 650004
on B1159, 6m E of North Walsham

Dating from the sixteenth century, this is a family-run freehouse and B&B with good facilities for children and pets – it has a family room as well as a garden. Elementary Ale is brewed locally to the pub's own recipe; they also offer Shepherd Neame Spitfire and two guest ales, which change regularly. Weiss beer is available in summer and the wine list offers a dozen moderately priced bins. Food on the printed menu leans towards the plain and simple, to which you can add your own speciality 'house sauce', while a board above the bar lists the specials.

Open *summer 12 to 11, Sun 12 to 10.30; winter Mon to Wed 12 to 3, 7 to 11, Thur to Sat 11 to 11, Sun 12 to 10.30*

HARBERTON

Devon   map 1

Church House Inn

Harberton TQ9 7SF
TEL: (01803) 863707
off A381 Totnes to Kingsbridge road,
2½m S of Totnes
Dating from about 1100, when it was
built to house the builders of the
church next door, this ancient hostelry
was a monks' chantry for many years
and passed out of church ownership
only in 1950. Bass and Charles Wells
Bombardier are joined by regularly
changing guest beers and locally made
farm cider. Ten wines are on offer by
the glass from a reasonable list. The
pub is child-friendly and has a family
room but no garden. Standard pub fare
is served and there are three bedrooms
for B&B.
Open *12 to 3 (4 Sat), 6 to 11, Sun 12*
to 4, 6 to 10.30

HARRIETSHAM

Kent   map 3

Ringlestone Inn

Ringlestone Road,
Harrietsham ME17 1EX
TEL: (01622) 859900
off A20, 3m NE of Harrietsham, take
B2163 N signposted Sittingbourne, turn
right towards Doddington at crossroads
by water-tower after Hollingbourne
Built in 1533, this former monks'
hospice became an alehouse after the
Reformation, and beer still matters
here. Casks behind the bar might
contain Theakston Old Peculier,
Greene King IPA, Nun's Delight or
Ringlestone Bitter; a wide range of
Ringlestone country wines and fruit
liqueurs is also stocked. The clapboard
building stands in eight acres of
grounds, but inside, it's darker than
suggested by the white-painted
exterior.
Open *Mon to Fri 12 to 3, 6 to 11, Sat*
12 to 11, Sun 12 to 10.30; closed
25 Dec

HARRINGWORTH

Northamptonshire   map 6

White Swan

Seaton Road,
Harringworth NN17 3AF
TEL: (01572) 747543
off B672, 6m N of Corby
This stone-built fifteenth-century
coaching inn is tucked away in a pretty
and unspoilt village in the Welland
Valley, close to the impressive, 82-arch
viaduct that traverses the valley. It is a
handy overnight resting place or
refreshment stop for tourists exploring
Uppingham and Oakham or visiting
nearby Rockingham Castle. Traditional
interior with stone walls, open fires,
old village photographs, and Greene
King ales on tap. In the heart of good
walking country.
Open *11.30 to 2.30, 6.30 to 11, Sun*
12 to 3, 7 to 10.30; closed evenings 25
and 26 Dec

HARTFIELD

East Sussex   map 3

Anchor Inn

Church Street, Hartfield TN7 4AG
TEL: (01892) 770424
village is on junction of B2026 and
B2110, 6m SE of East Grinstead
A.A. Milne, creator of Winnie the
Pooh, came from Hartfield, whose
mock-Tudor (modernised fifteenth-
century) village pub attracts many
sightseers and walkers. Real ales on
offer include Fuller's London Pride,
Bass and Wadworth 6X. In addition to
bar snacks, the printed menu offers a
range of fish dishes and grills. Children
are welcome. Two rooms are available
for B&B.
Open *11 to 11, Sun 12 to 10.30*

HASCOMBE

Surrey   map 3

White Horse

Hascombe GU8 4JA
TEL: (01483) 208258
on B2130, 3m SE of Godalming
A mecca for families – children love
climbing the venerable old trees in the
garden, and there is a family room
indoors – this attractive-looking pub

caters to the well-heeled local clientele. Fuller's London Pride, Adnams Best and Badger Champion are on draught, with five wines available by the glass. Food is not cheap, and the bar menu might include lamb and mint pie, or Thai-style salmon and prawn fishcakes.

Open *Mon to Fri 11 to 3, 5.30 to 11, Sat 11 to 11, Sun 12 to 10.30; closed 25 Dec*

HEATH

West Yorkshire   map 9

Kings Arms

Heath Common, Heath WF1 5SL
TEL: (01924) 377527

from A638 between Wakefield and Crofton take A655, then turning to Heath and Kirkthorpe

This traditional hostelry, dating from the early eighteenth century, is set on Heath common, a 100-acre area of common grassland, ideal for walking. Inside, the original bar retains an old black range. The beer range runs to Tetley, John Smith's, Clark's Traditional and Timothy Taylor Landlord, and there is a short wine list. Bar food ranges from snacks to main courses such as chicken curry or lasagne; also available is a separate restaurant menu in a more upmarket style.

Open *Mon to Fri 11.30 to 3, 5.30 to 11, Sat 11.30 to 11, Sun 12 to 10.30*

HELFORD

Cornwall   map 1

Shipwrights Arms

Helford TR12 6JX
TEL: (01326) 231235

on S side of Helford River

This fine thatched pub has terraced gardens dropping down to the water's edge, offering a peaceful, secluded view of the Helford River and the wooded creek on which the village lies. Sit among the palm trees and colourful flowers on a warm summer's day or relax in the traditional bar – oak settles, an open fire, nautical memorabilia – with a pint of Castle Eden Ale or Flowers IPA. Memorable summer evening barbecues.

Open *11 to 2.30, 6 to 11 (10.30 winter); closed Sun evening*

HELSTON

Cornwall   map 1

Blue Anchor

50 Coinagehall Street,
Helston TR13 8EL
TEL: (01326) 565765

One of the oldest pubs in the country to brew its own beer, the Blue Anchor dates back to the early fifteenth century, when it was a rest home for monks – it became a tavern after Henry VIII's Dissolution of the Monasteries. The potent ales are Spingo Best, Spingo Middle and Special, and Spingo also turns up in a beef dish on a menu where hearty pies and hotpots dominate.

Open *11 to 11, Sun 12 to 10.30*

HERMITAGE

West Sussex   map 3

Sussex Brewery

36 Main Road, Hermitage,
Emsworth PO10 8AU
TEL: (01243) 371533

on A259, just out of Emsworth towards Chichester

If you love sausages, then this rustic, seventeenth-century former brew pub should be high on your list of pubs to visit. Over 40 kinds of additive-free sausages top the bill on the menu. Sample various gourmet sausages, including O'Hagan's Special, Welsh leek, Sussex pigeon, drunken duck and chicken tikka masala, and wash them down with ales from Young's. Expect few frills – simple furnishings and sawdust on the floor. Walled garden.

Open *11 to 11 (10.30 Sun)*

HILDERSHAM

Cambridgeshire   map 6

Pear Tree

Hildersham CB1 6BU
TEL: (01223) 891680

off A604, 8m SE of Cambridge

Quiet, unpretentious one-room local, brown of décor and featuring a brick-built bar, a small wood-burning stove and an old coin-operated gaming machine. Nowadays, tables have legs but they used to be suspended on chains, some of which remain dangling from the ceiling. Among the drinks available are

Greene King IPA and Abbot Ale plus a modest selection of wines. Food is simple fare: steaks, ploughman's, chilli con carne, and so on.

Open *11.45 to 2, 6.30 (6 Fri and Sat) to 11, Sun 12 to 2, 7 to 10.30*

HOLBETON

Devon   map 1

Mildmay Colours

Holbeton PL8 1NA
TEL: (01752) 830248

off A379 Plymouth to Modbury road, 1m after National Shire Horse Centre, signposted Mothercombe and Holbeton
There are no limits to the horsiness of the menu at this seventeenth-century manor house: food is divided into sections opening with 'under starters orders' and continuing with meat dishes labelled 'and they're off' (which we trust is not true). Colours Best Bitter and S.P. are no longer brewed on the premises but are still local, as is Symons Farmhouse Cider. Also look out for Wild Blonde (a guest beer brewed by Sutton).

Open *11 to 3 (2.30 winter), 6 to 11, Sun 12 to 3, 7 to 11*

HOLNE

Devon   map 1

Church House Inn

Holne TQ13 7SJ
TEL: (01364) 631208

off A38 and A3357, just S of Ashburton
The whitewashed, timbered inn is in a small Dartmoor village set in wild countryside, approached via winding lanes. Simple and homely inside, with an eating area to the back of the bar as well as a separate restaurant, it presents a smiling welcome to the casual dropper-in. New owners took over in late 2000, too late for inspection, but the menu typically offers smoked salmon cornets, king prawns in garlic butter, sea bass in white wine and cream, and venison casserole. A fine range of real ales includes Butcombe's and Palmer's brews, and ten wines may be ordered by the glass. Reports, please.

Open *12 (11.30 Sat) to 3, 6 to 11, Sun 12 to 3, 7 to 10.30*

HOLYPORT

Berkshire   map 3

Belgian Arms

Holyport SL6 2JR
TEL: (01628) 634468

off M4, 2m S of Maidenhead
It was the Eagle until the First World War, when German prisoners held nearby would salute the pub sign – so the name was changed to the Belgian Arms. It is a friendly Brakspear house keeping their Best Bitter and Special, as well as serving six wines by the glass and traditional bar food. It is also near enough to the M4 to make it a useful alternative to motorway service stations. Food is not served some Sunday evenings.

Open *Mon to Thur and Sat 11 to 3, 5.30 to 11, Fri 11 to 11, Sun 12 to 3, 7 to 10.30*

HOLYWELL

Cambridgeshire   map 6

Old Ferry Boat Inn

Holywell PE27 4TJ
TEL: (01480) 463227

off A1123, 2m E of St Ives
At the end of a country lane and overlooking the meandering River Ouse, this low-built, whitewashed and thatched pub was originally a ferry house. Documents show that liquor has been sold here since AD 560. The beamed and partly panelled bar is said to be haunted by Juliet, a vivacious young girl who was a victim of unrequited love. Good river views can be enjoyed from the sun-trap terrace. Children are most welcome, and a peaceful night is assured in the upstairs bedrooms.

Open *11.30 to 11, Sun 12 to 10.30*

HOOK NORTON

Oxfordshire   map 5

Pear Tree Inn

Scotland End, Hook Norton OX15 5NU
TEL: (01608) 737482

off A361, 5m NE of Chipping Norton
Expect to find the full range of tiptop Hook Norton ales at this unspoilt village local, the 'brewery tap' to the

highly rated Hook Norton Brewery just 100 yards down the lane. The welcoming wooden-floored bar sports a rustic mix of furnishings, an open log fire and a loyal local following. Simple pub food, overnight accommodation and a large garden, with a stream and children's play equipment, complete the picture.

Open 11.30 to 2.30 (4 Sat and Sun), 6 to 11 (10.30 Sun)

HORSEBRIDGE

Devon   map 1

Royal Inn

Horsebridge PL19 8PJ
TEL: (01822) 870214
off A384, 5m W of Tavistock
This ancient, ivy-clad inn is set in the depths of unspoilt Devon countryside close to a superb fifteenth-century bridge over the River Tamar. Formerly a nunnery (note the high-arched windows), it was later patronised by Charles I (hence the name), who carved the royal seal on the doorstep. It is now a friendly, family-run inn offering excellent Sharp's ales from Cornwall and regularly changing guest brews in its two simply furnished, slate-floored bars. Children welcome lunchtimes only.

Open 12 to 3, 7 to 11, Sun 12 to 3, 7 to 10.30

HORSEY

Norfolk   map 6

Nelson Head

Beach Road, Horsey NR29 4AD
TEL: (01493) 393378
off B1159, 9m NE of Acle
Leased by the landlord from the National Trust, this unpretentious brick-built pub lies tucked away down a dead-end lane close to the beach and Horsey Mere. Traditional unspoilt charm characterises the two neat and simply furnished rooms, each adorned with nautical and farming artefacts and warmed by open log fires. Woodforde's ales and straightforward pub food await walkers and bird-watchers, having explored the delights of the windswept coast.

Open 11 to 2.30, 6 (7 winter) to 11, Sun 12 to 3, 7 to 10.30; closed evening 25 Dec

HUNDON

Suffolk   map 6

Plough Inn

Hundon CO10 8DT
TEL: (01440) 786789
off A143, 2m N of Haverhill, take right turn to Kedington, then 1m towards Hundon
Standing on a hilltop in acres of landscaped gardens with lovely views of the Stour valley, the Plough is a pub, restaurant, small hotel and conference centre. It offers Woodforde's Wherry and Greene King IPA plus a range of guest ales, supplemented by about 30 malt whiskies and nearly as many wines, of which ten can be had by the glass. As well as the bar menu there is a quarterly-changing restaurant menu majoring on fish, steaks and traditional pub desserts.

Open 11 to 2.30, 6 to 11, Sun 12 to 3, 7 to 10.30

HURLEY

Berkshire   map 2

Dew Drop

Batts Green, Hurley SL6 6RB
TEL: (01628) 824327
take Honey Lane off A423, just outside Hurley between Maidenhead and Henley-on-Thames, continue past council houses and through farm until wood; at T-junction take right turn on to smaller lane, inn is a few hundred yards on right
Built in the seventeenth century as a pair of cottages, this village pub has been licensed since the mid-1700s. It has a large garden for summer eating. Brakspear Bitter is stocked as well as occasional and seasonal ales such as Resolution, Downpour and O Be Joyful. Home-made pies feature on the menu, with steak and ale for carnivores, some vegetarians options, and for pastry addicts apple pie to finish.

Open 12 to 3, 6 to 11, Sun 12 to 3, 7 to 10.30

ICKLESHAM

East Sussex   map 3

Queens Head

Parsonage Lane,
Icklesham TN36 4BL
TEL: (01424) 814552
*just off A259 Hastings to Rye road, 2m
W of Winchelsea*

Look for the name in large slate
lettering on the roof of this
seventeenth-century inn near the village
church. The pub serves an excellent
range of real ales, including selections
from Forge, Rother Valley, Cotleigh,
Woodforde's, Harveys and Hampshire,
as well as Biddenden cider and over ten
wines by the glass. Ploughman's
lunches, salads, steaks and favourites
such as lasagne, chilli, and chicken,
ham and mushroom pie are the kind of
hearty pub fare to expect.
Open *11 to 11, Sun 12 to 10.30*

INGLEBY

Derbyshire   map 5

John Thompson

Ingleby DE73 1HW
TEL: (01332) 862469
off A514, 3m NW of Melbourne

John Thompson converted his
fifteenth-century farmhouse into a pub
in 1969 and started brewing beer on
the premises in 1977. Since the success
of Thompson's first beer, brewed to
commemorate the Queen's Jubilee, the
brewery business has thrived under the
name of Lloyds. Visitors to this
homely, traditionally furnished pub can
enjoy carvery-style lunches and sample
the Summer Gold, Porter and John
Thompson Special.
Open *10.30 (12 Sun) to 2.30, 7 to 11
(10.30 Sun); closed evening 25 Dec*

INGS

Cumbria   map 9

Watermill

Ings LA8 9PY
TEL: (01539) 821309
just off A591, 2m E of Windermere

Set back from the road in a quiet
backwater, this 250-year-old converted
wood mill is a popular base for
exploring prime Lakeland walking
country. Visitors will find comfortable
family accommodation in seven *en
suite* bedrooms. It specialises in real
ales, and the mind-boggling beer menu
lists up to 16 brews, perhaps including
Harviestoun Ptarmigan, Tisbury
Nadderjack and Mordue Radgie
Gadgie, alongside old favourites like
Black Sheep Bitter and Theakston Old
Peculier. There are tables outside by
the River Gowan.
Open *12 to 2.30 (3 Sun), 6 to 11
(10.30 Sun)*

INKBERROW

Worcestershire   map 5

Old Bull

Inkberrow WR7 4DZ
TEL: (01386) 792428
*off A422, Worcester to Stratford-upon-
Avon road, 5m W of Alcester*

Known to devotees of *The Archers* as
the model pub for the Bull at
Ambridge. Tucked away in a quiet
village close to the church, it is a fine
half-timbered Tudor pub and well
worth visiting for its splendid beamed
interior, notably the impressive collar-
beam-framed roof, and for the wealth
of memorabilia relating to the
programme. Flowers IPA, Marston's
Pedigree and Tetley Bitter are on
handpump. Traditional pub food runs
to fish and chips in newspaper on
Fridays.
Open *Mon to Fri 12 to 3, 5.30 to 11,
Sat and Sun 12 to 11*

IXWORTH

Suffolk   map 6

Pykkerell

High Street, Ixworth IP31 2HH
TEL: (01359) 230398
off A143 Bury St Edmunds to Diss road

The name of this fifteenth-century
high-street coaching inn is a variant of
the name for a small pike. Its exterior
features include a fine colonnaded
front portico and a listed barn at the
back. New licensees took over in spring
2000 and offer straightforward printed
and blackboard menus of traditional
fare, including the Pykkerell special (an
Abbot Ale sausage) and Irish stew.

Greene King Abbot Ale and IPA are on draught.

Open *10am to 11pm, Sun 12 to 10.30*

KELD

North Yorkshire   map 9

Tan Hill Inn

Keld DL11 6ED
TEL: (01833) 628246
off B6270 at Keld, then 4m N
Britain's highest pub (1,732 feet above sea level) – and one of its remotest – is proud of its horribly cold and windy winters, and the fact that it has no mains electricity. Yorkshire puddings dominate the menu while real ales are from Theakston and Black Sheep – Theakston Old Peculier and Black Sheep Riggwelter are always on tap, and seasonal and occasional ales are also stocked.

Open *11 to 11, Sun 12 to 10.30*

KINGSBRIDGE

Devon   map 1

Crabshell Inn

Embankment Road, Kingsbridge TQ7 1JZ
TEL: (01548) 852345
off A381, 8m SW of Totnes
On warm summer days, head for the waterfront terrace at this popular quayside pub and admire the views over the moorings and estuary. If the weather is inclement, the informal bar areas offer a genuinely friendly atmosphere, and children are made particularly welcome, especially in the well-equipped games room. Bass, Crabshell Bitter and Flowers IPA are on handpump, and the long menu gives plenty of choice.

Open *11 to 11*

KINGSTON NEAR LEWES

East Sussex   map 3

Juggs

The Street, Kingston near Lewes BN7 3NT
TEL: (01273) 472523
off A27, 2m SW of Lewes
A 'catslide' roof that slopes vertiginously down one side of the building gives this building its

character. Outdoor seating at the front, as well as a children's play area, makes it a popular summer destination, but you will be greeted all year round with Harveys and Adnams ales and a range of eight wines by the glass. Fried haddock, scampi and steaks are the principal business of the kitchen, but see also the blackboard specials, which might take in pork on the bone with broccoli, mash and a Chinese-flavoured sauce.

Open *summer 11 to 11, winter 11 to 3, 6 to 11, Sun 11 to 4, 6 to 10.30*

KNEBWORTH

Hertfordshire   map 3

Lytton Arms

Park Lane,
Old Knebworth SG3 6QB
TEL: (01438) 812312
from Knebworth on the B197 take side road signposted Old Knebworth
Devoted real ale fans should note that over 4,750 different beers have been served at this Victorian-style pub since the landlord arrived here in 1988. In addition to Fuller's London Pride, Bass and Adnams Best Bitter, aficionados can choose from five guest brews on handpump, and from a mind-boggling choice at the pub's spring and autumn beer festivals. The drinks list extends to 50 Belgian bottled beers and an equal number of malt whiskies.

Open *Mon to Thur 11 to 3, 5 to 11, Fri and Sat 11 to 11, Sun 12 to 10.30; closed evening 25 Dec*

KNIPTON

Leicestershire   map 5

Red House

Croxton Road, Knipton NG32 1RH
TEL: (01476) 870352
off A607, 6m SW of Grantham
This imposing Regency house is near Belvoir Castle in a picturesque setting on a hill looking down towards the village church. It is a pub with a split personality: extravagantly decorated restaurant on the one hand, busy, informal bar on the other. Adnams and Mansfield cask ales are kept to accompany a long menu of light bar snacks and grills; from the more

ambitious restaurant menu, chicken liver pâté and pickled herring with soured cream sauce have been singled out for praise.

Open *12 to 2.30, 6 to 11, Sun 12 to 2.30, 7.30 to 11*

LACOCK

Wiltshire   map 2

Red Lion

1 High Street, Lacock SN15 2LQ
TEL: (01249) 730456
on A350, 3m S of Chippenham
Décor in the bar of this spacious pub includes agricultural implements and a bellows huge enough to match the vast fireplace. Window seats overlook the village's grey stone houses, all more than 200 years old, and half-timbered cottages. There is the Abbey too, and a museum of the work of pioneering photographer Fox Talbot. Badger Tanglefoot, Wadworth 6X or IPA and a seasonal guest ale are kept. Mostly traditional cooking takes in things like beef and Stilton pie, and lamb and apricot casserole.

Open *summer 11 to 11, Sun 12 to 10.30; winter 11.30 to 2.30 (3 Sat), 6 to 11, Sun 12 to 3, 6 to 10.30*

LANGTON HERRING

Dorset   map 2

Elm Tree

Shop Lane, Langton Herring DT3 4HU
TEL: (01305) 871257
off B3157, 5m NW of Weymouth
A pleasant drive through Dorset farmland leads to this cream-painted, slate-roofed pub with a profusion of exterior flora to lighten the spirits. High-backed settles and an open fire with a funnel-shaped hood add a quirkiness to the interior. Two regularly changing real ales are always offered and everything on the wine list may be taken by the glass. Blackboard menus deal in traditional pub fare: rack of lamb, Cumberland sausage, or fish specials such as sea bass.

Open *11 to 3, 6 to 11, Sun 12 to 3, 6.30 (7 winter) to 10.30*

LANLIVERY

Cornwall   map 1

Crown

Lanlivery PL30 5BT
TEL: (01208) 872707
off A390, 2m W of Lostwithiel
Tucked away down a narrow lane close to the parish church, this rough-stone former farmhouse dates from the twelfth century and is reputedly Cornwall's oldest pub. Worth tracking down for the tiptop ales – Doom Bar Bitter, Eden and Own – from Sharp's Brewery, and the impressive, black slate-floored bar with its ancient beams, old settles and the priest hole in the chimney. Peaceful, secluded garden and overnight accommodation in two bedrooms.

Open *11 to 3, 6 to 11, Sun 12 to 3, 6.30 to 10.30*

LAPWORTH

Warwickshire   map 5

Navigation Inn

Old Warwick Road, Lapworth BN4 6NA
TEL: (01564) 783337
on B4439, 1m SE of Hockley Heath
Morris dancers, occasional live jazz concerts and performances by travelling theatre companies draw customers in summer to this eighteenth-century creeper-clad pub set beside the Grand Union Canal. In addition to the spacious canalside terrace, the pub has an unpretentious interior, with a friendly, flagstoned bar decorated with stuffed fish and canal related artefacts, and an attractive side extension with views of the water. Guest ales accompany draught Bass and Mitchells and Butler Brew XI on handpump.

Open *Mon to Fri 11 to 3, 5.30 to 11, Sat 11 to 11, Sun 12 to 10.30*

LITTLE CHEVERELL

Wiltshire   map 2

Owl

Low Road,
Little Cheverell SN10 4JS
TEL: (01380) 812263
on B3098 ¼m W of A360
An off-the-beaten-track local in a tiny
hamlet surrounded by farmland with
views of Salisbury Plain, the Owl has a
secluded and peaceful garden running
down to the Cheverell Brook. It's
homely and neat, with a wood-burning
stove, farming implements, an
assortment of wooden furnishings, and
fresh flowers. Expect a selection of
weekly-changing real ales, and dishes
cooked by the landlady listed on the
blackboard. No children inside.
Reports please.
Open *11.30 to 2.30, 6 to 11, Sun
11.30 to 2.30, 7 to 10.30; closed 25
and 26 Dec, 1 Jan*

LITTLE HADHAM

Hertfordshire   map 6

Nags Head

The Ford, Little Hadham SG11 2AX
TEL: (01279) 771555
*between B1004 and A120, 3m W of
Bishop's Stortford*
The Nag's Head has clocked up 400
years as a country inn, and continues to
please. It is a Greene King house
serving IPA, Abbot Ale and seasonal
beers; seven wines are served by the
glass, from a list of around 40. Fish is
the kitchen's first love, the long menu
typically opening with fried whitebait
or crab cocktail, and proceeding to
poached skate with black butter. Finish
with sticky toffee meringue or
chocolate fudge cake.
Open *11 to 3, 6 to 11, Sun 12 to 3, 6
to 10.30*

LITTLEHEMPSTON

Devon   map 1

Tally Ho!

Littlehempston TQ9 6NF
TEL: (01803) 862316
off A381, 2m NE of Totnes
Dating from the fourteenth century,
this creeper-shrouded pub stands by the
village church. The single bar has open
fires in winter, and in summer you can
enjoy the sun and the flowers on the
patio. Bass is joined by regularly
changing guest ales. Apart from snacks,
the menu offers steaks and poultry
together with fresh local fish. B&B
available.
Open *summer 12 to 3, 6 to 11, winter
12 to 2.30, 6.30 to 11*

LITTLE LONGSTONE

Derbyshire   map 8

Packhorse Inn

Little Longstone DE45 1NN
TEL: (01629) 640471
off B6465, 2m NW of Bakewell
Formerly two miners' cottages dating
from the sixteenth century, the
Packhorse became an inn in 1787. In
prime Peak District walking country, on
the Monsal trail between Bakewell and
Miller's Dale, it offers simple old-
fashioned character, with open log fires
and local prints and photos on the walls.
Live folk sessions (Wednesday nights)
and traditional pub games entertain the
customers to the accompaniment of
Marston's ales. Basic pub food is
available, children are welcome and the
garden has a fish pond.
Open *11.30 to 2.30, 5 to 11, Sun 12
to 10.30*

LITTLE STRETTON

Shropshire   map 5

Ragleth Inn

Little Stretton SY6 6RB
TEL: (01694) 722711
*on B4370, off A49, just SW of Church
Stretton*
Nestling at the foot of the Long Mynd
mountain in a pleasant wooded valley,
this handsome brick pub, built in 1663,
is a favourite watering hole among the
walking fraternity. The appeal, other
than pints of Hobsons Best Bitter, is the
choice of traditional home-cooked
food, served in the relaxing and
intimate oak-beamed lounge or in the
homely bar. Pleasant summer garden
with an unusual tulip tree.
Open *Mon to Fri 12 to 2.30, 6 to 11,
Sat 12 to 11, Sun 12 to 10.30*

LLANYBLODWEL

Shropshire   map 5

Horse Shoe Inn

Llanyblodwel SY10 8NQ
TEL: (01691) 828969

just off B4396, 5 SW of Oswestry

Tucked away in a sleepy hamlet just a
mile from the Welsh border, this
rambling sixteenth-century black-and-
white timbered building stands next to
the ancient bridge over the River
Tanat. Charming, old-fashioned
interior with low, blackened beams,
bare wooden floors, Bass and
Worthington real ales on tap, and a
short menu listing traditional, home-
made pub food. Children are made
very welcome. Picnic tables on the
riverbank are ideal for peaceful
summer drinking.

Open *11.30 to 3, 6.30 to 11, Sun 12
to 3, 7 to 10.30; closed Mon lunchtime,
and evening 25 Dec*

LONG PRESTON

North Yorkshire   map 8

Maypole Inn

Long Preston BD23 4PH
TEL: (01729) 840219

on A65 Skipton to Settle road

Overlooking the green and maypole in
a pretty Dales village not far from the
Carlisle to Settle Railway, this
comfortably refurbished 300-year-old
inn is noted for its choice of North
Country ales. Relax by the log fire in
the neat carpeted bar and sup a pint of
Moorhouses Premier or Timothy
Taylor Landlord or, if your tipple is
real cider, try Saxon Ruby Tuesday.
Daily specials enhance the printed pub
menu. Children are welcome, and the
pub has useful family accommodation.

Open *11 to 3 (2.30 winter), 6 to 11,
Sun 12 to 10.30*

LOW CATTON

East Riding of Yorkshire   map 9

Gold Cup Inn

Low Catton YO41 1EA
TEL: (01759) 371354

off A166, just S of Stamford Bridge

A modernised whitewashed pub near
the Derwent in a small village at the
foot of the Yorkshire Wolds. Well
patronised by walkers trekking the
Wolds Way near Thixendale, the
unpretentious interior comprises a
rambling three-roomed lounge, each
with welcoming log fires and a wealth
of bric-à-brac, and a games room to the
rear. Real ales include Tetley Bitter and
John Smith's. The spacious beer garden
has access to the river.

Open *Mon to Fri (exc Mon lunchtime)
12 to 2.30, 6 to 11, Sat and Sun 12 to
11; closed evening 25 Dec*

LOWER ASHTON

Devon   map 1

Manor Inn

Lower Ashton EX6 7QL
TEL: (01647) 252304

*from A38 S of Exeter, take B3193
towards Christow, signposted on right
after 5m*

The commitment to real beer here is
such that the Manor Inn has listed over
1,500 different guest ales. Even the
regular selection makes a change from
the usual suspects, embracing RCH
Pitchfork and Princetown Jail Ale. A
trio of blackboards lists fish, meat and
vegetarian dishes, typically including
grilled salmon, beef and red wine
casserole, or Stilton and mushroom
bake. Eight wines are offered by the
glass.

Open *Tue to Sat 12 to 2.30, 7 to 11,
Sun 12 to 2.30, 7 to 10.30*

LOWER PEOVER

Cheshire   map 7

Bells of Peover

The Cobbles,
Lower Peover WA16 9PZ
TEL: (01565) 722269

on B5081, 6m E of Northwich

The Bells in question are not the ones
in the neighbouring church, but a
family who once owned this village inn.
It's a very English pub where
Eisenhower and General Patton met in
the Second World War. Theakston
Cool Cask, and Marston's Pedigree are
kept together with Greenall's ales and
there are six wines by the glass. Bar
snacks are available every day, the

restaurant opens Friday and Saturday evenings.

Open *Mon to Fri 11.30 to 3, 5.30 to 11, Sat 11.30 to 11, Sun 12 to 10.30*

LOWICK

Northamptonshire   map 6

Snooty Fox

Main Street, Lowick NN14 3BS
TEL: (01832) 733434
just off A6116, 2m NW of Thrapston
Built in 1530, the Snooty Fox was formerly the home of the Countesses of Peterborough, but became a country inn in 1671. It presents a warm and welcoming impression within, with a wood-burning stove on view, and cooking that encompasses such favourites as prawn cocktail, grilled salmon in lemon butter, knuckle of lamb in red wine and garlic, and spotted dick. Greene King IPA and Adnams beers can usually be found among the regularly changing ale selection.

Open *12 to 3, 6.30 to 11, Sun 12 to 3, 7 to 10.30*

LOW NEWTON-BY-THE-SEA

Northumberland   map 10

Ship

Low Newton-by-the-Sea NE66 3EL
TEL: (01665) 576262
off B1340, 2m N of Embleton
A genuine unspoilt local tucked away in a cluster of attractive, whitewashed fishermen's cottages, the Ship overlooks the tiny green and is just a stone's throw from a National Trust-owned beach. Both beach and pub are packed in summer, while winter finds the Ship blissfully quiet and the domain of chatty locals. Charming creel-adorned bar, Northumberland microbrewery ales and simple lunchtime menu offering hearty soups and fresh crab sandwiches; limited evening blackboard menu. Children welcome.

Open *summer 11 to 4 (5 in school summer holidays), 6.30 to 11; winter 12 to 3, 8 to 11; opens 9pm Jan and Feb*

LUDGVAN

Cornwall   map 1

White Hart

Churchtown, Ludgvan TR20 8EY
TEL: (01736) 740574
off A30 between Hayle and Penzance at Crowlas; take turning signposted Ludgvan, continue 1m
This old pub is in the centre of the village, next to its sixteenth-century church. Inside is all beamed ceilings and panelled walls, plus a wood-burning stove and an inglenook fireplace. Menus, displayed on an upright piano, offer salads, breaded fish and steaks, while the specials board might bring on green-lip mussels, salmon in a prawn sauce or rabbit casserole. Whiskies are something of a bar speciality, while cask ales offer a choice of Bass, Flowers IPA or Marston's Pedigree.

Open *11 to 2.30, 6 to 11, Sun 12 to 3, 7 to 10.30*

LUGWARDINE

Herefordshire   map 5

Crown & Anchor

Cotts Lane, Lugwardine HR1 4AB
TEL: (01432) 851303
off A438, 3m E of Hereford
This unpretentiously old-fashioned pub is decorated with interesting vintage photographs of Weston's Cider Company staff, farming implements, a bunch of fishing rods, and hop garlands on beamed walls and ceiling. Especially attractive is the paved patio in a flowery garden, which clearly shows the power of some very green fingers. On draught are Worthington Best Bitter, Theakston XB and Butcombe Ale, and there are eight wines by the glass.

Open *12 to 11 (10.30 Sun)*

LYNMOUTH

Devon   map 1

Rising Sun Hotel

Harbourside, Lynmouth EX35 6EQ
TEL: (01598) 753223
on A39, 9m W of Porlock
Literary heritage is a draw at this thatched, harbourside inn: R.D.

Blackmore wrote part of Lorna Doone during a stay, and Percy Bysshe Shelley is believed to have spent his honeymoon in what is now one of the guest rooms. The proximity of Exmoor National Park exercises its own pull, and so might the hand-pumped Exmoor ales in the bar. Ten wines by the glass are offered from an enterprising list. An inventive streak runs through menus that encompass crab and couscous salad with herb and balsamic vinaigrette, and chicken breast on saffron potatoes.
Open *11 to 3, 5.30 to 11, Sun 12 to 2, 7 to 10.30*

MARSWORTH

Buckinghamshire   map 3
Red Lion
90 Vicarage Road,
Marsworth HP23 4LU
TEL: (01296) 668366
off B489, 2m N of Tring
The Red Lion is on the Grand Union Canal and handy for the bird-watcher's haven of Tring Reservoir. Fuller's London Pride and the Vale Brewery's Notley Ale, together with regularly changing guest beers and a selection of ciders from Weston's, are reasons enough to venture here, and the cooking is built around classic pub fare such as curries, burgers and sausages, with daily specials on the board; the likes of spotted dick or treacle sponge (both with custard) round things off.
Open *11 to 3, 6 to 11, Sun 12 to 3, 7 to 11; 11 to 11 Sat and Sun July and Aug*

MEYSEY HAMPTON

Gloucestershire   map 2
Masons Arms
Meysey Hampton GL7 5JT
TEL: (01285) 850164
off A417, 1½W of Fairford
A seventeenth-century inn on the southern edge of the Cotswolds, the Masons Arms has nine guest rooms, making it a handy stopover for those on the sightseeing trail. It sits by the village green, serving Hook Norton Best Bitter and Scrumpy Jack cider alongside nearly 20 wines. Those with

an appetite may dine on a starter portion of mashed potato with Stilton, bacon and garlic, or Cajun chicken salad, then a main course such as rack of lamb, followed perhaps by a traditional pudding like apple pie.
Open *11.30 to 2.45, 6 to 11, Sun 12 to 4, 7 to 10.30; closed Sun evening Nov to Mar*

MILTON ABBAS

Dorset   map 2
Hambro Arms
Milton Abbas DT11 0BP
TEL: (01258) 880233
off A354, 6m SW of Blandford Forum
Surrounded by rolling hills, the striking village of identical thatched houses was evidently moved in Victorian times to be rebuilt a suitable distance from Milton Abbey. The long, white-painted pub is thatched too, and, inside, décor is traditional, with a pool table dominating the public bar. The food is mostly standard pub fare – pan-fried lamb'sliver with bacon, or fresh cod in batter, for example – and on draught are Bass and Old Speckled Hen. Friendly service.
Open *11 to 3, 6 to 11, Sun 12 to 3, 7 to 10.30*

MILTON BRYAN

Bedfordshire   map 3
Red Lion
South End,
Milton Bryan MK17 9HS
TEL: (01525) 210044
just off A4012, 2½m S of Woburn Abbey and 3m E of M1 junction 12
A spotlessly maintained pub nestling in a peaceful old village and well placed for Woburn Abbey and Safari Park. The attractive exterior is festooned with colourful flower baskets in summer, and the interior has rug-strewn wooden floors and a wealth of beams and exposed brickwork. Expect to find Greene King IPA, Old Speckled Hen and Ruddles Best on handpump and a varied menu favouring fresh fish. There is a lovely garden, and children are very welcome inside and out.
Open *12 to 4, 6 to 11 (10.30 Sun)*

MONTACUTE

Somerset   map 2
Kings Arms
Montacute TA15 6UU
TEL: (01935) 822513
just off A3088, 4m NW of Yeovil
Built of golden-coloured local
hamstone and in an unspoilt village
close to the gates of Montacute House
(NT), this sixteenth-century coaching
inn was once a staging post on the
Plymouth–London route. Horses were
changed here before the gruelling climb
up Ham Hill. The civilised interior has
a good pubby bar with pleasing village
views, a candlelit restaurant, and
comfortable accommodation in 15 *en
suite* bedrooms. Children welcome.
Open *11 to 11, Sun 12 to 10.30*

MORWENSTOW

Cornwall   map 1
Bush Inn
Crosstown, Morwenstow EX23 9SR
TEL: (01288) 331242
*3m W of A39, between Bude and
Clovelly, 6m N of Bude*
Follow a breezy cliff-top walk with a
visit to Cornwall's most northerly
parish and savour a pint at the Bush
Inn, one of Britain's oldest pubs. Once
a monastic resting house (note the
Celtic piscina set in the wall) on the
pilgrim route between Spain and
Wales, this ancient inn dates back to
950AD. Not surprisingly, the interior is
unspoilt and traditional, with
flagstones, built-in settles, stone
fireplace, and St Austell HSD and
Worthington Bitter tapped from the
cask. Food is served at lunchtime only,
and not at all on Sundays. The parish
church is worth a look.
Open *12 to 3 (2.30 winter), 7 (6
winter) to 11, Sun 12 to 3, 7 to 10.30;
closed Mon winter*

NAUNTON

Gloucestershire   map 5
Black Horse
Naunton GL54 3AD
TEL: (01451) 850565
off B4068, 5m W of Stow-on-the-Wold
A pleasant day-long circular walk of
this sumptuous part of the Cotswolds,
beginning and ending in the all-day car
park at Bourton-on-the-Water, can be
planned to take in lunch at the Black
Horse. On the main street of a
delightful hill village, it dates from the
1870s and was once a row of farm
workers' cottages, retaining the original
flagged floors and open fireplaces. Fish
and chips, steaks and curries are the
bulwarks of the menu, with 'sinful
sweets' to follow. Donnington ales, as
well as West Country ciders from
Weston's and Stowford Press, are
supplemented by a short, fairly priced
wine list with four by the glass.
Open *11.30 to 3, 6 to 11, Sun 12 to 3,
7 to 10.30*

NEAR SAWREY

Cumbria   map 8
Tower Bank Arms
Near Sawrey LA22 0LF
TEL: (015394) 36334
on B5285, 2m SE of Hawkshead
Fans of Beatrix Potter may find the
Tower Bank Arms familiar: it is next
door to the author's home, Hill Top,
and featured in *The Tale of Jemima
Puddleduck*. The menu is divided into
cold and hot dishes; the former
comprises variations on ploughman's
and salads, the latter being things like
lasagne, battered Whitby scampi, and
Lakeland game pie. Beers are Theakston
Best Bitter and Old Peculier, and four
wines are available by the glass.
Open *11 to 3, 5.30 (6 winter) to 11*

NESSCLIFFE

Shropshire   map 7
Old Three Pigeons
Nesscliffe SY4 1DB
TEL: (01743) 741279
on A5, 8m NW of Shrewsbury
The real ale selection in this ancient
pub (built in 1405) changes weekly.

Typical ales are Moorhouses Pendle Witches' Brew and Highgate Fox's Nob. The selection of wines also changes frequently. Fish is much in evidence on the menu, ranging from plainly served oysters and lobster to soused mackerel. Children are welcome throughout the pub.

Open *Tue to Sun 12 to 3, 6 to 11*

NEWNHAM

Kent   map 3

George Inn

44 The Street, Newnham ME9 0LL
TEL: (01795) 890237
off A2, 5m SW of Faversham
This atmospheric old pub, opposite the church in this olde-worlde village, started life as a farmhouse in the fifteenth century. It is built of brick and hung with tiles and in summer is festooned with flowers in window boxes and hanging baskets. It is a Shepherd Neame house serving Master Brew, Spitfire and Bishop's Finger, plus a good selection of Old and New World wines (12 by the glass). Pies and puddings are the mainstays of the cooking, plus blackboard specials. Children are welcome in the eating areas and garden.

Open *11 to 3, 6.30 to 11, Sun 12 to 4, 6.30 to 10.30*

NEWTON

Cambridgeshire   map 6

Queens Head

Newton CB2 5PG
TEL: (01223) 870436
on B1368, 6m S of Cambridge
This charming brick cottage is a wonderful little pub. A real rural gem, it has been lovingly maintained by the Short family for some 30 years, and both Cambridge dons and local farm workers form part of the interesting mixed clientele that fill the simple, stone-tiled bars. They come for the friendly, timeless atmosphere, unmarred by gimmickry, the excellent Adnams ales on tap, and the straightforward bar food, notably mugs of hearty soup and good-value, cut-to-order sandwiches.

Open *11.30 to 2.30, 6 to 11, Sun 12 to 2.30, 7 to 10.30*

NEWTON UNDER ROSEBERRY

Redcar   map 10

King's Head

Newton under Roseberry TS9 6QR
TEL: (01642) 722318
on A173, 3m SW of Guisborough
Walkers following the Cleveland Way often stop off at this red-brick and stone inn, which gets busy at weekends. It focuses mainly on food, with John Smith's Magnet the only real ale, but has a wide selection of Old and New World wines, including 12 by the glass. The printed menu of things like chicken breast stuffed with tomato and mushrooms, or pan-fried cod with horseradish Yorkshire pudding and shrimp gravy, is supplemented by daily-changing chef's specials. A good-value mid-week lunch menu is also available.

Open *11.30 to 3, 5.30 to 11*

NORTH WOOTTON

Dorset   map 2

Three Elms

North Wootton DT9 5SW
TEL: (01935) 812881
on A3030 Sherborne to Sturminster Newton road, 2m SE of Sherborne
On the fringes of Blackmoor Vale, with great views towards Bulbarrow Hill (Dorset's highest point), this is a pub that conspicuously reflects its landlord's passions. It contains over 1,300 model cars and other vehicles from bygone days, among other memorabilia. Originally a cider house, the building has been extended by the present owner and has a pleasant garden. As well as several handpumped real ales, including Otter Bitter, Butcombe Bitter and local guest ales, this freehouse offers Burrow Hill cider and 15 wines by the glass. The extensive menu caters for smaller appetites and vegetarians.

Open *11 to 2.30, 6.30 (6 Fri and Sat) to 11, Sun 11 to 2.30, 7 to 10.30*

NORTON
Wiltshire   map 2
Vine Tree
Norton SN16 0JP
TEL: (01666) 837654
*from M4 junction 17 take A429
towards Malmesbury, turn left after
1½m signposted Hullavington, Norton
and Sherston and follow road for 2¼m
to Norton; turn right in village on road
signposted Foxley*
This converted eighteenth-century mill
house is on the edge of a sleepy south
Cotswolds village in rolling countryside
close to Malmesbury and Westonbirt
Arboretum. Three brightly coloured
rooms – two for eating – have
flagstones or carpets, and walls are
adorned with copious picures and
mirrors. There is an attractive, secluded
rear terrace and a huge garden with an
impressive children's play area. Archers
ales are on tap and seven wines by the
glass, including champagne. As the
Guide went to press the new owners
had introduced a seasonal menu that
has much of interest. Reports please.
Open *11.30 to 3, 6 to 11, Sun 12 to
10.30*

NUNNEY
Somerset   map 2
George
11 Church Street,
Nunney BA11 4LW
TEL: (01373) 836458
off A361, 2m SW of Frome
Spare a thought for victims of the
Bloody Assizes if you happen by the
George. Some of the condemned were
tried in one of its rooms and then
hanged by the neck in the garden.
Restore a sense of cheer with one of
the many real ales on tap, including
perhaps something from Exmoor Ales
or Wadworth, or Highgate Saddlers
Celebrated Best Bitter or Black Sheep
Best Bitter. Help yourself from the
lunchtime cart, or head for the
restaurant to eat sticky pork ribs, deep-
fried Camembert with raspberry coulis,
a fish speciality such as silver bream,
red snapper or swordfish – with maybe
tiramisù to finish.
Open *12 to 4 (3 winter), 6.30 to
11.30, Sun 12 to 3, 6 to 11.30*

ONECOTE
Staffordshire   map 5
Jervis Arms
Onecote ST13 7RU
TEL: (01538) 304206
*on B5053, 1m off A523 Leek to
Ashbourne road, 4m E of Leek*
Highly popular with holidaymakers,
this seventeenth-century stone inn
stands on the bank of the River Hamps
on the edge of the Peak District
National Park. A small footbridge over
the stream connects the car park with
the pub and riverside garden, where
picnic tables and a play area draw
families in summer. The welcome to
children extends to three family rooms,
while devotees of well-kept real ale will
rejoice at the sight of six handpumps
on the bar, including Whim Arbor
Light and three guest brews.
Open *11 to 3, 7 (6 Sat) to 11, Sun 12
to 10.30*

ORFORD
Suffolk   map 6
Jolly Sailor
Quay Street, Orford IP12 2NU
TEL: (01394) 450243
*at end of B1084; village signposted off
A12 at Woodbridge*
The full range of Adnams ales is on
show at this unspoilt former smugglers'
haunt close to the quay overlooking
Orford Ness. Old-fashioned hatches
and counters serve the series of cosy
little rooms that feature genuine old
timbers from wrecked seventeenth-
century ships. Although very much a
local drinkers' pub, those in search of
food will find a short bar menu
featuring local fish in home-made
batter. No children inside.
Accommodation available.
Open *11.30 to 2.30, 7 to 11, Sun 12
to 2.45, 7 to 10.30*

OSWALDKIRK
North Yorkshire   map 9
Malt Shovel
Oswaldkirk YO62 5XT
TEL: (01439) 788461
on B1363, 4m S of Helmsley
Built as a manor house in 1610, the Malt
Shovel became a coaching inn during the

eighteenth century and is now a Grade II listed building owned by the Samuel Smith Brewery. The taproom boasts a huge inglenook and a lofty beamed ceiling, and roaring log fires warm the two little bars. Old Brewery Bitter is on handpump. The pub is on the edge of the Yorkshire Moors close to Ampleforth College. The splendid south-facing terrace is a real suntrap.

Open *Mon to Fri 11 to 3, 6 to 11, Sat 11 to 11, Sun 12 to 3, 7 to 10.30*

OVING

West Sussex   map 3

Gribble Inn

Gribble Lane, Oving PO20 6BP
Tel: (01243) 786893
off A259, 4m E of Chichester
Home of the Gribble Brewery (owned by Hall & Woodhouse), this old thatched pub offers the brewery's full range of beers from Gribble Ale to Pig's Ear, and seasonal ales such as Winter Wobbler. Also on offer is a good choice of malt, rye and bourbon whiskies and a list of 30 wines that includes eight by the glass. The pub has a family room as well as a garden where children are welcome. Daily blackboard specials supplement the printed menu and there are always vegetarian options.

Open *11 to 3, 5.30 to 11, Sun 12 to 4.30 (3 winter), 7 to 10.30*

OWSLEBURY

Hampshire   map 2

Ship Inn

Owslebury SO21 1LT
Tel: (01962) 777358
off A33/A272, 4m S of Winchester
This seventeenth-century thatched pub offers Cheriton Pots Ale, Ruddles, Bateman's XXXB and Greene King IPA, together with a wide-ranging wine list (six by the glass). Superior snacks include Italian toasted sandwiches and a menu of above-average ambition and range, plus blackboard specials. Children are welcome throughout the pub and garden.

Open *summer Mon to Fri 11 to 3, 6 to 11, Sat 11.30 to 11, Sun 12 to 10.30; winter Mon 6 to 11, Tue to Sat 11 to 3, 6 to 11, Sun 12 to 10.30*

PAGLESHAM

Essex   map 3

Plough & Sail

East End, Paglesham SS4 2EQ
Tel: (01702) 258242
off B1013, 4m E of Rochford
In a peaceful location just a short stroll from the River Roach, this 400-year-old weatherboarded pub is full of character and interest. The blackboard menu features fresh fish and seafood; try the oysters from nearby beds at West Mersea and wash them down with a pint of Greene King IPA. The spacious garden areas – one with an aviary, the other with a tree house and swing – are great for families with children.

Open *11.30 to 3 (3.30 Sat), 7 to 11, Sun 12 to 3, 7 to 10.30*

PEACEMARSH

Dorset   map 2

Dolphin Inn

Peacemarsh SP8 4HB
Tel: (01747) 822758
on B3092, just N out of Gillingham
Formerly a farmhouse, this creeper-clad building is now a popular watering hole among the tourists exploring the Stour Valley and the north Dorset countryside. Well-kept Hall & Woodhouse real ales, Inch's cider and a choice of eight wines by the glass can be ordered to accompany something from the extensive menu. There is a garden and patio for summer al fresco sipping.

Open *11 to 3, 6 to 11, Sun 12 to 10.30*

PELDON

Essex   map 3

Peldon Rose

Mersea Road, Peldon CO5 7QJ
Tel: (01206) 735248
off B1025, 5m S of Colchester
This fourteenth-century inn with its higgledy-piggledy floors and doors affords fine views of the Pyefleet Channel and Essex saltmarshes from its garden. You can feast on smoked salmon pâté or herring roes on toast, followed by chicken breast in filo, or

one of the fish specials. Chocolate tart or vanilla cheesecake await at meal's end. Flowers IPA and Adnams Best Bitter are on draught, and there is a list of nearly 30 wines.

Open *11 to 11, Sun 12 to 10.30*

PELYNT

Cornwall · map 1

Jubilee Inn

Pelynt PL13 2JZ
TEL: (01503) 220312

on B3359, 3m NW of Looe

This white-painted sixteenth-century pub was renamed to commemorate the fiftieth year of Queen Victoria's reign, and the décor celebrates that period. Bar food is available throughout opening hours. Bass is one of the well-kept regular real ales, perhaps alongside local St Austell Daylight Robbery. There are 11 *en suite* rooms.

Open *Mon to Fri 11 to 3.30, 5.30 to 11, Sat and Sun 12 to 11*

PENELEWEY

Cornwall · map 1

Punch Bowl & Ladle

Penelewey TR3 6QY
TEL: (01872) 862237

from A39 3m S of Truro, take B3289 towards King Harry Ferry

Formerly a courthouse and a meeting place for Customs and Excise men, this rambling fifteenth-century thatched and rose-covered cottage is a handy pit stop for Trelissick Gardens (NT), nearby beaches and the King Harry Ferry. Inside is a charming series of interconnecting, low-beamed rooms with open fires, sofas and easy chairs, and a collection of rural bygones. Real ales range from Bass and Courage Directors to Sharp's Own and Doom Bar Bitter from Wadebridge.

Open *11.30 (12 Sun) to 3, 5.30 to 11 (10.30 Sun); open all day late July to mid-Sept*

PIERCEBRIDGE

Co Durham · map 10

George Hotel

Piercebridge DL2 3SW
TEL: (01325) 374576

just off A67, 5m W of Darlington

Handsome sixteenth-century coaching inn delightfully situated by the bridge over the River Tees. Two brothers who died at the George, and their grandfather clock which stopped at the same moment, prompted an 1850s American lyricist to pen a well-known song. The clock still stands in the civilised and comfortable bars. New owners offer Adnams Broadside and Timothy Taylor Landlord on handpump, a choice of around 30 wines, and a good range of food. Children are welcome throughout, and accommodation is available.

Open *11 to 11 (10.30 Sun)*

PILLATON

Cornwall · map 1

Weary Friar

Pillaton PL12 6QS
TEL: (01579) 350238

2m W of A38, between Saltash and Callington

This twelfth-century inn, adjacent to the village church (like many, the inn was built to house the church's builders), is set deep in the winding country lanes of South Cornwall. A wide selection of real ales includes Wadworth 6X, Sharp's Doom Bar and Butcombe Bitter, and four wines are available by the glass. Children are welcome if dining. The pub has a garden and a no-smoking area, plus 12 rooms for B&B.

Open *11.30 to 3.30, 6.30 to 11, Sun 12 to 3, 7 to 10.30*

PILSLEY

Derbyshire · map 8

Devonshire Arms

Pilsley DE45 1UL
TEL: (01246) 583258

off B6048, 2m NE of Bakewell

Visitors to Chatsworth House and walkers exploring the network of paths that criss-cross the vast estate will find this seventeenth-century, stone-built village pub a useful refreshment stop, especially as it's only a mile from the big house. Expect an unspoilt interior, good-quality beers from Mansfield and Camerons, and a friendly atmosphere. Changing blackboard menus list hearty pub food.

Open *11 to 2.30, 7 to 11, Sun 12 to 3, 7 to 10.30*

PITTON

Wiltshire   map 2

Silver Plough

White Hill, Pitton SP5 1DZ
TEL: (01722) 712266
on A30, 5m E of Salisbury
The skittle alley at the back of this attractive village pub does not mean it's a centre of local pub sports, as it is more of an agreeable diversion for visitors. Badger Best and Tanglefoot are the regular ales, the guest might be King & Barnes Sussex, and of 40 odd wines listed, seven are offered by the glass. Also available by the glass are 15 fruit wines. Food is served in both bar and restaurant.

Open *11 to 3, 6 to 11, Sun 12 to 3, 6 to 10.30*

PLUMLEY

Cheshire   map 7

Smoker

Plumley WA16 0TY
TEL: (01565) 722338
off A566, 3m SW of Knutsford
Smoker was a white charger bred as a racehorse but pressed into military service when England was under threat from Napoleon. The thatched pub now bearing the animal's name actually dates from Elizabethan times. Its comfortable sofas and open fires create a welcoming atmosphere. Robinson's Best Bitter is joined by seasonal guest beers, such as Stockport Bitter, and over 30 malt whiskies are on offer together with a range of mainly French wines. As well as snacks, traditional-style meals are served.

Open *11.30 to 3, 6 to 11, Sun 12 to 10.30*

POLKERRIS

Cornwall   map 1

Rashleigh

Polkerris PL24 2TL
TEL: (01726) 813991
off A3082, 2m W of Fowey
Coast Path walkers can dive straight in to the Rashleigh, known locally as the Inn on the Beach for its magnificent setting, tucked away in a tiny cove beside an isolated beach and restored jetty. Sit on the terrace to watch the sun set dramatically over the bay, and quaff Hicks Special Draught, drawn from the barrel, Sharp's Doom Bar Bitter or one of the two or three changing guests (about 300 annually). Fifteen wines are available by the glass.

Open *summer 11 to 3, 6 to 11, winter 11.30 to 2.30, 6.30 to 11, Sun all year 12 to 3, 6 to 10.30*

POLPERRO

Cornwall   map 1

Blue Peter

Quay Road, Polperro PL13 2QZ
TEL: (01503) 272743
on A387, 3m SW of Looe
This charmingly old-fashioned pub is set into the cliff face overlooking the harbour in the idyllic fishing village of Polperro – to call the setting picturesque would not do it justice. The well-kept beers are Sharp's Doom Bar Bitter, St Austell HSD and Tinners Ale, plus changing guest ales, and Belgian Chimay; Colin Vincent's scrumpy is also available in summer. No food is served, but customers may bring their own cold food.

Open *11 to 11, Sun 12 to 10.30*

POSTBRIDGE

Devon   map 1

Warren House Inn

Postbridge PL20 6TA
TEL: (01822) 880208
on B3212, between Postbridge and Moretonhampstead
Butcombe Bitter and Badger Tanglefoot are kept as regular ales, others may include Sharp's Special or Doom Bar Bitter, Shepherd Neame Spitfire or Butcombe Gold. With your

choice enjoy magnificent views over Dartmoor from the inn, constructed in 1845 to replace one which stood opposite. Home-made soup and rabbit pie are on the bar menu, and of course clotted cream accompanies most of the desserts.

Open *summer 11 to 11; winter Mon to Fri 11 to 3, 6 to 11, Sat and Sun 11 to 11*

POYNINGS

West Sussex   map 3

Royal Oak Inn

The Street, Poynings BN45 7AQ
off A281, W of A23
This square white building covered with plants has an atmospheric beamed bar, and the place is especially appealing to families as children are welcome throughout. Ales on draught might be Old Speckled Hen, Harveys Sussex Best Bitter or Courage Directors, and the menu takes in ploughman's, steaks, prawns wrapped in filo, and poached fillet of salmon with hollandaise.

Open *11.30 to 11, Sun 12 to 10.30*

PRIORS DEAN

Hampshire   map 2

White Horse Inn

Priors Dean GU32 1DY
TEL: (01420) 588387
from Petersfield, take road signposted Steep and Froxfield for 5m, turn right at crossroads signposted East Tisted, then second right; from A32, 5m S of Alton, turn on to Steep and Froxfield road, left at crossroads, then second right
The empty iron frame where the inn sign should be gives the pub its local nickname, the Pub With No Name. Its location may seem surprisingly bleak and windswept, but inside a warm atmosphere awaits in the form of stuffed sofas, leather armchairs, candles in bottles and farm gadgets. Real ales are the magnet here, with an eclectic and impeccable range that takes in Ringwood Fortyniner and Old Thumper and Gale's HSB, among others, as well as the latter brewery's fruit-based country wines.

Open *11 to 2.30, 6 to 11, Sun 12 to 3, 7 to 10.30*

RATTERY

Devon   map 1

Church House Inn

Rattery TQ10 9LD
TEL: (01364) 642220
1m off A385, from A38 S of Ashburton, 4m W of Totnes
This is one of the oldest pubs in Britain, with some parts dating back to 1028 when it housed craftsmen building the parish church next door, and was probably also a hostel for passing monks. Inside are reminders of its past – a massive oak screen, beams and standing timbers. Good ale traditions are maintained by Greene King Abbot Ale, Marston's Pedigree and Dartmoor Best Bitter.

Open *11 to 3, 6 to 11, Sun 12 to 3, 7 to 10.30*

REEDHAM

Norfolk   map 6

Reedham Ferry Inn

Ferry Road, Reedham NR13 3HA
TEL: (01493) 700429
off B1140, 6m S of Acle
Next to the chain ferry over the River Yare, close to the Strumpshaw bird sanctuary and Steam Engine Collection, this seventeenth-century inn is remarkable for having had the same licensees since 1949. The Archers serve Woodforde's Wherry, Adnams Broadside and St Peter's Mild, plus cider, from the handpumps; wines that include mulled and sangria; and traditional bar food. Children are welcome. Behind the pub is a campsite.

Open *11 to 3 (2.30 winter), 6.30 (7 winter) to 11, Sun 12 to 3, 7 to 10.30*

RIBCHESTER

Lancashire   map 8

White Bull

Church Street, Ribchester PR3 3XP
TEL: (01254) 878303
on B6245, 5m N of Blackburn
Ribchester is a Roman village in the heart of the Ribble Valley, complete with bathhouse and a Roman museum.

After taking in the sights, stop at the White Bull for an extensive menu of traditional pub food, from salads with Lancashire cheese or half a roast chicken, to grills, chilli, fish and chips and so on. Wash it down with one of the fine real ales, such as Bobbin's Bitter and Tackler's Tipple from Three B's, or Coachman's Best from Coach House.

Open *11.30 to 3, 6.30 to 11, Sun 12 to 10.30*

RIDGEWELL

Essex   map 6

White Horse

Mill Road, Ridgewell CO9 4SG
TEL: (01440) 785532
on A604, 10m N of Halstead

Despite its plain exterior, this pub on the village's main street has a friendly atmosphere, an unusual bar counter covered in old pennies and a spacious dining room. A menu of familiar pub dishes also includes fresh fish (not every day), and the cooking is of reasonable standard. The short wine list leans towards Australia. Ales include Greene King IPA and Adnams Bitter, while jugs of Pimms and sangria are strong warm-weather sellers.

Open *11 to 3, 6 to 11, Sun 12 to 10.30*

RINGMER

East Sussex   map 3

Cock

Uckfield Road, Ringmer BN8 5RX
TEL: (01273) 812040
just off A26, 2m NE of Lewes

This is a pleasant real ale pub, with views of the South Downs. The beer range takes in Harveys Sussex Best Bitter, Fuller's London Pride, Rother Valley Spirit Level and Harveys seasonal brews. Half a dozen wines from a list of about 20 are served by the large or small glass. Food-wise, a fair selection of traditional pub standards is displayed on the blackboard in the bar. Children are welcome.

Open *11 to 3, 6 to 11, Sun 12 to 3, 7 to 10.30*

RINGSTEAD

Norfolk   map 6

Gin Trap Inn

High Street, Ringstead PE36 5JU
TEL: (01485) 525264
off A149, 2m E of Hunstanton

Situated on the Peddar's Way close to the North Norfolk coast, this beautifully maintained seventeenth-century coaching inn is a popular stop-off for walkers and tourists alike. The opened-up split-level bar has low-beamed ceilings adorned with gin traps and cartwheels, and a cosy, welcoming atmosphere. East Anglian ales take pride of place and include those from Woodforde's, Greene King, Adnams, and the specially brewed, by Woodforde's, Gin Trap Bitter. A wide range of traditional pub food is listed on blackboards, and the rear garden is a pleasant place to sit on warm days.

Open *11.30 to 3 (2.30 winter), 6.30 (7 winter and Sun) to 11*

ROBIN HOOD'S BAY

North Yorkshire   map 9

Laurel Inn

New Road,
Robin Hood's Bay YO22 4SE
TEL: (01947) 880400
at end of B1447 (off A171), 5m SE of Whitby

Standing among fishermen's cottages in this much-loved cliffside village, famed for its narrow streets and dramatic seascapes, the tall and narrow Laurel Inn is one of the tiniest pubs in Yorkshire and worth searching out after a stroll along the beach. The beamed bar, carved from solid rock, makes a good setting for sampling Theakston ales and enjoying a traditional pub game. Soup and sandwiches are available during opening hours. Self-catering flat for two people is available.

Open *12 to 11 (10.30 Sun)*

ROKE

Oxfordshire　　　　map 2

Home Sweet Home

Roke OX10 6JD
TEL: (01491) 838249

turn at the signpost 'Home Sweet Home' on B4009, between Benson and Watlington

In a tranquil setting with sheep in the neighbouring field, and an attractive beer garden enclosed by low stone walls, this thatched pub has a cosy and 'un-corporate' feeling inside too. Many come to eat, in restaurant or bar, choosing from a long printed menu plus from perhaps a dozen specials on boards. Brakspear Bitter is the single real ale, and the landlady and her staff are cheerful and helpful.

Open *11 to 3, 6 to 11, Sun 12 to 3 (sometimes later); closed 25 Dec*

ROMALDKIRK

Co Durham　　　　map 10

Kirk Inn

Romaldkirk DL12 9GD
TEL: (01833) 650260

on B6277, 6m NW of Barnard Castle

On the village green, close to splendid walking country, including the Pennine Way, the rustic Kirk Inn is a real community local. Not only is it a favoured walkers' retreat for satisfying soup, sandwiches and more substantial fare, but this tiny, one-room pub doubles as the village post office each morning and specialises in excellent real ales from independent North Country breweries. Look out for beers from the Hambleton, Black Sheep, Rudgate and York Breweries. Children are welcome.

Open *Thur to Sun 12 to 2.30 (3 Sun), all week 6 to 11*

RYE

East Sussex　　　　map 3

Mermaid Inn

Mermaid Street, Rye TN31 7EY
TEL: (01797) 223065

The cobbled streets of the Cinque Port of Rye are full of beautiful black-and-white buildings, and the Mermaid holds her own among them. Enter through imposing old doors and continue down a corridor hung with portraits of Elizabethan and Tudor greats – Sir Walter Raleigh, the Earl of Leicester and some of Henry's wives for good measure. The bar is 'seriously atmospheric', with a huge inglenook fireplace virtually taking up one wall, pikes and swords and good-quality furnishings and fabrics. The bar menu deals in tradition, not surprisingly, and you can expect steak and kidney pudding, Sussex pork sausage casserole and fish pie. Drink Old Speckled Hen or Marston's Pedigree.

Open *11 to 11, Sun 12 to 10.30*

ST AGNES

Isles of Scilly　　　　map 1

Turk's Head

St Agnes TR22 0PL
TEL: (01720) 422434

A 20-minute boat journey from St Mary's brings you to this nineteenth-century slate-roofed cottage overlooking the harbour and quay on this tiny island. Bedecked with nautical memorabilia, it is popular with wildlife watchers, who flock to the island in search of seals and seabirds. A favoured tipple here is hot chocolate laced with St Agnes brandy, while traditional beers include Dartmoor Best and Turks Ale. The straightforward menu features locally made pasties. Children are welcome. One bedroom for overnight guests.

Open *11 to 11, Sun 12 to 10.30; closed some days winter*

ST BREWARD

Cornwall　　　　map 1

Old Inn

St Breward PL30 4PP
TEL: (01208) 850711

off B3266, 4m S of Camelford

Once a staging post for smugglers hauling contraband along the north Cornish coast, the Old Inn now plies a more respectable trade. As well as jacket potatoes, all-day breakfasts and ploughman's, a specials menu offers the likes of vegetable pithiviers, seafood thermidor and a home-made boozy cheesecake that blends Bailey's and Tia

Maria. Sharp's Doom Bar Bitter and Special are among the handpumped beers, and traditional scrumpy is drawn from a barrel. Four wines are served by the glass.

Open *Mon to Thur 11 to 3, 6 to 11, Fri and Sat 11 to 11, Sun 12 to 10.30; open 11 to 11 Mon to Thur June to Sept*

ST EWE

Cornwall   map 1

Crown Inn

St Ewe PL26 6EY
TEL: (01726) 843322
between B3287 and B3273, 5m SW of St Austell
Close to the Lost Gardens of Heligan, in a village named after the local saint, the Crown is a charming flower-bedecked hostelry with a sheltered garden. This St Austell house has Tinners, Daylight Robbery and HSD on tap, plus a wide-ranging wine list. Steaks, jackets and pasta feature on the menu. Children are welcome.

Open *summer 11 to 3, 6 to 11, Sun 12 to 3, 6 to 10.30, winter 12 to 3, 6 to 11, Sun 12 to 3, 6 to 10.30*

ST JUST

Cornwall   map 1

Star Inn

Fore Street, St Just TR19 7LL
TEL: (01736) 788767
on A3071/B3306, 4m N of Land's End
The granite-built Star stands in a terrace on the narrow road through the village, and is jam-packed with atmosphere and local characters. The friendly landlady welcomes locals and visitors alike, and all might be greeted by the sound of live accordion music. Drinks are from St Austell's, with Tinners Ale straight from the barrel or HSD and XXXX mild. Food is simple and hearty: crab sandwiches and chicken and mushroom pie are typical. Accommodation is available in three rooms.

Open *11 to 11, Sun 12 to 10.30*

SCALES

Cumbria   map 10

White Horse Inn

Scales CA12 4SY
TEL: (01768) 779241
just off A66 Keswick to Penrith road, 5m NE of Keswick
The White Horse and the house next door are on a bend of the old meandering A66 before it was straightened out into a dual carriageway. That said, its elevated site makes it a haven from the traffic, and it is seemingly a must-do for fell walkers fresh from a conquest of Saddleback behind. Long, low, beamed and homely, it offers comfort food of the likes of fried black pudding in mushroom sauce, simply grilled Borrowdale trout, steak and ale pie, vegetarian butter bean casserole and, of course, Cumberland sausage, with apple pie to round things off. Jennings ales and Black Sheep Best Bitter are served, and house wines are sold by the glass.

Open *12 to 4, 6.30 to 11 (10.30 Sun)*

SHALFLEET

Isle of Wight   map 2

New Inn

Main Road, Shalfleet PO30 4NS
TEL: (01983) 531314
A few minutes from Shalfleet Creek and the Newtown estuary, the inn is a valued retreat for yachting enthusiasts, but – as the literature has it – provides 'a warm welcome for landlubbers and mariners alike'. Extensive menus list all the expected pub favourites, alongside lunchtime offerings of baguettes, ploughman's and a children's selection, but there is also an enterprising restaurant-style menu that might include gratinated crab, medallions of pork with apples, prunes and brandy, and a commendable variety of fish dishes. End with chocolate truffle délices. Wadworth 6X and Shepherd Neame are among the real ales, and ten wines are served by the glass from a pedigree list. Reports please.

Open *11 (12 winter) to 3, 6 to 11, Sun 12 to 3, 6 to 10.30*

SHAMLEY GREEN

Surrey   map 3

Red Lion Inn

Shamley Green GU5 0UB
TEL: (01483) 892202
on B2128, 4m SE of Guildford
Opposite the green itself, this is a neat
white-painted pub with up-market bar
food: for example, ricotta and spinach
tortellini with pesto, and steak and
Murphy's pie, followed by raspberry
crème brûlée. There is a separate
restaurant. Marston's Pedigree and
Young's ales are regular beers, with
Adnams Broadside an occasional guest,
and six of the 28 wines listed are
available by the glass. Open for
breakfast.
Open *Mon to Fri 7am to 11pm, Sat
8am to 11pm, Sun 8am to 10.30pm*

SHARDLOW

Derbyshire   map 5

Malt Shovel

The Wharf, Shardlow DE72 2HG
TEL: (01332) 799763
off A6, 6m SE of Derby
Situated on the banks of the Trent &
Mersey Canal, the Malt Shovel, as its
name implies, is part of a converted
and greatly extended eighteenth-
century maltings. A terrace filled with
seating overlooks the waterway and
regularly plays host to summertime
Morris dancers, jazz musicians and a
theatre company. Expect Marston's
Pedigree and Banks's Bitter on
handpump; straightforward pub food is
served lunchtimes only. Children are
welcome throughout the pub.
Open *11 to 11, Sun 12 to 10.30;
closed evening 25 Dec*

SHEEPSCOMBE

Gloucestershire   map 2

Butchers Arms

Sheepscombe GL6 7RH
TEL: (01452) 812113
In summer, order a pint of Hook
Norton Best Bitter from the bar of this
seventeenth-century mellow-stone pub
at the heart of *Cider with Rosie*
country, then sit on the steeply sloping
lawn and marvel at the glorious views
over the rolling Stroud Valley. Log fires
warm the character bars in winter, and
the interesting range of food includes
home-cooked daily specials.
Open *11.30 to 3, 6 (6.30 winter) to
11, Sun 12 to 4, 7 to 10.30*

SHEEPWASH

Devon   map 1

Half Moon Inn

Sheepwash EX21 5NE
TEL: (01409) 231376
off A3072, 4m W of Hatherleigh
With ten miles of fishing rights on the
nearby River Torridge, this long,
white-painted village inn attracts
fishermen eager to cast a line for
salmon and sea and brown trout.
Facilities include a rod room, tackle
shop and personal tuition. The classic,
slate-floored main bar has a huge
inglenook, Ruddles, Courage and
Marston's ales on draught, a 200-
strong wine list, and an impressive
selection of malt whiskies. Simple
lunchtime snacks in the bar; set-price
restaurant dinners. Fourteen *en suite*
bedrooms.
Open *11.30 to 2.30, 6 to 11, Sun 12
to 2.30, 7 to 10.30*

SHENINGTON

Oxfordshire   map 5

Bell

Shennington OX15 6NQ
TEL: (01295) 670274
off A422, 6m W of Banbury
Fronting a three-acre green in a sleepy
Oxfordshire village, this cottagey,
stone-built pub dates from the
seventeenth century and is very much
at the heart of village life. The lively
locals' bar serves a tip-top pint of Hook
Norton Best, and a snug and
welcoming lounge/restaurant area is the
setting for a good choice of freshly
prepared food. Look out for hearty
soups and casseroles, and home-made
puddings such as treacle tart.
Accommodation is available in three
letting bedrooms.
Open *12 to 2.30, 6.30 to 11, Sun 12
to 3, 7 to 10.30; closed Mon lunchtime
Jan and Feb, evening 25 Dec*

SHIPTON-UNDER-WYCHWOOD

Oxfordshire   map 5

Shaven Crown Hotel

High Street,
Shipton-under-Wychwood OX7 6BA
TEL: (01993) 830330
on A361, 4m NE of Burford
Built in the fourteenth century of
honey-coloured stone, this hotel, now
part of a chain, was formerly a monks'
hospice. It retains several original
features, including the medieval hall
now used as a residents' lounge. Stables
have been converted into a small bar.
Together with Addlestone's cider, the
pub serves beers from Hook Norton,
alongside Old Speckled Hen and
Greene King Abbot ale. Food is
described on a jokey laminated menu
focusing on traditional British fare.
Open *11 to 2.30, 5 to 11*

SHRALEYBROOK

Staffordshire   map 5

Rising Sun

Knowle Bank Road,
Shraleybrook ST7 8DS
TEL: (01782) 720600
The Shraley Brook Brewery is based
here, producing three beers with
recipes devised by a group of local real
ale enthusiasts and named on a Civil
War theme. These are joined by several
other real ales, such as Wells
Bombardier Premium Bitter or Young's
Special. Bar food is straightforward
stuff; as well as omelettes, burgers,
salads and various pizzas are main
courses such as venison in red wine,
chicken Kiev, or salmon in asparagus
sauce. Vegetarians have their own
better-than-average menu.
Open *Mon to Thur 6 to 11, Fri to Sun
11.45 to 11 (10.30 Sun)*

SHUSTOKE

Warwickshire   map 5

Griffin

Shustoke B46 2LB
TEL: (01675) 481205
on B4114, 2½m E of Coleshill
This oak-framed former coaching inn
dates from the early seventeenth
century. One previous landlord used to
make coffins here – the churchyard is
next door – and the old coffin shop is
now Church End Brewery. Its range of
real ales is sold in the bar together with
scrumpy (in summer) and an extensive
selection of wines (30 by the glass).
The short menu concentrates on snacks
and grills. Children are welcome in the
conservatory.
Open *12 to 2.30, 7 to 11, Sun 12 to
2.30, 7 to 10.30*

SLEDMERE

East Riding of Yorkshire   map 9

Triton Inn

Sledmere YO25 3XQ
TEL: (01377) 236644
village on B1253 16m W of Bridlington
Sledmere House, in 2,000 acres laid out
by Capability Brown, contains
remarkable antique furniture and a
room which is a copy of a sultan's
apartments in Istanbul. The Triton was
built in the mid-eighteenth century as
the coach house just within the grounds.
The bar menu runs to lemon chicken,
and the hot beef baguette has been
recommended. On draught are Tetley,
John Smith's Bitter and Theakston ales.
Open *Mon to Sat (exc Mon lunchtime)
11.30 to 2.30, 7 to 11.30, Sun 12 to 3,
7.30 to 10.30*

SMART'S HILL

Kent   map 3

Spotted Dog Inn

Smart's Hill TN11 8EE
TEL: (01892) 870253
off B2188, 1m S of Penshurst
Close to picturesque Chiddingstone
and Penshurst Place, this
weatherboarded inn dating from 1520
is the haunt of walkers and locals alike.
Approach the entrance via a pretty
cottage garden to find an interior with
low ceilings and quarry-tiled or oak-
boarded floors; from the rear of the
pub are wonderful views across the
valley. Adnams and Greene King ales
are available, together with eight or so
wines by the glass. The pub is under
new management; reports please.
Open *11.45 to 2.15, 6 to 11, Sun 12
to 10.30*

SNAPE

Suffolk　　　　　　　　　　　map 6

Golden Key

Priory Road, Snape IP17 1SG
TEL: (01728) 688510

just off B1069, 3m S of Saxmundham

The nearby Snape Maltings makes not
beer but music during the Aldeburgh
Festival. At the Golden Key the beer is
Adnams Best Bitter and Fisherman, as
well as Tally Ho at Christmas. Adnams
supply the wines too, and six are
offered by the glass. The menu might
include Stilton and mushroom royale,
grilled sardines, steak and Guinness pie
and seasonal fish and game. Home-
made puddings might run to chocolate
brandy cake.

Open *11 to 3, 6 to 11 (7 to 10.30 Sun)*

SOUTH WOODCHESTER

Gloucestershire　　　　　　　map 2

Ram Inn

Station Road,
South Woodchester GL5 5EL
TEL: (01453) 873329

off A46, 2m S of Stroud

Don't be surprised to see bunting if
you're passing through South
Woodchester in 2001: the Ram is
celebrating its 400th birthday. If you
feel like joining in the festivity, pop in
for some hearty pub cooking of the
likes of steak, gammon, grilled fish or a
curry, preceded perhaps by Greek
salad, and rounded off by banoffi pie,
or crème brûlée. It might be enjoyed
with a pint of an ale from Wychwood
or Wickwar or some guest beer, or a
glass of one of the Australian house
wines.

Open *11 to 11 (10.30 Sun)*

SOUTH ZEAL

Devon　　　　　　　　　　　map 1

Oxenham Arms

South Zeal EX20 2JT
TEL: (01837) 840244

off A30, 4m E of Okehampton

Twelfth-century lay monks probably
built parts of this magnificent stone
edifice, incorporating a prehistoric
monolith now set in a wall. Other
features are a granite fireplace in the
lounge and a granite pillar supporting a
beam in the dining room. Contemplate
these and more while drinking one of
three ales drawn straight from the cask:
Princetown Dartmoor IPA or Jail Ale,
or Sharp's Will's Resolve.

Open *11 to 2.30, 6 to 11, Sun 12 to
2.30, 7 to 10.30*

SPELDHURST

Kent　　　　　　　　　　　　map 3

George & Dragon

Speldhurst TN3 0NN
TEL: (01892) 863125

*between A26 and A264, 2m NW of
Tunbridge Wells*

Set back from the village lane, this
magnificent black and white timbered
inn dates from 1213 and is reckoned to
be one of the oldest in southern
England. Judging by the massive
flagstones, heavy carved ceiling beams,
ancient wall panelling and huge
inglenook in the main bar, the claim is
probably true. A good range of real ales
includes local Harveys Sussex Best and
Larkins Traditional. Bar food is
modern – crispy duck or braised lamb
shank, for example – and a separate
restaurant is open Friday and Saturday
evenings and Sunday lunch. Reports
please.

Open *11 to 11, Sun 12 to 10.30*

SPREYTON

Devon　　　　　　　　　　　map 1

Tom Cobley Tavern

Spreyton EX17 5AL
TEL: (01647) 231314

*off B3219 (from A30), 7m E of
Okehampton*

This 400-year-old inn is located on the
northern edge of Dartmoor and is
popular with tourists. Cotleigh Tawny
is joined by various guest beers, and
there's a short, eclectic wine list.
Advance bookings are requested for the
restaurant, where the menu majors on
pies, lasagne and steak; home-made
pies (with chips) also feature among
bar snacks. B&B is also available (four
rooms). Children can use the garden
and games room.

Open *12 to 2, 6 to 11, Sun 12 to 3, 7
to 10.30*

SPROTBROUGH

South Yorkshire   map 9

Boat Inn

Nursery Lane,
Sprotbrough DN5 7NB
TEL: (01302) 857188
just off A1(M), 3m W of Doncaster
The riverside location of this Don
valley pub, with pleasant walks
upstream to a nature reserve, exerts a
strong appeal. Once a farmhouse, it
now offers John Smith's, Courage
Directors and Theakston ales on tap, a
wine list representing both Old and
New Worlds, and simple home-cooked
meals. It also has a garden.
Open *summer 11 to 11, winter 11 to
3, 6 to 11, Sun all year 12 to 10.30*

STAPLE FITZPAINE

Somerset   map 2

Greyhound Inn

Staple Fitzpaine TA3 5SP
TEL: (01823) 480227
*between A358 and B3170, 5m SE of
Taunton*
New owners had just taken over this
rambling, creeper-clad inn as the Guide
went to press. Built in 1640 as a hunting
lodge for the local lord, it enjoys a
peaceful rural location amid rolling
countryside close to the Blackdown
Hills. The front rooms are full of
character, with stone walls, flagstones
and open fires; the spacious dining area
is in a modern rear extension. The
changing real ales might be Bass,
Batemans and from Oakhill Brewery.
Overnight accommodation is available
in four bedrooms. Reports please.
Open *summer 11 to 11, winter 12 to
3, 6 (5 Fri and Sat) to 11, Sun all year
12 to 3, 7 to 10.30*

STEEPLE ASTON

Oxfordshire   map 5

Red Lion

South Street,
Steeple Aston OX25 4RY
TEL: (01869) 340225
*just off A4260, or B4030, 4m S of
Deddington*
Several local villages are called Aston,
and there is another lion (although

white) in this one, so don't be
confused. The bar menu in the Red
Lion takes in a wide variety of fare,
from sandwiches to game hotpot in
season. The regular ale is Hook
Norton Best Bitter, and the guest
might be Shepherd Neame Spitfire
Premium Ale. Over 100 hundred
wines are stocked, with four offered
by the glass.
Open *11 to 3, 6 to 11, Sun 12 to 3, 7
to 10.30*

STEYNING

West Sussex   map 3

Star Inn

130 High Street,
Steyning BN44 3RD
TEL: (01903) 813078
*just off A283, 5m NW of Shoreham-by-
Sea*
The village has a local museum, a
twelfth-century church, but goes back
even further to an old Saxon cottage
sometimes open to visitors. It also has
this pleasant, child-friendly pub with a
playroom and a safely fenced-off play
garden complete with climbing frame,
slide and picnic tables. The five regular
draught ales are Fuller's London Pride,
Young's Special and Bitter, Badger
Sussex, and Wadworth 6X. Bar food is
along the lines of lasagne and steak and
kidney pie.
Open *Mon to Fri 11 to 2.30 (3 Fri),
5.30 to 11, Sat 11 to 11, Sun 12 to
3.30, 7 to 10.30*

STOKE BRUERNE

Northamptonshire   map 5

Boat Inn

Stoke Bruerne NN12 7SB
TEL: (01604) 862424
just W of A508, 4m E of Towcester
In a prime location beside the Grand
Union Canal, opposite the fascinating
Canal Museum, this much-extended
seventeenth-century thatched inn is a
popular destination for families and
narrowboat enthusiasts. Owned and
run by the Woodward family since
1877, they can arrange boat trips as
well as serve food all day. Six real ales
are on handpump, there is a

characterful flagstoned bar, and a no-smoking room. Children are welcome.
Open *9am (9.30am winter) to 11pm (10.30pm Sun); closed 3pm to 6pm Mon to Thur winter*

STOKE FLEMING

Devon   map 1

Green Dragon

Church Road,
Stoke Fleming TQ6 0PX
TEL: (01803) 770238
take A379 S from Dartmouth
Opposite the church, this informal village pub is run by long-distance yachtsman Peter Crowther, and cuttings about his exploits adorn the walls in the bar. Unsurprisingly, a nautical theme pervades the entire pub – the dining area, for example, is called the Mess Deck – but the menu is more than just fish: alongside kiln-roasted salmon or seafood chowder might be Moroccan lamb, Italian meatloaf, or local sausages with mash. Four real ales are provided and eight wines by the glass.
Open *11 to 3, 5.30 to 11, Sun 12 to 3, 6.30 to 10.30*

STOUGHTON

West Sussex   map 3

Hare and Hounds

Stoughton PO18 9JQ
TEL: (023) 9263 1433
off B2147 at Walderton, 5m NW of Chichester
This 300-year-old brick-and-flint inn was originally two cottages and became a pub only about 80 years ago. It is hidden away in downland, with excellent walking, lovely views and Kingley Vale Nature Reserve nearby. Inside, the three knocked-through rooms feature plenty of exposed brick and several fireplaces. Supplementing the printed list of standard pub fare is a daily-changing blackboard list of things like rabbit casserole and pasta with spicy tomato sauce. Six real ales are always available, including Taylor Landlord, Bass and Gale's HSB, and the wine list includes eight by the glass.
Open *Mon to Thur 11 to 3, 6 to 11, Fri to Sun 11 to 11*

STRINESDALE

Greater Manchester   map 8

Roebuck Inn

Strinesdale OL4 3RB
TEL: (0161) 624 7819
from Oldham take A62 Huddersfield road, then left on to A672 Ripponden road, then right after 1m on to Turf Pit Lane; follow for 1m
Set in open country just outside Oldham, climbing towards the moors, the Roebuck is a cosy village pub with walls of exposed stone, and comfortable banquette seating in a separate dining room, although food may also be eaten in the bar. Plenty of seafood is in evidence among starters, while mains bring on the likes of steaks, chilli con carne, pies, and specialities such as duck or veal. Marston's Pedigree and Boddingtons Bitter are on handpump, and there are seven wines by the glass.
Open *12 to 3, 5 to 11, Sun 12 to 10.30*

SUSWORTH

Lincolnshire   map 9

Jenny Wren

East Ferry Road,
Susworth DN17 3AS
TEL: (01724) 784000
off A519, 3m W of Scotter
Open log fires and a large beer garden by the river are two of the attractions of this picturesque early-eighteenth-century inn. In addition to John Smith's, Old Speckled Hen and Marston's Pedigree on tap there is a selection of New World and European wines. The printed menu and daily-changing blackboard offer traditional fare. Children welcome in family room and garden.
Open *12 to 3, 5.30 to 11 (10.30 Sun)*

TEMPLE GRAFTON

Warwickshire   map 5

Blue Boar

Temple Grafton B49 6NR
TEL: (01789) 750010
off A46, 3m W of Stratford-upon-Avon
This creeper-covered seventeenth-century inn is close to where William Shakespeare was married. Red

patterned carpet, window seats, open fires and exposed stone set the scene inside. In summer, enjoy a drink on the flower-decked patio. Hook Norton Best, Theakston XB and Old Speckled Hen are supplemented by a weekly-changing guest beer, and seven wines from the extensive list are available by the glass. Food is standard bar fare. B&B provided in 15 rooms.

Open *11.30 to 12, Sun 12 to 11.30*

TESTCOMBE

Hampshire   map 2

Mayfly

Testcombe SO20 6AX
TEL: (01264) 860283
on A3057, between Stockbridge and Andover, by River Test
This lovely riverside pub, built of honey-coloured brick and framed by decorative white gables, is especially attractive in summer when you can sit in the garden watching the ducks and swans swim past. The interior has various eating and drinking areas with wooden tables and chairs, plus open fires in winter. Ales are Flowers Original, Wadworth 6X, Old Speckled Hen and Boddingtons, and a generous selection of wines by the glass is also offered.

Open *10 to 11, Sun 12 to 10.30*

THOMPSON

Norfolk   map 6

Chequers Inn

Griston Road, Thompson IP24 1PX
TEL: (01953) 483360
1m off A1075, 3m S of Watton
This pretty sixteenth-century thatched pub, festooned with colourful hanging baskets, offers a lengthy menu of mostly standard pub fare, from prawn cocktail to chicken tikka masala, as well as some less standard dishes like scallops wrapped in bacon with tomato and garlic sauce. More interesting is the blackboard of daily specials, which feature plenty of local game in season (pheasant and partridge, for example). Beers are from Adnams, Fuller's and Greene King, with occasional guests.

Open *11.30 to 2.30, 6.30 to 11, Sun 12 to 3, 7 to 10.30*

THREE LEGGED CROSS

East Sussex   map 3

Bull

Dunster Mill Lane,
Three Legged Cross TN5 7HH
TEL: (01580) 200586
take Three Legged Cross road signposted in centre of Ticehurst, off B2099
A typical Sussex pub, built of brick and hung with tiles, the Bull is in a peaceful and attractive location at the junction of two lanes, with a large lawn in front and excellent views to the rear. Colourful love birds can be seen in the wooden aviary. Inside the pub are old brick floors, a large open fire and dried hops on the beams. Real ales include examples from local breweries Harveys and Rother Valley; five wines are available by the glass. The menu offers standard pub fare and blackboard specials. There is a large children's play area and the inn offers B&B.

Open *11 to 11, Sun 12 to 10.30*

THURGARTON

Nottinghamshire   map 5

Red Lion

Southwell Road,
Thurgarton NG14 7GP
TEL: (01636) 830351
on A612, 3m S of Southwell
Scene of a gruesome murder in 1936, this sixteenth-century village inn began life as an alehouse for the monks of Thurgarton Priory. Today's customers are less ecclesiastical, and those not put off by the lurid framed newspaper account of the murder will find well-kept real ales to sup, including Courage Directors and Ruddles Best Bitter, and straightforward pub food (served all day at weekends). Children are welcome throughout the pub.

Open *Mon to Fri 11.30 to 2.30, 6.30 to 11, Sat 11.30 to 11, Sun 12 to 10.30*

TICHBORNE

Hampshire   map 2

Tichborne Arms

Tichborne SO24 0NA
TEL: (01962) 733760
off A31 or B3046, 2m SW of Alresford
Ringwood Best and four changing guest
ales are served from the cask at this
heavily thatched, red-brick pub set in a
tranquil rural hamlet in the Itchen
valley. It was rebuilt in 1939 after fire
destroyed the original thatched
building. Seek it out in summer for the
splendid, flower-filled rear garden.
Village photographs and documents
relating to the famous Tichborne
Claimant court case adorn one of the
bars. Excellent local walks.
Open *11.30 to 2.30, 6 to 11, Sun 12
to 3, 7 to 10.30; closed 25 and 26 Dec*

TIVETSHALL ST MARY

Norfolk   map 6

Old Ram Coaching Inn

Ipswich Road,
Tivetshall St Mary NR15 2DE
TEL: (01379) 676794
on A140, S of Norwich
This sympathetically restored
seventeenth-century coaching inn
provides comfortable accommodation
and food all day to travellers using the
A140 between Norwich and Ipswich.
The spacious and well-maintained
interior features standing timbers, brick
floors, pine furnishings, wood-burning
stoves and old farming implements.
Children are welcome throughout. A
good range of wines is available by the
glass, and ales on handpump include
Adnams Bitter, Bass, and Hancocks
HB. A long, laminated menu and daily
specials are offered, with breakfast
served from 7.30am.
Open *11 to 11, Sun 12 to 10.30
(breakfast from 7.30); closed 25 and 26
Dec*

TOLLARD ROYAL

Wiltshire   map 2

King John Inn

Tollard Royal SP5 5PS
TEL: (01725) 516207
*on B3081 (off A354), 14m SW of
Salisbury*
Built in 1859 to house the workforce
of the village's iron foundry, this
unpretentious inn in picturesque
Tollard Royal is well placed for walkers
exploring the ancient forests nearby.
Two guest ales complement the
Ringwood Best, Wadworth 6X and
Wells Bombardier, and Stowford Press
cider is also on draught. Both snacks
and a full menu are available. Children
are welcome.
Open *12 (11 Sat) to 2.30, 6.30 to 11,
Sun 12 to 2.30, 7 to 10.30*

TOOT HILL

Essex   map 3

Green Man

Toot Hill CM5 9SD
TEL: (01992) 522255
*off A414, between North Weald and
Chipping Ongar*
Refurbished Victorian coaching inn set
down narrow lanes in rolling Essex
countryside between Epping and Ongar.
Wines from a comprehensive 100-bin
list, and four real ales on handpump,
including Fuller's London Pride and
Young's Bitter, can be enjoyed with food
from an extensive menu, served in the
two restaurant areas. A meal might start
with king prawns in garlic butter, then
perhaps lamb cutlets and finish with jam
roly-poly. An award-winning floral
courtyard is a great place for summer
imbibing.
Open *11 to 3, 6 to 11, Sun 12 to 4, 7
to 10.30*

TOPSHAM

Devon   map 1

Bridge

Topsham EX3 0QQ
TEL: (01392) 873862
Topsham's village museum is devoted
to the ecology of the Exe estuary and
the history of shipbuilding. This pub is
mainly sixteenth century, but the

original building goes back another half a millennium. Up to ten locally brewed real ales, drawn straight from barrels, might include Branscombe Vale Bitter, Exmoor Valley, Black Autumn, and One-0-One, specially brewed for the Queen's visit when the Bridge celebrated 101 years of the same family's ownership.

Open *12 to 2.30, 6 to 10.30 (11 Fri and Sat); closed evenings 25 and 26 Dec and 1 Jan*

TREGADILLETT

Cornwall   map 1

Eliot Arms

Tregadillett PL15 7EU
TEL: (01566) 772051
off A30, 2m W of Launceston
Also known as the Square & Compass, this creeper-covered inn was built in 1625, modernised in 1840, and features a rambling series of five, softly lit little rooms with rug-strewn slate floors and an assortment of old furnishings. Much to entertain the eye includes splendid collections of clocks, old paintings and postcards, over 400 snuffboxes, and a host of other memorabilia. Good real ales and wines by the glass. Extensive menus. Overnight accommodation.

Open *11 to 3, 6 to 11*

TRESCO

Isles of Scilly   map 1

New Inn

Tresco TR24 0QQ
TEL: (01720) 422844
Very much geared to holidaymakers visiting this lovely car-free island (take the ferry or helicopter from Penzance), the New Inn makes a good base for exploring. Real ales are from mainland Cornish brewers Skinner's and St Austell; Hoegaarden wheat beer is also available, together with draught cider, 20 malt whiskies and 50 wines (seven by the glass). Bar snacks and restaurant menus feature local fish and cheese. The hotel has 14 guest rooms.

Open *summer 11 to 11, Sun 12 to 10.30; winter 11 to 3, 6 to 11, Sun 12 to 3, 6 to 10.30*

TRUDOXHILL

Somerset   map 2

White Hart

Trudoxhill BA11 5DP
TEL: (01373) 836324
1m off A361 Frome to Shepton Mallet road
Although the splendid Ash Vine ales are now brewed in nearby Frome, this creeper-clad, 300-year-old coaching inn continues to serve them on handpump, in addition to Bass, Wadworth 6X, farm cider and a mind-boggling choice of Gale's fruit wines. The long, opened-out bar has beams, two real fires and a relaxed atmosphere, and a wide choice of straightforward pub food is served. There is a sheltered side garden, and children are welcome.

Open *Mon to Thur 12 to 3.30, 5.30 to 11, Fri and Sat 11 to 11, Sun 12 to 10.30; closed lunchtime 26 Dec*

TURVEY

Bedfordshire   map 6

Three Cranes

High Street, Turvey MK43 8EP
TEL: (01234) 881305
on A428, 7m W of Bedford
This 300-year-old stone pub was renovated by the Victorians, and stands in a pretty village, adjacent to the parish church and close to an interesting abbey. A neat, open-plan bar is adorned with books, prints, plates and china. Real ales include Hook Norton Best, Fuller's London Pride and Courage Directors, with 12 wines also available by the glass. The varied menu is enhanced by blackboard specials. Overnight accommodation available in three *en suite* bedrooms.

Open *11 to 2.30, 6 to 11, Sun 12 to 3, 7 to 10.30*

VENTNOR

Isle of Wight   map 2

Spyglass Inn

The Esplanade, Ventnor PO38 1JX
TEL: (01983) 855338
The setting could not be better for this island favourite. With a terraced seating area stretching right to the sea

wall, it is the perfect spot in which to soak up the stunning views across the bay. On stormy days, watch the sea break over the wall from the enclosed verandah, or relax in one of five interconnecting rooms crammed full of nautical artefacts and memorabilia. Badger Best and Tanglefoot, Ventnor Golden and guest beers are on tap. Regular live music. Families are welcome.

Open *10.30 to 11, Sun 12 to 10.30; closed weekday afternoons Nov to Mar*

WARBLETON

East Sussex   map 3

War-Bill-in-Tun

Warbleton TN21 9BD
Tel: (01435) 830636
off B2096, S of Punnett's Town
The inn's name may be a play on the village's name or may refer to civil war events. Vegetarians will find stuffed mushrooms, nut roast and vegetable bake on the menu, and omnivores also have a wide choice, from lamb chops or steaks to poached salmon. On draught are Harveys Winter Ale and own-brew Ironmaster and Warbleton Special Bitter.

Open *11 to 3, 6.30 to 11, Sun 12 to 3, 7 to 10.30; closed evenings 25, 26 Dec and 1 Jan*

WASDALE HEAD

Cumbria   map 8

Wasdale Head Inn

Wasdale Head CA20 1EX
Tel: (019467) 26229
off A595, between Gosforth and Holmbrook; follow signs for 8m
In a remote, unspoilt part of Lakeland, this haven for ramblers, walkers and climbers has a bar named after the first landlord, the 'world's biggest liar', and a garden with beck-side tables. The beer policy is to stock only Cumbrian-brewed ales. Between six to eight at any one time come from brewers such as Jennings, Yates and Hesket Newmarket. For Europhiles they keep Hoegaarden and a selection of Belgian and German fruit wines.

Open *11 to 10.30 (11 Fri), Sun 12 to 10*

WATLINGTON

Oxfordshire   map 2

Chequers

Love Lane, Watlington OX9 5RA
Tel: (01491) 612874
take B4009 from M40 junction 6 and turn right down Love Lane just before Watlington, signposted Icknield School
Watlington, in the Chilterns, is a useful retreat from the M40, especially the garden and vine-decked conservatory of this old pub. The latter is one of the eating areas for bar food that runs from sandwiches and jacket potatoes to roast duck or Dover sole. This Brakspear house keeps the brewery's Bitter and Special, plus seasonal ales.

Open *12 to 2.30, 6 to 11, Sun 12 to 3, 7 to 10.30; closed evenings 25 and 26 Dec*

WELL

Hampshire   map 2

Chequers Inn

Well RG29 1PL
Tel: (01256) 862605
off A31, 5m W of Farnham
Lost down lanes in the heart of rolling Hampshire countryside, yet within easy reach of the M3 and Basingstoke, this seventeenth-century pub is the perfect rural retreat. Traditional in style, with beams, bare board floors, old scrubbed pine tables and an open log fire, the bar is supplemented in summer by a Continental-style seating area in front of the pub, beneath an amazing vine-covered pergola. The peaceful rear garden overlooking farmland and Badger ales on tap also help draw the crowds. The same menu is served throughout the pub.

Open *Mon to Fri 12 to 3, 6 to 11, Sat 11 to 11, Sun 12 to 10.30*

WEST HUNTSPILL

Somerset   map 2

Crossways Inn

Withy Road,
West Huntspill TA9 3RA
Tel: (01278) 783756
on A38, 3m S of Burnham-on-Sea
There's a breezy ambience in this haven of real ale amid the watery Somerset

Levels. The three regular ales are Thomas Hardy Royal Oak and Flowers Original and IPA, while three guests might include Cotleigh Barn Owl Bitter, Tisbury Fanfare, Adnams Broadside or Palmers 200. Six wines from the short list are offered by the glass.

Open *11 to 3, 5.30 to 11 (7 to 10.30 Sun)*

WEST TANFIELD

North Yorkshire   map 9

Bull Inn

Church Street,
West Tanfield HG4 5JQ
TEL: (01677) 470678
on A6108 Ripon to Masham road
This pleasant seventeenth-century village pub stands beside the River Ure on the edge of the Yorkshire Dales. The lovely riverside garden is a popular retreat for families on warmer days. Hand-pulled local Black Sheep Bitter and Riggwelter are served in the open-plan bar, and accommodation in five bedrooms is available. Bar food ranges from home-made soups, lasagne and chilli to lamb cutlets with redcurrant and rosemary.

Open *11 to 11, Sun 12 to 10.30*

WHALTON

Northumberland   map 10

Beresford Arms

Whalton NE61 3UZ
TEL: (01670) 775225
on B6524 from Morpeth
This very attractive nineteenth-century stone building stands in a country village of mainly Georgian houses. Family-run, it attracts a mature lunchtime clientele in the bar and comfortably furnished restaurant. The long menu takes in chef's special salads, Cumberland sausage with black pudding, and Asian-influenced chicken and duck dishes. There are no real ales, but Woodpecker and Strongbow cider are on draught and four wines are served by the glass.

Open *11 to 3, 6 to 11; closed Nov, Sun evening winter*

WHITTLESFORD

Cambridgeshire   map 6

Tickell Arms

1 North Road,
Whittlesford CB2 4NZ
TEL: (01223) 833128
off A505, or M11 junction 6, 7m S of Cambridge
The décor inside this blue and white inn that hides behind a narrow gateway is as idiosyncratic as the name, looking as it does like the result of much productive rummaging in antique shops. A conservatory extension gives views on to a charming sheltered garden with pond and fountain. Beers from Adnams and Greene King Abbot Ale are on handpump, and ten wines are offered by the glass. With these, you may eat the likes of seafood gratiné, pheasant pie, stuffed duck leg, or Moroccan lamb, with crème brûlée or chestnut meringue to finish.

Open *Tue to Sat 11 to 2.30, 7 to 11, Sun 12 to 4, 7 to 10.30*

WIDECOMBE IN THE MOOR

Devon   map 1

Rugglestone Inn

Widecombe in the Moor TQ13 7TF
TEL: (01364) 621327
off A38, 5m NW of Ashburton
This honey-coloured Dartmoor hostelry offers local farm cider as well as Bass and Butcombe Bitter and six wines by the glass from a short, largely French, list. Hearty pub cooking, including a few local items, is described on blackboards. Children are welcome only in the lawned garden, which contains a large shelter – a bolt-hole to use in the event of a downpour.

Open *summer 11 to 2.30 (3 Sat), 6 to 11, Sun 12 to 3, 6 to 10.30; winter 11 to 2.30 (3 Sat), 7 to 11, Sun 12 to 3, 7 to 10.30*

WILDBOARCLOUGH

Cheshire   map 8

Crag Inn

Wildboarclough SK11 0BD
TEL: (01260) 227239
off A54, 5m SE of Macclesfield
The dictionary says that clough is a
valley or ravine, but locals say it's no
good fishing for wild boar in the
stream as it's actually a wild bore that
runs up it. The inn is popular with
Peak District walkers although they are
asked to remove muddy boots before
coming in for regular ales, Theakston
XB and Worthington Bitter, or the
guest, perhaps Old Peculier or Old
Speckled Hen. Traditional food is
served in the bar and separate
restaurant.
Open *12 to 3, 7 to 11, Sun 12 to 6
closed Mon winter*

WISBOROUGH GREEN

West Sussex   map 3

Cricketers Arms

Wisborough Green RH14 0DG
TEL: (01403) 700369
village on A272 W of Billingshurst
The pub has tables outside so
customers can watch the cricket on the
green. Alternatively, go inside for the
relaxed and atmospheric nooks and
crannies of an old-style pub decorated
with sporting prints and with a stove in
a double-sided fireplace. Live music
sessions are held regularly. Drink
Fuller's London Pride, Flowers
Original, or Wadworth 6X; Cheriton
Pots Ale might be a guest.
Open *Mon to Fri 11 to 2.30, 5.30 to
11, Sat 11 to 11, Sun 12 to 10.30;
closed evening 25 Dec*

WISTANSTOW

Shropshire   map 5

Plough

Wistanstow SY7 8DG
TEL: (01588) 673251
*off A49 Church Stretton to Ludlow
road, 2m N of Craven Arms*
Real ale buffs travelling on the A49
should make time to visit this village
local as it stands right next to the
Wood Brewery, one of the best small

independent country breweries in
Britain. You can arrange to tour the
brewery and sample the full range of
ales – Shropshire Lad, Special and
Parish – in the simply furnished bar.
Traditional English cooking includes
venison sausages, lamb hotpot and
beery beef casserole. Seats outside
overlook the Shropshire hills and
Wenlock Edge.
Open *11.30 to 2.30 (2 winter), 6.30 (7
winter) to 11, Sun 12 to 2.30, 7 to
10.30*

WOODBASTWICK

Norfolk   map 6

Fur & Feather Inn

Slad Lane,
Woodbastwick NR13 6HQ
TEL: (01603) 720003
1½m N of B1140, 8m NE of Norwich
Beers from Woodforde's are well
represented at this thatched Norfolk
Broads pub: hardly surprising as the
brewery is next door. The full range of
eight brews is offered, and are
occasionally used in the cooking – for
example, in a Yorkshire pudding filled
with beef and mushrooms cooked in
Norfolk Nog. The printed menu offers
a wide range of traditional pub food.
Open *12 to 3, 6 to 11, Sun 12 to 3, 7
to 10.30*

WOOLLEY MOOR

Derbyshire   map 5

White Horse Inn

Badger Lane,
Woolley Moor DE55 6FG
TEL: (01246) 590319
*on W side of Ogston Reservoir, off
B6014, between Matlock and Stretton*
A 'real Dales pub', high up in 'the
middle of nowhere', this squat, stone-
built inn is worth knowing about for its
real ales: the regularly changing
selection of four might include Adnams
Best and Broadside, and Bateman
XXXB. Those with children will also
appreciate the outdoor play area. The
lounge bar and the modern
conservatory are used mainly for
dining, and the vast menu (printed and
blackboard) includes a few home-made
items.

Open *summer 11.30 to 3, 6 to 11, Sun 12 to 10.30; winter 12 to 3, 6 to 11, Sun 12 to 10.30*

WRENINGHAM

Norfolk   map 6

Bird in Hand

Church Road,
Wreningham NR16 1BH
TEL: (01508) 489438
off B1113, 5m S of Norwich
This extended and tastefully refurbished red-brick pub with a sheltered rear terrace enjoys an isolated rural position close to Wymondham and the Lotus car factory. It's a popular country destination for its friendly atmosphere, good range of real ales, including Woodforde's Wherry Best Bitter, Adnams Best Bitter and Greene King Abbot Ale, and a good choice of wines: seven are available by the glass. There are separate bar and restaurant menus which change regularly, plus interesting daily specials.
Open *11.30 to 3, 5.30 (6 winter) to 11, Sun 12 to 3, 7 to 10.30*

YANWATH

Cumbria   map 10

Gate

Yanwath CA10 2LF
TEL: (01768) 862386
from A6 turn right on to B5320 Pooley Bridge road after Eamont Bridge
Set in lovely countryside on the approach to Ullswater, this black and white inn is the main building in the little hamlet of Yanwath. Inside, the wide, open-plan room is furnished with beer-barrel tables and seats, while outside in the charming garden are bench tables for al fresco eating. Theakston Best and Skiddaw Special are on draught, and bar snacks and a full restaurant menu are available. Black pudding in the form of 'hot black devils' is among dishes to have drawn approving comment.
Open *summer 12 to 3, 6 to 11, Sun 12 to 3, 6 to 10.30; winter 12 to 2.30, 7 to 11, Sun 12 to 3, 7 to 10.30*

YARDE DOWN

Devon   map 1

Poltimore Arms

Yarde Down EX36 3HA
TEL: (01598) 710381
take Blackmoorgate Road of A361 for 1m, then follow signs for Simonsbath for 4m
High up on the edge of remote Exmoor, this isolated pub was built over 300 years ago as a coaching inn and has great views across the Devon countryside. In keeping with the rustic setting, the interior is simply furnished and the atmosphere relaxed, with local farmers, huntsmen and visitors enjoying the traditional range of pub food and real ales. Cotleigh Tawny and a guest are drawn straight from the barrel.
Open *12 to 2.30, 6.30 to 11, Sun 12 to 2.30, 7 to 10.30; closed all day Mon and lunchtimes Tue to Fri from Jan to Mar*

SCOTLAND

BROUGHTY FERRY

Dundee   map 11

Fisherman's Tavern

10–14 Fort Street,
Broughty Ferry DD5 2AD
TEL: (01382) 775941
off A930 (shore road)
Originally a fisherman's cottage, this listed seventeenth-century house is now a destination for real ale fans: on offer are Belhaven St Andrew's Ale and IPA, Inveralmond Ossian's Ale, McEwan 80/- and Fraoch Heather Ale. Wine drinkers also do well, with ten by the glass. Food is straightforward, ranging from snacks and light dishes such as minute steak on ciabatta or chilli burgers to main courses of steak and ale pie, or grilled Tay salmon with parsley butter and lemon.
Open *11 to 12*

CANONBIE

Dumfries & Galloway   map 11

Riverside Inn

Canonbie DG14 0UX
TEL: (013873) 71512
just off A47, 6m S of Langholm
Robert Phillips left the Riverside after
twenty-five years and the new owners
do not seem to have made sweeping
changes, although some refurbishment
is planned. The large white inn is a
rather grand edifice, but the interiors
are much more homely in feel than the
outside might suggest. The chef is still
in situ, so the blackboard menu should
continue to deal in soups and salads,
fresh fish dishes such as wild poached
salmon with parsley cream sauce, and
casseroles such as shoulder of lamb
cooked in red wine with a touch of
chilli. A fixed-price menu is also
available. Caledonian IPA and Yates
Bitter are on tap, and there is an
extensive wine list. Reports please.
Open *11 to 2.30, 6.30 to 11, Sun 12
to 2.30, 6.30 to 11; closed 2 weeks in
Nov and Feb*

CLOVENFORDS

Borders   map 11

Clovenfords Hotel

1 Vine Street, Clovenfords TD1 3LU
TEL: (01896) 850203
on A72, 3m W of Galashiels
This hotel is in a small village in the
tweed and woollen country around
Galashiels where links with Sir Walter
Scott are many. The connection here is
direct for a statue outside this
eighteenth-century coaching house
commemorates his frequent use of one
of its rooms. Real ale is taken seriously
at Clovenfords, with Caledonian 80/-
as the regular draught, joined by eight
guests – perhaps something from
Orkney or Young's. The printed menu
and blackboard display hearty food
along the lines of wild game soup or
haunch of venison with juniper sauce.
Open *Mon to Thur 11 to 11, Fri and
Sat 11 to 12, Sun 12 to 11*

GATEHEAD

East Ayrshire   map 11

Cochrane Inn

45 Main Road, Gatehead KA2 0AP
TEL: (01563) 570122
on A759 just SW of Kilmarnock
This white-painted, unshowy pub with
its neat flower border is on a T-junction
on the Kilmarnock to Troon road.
Flagstone floors, dark beams and dark
wooden tables with wrought-iron legs
create the right impression inside, and
the cooking revolves around an
extensive choice of traditional Scottish
fare, such as Cullen skink, Scotch broth,
and haggis with neeps and tatties, as
well as such dishes as seared salmon
with a tomato and cheese glaze.
Open *11 to 3, 5 to 11 (12 Sat and Sun)*

GLENCOE

Highland   map 11

Clachaig Inn

Glencoe PH49 4HX
TEL: (01855) 811252
*just off A82, Crianlarich to Fort
William road*
The Clachaig describes itself as 'the
outdoor inn', perhaps because it has
some of the most spectacular views in
Britain, including some of Scotland's
highest peaks. Certainly it serves the
outdoor fraternity of walkers and
climbers – indeed, it doubles as a
mountain-rescue centre. Unusually for
this area there is a good selection of
Scottish cask-conditioned beers,
including Fraoch Heather Ale and Isle
of Skye beers. Local produce including
venison and salmon, not to mention
haggis, is featured on the menu.
Children are welcome, and B&B is
offered.
Open *11 to 11 (11.30 Fri and Sat),
Sun 12.30 to 12*

ISLE OF WHITHORN

Dumfries & Galloway   map 11

Steam Packet

Harbour Row,
Isle of Whithorn DG8 8HZ
TEL: (01988) 500334
off A750, 12m S of Wigtown
Taking its name from the paddle
steamer which in Victorian times

operated between Liverpool and the Galloway coast, this harbourside freehouse serves Theakston XB plus guest ales such as Deuchars IPA and Sulwath Cuil Hill. A respectable selection of wines includes five by the glass. The simple cooking takes in haggis with chips and fried egg, moules marinière, various steaks, and blackboard specials such as monkfish wrapped in bacon with white wine sauce. Children are welcome, and B&B is offered.

Open *summer 11 to 11, Sun 12 to 11, winter Mon to Thur 11 to 2.30, 6 to 11, Fri and Sat 11 to 11, Sun 12 to 11*

KIPPFORD

Dumfries & Galloway map 11

Anchor Hotel

Kippford DG5 4LN
TEL: (01556) 620205
off A710, 4m S of Dalbeattie
This small family-run hotel in an attractive village is busiest in summer, when it is popular with yachtsmen from the marina the pub overlooks. For sustenance, there are real ales – Theakston, Boddingtons and guests – plus a selection of malt whiskies and 15 wines, and an extensive menu featuring the day's catch as well as eclectic house specialities ranging from steak pie to fajitas. B&B is available and the beach is within walking distance.

Open *summer 11am to midnight; winter Mon to Fri 11 to 3, Sat 11 to 11, Sun 12 to 11*

KIRKTON OF GLENISLA

Angus map 11

Glenisla Hotel

Kirkton of Glenisla PH11 8PH
TEL: (01575) 582223
from Alyth head N on B954, turn left on to B951 and follow signs
The Glenisla is a rarity in Scotland, being a good place for real ales, and they are all Scottish brews, such as Independence and Lia Fail from the Inveralmond Brewery and Formakin from the Houston Brewing Company. Less surprising is the range of over 50 malt whiskies. Menus also use plenty of home-grown produce, including Glamis duck with orange and cranberry sauce, pan-fried langoustines with white wine and garlic, and local lambs' liver in a creamy Drambuie sauce.

Open *11 (12.30 Sun) to 11 (12 Fri and Sat); closed 25 Dec*

LINLITHGOW

West Lothian map 11

Four Marys

65 High Street,
Linlithgow EH49 7ED
TEL: (01506) 842171
The complicated history of this tall townhouse starts about 1500, but it remained unlicensed until 1975. The name refers to four ladies-in-waiting of Mary Queen of Scots, whose life and death are commemorated in the fascinating décor. Now it's a monument to Scottish brewing with Caledonian Deuchars IPA, and Bellhaven 70/-, 80/- and St Andrews as regulars; guests might be from other well-respected Scottish breweries like Harviestoun, Broughton, or Orkney. Food is traditional pub fare, Scottish style.

Open *Mon to Wed 11 to 11, Thur to Sat 11am to midnight, Sun 12.30 to 11*

LOCH CLUANIE

Highland map 11

Cluanie Inn

Loch Cluanie IV63 7YW
TEL: (01320) 340238
on A87, between Loch Ness and Skye ferry, at W end of Loch Cluanie
Walkers and climbers, and everyone else, will find a warm welcome at this remote hostelry. Soups or pâté might be followed by something like steak and ale pie, haggis, or steaks, then apple pie or ice cream sundae. Snacks are available all day. McEwan 80/- is on draught, four wines are sold by the glass and there is an extensive collection of malts. Dogs and children are welcome, and there are 15 guests' bedrooms.

Open *11 to 11, Sun 12 to 10.30*

RATHO

Edinburgh   map 11

Bridge Inn

27 Baird Road, Ratho EH28 8RA
TEL: (0131) 333 1320

*off M8 and A8, 8m W of Edinburgh;
follow signs for Edinburgh Canal
Centre from Newbridge roundabout;
pub is alongside canal*

Close to the canal about 20 minutes
out of Edinburgh, the Bridge boasts a
warren of small rooms and eating
areas. The 'Pop Inn' bar menu offers
Bargee's Broth as one of the starters,
and burgers, battered fish, sausages and
the like for mains, with a more unusual
dish of the day, which might be fillet
steak with haggis in Drambuie and
mushroom sauce. Cranachan is one
way of finishing, or you might risk fatal
attraction, elaborately garnished
chocolate ice cream. Belhaven 80/- Ale
is always available, and there are
usually a couple of guest beers,
together with three wines by the glass.
Open *Mon to Thur 12 to 11, Fri 12 to
12, Sat 11 to 12, Sun 12.30 to 11*

ST MARY'S LOCH

Borders   map 11

Tibbie Shiel's Inn

St Mary's Loch TD7 5LH
TEL: (01750) 42231

100yds off A708, 13m W of Selkirk
Isabella (Tibbie) Shiel's idyllically
situated cottage was a favourite haunt
of poets in the nineteenth century.
Today the clientele is more likely to
comprise walkers and windsurfers, but
despite its gorgeous scenery the area is
not that well known to tourists.
Scottish real ales on tap here are from
Greenmantle and Belhaven, alongside
Stowford Press cider, some interesting
Scottish bottled beers and a great many
single malt whiskies. Three-dozen
wines are on offer, but only two by the
glass. Homely Scottish fare includes
traditional high teas as well as hearty
main dishes and snacks. Children are
welcome. B&B is available too.
Open *summer Mon to Thur 11 to 11,
Fri and Sat 11am to midnight, Sun
12.30 to 11; winter Thur 11 to 11, Fri
and Sat 11am to midnight, Sun 12.30
to 6*

STROMNESS

Orkney   map 11

Ferry Inn

John Street, Stromness,
Orkney KW16 3AA
TEL: (01856) 850280

*take the ferry from Aberdeen or
Scrabster*

This tall, steep roofed, town inn
overlooks the bustling harbour and
views extend to Scapa Flow, a name
still resonating with memories of both
World Wars. In the modernised bar,
fitted out in mahogany to resemble the
interior of a schooner you can enjoy
the Orkney Brewery Dark Island real
ale. They specialise in local seafood and
local beef, and there is a selection of
vegetarian dishes too. Twelve
bedrooms are available for B&B.
Open *Sun to Wed 11 to 12, Thur to
Sat 11 to 1am; closed 1 Jan*

WESTRUTHER

Borders   map 11

Old Thistle Inn

Westruther TD3 6NE
TEL: (01578) 740275

*from A697, between Lauder and
Greenlaw, take B6456*

Set in remote moorland near the
Lammermuir Hills, this simple, homely
pub in a whitewashed terrace of
Victorian cottages is open only in the
evening, except at weekends when food
is served all day. The bar and slightly
more formal restaurant share the same
menus of pub favourites together with
steaks from 8 to 16 ounces. There are
no real ales but several Tennants
bottled beers are kept.
Open *Mon to Fri 5 to 12, Sat and Sun
12 to 12*

WALES

ABERGORLECH

Carmarthenshire   map 4

Black Lion Inn

Abergorlech SA32 7SN
TEL: (01558) 685271
on B4310, S of Llansawel
In late 2000 a new owner took over
this unassuming village pub in a
sixteenth century building which has
successfully maintained its period
charm. In the characterful bar is a large
oak table and pair of high-backed
settles, while outside the river Cothi
flows past the garden. Worthington is
the real ale kept, and guests may be
brought in if the demand is there. Eat
traditional food in the bar or
restaurant.
Open *12 to 3, 7 to 11*

ALLTWEN

Neath Port Talbot   map 4

Butchers Arms

Alltwen Hill, Alltwen SA8 3BP
TEL: (01792) 863100
on A474, 1m SE of Pontardawe
Not as rural as most pubs in this guide,
this one is half-way up a hill with views
over the Swansea valley, and attracts
serious local beer-drinkers. They find
Everards Original, Wadworth 6X,
Courage Directors and John Smith's
Cask Bitter as regulars while the single
guest, which changes about three times
a week, might be Fuller's ESB, Archers
Golden Bitter, or Swansea Three Cliffs
Gold. Food is not served on Sunday
nights.
Open *12 to 3, 6.30 to 11, Sun 12 to 3,
7 to 10.30; closed evening 25 Dec*

BODFARI

Denbighshire   map 7

Dinorben Arms

Bodfari LL16 4DA
TEL: (01745) 710309
off A55, 4m NE of Denbigh
This heavily timbered seventeenth-
century inn in the heart of the Clwyd
Vale is noted for its amazing flower-
filled terraced gardens, the mind-
boggling collection of over 200
whiskies behind the bar, and the
popular lunchtime self-served
smorgasbord. Ale aficionados will find
Tetley Bitter, Old Speckled Hen and
Batemans XB on handpump, while the
private cellar choice will delight wine
drinkers. Children are welcome
throughout; dogs in the gardens only.
Open *Mon to Fri 12 to 3.30, 6 to 11,
Sat 12 to 11, Sun 12 to 10.30*

BWLCH-Y-CIBAU

Powys   map 7

Stumble Inn

Bwlch-y-Cibau SY22 5LL
TEL: (01691) 648860
on A490, 3m SE of Llanfyllin
Extensive refurbishments undertaken
here have provided an expanded no-
smoking dining area and comfortable
lounge with domestic-style furniture,
including a chesterfield. The lengthy
menus go in for some speculative
cooking, combining oriental and
Mexican influences, with inventively
handled vegetables. If you're not ready
for chicken bang-bang or Thai
monkfish, have a steak. Old Speckled
Hen and Wells Bombardier Premium
Bitter are on handpump, and there are
four wines by the glass.
Open *Tue to Sat 11 to 2, 6 to 10, Sun
12 to 2, 7 to 9; closed Tue and Sun
winter, first week Oct*

CILGERRAN

Pembrokeshire   map 4

Pendre Inn

Cilgerran SA43 2SL
TEL: (01239) 614223
off A478, 3m S of Cardigan
Outstanding value for money
distinguishes this ancient whitewashed
inn not far from Cardigan Bay and
Cilgerran Castle. The food delivers
some unusual ideas, perhaps délices of
salmon with onion and honey sauce, or
liver and bacon Maltese (with capers,
gherkins, olives and cream). Fixed-
price 'gourmet night' dinners are a steal
at £15 for three courses, plus Buck's
Fizz and canapés. Tomos Watkin
Whoosh is a beer with a name to

conjure with, and three house wines are served by the glass.

Open *12 to 3, 6 to 11, Sun 12 to 3, 7 to 10.30*

EAST ABERTHAW

Vale of Glamorgan   map 4

Blue Anchor Inn

East Aberthaw CF62 3DD
TEL: (01446) 750329

off B4265, between St Athan and Barry

Parts of this brown-thatched, creeper-covered inn date from 1380 and it is said to have been the haunt of smugglers. In the main bar, the ancient walls have been darkened by smoke from the massive open fire, and the adjacent warren of charming rooms bristle with nooks and alcoves. The pub attracts custom from miles around, particularly at weekends and in the evenings. Ales include Buckleys Best, Wadworth 6X and guest beers. Three wines are offered by the glass.

Open *11 to 11, Sun 12 to 10.30*

HOWEY

Powys   map 4

Drovers Arms

Howey LD1 5PT
TEL: (01597) 822508

off A483, 1m S of Llandrindod Wells

Despite a rather uninspiring façade, this solid Victorian red-brick pub is worth seeking out for the excellent Drovers Ale (brewed by the Wood Brewery) served on handpump in the rustic bar. Try also the traditional ploughman's lunch, a generous platter of Welsh and English cheeses with home-made bread and chutney. Three bedrooms are available. No children inside.

Open *12 to 2.30, 7 to 11; closed Tue lunchtime*

HUNDLETON

Pembrokeshire   map 4

Speculation Inn

Hundleton SA71 5RU
TEL: (01646) 661306

at junction of B4320/B4319 at Pembroke, follow Texaco and power station signs

This eighteenth-century roadside inn has been in the same family ownership since the time of the First World War. It is a friendly and convivial place, serving good Welsh ales such as Felinfoel Dragon, as well as cider from Stowford Press. Bar snacks are the full extent of the catering, but they include a decent choice of pies, pizzas, burgers and sandwiches (plain or toasted) at fair prices.

Open *12 to 3 (2 winter), 6 to 11, Sun 12 to 3 (2 winter), 7 to 10.30*

LIBANUS

Powys   map 4

Tai'r Bull Inn

Libanus LD3 8EL
TEL: (01874) 625849

on A470, 3m SW of Brecon

The Brecon Beacons rise to nearly 3000 feet leaving much of Pen-y-Fen to climb from this pub although it is one of Wales' highest. The no-smoking restaurant shares its menu with the bar, featuring home-made soups such as cream of chicken or leek and potato, and substantial curries. Steve Coop, the new landlord since late 2000, plans to add summer guest ales to regulars, Wadworth 6X and Bass. Accommodation is available.

Open *12 to 11, Sun 12 to 10.30; closed Mon lunchtime winter*

LLANDAROG

Carmarthenshire   map 4

Butchers Arms

Llandarog SA32 8NS
TEL: (01267) 275330

off A48, 5m E of Carmarthen

Locally brewed Felinfoel Best and Double Dragon are the real ales to go for, and wines include specials by the glass, changing every three weeks. On the food specials board you might find whole shoulder of lamb in Cumberland sauce or pan fried cockles, bacon and laverbread. All this, plus masses of flowers adorning the pub and a friendly welcome makes this a most attractive destination. Note that the pub is not open on Sundays.

Open *Mon to Fri 12 to 3, 6 to 11, Sat 11.30 to 3, 5 to 11; closed 25 and 26 Dec*

White Hart Inn
Llanddarog SA32 8NT
TEL: (01267) 275395

This pretty 600-year-old thatched pub has a large standard menu, with a daily specials board worthy of closer attention. The home-brew beers are a real draw, and two are on at any one time; Cwrwblafur Ale, perhaps, or Roasted Barley Stout, Beetroot Ale, or Parsnip Ale. Sit on picnic tables outside and admire the hanging baskets, tubs, and fine views over the countryside.

Open *11.30 to 3, 6.30 to 11, Sun 12 to 3, 7 to 10.30*

LLANDINAM
Powys   map 4

Lion Hotel
Llandinam SY17 5BY
TEL: (01686) 688233

on A470 in village centre, 8m SW of Newtown, 6m N of Llanidloes

In summer you can eat in this rustic pub's garden, separated only by a meadow from the banks of the Upper Severn. New owners still offer hearty casseroles on the specials board in addition to pub favourites: perhaps Welsh lamb hotpot with port, plums and ginger, or Montgomery beef with herby dumplings. The two changing ales might be Elgood's Golden Newt and Old Speckled Hen.

Open *12 to 3, 6.30 to 11, Sun 12 to 3, 7 to 10.30*

LLANGYBI
Monmouthshire   map 4

White Hart
Llangybi NP15 1NP
TEL: (01633) 450258

just off A449, between Newport and Usk

Built in the twelfth century for Cistercian monks and later commandeered by Henry VIII as part of Jane Seymour's wedding dowry, this whitewashed, slate-roofed freehouse enjoys a secluded village location in the beautiful Vale of Usk. Worth seeking out for its authentic, unspoilt character, including heavy beams, flagstones and open fires, and real ales, perhaps Bass and Hancock's HB on handpump. Straightforward bar food; overnight accommodation is available.

Open *Mon to Fri 11.30 to 3.30, 6 to 11, Sat 11.30 to 11, Sun 11 to 4, 7 to 10.30*

LLANGYNWYD
Bridgend   map 4

Old House
Llangynwyd CF34 9SB
TEL: (01656) 733310

off A4063, 2m S of Maesteg

The beer garden of this welcoming, thatched, twelfth-century country pub overlooks the Llynfi, and its restaurant was the valley's first Nonconformist chapel. Old-time music hall devotees please note that the figure still annually celebrated is Mari Lwyd, not Marie Lloyd, and the poetic link is with Wil Hopkin. More familiar are the names on the pumps: Flowers Original, Bass, Worthington and Brains.

Open *11 to 11*

LLANHENNOCK
Monmouthshire   map 2

Wheatsheaf
Llanhennock NP18 1LT
TEL: (01633) 420468

off B4236, 2m N of Caerleon

In a tiny hill-side village this pub is an example of old world charm with tables and chairs in the front garden of what still looks like the farmhouse it once was. Mrs Powell's enormous portions of home-cooked pies might be deemed satisfying even to inhabitants and visitors in wilder mountain regions. Bass and Worthington are regular draught beers, the guest could be Fisherrow Bears Ale.

Open *summer 11 to 11, Sun 12 to 3, 7 to 10.30; winter Tue, Thur, Fri and Sat 11 to 11, Mon and Wed 11 to 3, 5.30 to 11, Sun 12 to 3, 7 to 10.30*

LLANTHONY

Monmouthshire   map 4

Llanthony Priory

Llanthony NP7 7NN
TEL: (01873) 890487
on B4423, 9m N of Abergavenny

In a stunning setting surrounded by beautiful trees and soaring mountains, this remote pub once formed part of a twelfth-century Augustinian abbey. Approach through a wall straight into the open cloisters, 'all green lawns and towering, broken stone pillars and arches', and there you find this old prior's house, built into the ruins (worth a visit in their own right), its old stone now lichen-covered and highly atmospheric. The tiny bar in the vaulted crypt offers Bass and Felinfoel ales plus a short menu of simple, hearty fare.

Open *summer Mon 10 to 3, Tue to Fri 10 to 3, 6 to 11, Sat 10am to 11pm, Sun 12 to 10.30 (open 11 to 11 every day in July and Aug); winter Fri 6 to 11, Sat 10 to 11, Sun 12 to 10.30*

LLANVIHANGEL CRUCORNEY

Monmouthshire   map 4

Skirrid Mountain Inn

Llanvihangel Crucorney NP7 8DH
TEL: (01873) 890258
off A465, 4½m N of Abergavenny

Dating from 1110 and full of brooding history that takes in Owain Glyndwr, the Monmouth Rebellion, and legends of some 180 hangings, this remote stone hostelry lays claim to being the oldest in Wales. Set below the Skirrid Mountain and overlooking the Monnow Valley, it is worth seeking out for its immaculately preserved interior, complete with medieval beams,

windows and panelling, and the cosy atmosphere. Expect Ushers ales on handpump and hearty bar food. Accommodation is available.

Open *summer 11 to 11, Sun 12 to 10.30; winter Mon to Fri 12 to 3, 6 to 11, Sat 11 to 11, Sun 12 to 10.30*

LLWYNDAFYDD

Ceredigion   map 4

Crown

Llwyndafydd SA44 6BU
TEL: (01545) 560396
off A487 at Synod Inn, take A486 signposted for New Quay, turn left at Cross Inn

An extensive menu served in the restaurant, bar or garden (with children's play area) is available at this 200-year-old pub in a pretty, wooded valley. Flowers Original and IPA are regularly on tap while among the guests may be Old Speckled Hen. Sixty-two wines include four by the glass. It's a useful base for visiting New Quay with its reputation for having inspired *Under Milk Wood*, and for its National Trust cliffs.

Open *12 to 3, 6 to 11, Sun 12 to 3, 7 to 10.30; closed Sun evening Sept to Easter*

MONTGOMERY

Powys   map 4

Dragon Hotel

Montgomery SY15 6PA
TEL: (01686) 668359
on B4385, 3m E of A483 Newtown to Welshpool road

With its distinctive black and white façade, this family-run former coaching inn, dating from the seventeenth century, is easy to identify at the top of Montgomery's old market square. Wood's Best Bitter and Boddingtons are always available, and guests might include Brains Bitter, Castle Eden Bitter, Fuller's London Pride and Wadsworth 6X. There's a good selection of wines (five by the glass), too, a bar menu supplemented by daily specials, and, in the restaurant, food that is described as 'modern English and Welsh with a Mediterranean

influence'. Children are welcome. Live jazz is played here on Wednesday nights and the hotel has 20 rooms.
Open *11 to 11, Sun 12 to 10.30*

NEVERN

Pembrokeshire   map 4

Trewern Arms
Nevern SA42 0NB
TEL: (01239) 820395
on B4582, 2m E of Newport
While visiting the historical pilgrims' church, with its Celtic crosses and 'bleeding' yew tree, in this hidden hamlet, it is worth venturing across the medieval bridge over the river for refreshment at this seventeenth-century creeper-clad inn. The original bar is still a wonderfully cluttered showpiece, filled with a fascinating collection of old farm implements, Welsh cauldrons and lanterns. Wadworth 6X, Castle Eden Ale and Flowers IPA are on handpump. Useful family accommodation.
Open *11 to 3, 6 to 11, Sun 12 to 3, 7 to 10.30*

OLD RADNOR

Powys   map 4

Harp Inn
Old Radnor LD8 2RH
TEL: (01544) 350655
off A44, between New Radnor and Kington
Looking out on the fine fifteenth-century church of St Stephen, the Harp, an inn of similar vintage, serves holidaymakers as well as the small local community. It stands in a peaceful spot on a hillside in the Marches and offers a warm and welcoming haven from the wind. Several real ales are served, including Sharp's Doom Bar, plus a range of malt whiskies and some French organic wines. Bar food ranges from ploughman's to pasta and Stilton bake. Children are welcome and five rooms are available for B&B.
Open *Mon to Fri 7 to 11, Sat and Sun 12 to 3, 7 to 11 (10.30 Sun)*

REYNOLDSTON

Swansea   map 4

King Arthur
Higher Green,
Reynoldston SA3 1AD
TEL: (01792) 390775
Set at the base of Cefn Bryn on the Gower Peninsular, this black and white building dotted with hanging baskets looks out on grassland to the front and woodland to the rear. When the moon is full the ghost of King Arthur is said to emerge from the Cromlech and traverse this scenic landscape. The pub's interior is basic, but the views compensate. Sporting memorabilia is much in evidence. Real ales are Bass, Worthington and Felinfoel Double Dragon. Children are welcome and B&B is available.
Open *11 to 11*

RHYD-DDU

Gwynedd   map 7

Cwellyn Arms
Rhyd-ddu LL54 6TL
TEL: (01766) 890321
on A4085, between Caernarfon and Beddgelert
From this stone-built pub you can view Snowdon's western slopes, and the waters of Lyn y Gadair, Lyn Cwellyn and Beddgelert Forest. Outside there is a beer garden and children's playground. Nine real ales on at a time might include something from the Wye Valley Dorothy Goodbody range, Everards Tiger Best, Young's Special, and Bateman XXXB.
Open *11 to 11, Sun 12 to 10.30*

ST DOGMAELS

Pembrokeshire   map 4

Ferry Inn
St Dogmaels SA43 3LF
TEL: (01239) 615172
on B4546, 1m W of Cardigan
Despite the proximity to Cardigan, this inn is just over the Pembrokeshire border, with the Teifi running by its garden. The ferry was for centuries rowed across here, where the river became tame enough to cross. There are no regular ales but changing guests,

one in winter, more in summer, might include Wadworth 6X, Brains Reverend James or seasonal St David's. As the Guide went to press there were plans to make the food more Mediterranean in style. Reports please.

Open *12 to 3, 7 to 11, Sun 12 to 3, 7 to 10.30*

SOLVA

Pembrokeshire   map 4

Cambrian Inn

Main Street, Solva SA62 6UU
TEL: (01437) 721210

off A487, 3m W of St David's

This quiet and unpretentious pub is at the bottom of the steep valley in a small fishing village near Pembrokeshire's most westerly point. Food is served throughout from a menu that focuses on steaks and fish; portions are large, and the bread-and-butter pudding with Amaretto has drawn praise. Marston's Pedigree and Worthington Best are on draught, and five of the 20 wines are available by the glass.

Open *summer 11.30 to 3, 6 to 11, Sun 11.30 to 3, 6 to 10.30; winter 12 to 2.30, 7 to 11, Sun 12 to 2.30, 7 to 10.30*

TALYBONT

Powys   map 4

Star Inn

Talybont LD3 7YX
TEL: (01874) 676635

½m off A40, 6m SE of Brecon

Variety is the spice of life at the Star, and the ever-changing list of ales provides an exceptional range. In the summer you will find 10 or 12 (half that in winter), perhaps Brains Bitter, Felinfoel Double Dragon and Wadworth 6X among them. Food is simple, and traditional, and wine amounts to a choice of two. Accommodation is available.

Open *Mon to Fri 11 to 3, 6.30 to 11, Sat 11 to 11, Sun 12 to 3, 6.30 to 10.30*

INDEX OF ENTRIES

Index

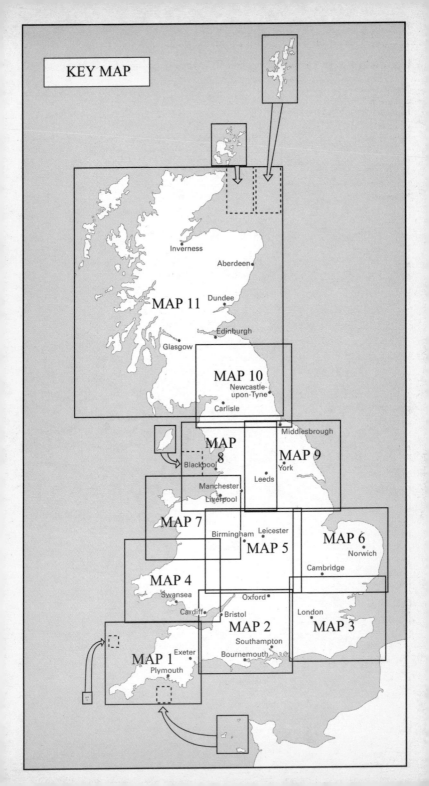

KEY MAP

MAP 11

Inverness
Aberdeen
Dundee
Edinburgh
Glasgow

MAP 10

Newcastle-upon-Tyne
Carlisle

Middlesbrough

MAP 8

Blackpool

MAP 9

York
Leeds

Manchester
Liverpool

MAP 7

Birmingham
Leicester

MAP 5

MAP 6

Norwich

Cambridge

MAP 4

Swansea
Cardiff
Bristol

Oxford

London

MAP 2

MAP 3

Southampton
Bournemouth

MAP 1

Exeter
Plymouth

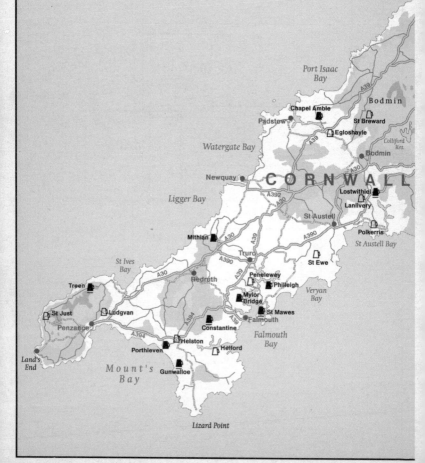

MAP 1

Main entries
Main entry with accommodation
Out & About entries
Main and Out & About entries
Main entries with accommodation, and Out & Abouts

| 0 | | 5 | | 10 miles |
| 0 | | | 15 kms |

Lundy Island

Isles of Scilly
28 miles WSW of Land's End

Bryher
St Martin's
Tresco
St Mary's
St Agnes

Bude Bay

Port Isaac Bay

BODMIN

Chapel Amble
Padstow
St Breward
Egloshayle
Bodmin
Colliford Res.

Watergate Bay

Newquay
CORNWALL

Lostwithiel
Lanlivery

Ligger Bay

Mithian
St Austell
Polkerris
St Austell Bay

Truro
St Ewe

St Ives Bay

Redruth
Penelewey
Philleigh

Treen
Mylor Bridge
St Mawes
Veryan Bay

St Just
Ludgvan
Constantine
Falmouth

Penzance
Helston
Helford
Falmouth Bay

Porthleven

Land's End

Mount's Bay
Gunwalloe

Lizard Point

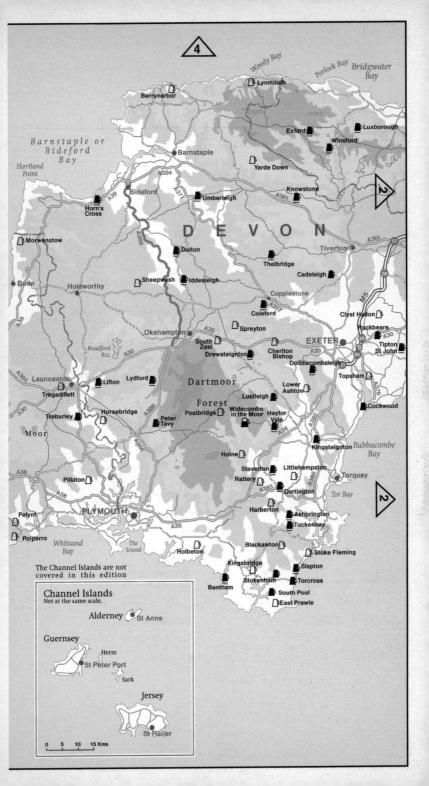

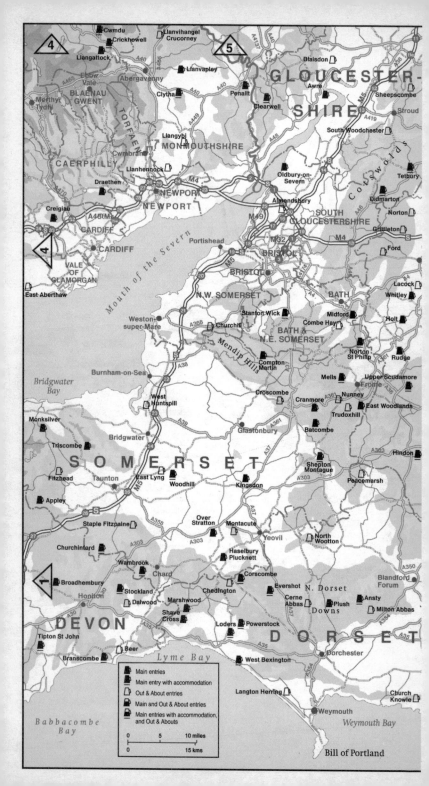

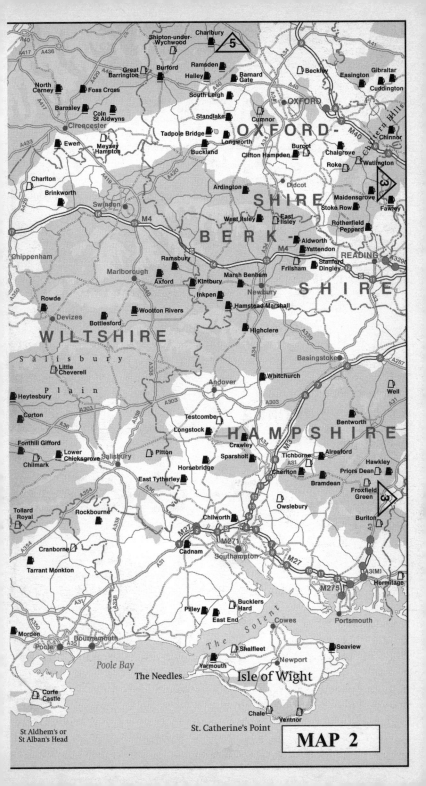

MAP 2

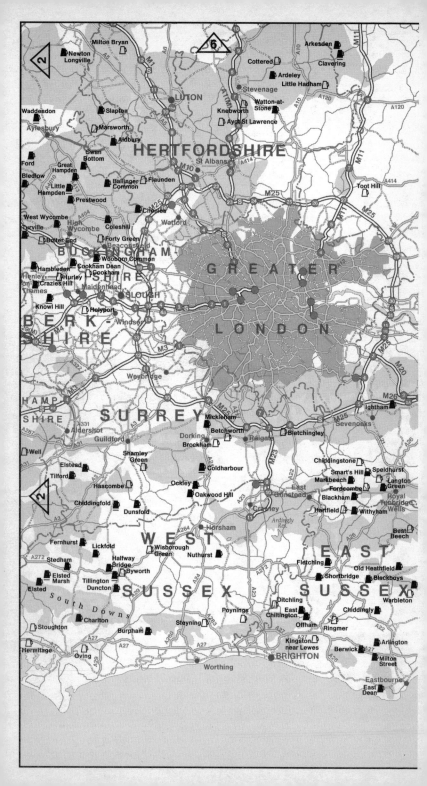

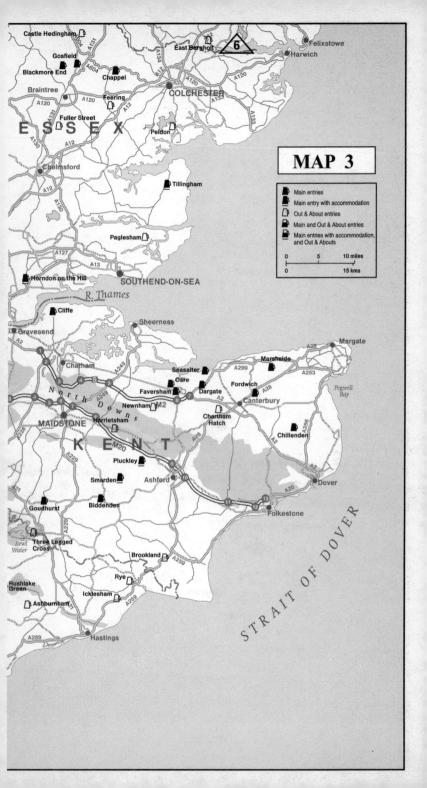

MAP 4

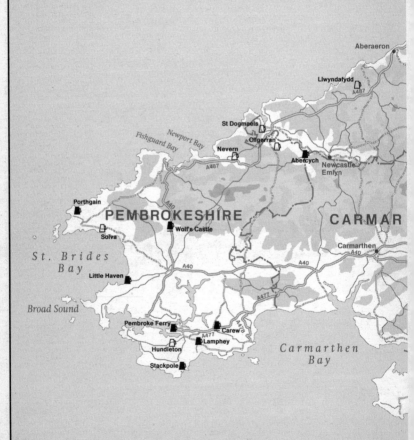

Main entries
Main entry with accommodation
Out & About entries
Main and Out & About entries
Main entries with accommodation, and Out & Abouts

| 0 | 5 | 10 miles |
| 0 | | 15 kms |

CARDIGAN

BAY

Aberaeron

Llwyndafydd

A487

Newport Bay

St Dogmaels

Fishguard Bay

Cilgerran

Nevern

A487

Abercych

Newcastle Emlyn

CARMAR

Porthgain

PEMBROKESHIRE

Carmarthen

A40

Solva

St. Brides Bay

A40

A40

Little Haven

Broad Sound

A477

Pembroke Ferry

Carew

Carmarthen Bay

A477

Hundleton

Lamphey

Stackpole

BRISTOL

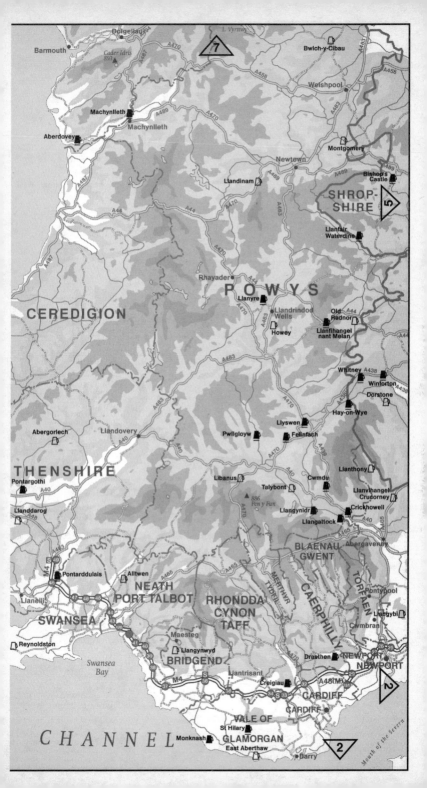

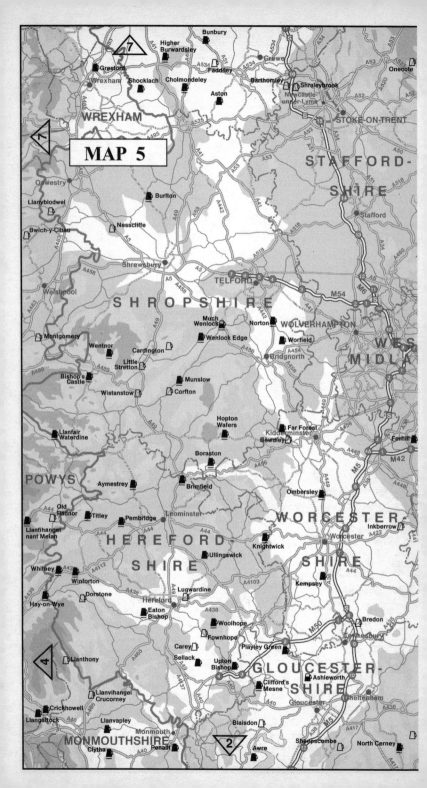

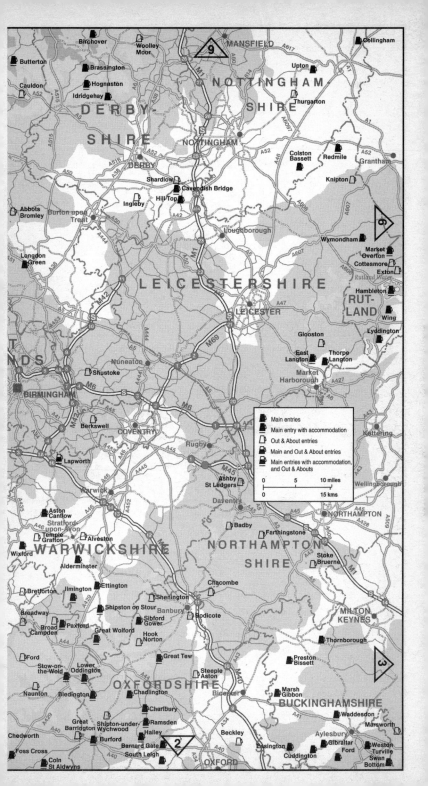

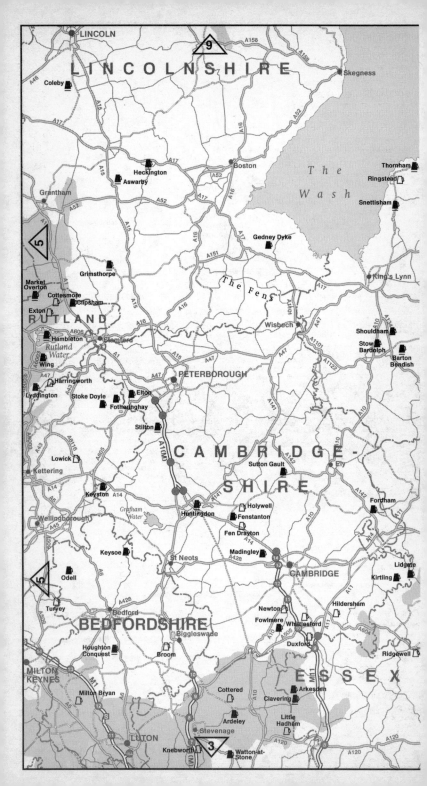

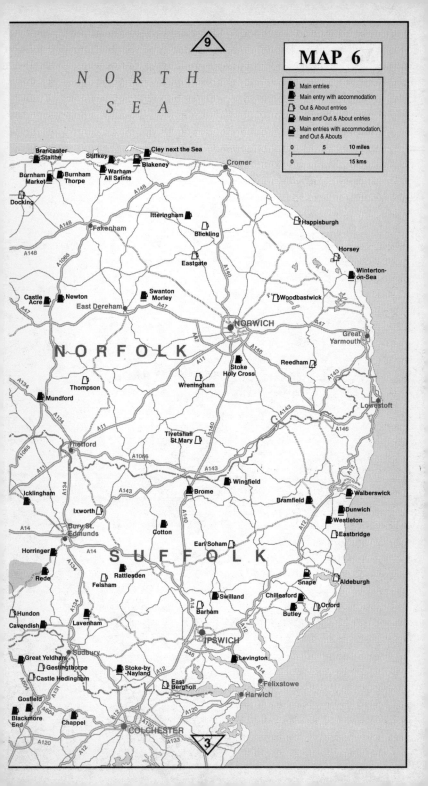

MAP 6

Main entries
Main entry with accommodation
Out & About entries
Main and Out & About entries
Main entries with accommodation,
and Out & Abouts

0   5   10 miles
0   15 kms

NORTH
SEA

Cromer

Brancaster
Staithe   Stiffkey   Cley next the Sea
Burnham   Blakeney
Market   Burnham   Warham
Thorpe   All Saints
Docking

Itteringham   Happisburgh

Fakenham   Blickling   Horsey

Eastgate   Winterton-
on-Sea

Castle   Newton   Swanton
Acre   Morley   Woodbastwick
East Dereham

NORFOLK   NORWICH   Great
Yarmouth

Stoke   Reedham
Thompson   Holy Cross
Mundford   Wreningham

Thetford   Tivetshall   Lowestoft
St Mary

Icklingham   Wingfield

Ixworth   Brome   Walberswick
Cotton   Bramfield   Dunwich
Bury St.   Westleton
Edmunds   Earl Soham   Eastbridge

Horringer   SUFFOLK
Rede   Rattlesden   Snape   Aldeburgh
Felsham   Swilland   Chillesford
Hundon   Barham   Orford
Cavendish   Lavenham   Butley

Great Yeldham   Sudbury   IPSWICH
Gestingthorpe   Levington
Castle Hedingham   Stoke-by-
-Nayland   Felixstowe
Gosfield   East   Harwich
Blackmore   Bergholt
End   Chappel   COLCHESTER

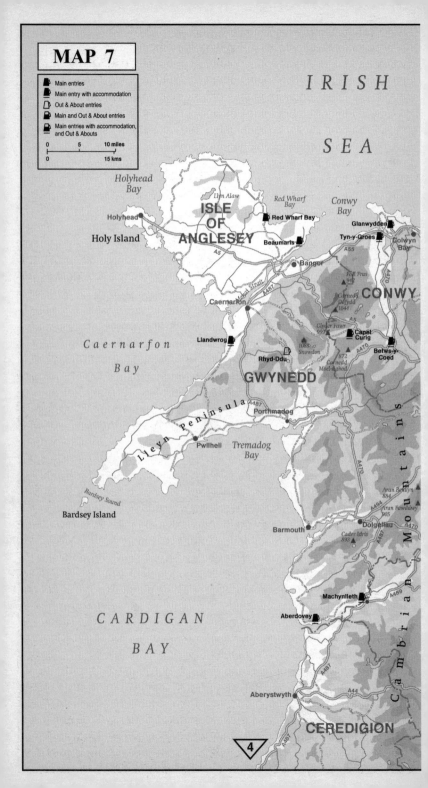

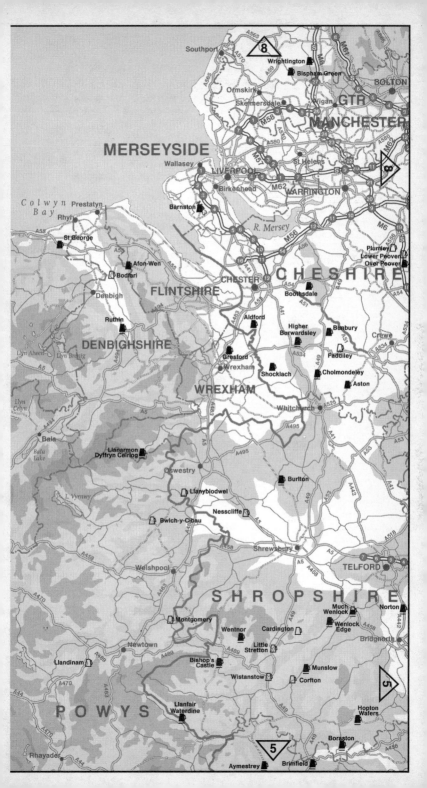

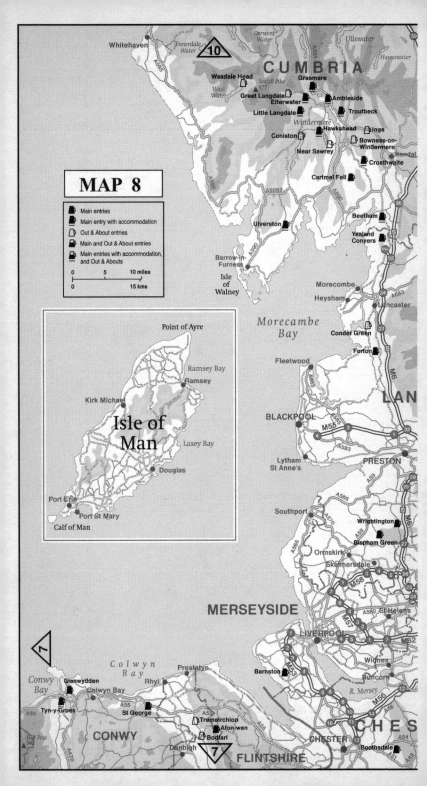

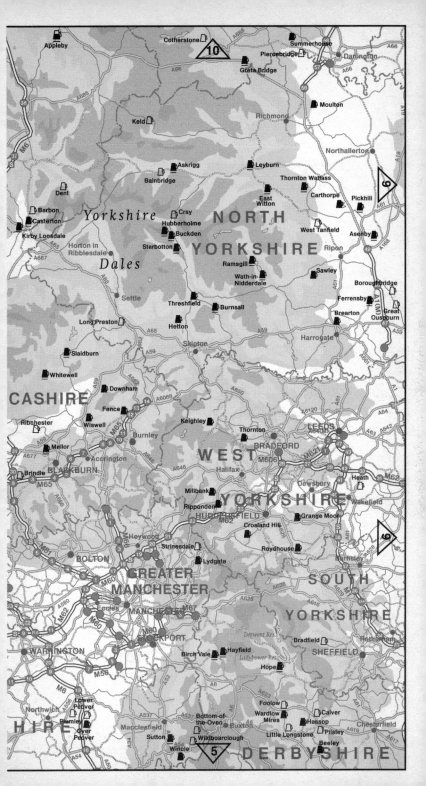

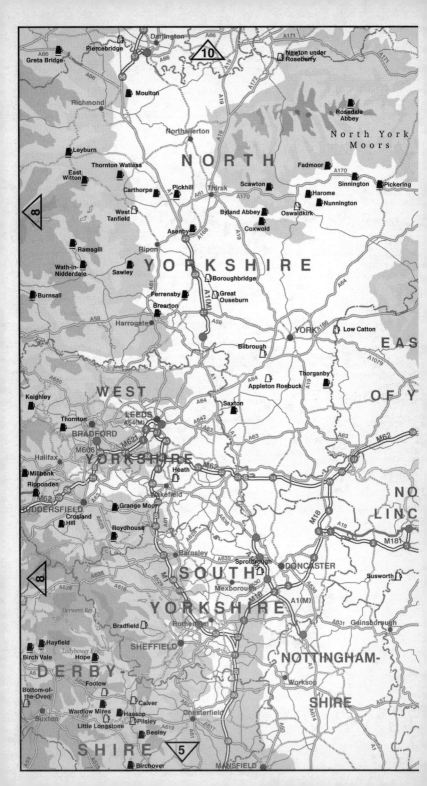

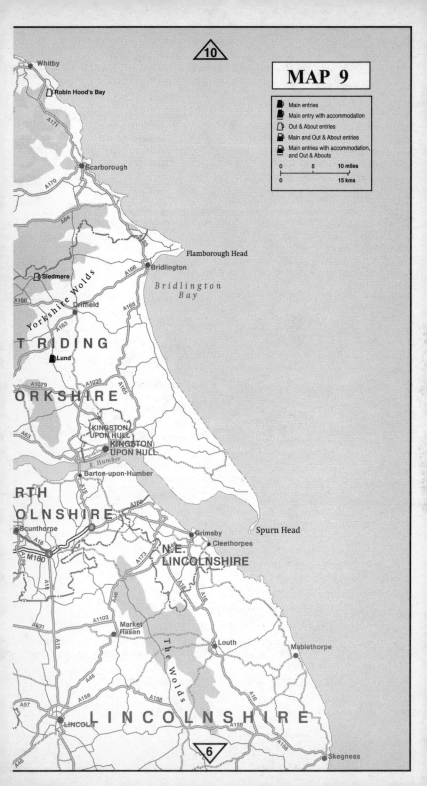

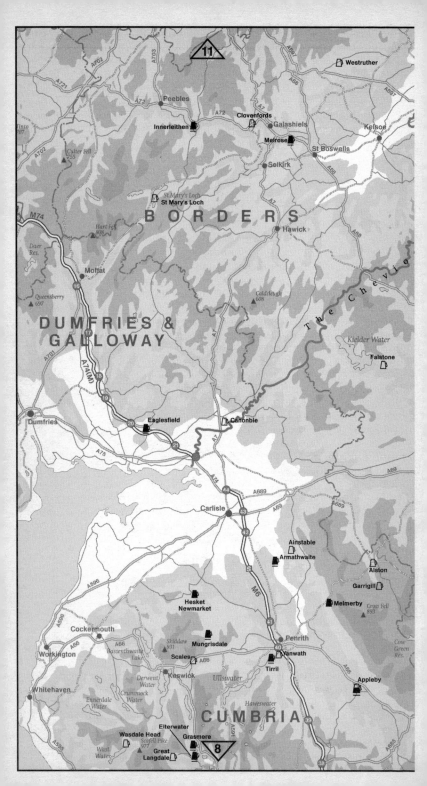

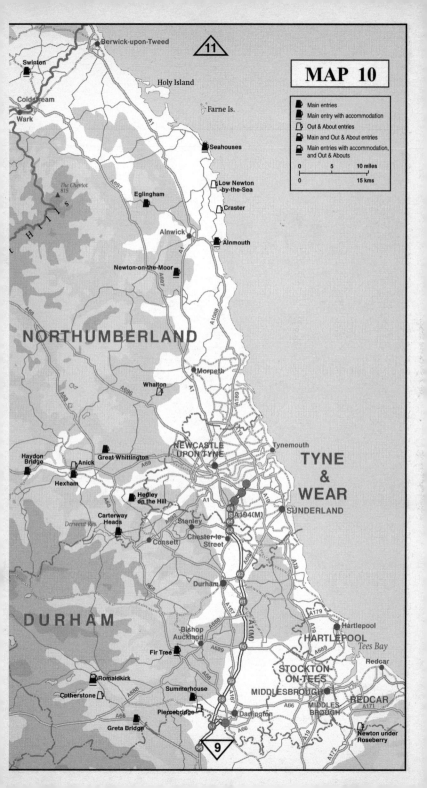

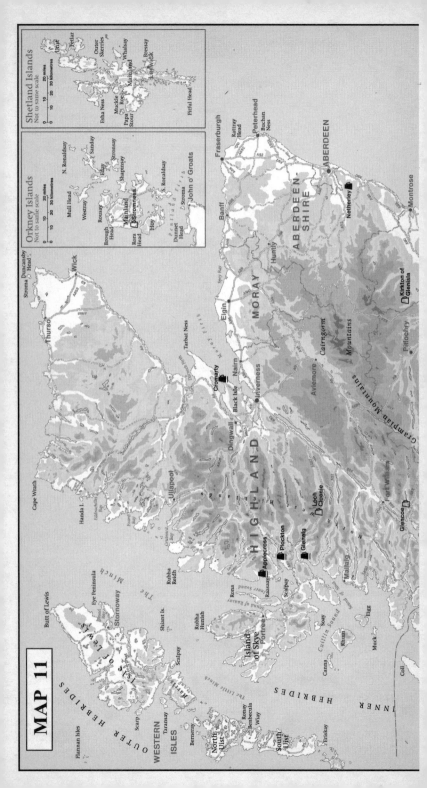

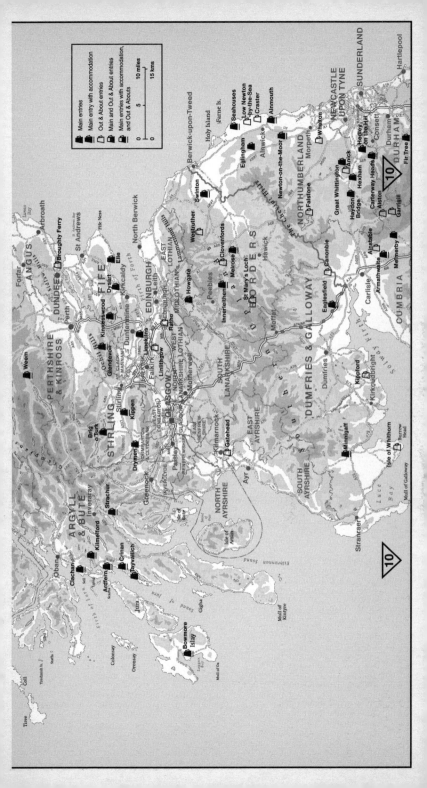

Report form

To *The Which? Guide to Country Pubs,*
FREEPOST, 2 Marylebone Road, London NW1 4DF

Or email your report to: *whichcountrypubs@which.net*

PUB NAME _____

Address _____

_____ Telephone _____

Date of visit _____

From my personal experience this establishment should be
(please tick)

main entry ☐   'Out and About' entry ☐   excluded ☐

Please describe what you ate and drank (with prices, if known), and
give details of location, service, atmosphere etc.

My meal for ___ people cost £___ Value for money? yes ☐ no ☐

I am not connected in any way with the management or proprietors.

Name and address (BLOCK CAPITALS) _____

_____

_____

Signed _____

Report form

To *The Which? Guide to Country Pubs,*
FREEPOST, 2 Marylebone Road, London NW1 4DF

Or email your report to: *whichcountrypubs@which.net*

PUB NAME _____

Address _____

_____ Telephone _____

Date of visit _____

From my personal experience this establishment should be
(please tick)

main entry ☐   'Out and About' entry ☐   excluded ☐

Please describe what you ate and drank (with prices, if known), and
give details of location, service, atmosphere etc.

Please turn over

My meal for ___ people cost £___ Value for money? yes ❏   no ❏

I am not connected in any way with the management or proprietors.

Name and address (BLOCK CAPITALS) _____

_____

_____

Signed

To *The Which? Guide to Country Pubs,*
FREEPOST, 2 Marylebone Road, London NW1 4DF

Or email your report to: *whichcountrypubs@which.net*

PUB NAME _____

Address _____

_____ Telephone _____

Date of visit _____

From my personal experience this establishment should be
(please tick)

main entry ☐   'Out and About' entry ☐   excluded ☐

Please describe what you ate and drank (with prices, if known), and
give details of location, service, atmosphere etc.

Please turn over

My meal for ___ people cost £____ Value for money? yes ❑   no ❑

I am not connected in any way with the management or proprietors.

Name and address (BLOCK CAPITALS) _____

_____

_____

Signed